FUNDAMENTALS OF LOGIC

James D. Carney
The University of Otago, New Zealand

Richard K. Scheer
The University of Missouri

FUNDAMENTALS OF
LOGIC

THE MACMILLAN COMPANY, NEW YORK
COLLIER-MACMILLAN LIMITED, LONDON

First Printing

THE MACMILLAN COMPANY, NEW YORK

COLLIER-MACMILLAN CANADA, LTD., TORONTO, ONTARIO

Library of Congress catalog card number: 64–16050

Printed in the United States of America

DESIGNED BY ANDREW P. ZUTIS

The quotation appearing as Exercise 14 on page 86 is from
Nineteen Eighty-four by George Orwell, Copyright 1949. Used by
permission of Secker and Warburg Ltd. and Brandt and Brandt
(New York).

To O. K. Bouwsma

PREFACE

This text introduces much material that is new to logic texts. Most of this new material has been taken from the writings of philosophers who, in the last sixty years, have greatly enriched our understanding of language and the nature of inference. The writings of Ludwig Wittgenstein and, in the philosophy of science, the writings of Ernest Nagel influenced our conception of what ought to be treated in the text. They (and others mentioned below) are primarily responsible for whatever merit the text has over and above our treatment of the standard topics. The student should be informed, therefore, that many of the ideas he will find in the text are not—or are not yet—"accepted doctrine." And he should be informed that it is often difficult, and sometimes impossible, to expound with precision, in an elementary text, ideas which are treated in isolation from the considerations that gave rise to them.

Part I, Informal Logic, contains both new and traditional topics and some novel treatment of traditional topics. Informal fallacies, which are useful in motivating students in the study of logic, are treated in the traditional manner. The standard topics—analogy, dilemmas, uses of language, classifications of methods of defining terms and types of definitions—are also discussed in this part. But two topics are introduced—paradoxes and nonsense—which are not found in many introductory logic textbooks. The discussions of nonsense and the uses of language are designed to bring to the attention of the student some of the immediate connections between logic and language and to show the student the significance of logic to philosophy. The discussion of paradoxes is introduced partly because of their inherent interest and partly because of their connections with the important results that logicians have achieved.

In Part II, Formal Logic, we have introduced the student to a variety of ideas. Instead of limiting the presentation to the study of deduction as involved in argument, we have introduced the concept of an axiom system. Thus the student gains some familiarity with a formal deductive system. This is necessary, in our opinion, if the student is to understand the structure of science and the role of inference in science (Part III). Sentential logic is introduced by truth tables, through rules of inference, and as an axiomatic system. A significant part of quantification theory is developed from sentential logic through additional rules of inference —which, though not adequate to show the validity of all valid arguments in quantification theory, do provide a relatively simple procedure for showing the validity of many complex ones. The classical syllogism is introduced as of primarily historical interest. Finally, an introductory treatment of class logic is given as an interpretation of sentential logic and as an axiom system. In this part we have used many ideas from other works on logic, especially:

A. H. Basson and D. J. O'Connor: *Introduction to Logic*
P. F. Strawson: *Introduction to Logical Theory*
Patrick Suppes: *Introduction to Logic*
W. V. Quine: *Methods of Logic.*

Part III, The Logical Structure of Science, is a somewhat marked departure from what is usually found in an elementary logic text. We attempt in this part to show how the topics in science that are of interest to the logician—hypotheses, laws, theories, explanations, and so on— are related to one another and how they change as science progresses. Here, as in Part I, we have introduced points of view, but the style of presentation should not mislead readers into thinking that we are always expounding accepted doctrines. Chapter 16 is a discussion of explanations. In Chapter 17, which is a treatment of crucial experiments, we have borrowed from P. Duhem's *The Aim and Structure of Physical Theory.* The chapter ends with a discussion of Mill's methods. The classification of types of explanation is, on the whole, that of Ernest Nagel's *The Structure of Science: Problems in the Logic of Scientific Explanation.* Our discussion of the demarcation of scientific explanations from non-scientific ones uses some of the ideas of K. Popper, especially those in his *Conjectures and Refutations.* In the last chapter the discussion of theories and laws also owes much to Nagel's discussions and to John Kemeny's *A Philosopher Looks at Science.*

We want to acknowledge our debt to those who helped with the manuscript: the publisher's readers who are anonymous to us; Professors Newton Garver and James Willard Oliver, who read parts of the manuscript; Professor Robert Herbert, who read the entire manuscript; Mr. John D. Moore, our editor, who helped in a number of different ways; and Mrs. James D. Carney, who handled many of the tedious aspects of manuscript preparation.

James D. Carney
Richard K. Scheer

CONTENTS

Preface *vii*

Part **I**

INFORMAL LOGIC *1*

Chapter One: APPRAISING ARGUMENTS LOGICALLY *3*

Arguments *3*
The logical correctness of an argument *9*
Correctness of an argument and truth of the premisses *10*
Fallacies *11*
The general circumstances of arguments *12*

Chapter Two: TRADITIONAL INFORMAL FALLACIES *19*

The material fallacies of relevance *20*
The material fallacies of insufficient evidence *39*
The fallacies of ambiguity *46*

Chapter Three: DEFINITIONS *66*

Two aspects of ordinary words *66*
Verbal disputes *88*
Methods and types of definitions *97*

Chapter Four: USES OF LANGUAGE 112

Three common uses of sentences 112
Form, purpose and effect 116
The countless uses of sentences 118
The value of distinguishing sentence uses 120
The informative use of language and nonsense utterances 128
Context and category-mixing 131
Context- and category-mixing fallacies 132
Nonsense and the metaphorical use of language 134

Chapter Five: ANALOGY 141

Three uses of analogy 141
Explanatory analogies 143
Analogies which suggest hypotheses 145
Argumentative analogies 146
Evaluating analogical arguments 148
Some poor analogical arguments 151
Criticism by logical analogy 153

Chapter Six: DILEMMAS AND PARADOXES 164

What is a dilemma? 164
The value of the dilemma 166
Appraising a dilemma 166
The counterdilemma 170
What is a paradox? 175
Two classical logical paradoxes 176
Falsidical and veridical paradoxes 177
The liar's paradox 178
Antinomies 179

Part 2
FORMAL LOGIC 185

Chapter Seven: VALIDITY 187

Deductive arguments 187
The validity or invalidity of a deductive argument 188
Logical form 189
Contingent truths and logical truths 192
Terminology 193

Chapter Eight: STATEMENT CONNECTIVES   *199*

    '∼' and English "not"   *199*
    '·' and English "and"   *200*
    'v' and English "or"   *202*
    '⊃' and English "if-then"   *204*
    '≡' and necessary and sufficient conditions   *207*
    Complex statements and the scope of statement connectives   *208*

Chapter Nine: TRUTH TABLES   *214*

    Truth tables for the logical connectives   *214*
    Relations between the logical connectives   *216*
    Tautologies, contradictions and contingent statements   *219*
    Testing validity   *223*
    Truth table short cut   *227*

Chapter Ten: ELEMENTARY INFERENCES   *230*

    A rule of inference—*modus ponendo ponens*   *230*
    Relation between "implies" and '⊃'   *231*
    Other rules of inference   *232*
    The validation of inferences   *234*
    Conditional validation   *235*
    The *reductio ad absurdum* rule   *237*
    Consistency (S) of premisses   *238*

Chapter Eleven: QUANTIFICATION   *249*

    The existential quantifier   *250*
    The universal quantifier   *252*
    Context   *254*
    Individual constants   *257*
    Multiple quantifiers and many-placed predicates   *259*

Chapter Twelve: ARISTOTELIAN LOGIC   *266*

    Syllogisms   *266*
    The six conditions of validity   *267*
    Sorites and enthymemes   *269*

Chapter Thirteen: INFERENCE INVOLVING QUANTIFIERS   *273*

    Universal generalization   *273*
    Notation and terminology   *274*
    Universal instantiation   *276*

Chapter Thirteen (Continued)

Existential instantiation	*278*
Existential generalization	*279*
Restrictions	*279*
Examples	*281*
General rules	*284*
Invalid arguments	*286*

Chapter Fourteen: AXIOM SYSTEMS   *293*

The anatomy of an axiom system	*293*
The vocabulary, axioms, and rules of inference	*297*
Theorems	*301*
Derived rules	*303*
Interpretation	*304*
Consistency	*304*
Independence of the axioms	*307*
Completeness	*308*

Chapter Fifteen: CLASSES   *314*

Membership and inclusion	*314*
Class complement, the null class, and the universe of discourse	*317*
Operations on classes	*318*
Categorical statements	*320*
Venn diagrams and the validity of arguments	*321*
Identities	*326*
Boolean algebra as an axiom system	*328*

Part **3**

THE LOGICAL STRUCTURE OF SCIENCE   *335*

Chapter Sixteen: SCIENCE AND HYPOTHESES   *337*

Four episodes from the history of science	*338*
Empirical and theoretical hypotheses, theories, and laws	*348*
Induction and deduction	*351*

Chapter Seventeen: CRUCIAL EXPERIMENTS AND INDUCTIVE TECHNIQUES   *363*

Crucial experiments and empirical hypotheses	*363*
Crucial experiments and theoretical hypotheses	*364*
"Death blows"	*367*

Chapter Seventeen (Continued)

Fact of the cross   *368*

Traditional inductive techniques and correct inductive arguments   *374*

Chapter Eighteen: PATTERNS OF SCIENTIFIC EXPLANATIONS   *389*

Deductive explanations   *389*

Probabilistic explanations   *394*

Historical explanations   *396*

Functional explanations   *398*

.Empathetic explanations   *398*

Genuine and pseudoscientific explanations   *409*

Satisfactory and unsatisfactory explanations   *418*

Chapter Nineteen: SOME LOGICAL FEATURES OF SCIENCE   *428*

The logical character of scientific laws   *428*

The logical structure of a fully developed science   *435*

Ideal laws   *439*

Science and common sense   *447*

Appendix   *457*

The Aristotelian square of opposition   *457*

The Boolean square of opposition   *458*

Criticisms and defense of the Aristotelian square   *460*

Criticisms and defense of the Boolean square   *462*

FUNDAMENTALS OF LOGIC

Part I

INFORMAL LOGIC

Chapter One

APPRAISING ARGUMENTS LOGICALLY

ARGUMENTS

The primary interest of this book is the logical appraisal of arguments. Let us begin by indicating what an argument is.

In logic an *argument* is a group of two or more statements, one of which is affirmed on the basis of the other or others. The statement which is affirmed is called the *conclusion* of the argument. The statement or statements which supply the reason or reasons for affirming the conclusion are called the premisses of the argument.

Consider this simple example of an argument:

Project Apollo, the 20 billion (or more) program to put a man on the moon, should be abandoned because these billions should be spent on basic scientific research of space, and the project is nothing more than a spectacular stunt.

Here the statement—Project Apollo should be abandoned—is affirmed as true on the basis of the statements: the billions should be spent on basic scientific research of space; and the project is nothing more than a spectacular stunt. The first statement is the conclusion of the argument and the last two statements are the premisses. This argument can be explicitly written as follows:

Premisses: The billions advocated to project Apollo should be spent on basic scientific research of space.
The project is nothing more than a spectacular stunt.

Conclusion: Project Appollo should be abandoned.

A more complex example of an argument is found in the following paragraphs of an editorial:

3

This week the Federal Trade Commission charged a Brooklyn bubble gum manufacturer with illegally monopolizing a growing industry—the distribution of picture cards of major league baseball players. The commission charged that the manufacturer had exclusive picture card contracts with all but seven of the 421 major players, and he was violating the FTC Act by creating a monopoly in detriment of free competition in the bubble gum and picture card industries.

The FTC may have been only carrying out the provisions of a federal law, but it was at the same time penalizing enterprise and ingenuity—qualities which were instrumental in lifting America to the forefront of all other nations. The absence of these qualities, due to their discouragement by legislation or by any other means, could change a vigorous nation into one without the drive and imagination which are essential to progress and growth.

The primary argument in this editorial is:

Premisses: Discouragement of enterprise and ingenuity could deprive the nation of what is necessary for progress and growth.
The FTC is carrying out monopoly laws which in the bubble gum case discourage enterprise and ingenuity.

Conclusion: The FTC is doing things which could deprive the nation of what is necessary for progress and growth.

Also implicit in this passage is this argument:

Premiss: Enterprise and ingenuity were factors which caused America's rise in world power and greatness.

Conclusion: Lack of these qualities could deprive the nation of its greatness and power.

EXERCISES I

For each of the following: First, indicate any arguments. Second, identify the premisses and conclusion of each argument in the way this was done above with the bubble gum editorial. Third, supply, if necessary, any missing premiss.

It will be helpful to keep in mind that words like "if," "so," "therefore," "for," "since," "because," and "hence" generally indicate that a passage contains an argument. For example, arguments are often phrased in the following ways:

If (premisses), then (conclusion)
(premisses), so (conclusion)
(premisses), therefore (conclusion)
(conclusion), for (premisses)
(conclusion), since (premisses)
(conclusion), because (premisses)
(premisses), thus (conclusion)
(premisses), hence (conclusion)
(premisses), consequently (conclusion)

1. Advertising is something we *should* have in America since it stimulates the economy by inducing the public to buy what they do not essentially need, and it creates mass production, employment, and greater physical well-being by informing people of the availability of new or improved products.

2. Trade with satellite countries like Yugoslavia prevents their complete dependence on the U.S.S.R. Such trade also helps to promote liberalization trends in countries like Poland. In addition, to lose our trade with these countries would not only hurt us because it would reduce Communist trade with Western Europe, but the loss of such trade would strengthen the hand of those who say that a peaceful accommodation between East and West is impossible. Thus we should not listen to the extreme Right; we should not end trade with Communist satellite countries.

3. . . . "Goodbye, till we meet again!" she said as cheerfully as she could.

"I shouldn't know you again if we *did* meet," Humpty Dumpty replied in a discontented tone, giving her one of his fingers to shake: "you're so exactly like other people."

"The face is what one goes by, generally," Alice remarked in a thoughtful tone.

"That's just what I complain of," said Humpty Dumpty. "Your face is the same as everybody has—the two eyes, so—" (marking their places in the air with his thumb) "nose in the middle, mouth under. It's always the same. Now if you had the two eyes on the same side of the nose, for instance—or the mouth at the top—that would be *some* help."

(LEWIS CARROLL, Through the Looking Glass)

4. ". . . there's the King's Messenger. He's in prison now, being punished: and the trial doesn't even begin till next Wednesday: and of course the crime comes last of all."

"Suppose he never commits the crime?" said Alice.

"That would be all the better, wouldn't it?" the Queen said. . . .

Alice felt there was no denying *that.* "Of course it would be all the better," she said: "but it wouldn't be all the better his being punished."

"You're wrong *there,* at any rate," said the Queen. "Were *you* ever punished?"

"Only for faults," said Alice.

"And you were all the better for it, I know!" the Queen said triumphantly.

"Yes, but then I *had* done the things I was punished for," said Alice: "that makes all the difference."

"But if you *hadn't* done them," the Queen said, "that would have been better still. . . ."

(LEWIS CARROLL, Through the Looking-Glass)

5. When she got back to the Cheshire-Cat, she was surprised to find quite a large crowd collected round it: there was a dispute going on between the executioner, the King, and the Queen, who were all talking at once, while the rest were quite silent, and looked very uncomfortable.

The moment Alice appeared, she was appealed to by all three to settle the question, and they repeated their arguments to her, though, as they all spoke at once, she found it very hard to make out exactly what they said.

The executioner's argument was, that you couldn't cut off a head unless there was a body to cut it off from: that he had never had to do such a thing before, and he wasn't going to begin at *his* time of life.

The King's argument was that anything that had a head could be beheaded, and that you weren't to talk nonsense.

The Queen's argument was that, if something wasn't done about it in less than no time, she'd have everybody executed, all round.

(LEWIS CARROLL, *Alice in Wonderland*)

6. I mentioned Hume's argument against the belief of miracles, that it is more probable that the witnesses to the truth of them are mistaken, or speak falsely, than that the miracles should be true. JOHNSON. "Why, Sir, the great difficulty of proving miracles should make us very cautious in believing them. But let us consider; although GOD has made Nature to operate by certain fixed laws, yet it is not unreasonable to think that he may suspend those laws, in order to establish a system highly advantageous to mankind. Now the Christian religion is a most beneficial system, as it gives us light and certainty where we were before in darkness and doubt. The miracles which prove it are attested by men who had no interest in deceiving us; but who, on the contrary, were told that they should suffer persecution, and did actually lay down their lives in confirmation of the truth of the facts which they asserted. Indeed, for some centuries the heathens did not pretend to deny the miracles; but said they were performed by the aid of evil spirits. This is a circumstance of great weight. Then, Sir, when we take the proofs derived from prophecies which have been so exactly fulfilled, we have most satisfactory evidence. Supposing a miracle possible, as to which, in my opinion, there can be no doubt, we have as strong evidence for the miracles in support of Christianity, as the nature of the thing admits."

(JAMES BOSWELL, *Life of Samuel Johnson*)

7. The means to real peace. No government admits any more that it keeps an army to satisfy occasionally the desire for conquest. Rather the army is supposed to serve for defense, and one invokes the morality that approves of self-defense. Moreover, the reasons we give for requiring an army imply that our neighbor, who denies the desire for conquest just as much as does our own state, and who, for his part, also keeps an army only for reasons of self-defense, is a hypocrite and a cunning criminal who would like nothing better than to overpower a harmless and awkward victim without any fight. Thus all states are now ranged against each other: they presuppose their neighbor's bad disposition and their own good disposition. This presupposition, however, is *inhuman,* as bad as war and worse. At bottom, indeed, it is itself the challenge and the cause of wars because, as I have said, it attributes immorality to the neighbor and thus provokes a hostile disposition and act. We

must abjure the doctrine of the army as a means of self-defense just as completely as the desire for conquest.

(NIETZSCHE, *The Wanderer and His Shadow*) [1]

8. In 1962 the merits of the RS-70, an Air Force bomber, were debated.
Each side claimed that the other was absolutely wrong.

The Argument For. General Curtis LeMay, the Air Force Chief of Staff,
flew B-17's against Europe, directed the B-29 attacks against Japan, developed
the Strategic Air Command as the carrier of nuclear deterrent, and still has
deep faith in manned aircraft no matter how fast the art of the missile has
advanced. LeMay argues that a man can operate better in the inevitable confusion of combat than the robot brain of a missile. For the advantages of
manned aircraft at whatever speed or altitude, he has only to point to the
recent experiences of Astronaut John Glenn, who personally took the controls of *Friendship 7* when the automatic equipment performed erratically.
Even more important, if radar were to pick up signs of an attack on the U.S.,
an RS-70 could be sent on its way—and recalled later if the warning turned
out to be false. No one can call back a missile: it goes or it stays.

The RS-70 advocates maintain that the nuclear deterrent must have the
proper "mix" of bombers and missiles to overwhelm an enemy with a variety
of weapons systems. If one does not work, another will—and the RS-70 is a
whole new weapons system in itself. Those same advocates point out that production will stop this year on the Air Force's last two bombers—the 600-
m.p.h. B-52 and the 1,300-m.p.h. B-58. If the RS-70 is held back, they say, the
entire U.S. bomber fleet will eventually be obsolete.

The Air Force argues that the RS-70 would be a hard target to hit. Even
if the Russians built a fighter that could fly 2,000 m.p.h., intercepting an
RS-70 covering 30 miles a minute would be a tricky task. One of the RS-70's
defenses against missiles would be highly secret electronic countermeasures.
The Air Force admits that some RS-70's would be shot down; but many
would get through to annihilate the enemy.

The Case Against. Defense Secretary McNamara trusts his charts, tables and
economic projections just as much as General LeMay trusts his own experiences and intuition. McNamara's figures indicate that the money that would
have to go into the RS-70 could be better spent elsewhere. For the $10 billion
the Air Force wants to spend on RS-70's by 1970, McNamara says the U.S.
could buy 2,000 Minuteman missiles, install them with all their equipment in
concrete silos buried deep in the ground. What is more, it would cost $3 bil-
lion to maintain the RS-70 fleet for five years, *v.* $2 billion for the 2,000
Minutemen.

McNamara also argues that the RS-70 would be useless unless equipped
with target-spotting radar and target-obliterating nuclear missiles that have
not yet been designed—and might never be. The proposed radar would have

[1] Friedrich Nietzsche, *The Wanderer and His Shadow*, in *The Portable
Nietzsche*, Walter Kaufmann, trans. and ed. (New York: The Viking Press, 1954),
pp. 71–72.

to scan 100,000 sq. mi. an hour while the plane was traveling at 2,000 m.p.h. at 70,000 ft. To separate two points at that height, McNamara argued, would require a radar screen 15 ft. wide and 15 ft. high. By the late '60's, Mc-Namara feels that the job of reconnaissance could be done by advanced versions of the Samos spy-in-the-sky satellite.

("RS-70: Bust or Superplane?" *Time*, March 30, 1962) [2]

9. In March 1961, there were rumors widespread in the United States that this country was planning to support an invasion of Cuba by a group of Cuban refugees. The following argument against such a plan is reported to have been presented to President Kennedy by Senator J. William Fulbright:

The problem in Latin America was not with governments. It was with people, particularly with workers, peasants and students. If so, the argument that Castro must go in order to keep his influence from spreading further among these groups failed to take into account the fact that Castro's influence had already gone far beyond the personal appeal of Castro the individual. It would persist as a doctrine of radical social reform with anti-Yanqui overtones long after Fidel Castro.

Furthermore, on the provisional assumption that an attempt would be made by Cuban refugees to overthrow him, and on the further assumption that the attempt succeeded, it was worth asking whether the successor government would be equal to the task facing it. The evidence about the leaders of the Democratic Revolutionary Front who presumably would constitute that government pointed to a discouraging conclusion. As an uncomfortable coalition of dissident interests, it had no men in it who could provide vigorous, progressive government. If they came to power, and failed on the social and political front, the U.S. would be blamed; if they were partly successful, the U.S. would be blamed, not only in Cuba but elsewhere, for their shortcomings.

Finally, the political question to one side, what should the U.S. do if Cuban exiles failed? Should the U.S. let the enterprise fail, in the probably futile hope of concealing the U.S. role in it? Should it respond openly with whatever assistance might be necessary to insure the success of the invasion? Overt assistance would undo the work of 30 years in trying to live down earlier U.S. interventions in Latin American affairs. Even covert support of a Castro overthrow would be in violation of the spirit, and probably the letter as well, of domestic legislation and of treaties to which the U.S. was a party. Besides, covert support would be of a piece with the hypocrisy and cynicism for which the United States was constantly denouncing the Soviet Union. And the point would not be lost on the world.

Provided that the Soviet Union used Cuba only as a political and not as a military base, the Castro regime should be viewed as a thorn in our flesh, not a dagger in our heart. If so, the real question was whether Castro could in fact succeed in providing a better life for the Cuban people; and whether

[2] "RS-70: Bust or Superplane?" *Time*, March 30, 1962, p. 15. Courtesy TIME; Copyright Time Inc., 1962.

he could do a better job in this respect in Cuba than the U.S. and its friends could do elsewhere in Latin America. It would be a fatal confession of failure in ourselves and our values if we decreed that Castro must go because he might succeed.

What the U.S. had to do immediately, Fulbright suggested, was to address itself to the sadly neglected political orientation of its economic aid program. Insofar as they had political content at all, these programs had usually been keyed to support a given government in power, and too often this had been a traditional, oligarchical government on its way out.

We must sometime stop supporting governments which paid lip service to social reforms, but which did not really have it in their hearts. We must perforce deal with these governments, but if they could not be corrected in their ways, they were going to be overthrown. We must make it clear to them that the time for conversion was growing short; that if they were converted to the cause of genuine social reform, we would help them; but that if they were not, we did not propose to be overthrown with them.

(SIDNEY HYMAN, "Fulbright of Arkansas") [3]

THE LOGICAL CORRECTNESS
OF AN ARGUMENT

There are many ways to appraise an argument; for example, one can ask: Are the premisses true? This will not be our interest in appraising arguments. Rather we will be interested in whether an argument is logically correct or incorrect. An argument is *correct,* as we will use the word, when the premiss or premisses constitute good grounds for affirming the conclusion.

Consider again the first argument on page 3, the Project Apollo argument. Of this argument it can be asked: Is it a correct argument? Do the premisses constitute good grounds for affirming the conclusion? That is, supposing that the billions advocated to Project Apollo should be spent on basic scientific research of space and that the project is nothing more than a spectacular stunt, does this provide good grounds for affirming that Project Apollo should be abandoned? The answer is clearly "Yes." That is, if it is true that the billions advocated to the project should be spent on basic scientific research of space, and if it is true that the project is nothing more than a spectacular stunt, then this provides strong grounds indeed for thinking that Project Apollo should be abandoned. The exercises at the end of the first section also provide examples

---

[3] Sidney Hyman, "Fulbright of Arkansas," *The New Republic,* Vol. 146, No. 20, May 14, 1962, p. 24. Copyright © 1962 by Harrison-Blaine, Inc. Used by permission of *The New Republic.*

of correct arguments. For example, the cases made on *each* side of the RS-70 controversy are correct. Of course, since the conclusions of the two arguments are incompatible, the arguments do not establish the conclusion; but, nevertheless, the arguments are both correct. As another example, Fulbright's argument concerning the 1961 invasion of Cuba is a logically correct argument.

A clear-cut example of an incorrect argument is the following:

The Exodus from Egypt did take place, for the account of this event has been a source of inspiration to millions throughout the centuries.

The premiss—the account of this event has been a source of inspiration to millions—does not provide good grounds for affirming the conclusion —the Exodus from Egypt did take place. In fact, we would say that the premiss or reason is irrelevant to the truth of the conclusion. Reasons relevant to the truth of the conclusion would touch on such things as historical records, eyewitness reports, and archaeological findings.

CORRECTNESS OF AN ARGUMENT AND TRUTH OF THE PREMISSES

The correctness of an argument is determined independently of the truth of the premisses of the argument. For to ask if an argument is correct is to ask: Supposing the premisses are true, do they provide good grounds for affirming the conclusion? The independence of the correctness of the argument from the truth of the premisses can be brought out in this way: A correct argument can have false premisses, and an incorrect argument can have true premisses.

For example, in this correct argument the premiss is false:

That Moses was a historical figure can be doubted because we have no written record of Moses' life.

The premiss—we have no written record of Moses' life—provides good grounds for affirming the conclusion. But this premiss is false since we have the Old Testament account. An example of an incorrect argument with a true premiss is:

Freud is a confessed atheist and does not believe in the Bible, so we can conclude that his view that Moses was an Egyptian is false.

Since the truth of the premiss is irrelevant to the truth of the conclusion, this argument is clearly incorrect. That is, in determining whether Moses was an Egyptian, one would not count Freud's atheism. It is true, however, that Freud was an atheist.

From this it is clear that the truth or falsity of the premisses does not determine the correctness or incorrectness of the argument. Thus to ask if the premises of an argument are true is one thing, and to ask if the argument is logically correct is another thing.

EXERCISES II

Consider again the arguments found in the last exercises. Which arguments are correct? Indicate, as far as is possible, those premisses which are true.

FALLACIES

A *fallacious* argument in logic is an incorrect argument. It is also customary to restrict the word "fallacious" to incorrect arguments which in certain contexts *seem* to some to be correct. The two examples of incorrect arguments we have considered are:

1. The Exodus from Egypt did take place, for the account of this event has been a source of inspiration to millions throughout the centuries.
2. Freud is a confessed atheist and does not believe in the Bible, so we can conclude that his view that Moses was an Egyptian is false.

In our terminology each one is fallacious. In certain circumstances, (1) and (2) might be erroneously regarded as correct arguments. In (2) we see that the arguer, rather than presenting reasons relevant to the falsity of Freud's view, attacks Freud himself. The same thing happens in this incorrect or fallacious argument:

3. Professor Breasted is a confessed theist and believes in the Bible, so we can conclude that his view that Moses was not an Egyptian is false.

In both (2) and (3) the man is attacked and it is inferred from statements about him that his view is false. No reason is given which is relevant to deciding whether his view is true. These incorrect arguments thus exemplify a common pattern. Incorrect arguments with this particular pattern are commonly called *ad hominem* arguments. This type of fallacy and other types will be discussed in the next chapter.[4]

In (1), (2), and (3), as we have seen, the truth of the premises of the argument is irrelevant to the conclusion. To say that the truth of the

---

[4] Later (in Parts II and III) the distinction is made between deductive and inductive arguments. A valid deductive argument is, of course, a correct argument, and an invalid deductive argument is an incorrect argument. Certain kinds of invalid deductive arguments have been given names and are classed under formal fallacies. Most of the fallacies considered in this Part are informal fallacies—that is, nondeductive (of one of the kinds of inductive arguments) incorrect arguments. We will reserve the term "valid" for appraising deductive arguments. Valid arguments, following this convention, are thus one kind of correct argument.

premiss(es) is irrelevant to the conclusion means—to be more specific—that the premiss(es) should not be considered in determining whether the conclusion is true. To determine whether the Exodus took place, we would not consider the fact that the account of the Exodus has been a source of inspiration to millions. We would consider written records, archaeological findings, and the like. Similarly, our grounds for concluding either that Moses was or was not an Egyptian should not include statements about the religious beliefs of those who hold one view or the other.

Often in a fallacious argument the truth of the premiss(es) is irrelevant to the truth of the conclusion. But in some fallacious arguments this will not be so, for they are fallacious for other reasons. Consider, for example, this passage from *Huckleberry Finn:*

4. Well, I was getting to feel that way myself, though I've always reckoned that looking at the new moon over your left shoulder is one of the carelessest and foolishest things a body can do. Old Hank Bunker done it once, and bragged about it; and in less than two years he got drunk and fell off of the shot-tower and spread himself out so that he was just kind of a layer, as you may say; and they slid him edgeways between two barn doors for a coffin, and buried him so, so they say, but I didn't see it. Pap told me. But anyway it all come of looking at the moon that way, like a fool.

The argument which can be constructed from this passage is:

5. Old Hank Bunker looked at a new moon over his left shoulder and got drunk and fell off a tower and died. Therefore looking at the new moon over his left shoulder caused his death or, generally, looking over your left shoulder at the new moon causes bad luck.

This argument is incorrect. Obviously the bad luck (falling off the tower) following the look at the moon is not good grounds for concluding that the look caused the bad luck. However, in establishing whether such a look causes bad luck (that is, unfortunate events) or does not cause bad luck (if anyone would ever be interested in this question), the fact that Hank Bunker looked at the moon and then died would have to be considered.

THE GENERAL CIRCUMSTANCES
OF ARGUMENTS

The phrase *general circumstances of an argument* means such things as:

The shared beliefs of the audience to which the argument is addressed.
Innuendo, verbal emphasis, and gestures, if such things accompany the argument.

What is said or written before and after the presentation of the argument.
The physical surroundings.
Events which happened before or at the time of the argument.

In fact, it would be difficult to name anything which *could not* be part of the general circumstances of an argument.

It happens that sometimes we misappraise an argument as correct or incorrect because we lack knowledge of some aspect of the general circumstances. And sometimes an argument in one set of circumstances will be incorrect while the same argument will be correct in another set of circumstances. To illustrate this latter possibility first, consider these incorrect arguments:

1. Mr. Corpulent, my husband deserves a raise in pay. We can just barely feed our six children on his pay. Another one is on the way; and if our youngest is ever to walk she needs an operation.
2. No scandal has ever touched Senator Snort, so we can conclude that he is incorruptible.

The first is ordinarily classified as incorrect because, ordinarily, a man's output and not his need is relevant to the question of whether his wages should be increased. But we could imagine that in some circumstances need is one of the relevant factors considered in determining a man's wage. In these circumstances (1) would not be easily classified as incorrect. Also the wife might be using "deserves" to mean "needs," in which case (1) would not be fallacious. The second is classified as incorrect because, it is argued, a person's not ever being touched by scandal does not provide good grounds for concluding that he is incorruptible. (Notice, by the way, that even if the argument is fallacious, the premiss is not irrelevant to determining whether the conclusion is true.) But let us suppose that during Senator Snort's term of office there were great and powerful forces leading senators into corruption. And let us suppose that the press was good at detecting and reporting scandal. In these circumstances we might hesitate to call (2) incorrect.

A real-life case which one may be inclined to misappraise is this: In 1961 the Faculty Council of the Ohio State University prevented the Ohio State football team from going to the Rose Bowl. A state representative in the legislature was reported to have opposed this decision and his argument was:

Many thousands of dollars of taxpayers' money are spent on faculty trips to various places for various purposes; therefore the football team should go to the Rose Bowl.

This argument, taken apart from circumstances, seems incorrect. The reason does not seem to be at all relevant to the conclusion, especially since, as the representative knew, the Rose Bowl organization pays the expenses of the two participating teams. But with a knowledge of the circumstances in which this argument was given, we find that the argument (in its circumstances) is no longer obviously incorrect. The argument was given on the floor of the Ohio State Assembly. All the representatives were fully acquainted with the justifications for tax money going to a state university. All or most of them shared the belief that a state university is justified because it is in the state's interest. This plus other knowledge of the circumstances helps us to see that the representative's argument amounted to the following:

Since we spend many thousand of dollars on faculty trips (and, for that matter on the state university itself) to promote the interests of the state, it follows that we should send the team to the Rose Bowl, since this promotes the interests of the state and is free. [Most of the representatives thought sending the team would promote the interests of the state.]

As we can see, the reasons no longer seem irrelevant to the conclusion.

SUMMARY

Arguments can be appraised as correct or incorrect. To ask whether an argument is correct is to ask: If the premisses are true, do they constitute good grounds for affirming the conclusion? The incorrect arguments we have considered can be divided into two groups. First, those which are such that the truth of the premisses is irrelevant to deciding whether the conclusion is true. By "irrelevant" is meant that the premisses would not or should not be placed among the evidence which would be considered in determining whether the conclusion is true or false. Second, there are arguments which are such that the premisses, though relevant, do not constitute sufficient evidence for affirming the conclusion. The correctness or incorrectness of the arguments we consider is independent of the truth or falsity of the premisses. However, as a rule, knowledge of the general circumstances is necessary to judge with certainty whether an argument is correct.

In Part I we will examine certain kinds of incorrect arguments and consider the logic of ordinary language. The purpose of the latter is to help us to see mistakes in reasoning and incorrect arguments which result from the ambiguities of ordinary language.

EXERCISES III

A. Follow directions given on page 4 for the exercises at the end of the section "Arguments." In addition, try to determine which arguments are correct and which are incorrect.

1.   Marx said that there are certain irreversible laws operating in history. One of the consequences of these laws is that Capitalism will shatter and out of it will come Communism. Communism could emerge only from Capitalism. Russia was one of the first countries where Communist ideas flourished. Yet Russia at that time was a backward country and would take many years to catch up to the stage Marx called "Capitalism." In 1881 a member of the Populists in Russia wrote to Marx and asked for his support in their movement. Marx was in a dilemma. If he encouraged the movement, then this would conflict with his theory. If he didn't encourage the movement, then perhaps the strongest Communist movement would die or be taken over by other ideologies.

2.   During the Berlin crisis in 1961 an editorial appeared in a newspaper which (in substance) argued: Mobilization can't be wrong. If the United States mobilization calls the Soviet bluff, then it merely brings out the fact that the Soviets do not intend to go to war over Berlin. On the other hand, if the Soviets are planning to initiate a war of conquest in order to spread their slavery over the world, then it is essential to mobilize. In both cases mobilization is either worth it or essential; thus no error can be made in mobilizing now.

3.   We are not alone. There is life on other planets. For, first, the conservative estimate of the number of stars is 10^{21}; second, these stars' origin is the same as that of our sun; third, many of the stars which radiate energy suitable for the complex biological activity that we call life are accompanied by planets; and, last, biochemistry has gone so far in bridging the gap between the inanimate and the living that we can no longer doubt but that whenever the physics, chemistry, and climates are right on a planet's surface, life will emerge, persist, and evolve.

(Adapted from HARLOW SHAPLEY, *Of Stars and Men*) [5]

4.   GLENDOWER: . . . at my nativity
The front of heaven was full of fiery shapes,
Of burning cressets; and at my birth
The frame and huge foundation of the earth
Shak'd like a coward.

HOTSPUR: Why, so it would have done at the same season if your mother's cat had but kittened, though yourself had never been born.

(SHAKESPEARE, *Henry IV*, Part I)

5.   Hoffa's Teamsters were expelled from the AFL-CIO after the McClellan Committee of the United States Senate presented volumes of evidence that the union was crawling with extortionists and racketeers. Joseph Curran, the president of the National Maritime Union, gives these reasons why the Teamsters should be taken back into the organization:

[5] Harlow Shapley, *Of Stars and Men* (New York: Washington Square Press, 1960), pp. 99–101.

1. Anyone who would stand up and say that he didn't want the Teamsters back is not a trade unionist.
2. Hoffa's been cleared by the courts, hasn't he? Who am I to say he's guilty—or you. Of course some people aren't satisfied with the courts, or with democracy either.
3. Expulsion has played into the hands of labor's enemies who are using Hoffa to get at all of organized labor.
4. Why demand reform concessions from Hoffa, who is legally in the clear, and not from Maurice Hutcheson, the Carpenters' president who was actually convicted?

(Adapted from *The Reporter*) [6]

6. Lenin organized a military insurrection to overthrow the Kerenski government in 1918. Following the revolution there was a general election to determine membership of the Constituent Assembly. The results disappointed Lenin. Of some 700 elected members 410 were Socialist Revolutionaries and 175 were Lenin's Bolsheviks. So Lenin dissolved the assembly. He gave three reasons for doing so:
1. The S.R. party "no longer existed" since after the election 40 of the 410 members split off from the party.
2. The Soviets were a "higher form of democratic principle" than the Assembly. (The Soviets were small organizations among the workers, soldiers, and peasants, where the Bolsheviks had won a great deal of support.)
3. The results of the election were not representative since the election was held at a time when "the people could not yet know the full scope and meaning" of the Bolsheviks' insurrection.

(Adapted from HUGH SETON-WATSON, *From Lenin to Khrushchev*) [7]

7. The purpose of this brief talk is to prove to you that the Soviet concept of personal liberty, which I shall tag "economic liberty," agrees more impressively than the Western concept with truths which any reasonable man must assent to. In extending "economic liberty" to her citizens, the USSR in fact denies them the right to starve, to be malnourished, to be victimized by their employers, to be put out of work in depressions, and in general to suffer under conditions which parade themselves so enticingly under the mask of personal liberty. Our system is geared to protect every citizen from exercising such "freedoms."

Now you will object that the Soviet citizen is guaranteed food, clothes, housing, employment, and medical care only at the cost of his complete subservience to the community and at the total sacrifice of personal mobility. There is of course a sense in which the Soviet citizen of today lacks certain prerogatives.

[6] Robert Bendiner, "What's Wrong in the House of Labor?" in *The Reporter*, October 12, 1961.

[7] Hugh Seton-Watson, *From Lenin to Khrushchev* (New York: Praeger, 1960), pp. 36–37.

He may not strike, or criticize, or take a day off when he is bored and weary, or choose among a general abundance of consumer goods, or offer his children religious training. However, these lacks are not to trouble the Soviet man indefinitely. Succeeding generations will either cease to feel them as lacks or else see them satisfied. There is one great point that you Westerners, on your Roman couch of luxury, tend to forget, namely that every Soviet citizen is spiritedly working for a *cause*. That cause is the classless society to come. So inspired, they do not chafe as you do under every little temporary unpleasantness. They are indeed rather like your religious workers—priests and brothers and nuns, rabbis and ministers, who in their devotion neither strike, nor complain, nor cry out, nor ask for a day off, nor cherish consumer goods.

The main line of my argument, however, is this. If a government takes no steps whatever to insure its own stability against capricious elements of the populace, including those whose interests are anarchical and antiprogressive, then obviously that government cannot long operate as a government. It cannot govern. For this reason every city has its police force, every hamlet its sheriff, every regiment its guardhouse. For the same reason the several states of the American Union became a federation, and for the same reason every government duly constituted has the absolute duty to have a say in whatever public actions affect its power to govern. Now if this is the case, and I see by your faces that no one here is addled enough to disagree with me, we can go one step further. All of the things I am about to list, and many others besides, have major consequences for government in the long run: what political party a citizen belongs to, how many children he raises, what soldiers do with their leisure, how workers spend their money, what broadcasters say on the radio, and how much editorial freedom is tolerated in the newspapers—but I could go on listing things all evening. The point is this: you have already agreed with me that actions which affect the government ought to be subject to review and approval by the government if it wishes to survive. A very great number of actions by private citizens have some sort of influence, whether at short range or long, on the government. It follows with certainty, then, that these actions should be controlled by farsighted officials and not left to the citizen himself to decide. To deny this is to give license to spies, counterfeiters, tax-evaders, anarchists, monopolists, and other seamy elements. Thus, the Soviet concept of "economic liberty" is already materially recognized and approved in principle in your own lands, as evidenced by those agencies of your governments whose duty is to counteract such elements as threats to the ability of government to exercise its functions.[8]

B. Imagine circumstances in which each of the following arguments would be correct, and imagine circumstances in which each argument would be incorrect.

  1. You can tell that Noodles Romanoff is a disreputable person by the char-

---

[8] This example was created by Professor Harry Nielsen of the University of Notre Dame, and is used here with his permission.

acter of his associates, for the kind of people who go around with people such as he are the lowest type.

2. You ought to vote for a union shop, Utah Jenkins. If you don't we'll see that you lose your job.

3. Vote for Senator Snort. He was wounded twice in the Laosian war. He has ten pounds of shrapnel in his right leg. He is married and has seven children. In addition, he has to support two unemployed brothers-in-law.

4. Catfish State Teachers College has an excellent faculty. Professor Zool, a member of it, must therefore be an excellent teacher.

5. As creators, women are superior to men since men can only create works of art, science, or philosophy, whereas woman can create life.

6. "How do you know you've got what it takes?" Mrs. Ogmore-Pritchard: "Most of us take it for granted that we have what it takes. The proof is that if we don't have it, people will quickly tell us. No, I haven't been told of any real or supposed shortcomings. I have what it takes!"

7. The achievement of our aims in the Middle East demands the continued support in Congress of that policy which has so far proven successful in that area. No evidence has been forthcoming which would indicate that our present Middle Eastern policy has been unwise. It therefore seems reasonable to recommend the passage of this bill.

8. Could the reason for the unexcelled superiority of American optical goods be this: they have been made under a competitive system?

9. Why should I support your bill? Last year you opposed the very measure which you now advocate.

10. We should have a fallout shelter program not to make deterrence credible, nor to give our diplomacy muscle, but merely as insurance. A home owner buys fire insurance to save himself from the financial loss that would follow a fire, so we should invest a few hundred dollars in a shelter that might save us from the perils of radiation that would follow a nuclear attack.

Chapter Two

TRADITIONAL
INFORMAL
FALLACIES

Many kinds of incorrect arguments have been studied by logicians and given names. The *ad hominem* fallacy, which was discussed briefly in the first chapter, is one such kind. In this chapter we will consider many of the fallacies traditionally discussed in logic texts. Several of them were first discussed by Aristotle, the famous Greek philosopher.

In accordance with an ancient tradition which began with Aristotle's short treatise *De Sophistici Elenchi,* we will divide the traditional fallacies into two groups: material fallacies and fallacies of ambiguity. *Fallacies of ambiguity* are arguments which are incorrect or invalid because of some ambiguity in the language, for example, because a word, phrase, or statement can be understood in different ways. The *material fallacies* are arguments which are incorrect for reasons other than the ambiguity of language. As Aristotle said, they arise from the subject matter of the argument and cannot be detected and set right by those unacquainted with the subject matter.

We will, in addition, divide material fallacies into fallacies of relevance and fallacies of insufficient evidence. The material fallacies of *relevance* are arguments whose premises are irrelevant to establishing the truth of the conclusion. Material fallacies of *insufficient evidence* are arguments whose premises are relevant to the conclusion but are not good grounds for affirming the conclusion.

At the end of the last chapter it was noted that an argument can be fallacious in one set of circumstances and not fallacious in another. Thus to be certain that an argument is fallacious, one must have knowledge of the circumstances in which the argument is presented. In this

19

chapter some of the examples of fallacious arguments are from real-life and some are made up. While it is not practically possible to provide the general circumstances for either type, some of the relevant context is given for the real-life examples. Consequently, for many of the arguments one can, with some imagination, describe circumstances in which the argument would not be fallacious. The reader is thus asked to presuppose circumstances which would make the argument fallacious.

THE MATERIAL FALLACIES
OF RELEVANCE

The *ad Hominem* Fallacy

The *ad hominem* fallacy (fallacy directed to the man) is committed when the conclusion of an argument states that a view is mistaken, and the reasons given for this conclusion amount to no more than a criticism of the person or persons maintaining the view.

There are a number of ways to criticize a person. One common way is to criticize his *character*. For example, in 1961 the Ohio State football team was invited to the Rose Bowl. The Faculty Council turned down the invitation. Some of the letters protesting this decision are reflected in this letter:

Never have I been so disgusted and ashamed of a group of so-called "intellectuals" as I was when I read the decision not to allow our fine football team to play in the Rose Bowl on January 1. They obviously showed extremely poor judgment in the Rose Bowl matter. For the faculty is a hypocritical bunch of jerks. I think the faculty is just plain jealous of what little notoriety the players and coaches get from a game like the Rose Bowl. It is most unfortunate that 28 near-sighted introverts can call the shots, for we all know what judgments these people make.

"SOCKO" FRIENDLY, '59

As we can see, the author opposes the decision of the Faculty Council. The reasons he gives are that the Council is made up of "near-sighted introverts," "hypocrites," and men who are jealous of the notoriety of the players and coaches. Of course none of this is true, but even if it were, it would not constitute good grounds for stating that the decision reflects poor judgment. Since the conclusion of this argument is that a view is mistaken, and since the reasons given for this conclusion amount to no more than a criticism of the party supporting the view, the *ad hominem* fallacy is committed.

In opposing someone's view there are ways to criticize him other than trying to discredit his character. Here are examples of three other common ways in which an *ad hominem* fallacy is committed:

The Administration appointed, and the Senate approved, the nomination of Tom Sawyer to the Civil Rights Commission. Sawyer, now dean of the Harvard Law School, has long been an active member and one of the chief protagonists of the National Association for the Advancement of Colored People. The Civil Rights Commission, so-called, exercises a quasijudicial function. It decides whether something is wrong and makes recommendations to the Justice Department, which then prosecutes. It also makes recommendations for "civil rights" laws. Appointment of Sawyer is the same thing as making the NAACP an arm of the Justice Department, and of making a judge out of a party to a suit. There can be no unbiased findings, and no true justice, under such an arrangement.

The argument is that since Sawyer is an "active member" and a "chief protagonist" of the NAACP, his findings will be biased and his decisions unjust as a member of the Civil Rights Commission—in a word, his *special circumstances* will make him biased. Now this might be a reason to be skeptical of his findings and decisions as a member of the federal commission, but it is not a reason to conclude that his findings will be biased and his decisions unjust.

Air Force General "Flip-Flop" Herbert has testified in favor of our starting to manufacture the new RS-1099E. In fact it is his view that it would be absolutely disastrous to our defenses if we do not immediately start building these bombers in great quantity. But his views are ridiculous and are nothing more than the expression of ruthless self-interest. For in two months General Herbert will retire and become a high-level executive and stockholder in the bomber division of General Juggernaut Corporation—the very people who will build the RS-1099E.

The criticism of the man here takes the form of arguing that his views are mistaken because it is in some way in his *interest* to have us believe his views. In this case it is argued that General Herbert's views about the RS-1099E are mistaken because it is to his financial interest that certain people believe his views. Now it might be that the general's views are mistaken, but the fact that he profits from people believing him is irrelevant to the question of whether his views are true. However, this knowledge about the general's new job would certainly be a good reason to examine the evidence for and against his views.

A debate took place one time over the issue whether the military in the United States should educate the people to the nonmilitary dangers of Communism. One of the senators who strongly maintained that the military should educate the people opposed federal aid to education on the grounds that it would bring the federal government into an area reserved to the states. An Arkansas senator who wanted to discourage the military from educating the people in this way argued: "The South Carolina senator who opposed federal aid to education apparently wants the military to educate the people."

The Arkansas senator is suggesting that the South Carolinian's views on the military are inconsistent with his views on federal aid to education. If one inferred from this claimed inconsistency that the senator's views on the military are mistaken, this would be an *ad hominem* fallacy. If someone's views are shown to be inconsistent, what is shown is only that they *all* cannot be true. Here, then, is a case of criticizing a man by showing an *incompatibility* of the view under consideration with his other views.

It should not be overlooked that not all arguments criticizing a man are fallacious. For example, consider this fictitious argument:

President Kennedy while in office has accepted immense bribes, imprisoned his political opponents, taken vast sums of money from the United States treasury and put it in Swiss banks, and he has made plans for declaring himself king. Therefore we should impeach him.

This clearly is an attack on a man. However, if the premisses of this argument were true, this would be good grounds indeed for affirming the conclusion. Consequently, the argument is quite sound.

The *Tu Quoque* Fallacy

Tu quoque means "you're another." The *tu quoque* fallacy is committed when one tries to reply to a charge made by an opponent by making the same or a similar charge against him. Consider these two examples:

So these are your grounds for criticizing the way we treat our native population. In answer let me just say, "Who was it that killed most of the American Indians?"

The charge has been made by my opponent that I illegally acquired the money for this campaign. In reply to this I want it to be known that all the money my opponent has for his campaign is illegally acquired.

These arguments are both instances of the *tu quoque* fallacy. In each case someone answers a charge by making a similar charge. These arguments are fallacious because no relevant reason is given for why the policy toward the native population should be continued or for why we should believe that the campaign money was not illegally acquired.

Stuart Chase, in his *Guides to Straight Thinking*, reports this amusing story which can be organized into a *tu quoque* fallacy: [1]

---

[1] Stuart Chase, *Guides to Straight Thinking* (New York: Harper, 1956), p. 65.

The story runs that when the Moscow underground was first opened to visitors in the 1930's, an American tourist was invited to inspect one of the stations. He was shown the self-registering turnstiles and the spotless washrooms. "Fine," he said; then, looking down the tracks, "How about the trains?" They showed him the safety devices and the excellent tile frescos on the tunnel walls. He was again impressed, but continued to look anxiously down the tracks. "How about the trains?" snapped his guide. "How about the trains? How about the share-croppers in Alabama?"

The *ad Populum* Fallacy

Sometimes in an argument one tries to persuade someone of the truth or falsity of a view by appealing to his emotions and prejudices in some way rather than by giving reasons which support the truth or falsity of the view. When this is done, the fallacy called the *ad populum* fallacy is committed. This excerpt from Ingersoll's nomination speech for James G. Blaine for President in 1876 is, on the whole, an *ad populum* argument:

Our country, crowned with the vast and marvelous achievements of its first century, asks for a man worthy of her past—prophetic of her future; asks for a man who has the audacity of genius; asks for a man who is the grandest combination of heart, conscience, and brains beneath the flag. That man is James G. Blaine.

For the Republican host led by that intrepid man there can be no such thing as defeat.

This is a grand year—a year filled with the recollections of the Revolution; filled with proud and tender memories of the sacred past; filled with the legends of liberty; a year in which the sons of freedom will drink from the fountain of enthusiasm; a year in which the people call for a man who has preserved in Congress what our soldiers won upon the field; a year in which we call for the man who has torn from the throat of treason the tongue of slander—a man who has snatched the mask of democracy from the hideous face of rebellion—a man who, like an intellectual athlete, stood in the arena of debate, challenged all comers, and who, up to the present moment, is a total stranger to defeat.

Like an armed warrior, like a plumed knight, James G. Blaine marched down the halls of the American Congress and threw his shining lances full and fair against the brazen foreheads of every defamer of his country and maligner of its honor.

For the Republican party to desert a gallant man now is worse than if an army should desert their general upon the field of battle.

James G. Blaine is now, and has been for years, the bearer of the sacred standard of the Republic. I call it sacred because no human being can stand beneath its folds without becoming, and without remaining, free.[2]

2 *The World's Famous Orations*, ed., William Jennings Bryan, Vol. X (New York: Funk and Wagnalls, 1906), pp. 79–80.

In this example, no reasons are given, for instance, for Blaine's being a prophet of America's future and for his being "the grandest combination of heart, conscience, and brains beneath the flag." Perhaps in a convention like that of 1876, all the delegates knew the reasons, so all that was called for was an emotionally stirring speech to get them to *act* on their knowledge. Nevertheless, we have little more here than an emotional appeal by use of words and phrases like "the flag," "the Revolution," "legends of liberty," "sons of freedom," and "sacred past."

Socrates in 399 B.C. was accused of not worshipping the gods whom the state worshipped and of introducing new and unfamiliar religious practices; he was further accused of corrupting the youth of Athens. Socrates gave a rational and what seems a conclusive defense against these charges. Nevertheless he was found guilty. Socrates, in the passage below, indicates the kind of defense which would have led the jury to find him innocent and thus render a just decision. As we can see, it is an appeal to pity:

Well, Athenians, this and the like of this is all the defence which I have to offer. Yet a word more. Perhaps there may be some one who is offended at me, when he calls to mind how he himself on a similar, or even a less serious occasion, prayed and entreated the judges with many tears, and how he produced his children in court, which was a moving spectacle, together with a host of relations and friends; whereas I, who am probably in danger of my life, will do none of these things. The contrast may occur to his mind, and he may be set against me, and vote in anger because he is displeased at me on this account. Now if there be such a person among you—mind, I do not say that there is— to him I may fairly reply: My friend, I am a man, and like other men, a creature of flesh and blood, and not "of wood or stone," as Homer says; and I have a family, yes, and sons, O Athenians, three in number, one almost a man, and two others who are still young; and yet I will not bring any of them hither in order to petition you for an acquittal. And why not? Not from any self-assertion or want of respect for you. Whether I am or am not afraid of death is another question, of which I will not speak. But, having regard to public opinion, I feel that such conduct would be discreditable to myself, and to you, and to the whole state.

(PLATO, *Apology*)

The means of defence which Socrates did not choose to use was clearly an argument which appeals to emotions.[3] In this case the emotion appealed to is pity. When such an appeal is used to (supposedly) support a contention of some sort a fallacy is committed: an *argumentum ad misericordiam* (fallacy of appeal to pity).

[3] From the context of the *Apology* it can be seen that Socrates is neither directly nor indirectly using an appeal to emotion. The majority of the jury reacted to this as an insult and Socrates knew that this would be its effect.

Another type of appeal to emotion is found in this example:

In 1961 the Western Powers held that they had certain rights in West Berlin, while the Soviet Union denied that they had such rights. Other nations were placed by both powers in the position of having to take sides. At that time the Soviet Union announced and tested a nuclear bomb that was about a hundred times more powerful than any United States bomb.

Suppose the Soviet Union had argued: We have the largest bomb in the world, consequently our claims about Berlin are true. This would be an instance of the fallacy which bears the name *argumentum ad baculum* (fallacy of appeal to force). If someone were led to conclude from this argument that the Soviet Union's claims were true, he would have fallen victim to an *ad baculum* fallacy. Here it should be noted that not all appeals to force are or involve fallacies. For example, simple threats ("Your money or your life") are appeals to force, but are not or do not involve fallacies.

There is yet another observation to be made concerning the *ad baculum* fallacy. Of the nuclear bomb example we said that if it is correct that the fear of these new bombs led some to conclude that the Soviet Union's claims were true, then they fell victim to an *ad baculum* fallacy. But it seems to be highly unlikely that the fear of new bombs (or of anything else) would lead anyone to *conclude* that the Soviet Union's claims were *true*. Fear might indeed lead some to *say* that those claims were true, but hardly to *believe* (or conclude) that they were. We suppose that in such a case fear of (possible) consequences would not befog the mind, would not cause one to be duped into thinking a certain claim true, though this fear might well lead one to give lip service to the claim. If this observation is correct, then there exists serious doubt that what have traditionally been called fallacies of appeal to force, or *ad baculum* fallacies, are fallacies at all, since one is not taken in by the "argument," but at best only wishes to appear to be taken in—because he is afraid.

The *ad Verecundiam* Fallacy

The *ad verecundiam* fallacy (appeal to authority fallacy) occurs when one supports a view by appealing to the endorsement of the view by someone who is not in fact an authority on the subject matter being considered. Thus if someone argues that Soviet Russia will take over the United States before 1970 and supports this claim by citing the fact that Mr. X says they will, and Mr. X is not an authority on the Cold War and the world situation, this would be an instance of the *ad verecundiam* fallacy. If, on the other hand, Mr. X is an expert in the field, the argument would be correct. Thus in order for an argument which is an appeal to authority to be a fallacy, it must be the case that the person whose opinion is being appealed to is not an authority in the area under consideration.

In 1958, to consider a real-life example, Robert Welch, the founder of the John Birch Society, in a series of talks which were collected in what is called *The Blue Book,* said such things as: (a) Unless we can reverse the seemingly relentless forces now at work, the United States in only a few more years will become four separate provinces in a world-wide, Kremlin-based Communist dominion. (b) The method by which the Communists are trying to take over the United States is to induce the gradual surrender of United States sovereignty to various international organizations, for example, the United Nations, and to change the economic and political structure of the United States so that it can comfortably merge with Soviet Russia. (c) Although our real danger is internal—from Communist influences and treason in our government—the American people are being led to believe that the danger is external—from Russian military superiority. (d) The only thing which the Communists fear is that, in spite of their tremendous influence in our government and their control of mass media, the American people will someday wake up to what is happening.

According to Welch this is all "the facts," but during these talks little evidence is given other than Welch's testimony. Who then is Welch? He has been in the candy manufacturing business all of his adult life. In addition, to quote Welch:

> . . . I should like to make clear in my own defense that my credentials for the task are not based simply on my association with other anti-Communists. It's true that I have been to Formosa, and talked with Chiang Kai-shek and to practically every high official in the Chinese Nationalist Government—with some of them at considerable length. I have been to West Germany, and talked with Chancellor Adenauer. I have been in personal association or continuous correspondence with many if not most of the leading anti-Communists in this country and throughout the world. And I have diligently studied the anti-Communist books and objective histories which reveal piecemeal the horrifying truth of the past two decades.
>
> None of that, however, constitutes the best support of my right to express the opinion I am going to give you. The opinion is: The Communists have already gone at least one-fourth of the way in their third and final step—taking over the United States, and with it the world. That right comes primarily from a study of the Communists' own periodicals and literature.

In another place he says that he has been studying the problem of Communism increasingly over the past nine years and almost full time for the last three years. He also points out that his lifetime spent in the candy manufacturing business enables him to see the weakness of the economic theory of Communism "more readily than might some scholar coming into that study from the academic cloisters." His lifetime interest in world history, Welch adds, gives him an advantage over many businessmen in seeing this weakness. These credentials do not, as we can see, reveal Welch as an expert in international matters. Thus his testimony alone is not grounds for affirming the above statements. If someone were to affirm these statements and his only reason was the testimony of Welch or people with similar backgrounds, then he would commit the fallacy of appeal to authority.

A less obvious example of the error in reasoning is found in this kind of commonly encountered argument:

We should abolish NATO, get out of SEATO, leave the UN, and end foreign aid. For George Washington, the Father of Our Country, and the very man who appears on our five-cent stamp, gave this wise counsel to Congress in his Farewell Message: The United States should stay out of entangling alliances.

Washington no doubt was an expert in these matters. But the opinions of an eighteenth-century expert do not ordinarily constitute good counsel for contempory problems. (It is interesting, however, to speculate as to what a man like Washington *would* say about the problems confronting us today.) This argument and others like it are instances of the fallacy of appeal to authority.

The *ad Ignorantiam* Fallacy

Arguments which are called *ad ignorantiam* fallacies must have one of these two forms (where S stands for some statement):

1. *S* is true
   because it has not been proved false (or there is no reason for S to be false).
2. *S* is false
   because it has not been proved true (or there is no reason for S to be true).

At one time there was no proof that the earth revolves around the sun. If someone had argued:

The earth does not revolve around the sun, since there is no proof that it does,

this would be an instance of an *ad ignorantiam* fallacy. For, as we can see, man's ignorance of reasons for the earth revolving around the sun does not support the conclusion that the earth does not revolve around the sun. This argument has the second form.

Here is an *ad ignorantiam* which has the first form: Alexander Hall, a nineteenth-century Methodist minister, defended a theory of physics called "substantialism." According to Hall, all forces like gravity are composed of particles. In magazines which he edited, he is supposed to have tried for years to prod scientists into debating with him. They all, of course, refused. It is reported that Hall responded in this way: [4]

Since no one comes up with any reasons against my theory, it must be true.

This is an *ad ignorantiam* fallacy. From the fact that no one objected to his view, it does not follow either that the view is true or that it is false. In Hall's case, scientists felt the view was too absurd to take the trouble to refute.

The *ad ignorantiam* fallacy is commonly committed in examples like:

No one has ever proved that reincarnation does not take place, so it must be true that there is reincarnation.

or

No one has ever proved that I don't have an immaterial soul in my head, so it must be true that I do have one.

Now these two examples differ from the earlier ones in an interesting way. It is generally maintained that the notion of reincarnation and the notion of an immaterial soul are not significant empirical notions. That is, they are not the kind of thing which can either be proved to exist or proved not to exist, as one can prove that the earth revolves around the sun and as one can prove that the human body does not have two livers. If this is so, then it would follow that we cannot prove that there is reincarnation or the existence of an immaterial soul. But from this it doesn't follow that reincarnation and the existence of an immaterial soul are false notions, nor, for that matter, does it follow that they are true. One cannot empirically prove that there is not an undetectable gremlin in one's stomach, but it doesn't follow that such a gremlin is indeed there.

In the last chapter it was noted that often in one set of circumstances an argument is fallacious, whereas in others it is not. This is especially true of arguments with the form of (1) and (2). For example, in a law court if it is not proved that X is guilty, it follows that X is not guilty. Even though this argument has the form of an *ad ignorantiam*, it is not fallacious because of the wise principle employed in our law courts that a person is presumed innocent until proven guilty.

[4] Cf. Martin Gardner, *Fads and Fallacies in the Name of Science* (New York: Dover, 1952), pp. 81–82.

The *Petitio Principii* Fallacy

There are two argument forms which are traditionally called the fallacy of *petitio principii* (begging the question). They are:

1. *S* is true
   because *S* is true (sometimes other statements are included with *S* in the premisses).
2. *S* is true
   because *A* is true. And *A* is true because *B* is true. And *B* is true because *S* is true (the length of this chain can vary).

Arguments having the second form are called "circular arguments." If an argument has either form, it is self-evident that the alleged reason is not a reason at all.

Each of the following is an instance of the *petitio principii* fallacy of the first form:

3. A physician in one of Molière's plays accounts for the sleep-giving power of opium by saying that the drug possesses "a dormative virtue."
4. To allow every man unbounded freedom of speech must always be, on the whole, advantageous to the state; for it is highly conducive to the interests of the community that each individual should enjoy a liberty perfectly unlimited of expressing his sentiments.

(WHATELY, Elements of Logic) [5]

5. He that hath wife and children hath given hostages to fortune; for they are impediments to great enterprises, either of virtue or mischief.

(BACON)

That the reason repeats the conclusion is quite obvious in (3), not so obvious in (4), and less so in (5). In (3) "a dormative virtue" is a synonym for "sleep-giving power." In (4) "advantageous" and "highly conducive to the interests of the community" are synonymous. And in (5) the "reason" is merely an explanation of "hostages to fortune." Sometimes the reason can be a carefully disguised restatement of the conclusion.

Reasoning in a circle is a more complicated instance of an argument which has the basic form: *P* is true because *P* is true. There are more steps between the conclusion *P* and the reason *P*. An example of such an argument is found in the following:

All the statements in the Koran are true because they are the word of God.
We know the Koran is the word of God because Mohammed said it was.
We can rely on what Mohammed said because he was God's prophet.

[5] Richard Whately, *Elements of Logic* (Boston: J. Monroe, 1843) p. 196.

And we know he was God's prophet because the Koran says so, and whatever is said in it is true.

It is clear that this argument is circular and has the second form indicated above.

The famous law of effect in learning theory has at times been so formulated that it mirrors a *petitio*. Here is one formulation of the law:

> Of several responses made to the same situation, those which are accompanied or closely followed by satisfaction to the animal will, other things being equal, be more firmly connected with the situation, so that, when it recurs, they will be more likely to recur; those which are accompanied or closely followed by discomfort to the animal will, other things being equal, have their connections with the situation weakened, so that, when it recurs, they will be less likely to occur. The greater the satisfaction or discomfort, the greater the strengthening or weakening of the bond.

How does one tell when an animal is satisfied or dissatisfied with something? If the answer is: one tells by seeing whether the animal seeks or avoids the thing in question, then the above explanation (that is, the law of effect) is a *petitio* argument.

Complex Question

In Sophocles' *King Oedipus*, Tiresias, the blind prophet, tells Oedipus that he is responsible for the curse that is on Thebes since it was he who slew Laius, the King of Thebes before Oedipus. Oedipus in his rage accuses Creon, his brother-in-law, of getting Tiresias to say this so that Creon might become king. When Creon hears of this he goes to Oedipus to deny the charge since it is not true. When he meets Oedipus, the latter says:

What brought you here: have you a face so brazen that you come to my house— you, the proved assassin of its master—the certain robber of my crown? Come, tell me in the face of the Gods what cowardice, or folly, did you discover in me that you plotted this? Did you think I would not see what you were at till you had crept upon me, or seeing it would not ward it off?

(SOPHOCLES, *King Oedipus*) [6]

Most of these questions are *complex questions*, for they presuppose that Creon plotted to become king. Take, for example, the last: "Did you think that I would not see what you were at?" If Creon answers "No," then he would be assenting to the claim that he was guilty, and if he

[6] Sophocles, *King Oedipus*, trans. W. B. Yeats, in *Collected Plays of W. B. Yeats* (New York: Macmillan, 1952), p. 489. Used by permission of The Macmillan Company.

answers "Yes," he would also be assenting. Or, to put it another way, Oedipus' question is a complex question because two questions are involved in it: First, Did you plot to become king? and, second, Did you think I would not see it?

The *fallacy of complex question* is committed in this example:

Why has the Administration refused to avail itself of the help of Chiang's 800,-000 well-trained fighters instead of playing into the Communists' hands by keeping them immobilized on Formosa? It is clear that the government's policy is incapable of bringing us victory in the Far East.

Notice, first, that we have a complex question which makes up the reason. The two questions involved in it are: Why has the Administration not used the troops? and, Why has it played into the Communists' hands by keeping them immobilized? Second, the question is employed in an argument. Third, it is supposed that the hearer or reader will respond to the question. The response which is appropriate is "Why?" or "I don't know." Fourth, this response commits the reader to agreeing with the presupposition. The presupposition is that the Administration has played into the Communists' hands. Last, this committal is then employed in supporting the conclusion. All these five elements need to be present to have the *fallacy* of complex question.

The Fallacy of Accident

The *fallacy of accident* consists in arguing from an accepted rule or principle to a special case, when the rule is not applicable to the special case. The *converse fallacy of accident* occurs when one erroneously argues from a special case to an accepted rule or principle.

Examples of the fallacy of accident are found in the following:

All men have a right to express their opinions, therefore a judge should have the right to express his political opinions in the courtroom.

This country is a democracy and is dedicated to the proposition that all men are created equal. Why then do we hypocritically continue to employ certain tests in admissions to colleges and universities?

This country is a democracy and is dedicated to the proposition that all men are free and cannot be deprived of their liberties. Therefore we should stop imprisoning criminals and lunatics.

In each case, a general rule which, at least in our country, is regarded as holding, is applied to particular cases. However, as is evident, these rules do not apply to such cases, The converse fallacy of accident can be illustrated by simply reversing the conclusions and reasons of the above in this way:

Since a judge cannot express his political opinions in a courtroom, it follows that all men do not have a right to express their opinions.

Admission to colleges is based on the fact that some candidates have greater abilities than other candidates; thus it is not true that all men are created equal, as we have been led to believe by Jefferson and others.

Criminals and lunatics are put in institutions against their will. I could name more. But enough is said to see that our country is not truly dedicated to the proposition that all men are free and that one of their rights is liberty.

In each of these examples the reason given is irrelevant to the truth of the conclusion. The reason for this is that in the first group a general statement has been misapplied, whereas in the second group a particular case is considered which does not come under the general statement.

The Genetic Fallacy

When someone gives an account of what led someone (or a group) to a view and argues that since this (the account) is true, the view is false, this is called the *genetic fallacy*. Such an argument is incorrect since what led someone to a view is irrelevant to determining whether the view is true. In many of its instances the genetic fallacy is a variation of the *ad hominem* fallacy. Consider this imagined argument:

Lafayette Jones, owner of Special Foods, Inc., an Indianapolis firm which produces skim milk, brewer's yeast, wheat germ, yoghurt, tiger's milk, and blackstrap molasses, realized how someone could profit from the sale of these "wonder foods" if people came to believe that the regular use of these foods would maintain good health and add years to their lives. So he lectured and published articles making these claims. Thus we can clearly see that Mr. Jones's views about these "wonder foods" are worthless and erroneous.

Would this be grounds for concluding that Lafayette Jones's claim is false? It would make us skeptical of its truth, but only evidence that the five foods have no such value would be reasonable grounds for concluding that the view is false. The arguer has described what led someone to a view and infers from this that the view is false.

Another example of this fallacy is found in the following:

John Stuart Mill's views about the equality of men can be dismissed as myths. We all know that John's father, James, told his son, in order to prevent Johnny from becoming conceited, that if one showed more ability than another, it was entirely due to a better education.

(It should be noted that John Stuart Mill was a genius.) Even supposing that Mill's father did this, and that this is how Mill came to his views about equality, this does not provide grounds for dismissing his views.

Our last illustration of the genetic fallacy is from real life:

A study of primitive tribes shows that early man had many fears—his principal fears were those of illness, being crushed under a falling tree, and being killed by wild animals. Certain men gained influence in tribes by offering various charms and incantations to ward off these dangers or by asserting that some benevolent spirit more powerful than these dangers would protect those who approached him in the right way. The ones who preferred the second policy were those who introduced religion. Since this is the origin of belief in God, it is little more than superstition, as you can see, and, consequently, the thinking man should reject religion.

Even supposing this is what led men at first to religious beliefs, it still does not follow from this that religious claims are to be rejected. Thus the genetic fallacy is committed.

Ignoratio Elenchi

From time to time statements are misunderstood. Sometimes they are then refuted (or supported, or proved). When someone misunderstands a statement (intentionally or unintentionally) and employs it in this way, the resulting incorrect argument is called the *ignoratio elenchi* fallacy.

Consider this example of an *ignoratio elenchi:*

The man who said "Miracles don't happen" is as blind as a mole in a tar-barrel. I guess he never heard of penicillin. TV is unknown to him. "Astronauts" is a new word to him. The news about Crest hasn't reached him yet. I tell you this is an age of miracles. I could name a thousand more.

In the example, the arguer, if serious, has taken "Miracles do not happen" to mean that extraordinary inventions cannot take place. And, obviously, he has successfully shown the statement, understood in this way, to be false. But is this how those who say "Miracles do not happen" are to be understood? This depends on the context in which the denial is made. Sometimes what is meant by the denial is that events which go against natural law or happen while natural law is suspended and are caused by supernatural forces, do not happen. And, of course, the arguer in our example has not shown or even given a reason why this view is false.

Consider this real-life example of this fallacy:

Does Communism come out of poverty? Is it true that if you feed the people you can stop Communism? A United States senator at one time answered no to both questions, and here are the two reasons he gave:
(a) "I suppose that some of the people of our country have learned that some Indians and some of the poor people of America have not had enough

economic opportunity. But these citizens have not been enrolled among the group led by the Communists or the group of Communist supporters."

(b) "But as to Communists being brewed out of poverty and Communists coming up from hunger, I will venture the statement that there is not a single hungry Communist in Russia. There are only a few million members of the Communist Party there. They are the elite; the privileged class. Lots of people are starving there, but they are the poor people who are oppressed by the Communists."

Now it might well be true that hunger does not breed Communism, but the reasons given by the senator are not relevant to the view that hunger breeds Communism. The first reason is a refutation of the view that if someone is poor, then he is a Communist. His second reason is a refutation of the view that if someone is a Communist, then he is poor. Neither view, of course, is involved in the opinion held by some that hunger breeds Communism.

Sometimes arguments in which the premises are entirely unrelated to the conclusion are called *ignoratio elenchi*. Here is an example taken from a military manual:

Communist philosophy is demonstrably false. Communist tactics—individual and mass terrorism, infiltration and subversion, the abrogation of treaties, to mention just a few—are abhorrent to the entire civilized world. Yet Communism represents a massive effort to transform not only the world but human nature itself. It offers the dream of a worldwide society in which, it is claimed, there will be lasting peace and harmony. The fact that this offer continues to deceive people makes it evident that the power of a myth is still a factor to reckon with in human relations.

The argument is:

Communist tactics are abhorrent to the civilized world.
Communism represents an effort to transform human nature.
Communism offers the dream of a worldwide society in which there will be peace and harmony.
The Communist offer continues to deceive people.
The power of a myth is still a factor to reckon with in human relations.
Therefore Communist philosophy is false.

In this example the premises of the argument are unrelated to the truth or falsity of the conclusion.

EXERCISE I

In each of the following passages, first decide whether it is an argument. Second, if it is an argument, state the conclusion and the reasons given for the conclusion. Third, decide whether the argument is fallacious. Fourth, if the argument is fallacious, indicate what kind of fallacy it is, selecting from those discussed above. If some of the arguments are fallacious but of a type not discussed above, use the category "none of these." Fifth, give reasons for your opinion. Remember that each item can be regarded in different ways, since what we call "the general circumstances" in Chapter One cannot be completely provided. Consequently, at times you will need to stipulate a context in order to classify an argument as fallacious and to indicate the kind of fallacy committed in the argument.

1.   The time has come for us to realize that our Founding Fathers had some mistaken ideas. For example, in the Preamble to the Constitution we read that "all men are created equal." But this is obviously false. Some are stronger than others. Some have more intelligence than others. Some have drives which lead to success, while others seem to lack these drives. All men are not created equal.

2.   Christians, to arms! The enemy is at the gate. Buckle on the armor of the Christian and go forth to battle. With education, evangelism, and dedication let us smite the Communist foe and if necessary give up our lives in this noble Cause! We cry, "We shall not yield! Lift high the blood-stained banner of the Cross and on to victory!" Coexistence is impossible. Communism is total evil. Its methods are evil and its ends are evil. We must hurl this thing back into the pit from whence it came!

3.   In our opinion the Evening *Bugle* should add five regular Negro truck drivers to its force of 200, or eight Negro men and boys among its 100 white mechanical and press-room employees, or 15 clerical and office workers to its staff of perhaps 2,000. We are sure you see that you should do this hiring, and in addition, we are sure you will want to show that you do not discriminate. For, let us remind you, there are 700,000 Negroes in this community who are capable of "selective patronage."

4.   The business executives who say the workers' wishes for unemployment insurance and old age pensions are degenerate wishes are the same ones who would never have taken their present jobs if they were subject to arbitrary discharge or if they were not given adequate pension arrangements. We can easily see that their views have no substance to them.

5.   The Constitution supposedly guarantees freedom of speech. But I know that I don't let my little girl say just anything she wishes. We also don't let criminals and dangerous enemies say what they want. So let us stop being hypocrites. We *say* we have freedom of speech here, but it is clear that in our *actions* we do not *practice* it.

6.   My uncle Noodles Romanoff, who is now in prison, used to preach to us kids about self-control, but I can't see any value in his ideas if he cannot live up to them himself.

7.   Voters of Massachusetts, we have charged my opponent with dishonesty in public office. We have offered him numerous chances to rebut us. He has not done so. Do you, then, citizens of this great state, wish to elect a dishonest man?

8.   It is silly to talk about abolishing poverty. Even if all your proposals went

through, there would always be some people who had less than others. So no matter what steps are taken there will always be poverty.

9. Jesus said, ". . . In very truth I tell you, if anyone obeys my teaching he shall never know what it is to die."

The Jews said, "Now we are certain that you are possessed. Abraham is dead; the prophets are dead; and yet you say, 'If anyone obeys my teaching he shall never know what it is to die.' Are you greater than our father Abraham, who is dead? The prophets are dead too. What do you claim to be?"

(John 8: 51-53)

10. The gift of reasoning to men is the crowning proof of God's providential care. He who cannot in this see God's providential care lacks the gift himself.

11. On the Senate floor in 1950, Joe McCarthy announced that he had penetrated "Truman's iron curtain of secrecy." He had 81 case histories of persons whom he considered to be Communists in the State Department. Of Case 40, he said, "I do not have much information on this except the general statement of the agency that there is nothing in the files to disprove his Communist connections."

(Taken from RICHARD H. ROVERE's *Senator Joe McCarthy*)[7]

12. Those who say that Nehru and Nasser are not Communists are wrong, since they are the very same people who insisted that Mao Tse-tung was not a Communist.

13. You ought to try to sell more cars this year, Figby, because it will spare your wife the embarrassment of a letter from the main office telling her you're slipping.

14. A columnist visited the Argonne Laboratories, where the A-bomb had been pioneered, and found that neither the institution itself nor any of the scientists he interviewed had a shelter. Even the top government officials seemed to have little faith in the idea, for not a single one of the fourteen high officials of the National Security Council had built a shelter for his own family. Neither had Vice-President Lyndon Johnson or Attorney General Robert Kennedy. Assistant Secretary of Defense Steuart Pittman, who is in charge of the national civil defense program, told a reporter that he had not built a shelter for his family because he was studying the "'range of choices." Why should we do anything? If these people don't have shelters, then we shouldn't.

15. In 1907 *Collier's* magazine said in an editorial that a Grape-Nuts ad produced the impression that Grape-Nuts will obviate the necessity for an operation for appendicitis and that this is a lie. C. W. Post, head of the Postum Company, Ltd., in reply to this charge, ran the following advertisement:

"To call a man a liar seems rude, so we will let the reader select his own term. Sometime ago the manager of *Collier's Weekly* got very cross with us because we would not continue to advertise in his paper. We have occasionally been attacked by editors who have tried to force us to advertise in their papers at their own prices, and on their own conditions, failing in which we were

[7] From *Senator Joe McCarthy*, by Richard H. Rovere. (New York: Harcourt, Brace and World, 1959).

to be attacked through their editorial columns. The reader can fit a name to that tribe.

"We had understood that the editor of *Collier's* was a wild cat of the Sinclair 'jungle bungle' type, a person with curdled gray matter, but it seems strange that the owners would descend to using their editorial columns, yellow as they are, for such rank out-and-out falsehoods as appear in their July 27th issue, where the editor goes out of his way to attack us, and the reason will appear tolerably clear to any reader who understands the venom behind it.

"When a journal wilfully prostitutes its columns, to try and harm a reputable manufacturer in an effort to force him to advertise, it is time the public knew the facts. The owner or editor of *Collier's* cannot force money from us by such methods!"

(Taken from CLARK GAVIN's *Famous Libel and Slander Cases of History*) [8]

16. It is curious to observe how the theory of what is called the Christian Church, sprung out of the tail of the heathen mythology. A direct incorporation took place in the first instance, by making the reputed founder to be celestially begotten. The trinity of gods that then followed was no other than a reduction of the former plurality, which was about twenty or thirty thousand. The statue of Mary succeeded the statue of Diana of Ephesus. The deification of heroes changed into the canonization of saints. The Mythologists had gods for everything; the Christian Mythologists had saints for everything. The church became as crowded with the one, as the pantheon had been with the other; and Rome was the place of both. The Christian theory is little else than the idolatry of the ancient Mythologists, accommodated to the purposes of power and revenue; and it yet remains to reason and philosophy to abolish the amphibious fraud.

(THOMAS PAINE, *The Age of Reason*)

17. In 1878 the American painter James Whistler sued the foremost British art critic and leading literary figure John Ruskin because Ruskin wrote that Whistler was an imposter and wrote of Whistler's "Nocturne": "I . . . never expected to hear a coxcomb ask 200 guineas for flinging a pot of paint in the public's face."

The trial began with the Attorney-General examining Whistler:

WHISTLER: ". . . It [the "Nocturne"] was marked 200 guineas."

ATTORNEY-GENERAL: "Is not that what we, who are not artists, would call a stiffish price?"

WHISTLER: "I think it very likely that may be so."

ATTORNEY-GENERAL: "But artists always give good value for their money, don't they?"

WHISTLER: "I am glad to hear that so well established." (Laughter)

ATTORNEY-GENERAL: "Now, Mr. Whistler, can you tell me how long it took you to knock off that nocturne?"

WHISTLER: "I beg your pardon!" (Laughter)

(Taken from CLARK GAVIN's *Famous Libel and Slander Cases of History*)

[8] Clark Gavin, *Famous Libel and Slander Cases of History* (New York: Collier Books, 1962).

18. I have been asked tonight to state the South's case for segregation. It's quite simple. We read, for example, this statement from the platform of the Democratic Party of Massachusetts: "We express our deep concern and manifest indignation at any effort by any group, anywhere in the land, whereby the Constitution, as interpreted by the Supreme Court, is flaunted (sic) for the base reason of maintaining a decadent way of life which from its inception was alien to the American ideal." Such vitriolic statements come from a state which in large measure is responsible through its New England slave trade for creating the Negro problem in the South. Similar excoriations, in equally bad taste, have come from the land of anti-Asiatic hysteria—California—and the lands of race riots—Illinois and Michigan. Just think how these states would react if their Negro population were the same as Mississippi's! The South's case for segregation rests!

19. How did Freud discover that all dreams are wish-fulfillments? Like this: During an interview it suddenly became clear that the patient who had certain strong erotic or ambitious wishes was having dreams in which these wishes were being fulfilled. He saw, then, how any number of dreams which came to mind and which were reported to him could be regarded in this way, and concluded that dreams are simply wish-fulfillments. If the first patient had had strong fears and was having dreams in which these fears were expressed, Freud might have concluded that all dreams are simply expressions of fear after seeing how many dreams could be looked at in this way. As we can see from this, his views amount to nothing.

20. Once again Jesus addressed the people: "I am the light of the world. No follower of mine shall wander in the dark; he shall have the light of life." The Pharisees said to him, "You are witness in your own cause; your testimony is not valid." Jesus replied, "My testimony is valid, even though I do bear witness about myself . . . "

(John 8: 12-15)

21. Edmund Ross' vote as a Republican United States Senator from Kansas is considered to be the vote which prevented Andrew Johnson's removal from office by the Radical Republican majority in the Senate. Ross felt, as do historians, that the Radical Republicans acted from insufficient proof and from partisan considerations. This editorial in a Kansas newspaper appeared after this important vote:

"On Saturday last Edmund G. Ross, United States Senator from Kansas, sold himself, and betrayed his constituents; stultified his own record, basely lied to his friends, shamefully violated his solemn pledge . . . and to the utmost of his poor ability signed the death warrant of his country's liberty. This act was done deliberately, because the traitor, like Benedict Arnold, loved money better than he did principle, friends, honor and his country, all combined. Poor, pitiful, shriveled wretch, with a soul so small that a little pelf would outweigh all things else that dignify or ennoble manhood."

(Taken from JOHN F. KENNEDY's *Profiles in Courage*)[9]

[9] John F. Kennedy, *Profiles in Courage* (New York: Pocket Books, 1957), pp. 120–121.

22. But why do we infer that if the experiment be repeated, the same two bodies, or any other bodies, will behave the same way? Because we feel assured that the same cause will invariably be followed by the same effect, or, to speak more accurately, that the same cause or combination of causes will, if unimpeded by the action of any other cause or combination of causes, be invariably followed by the same effect or combination of effects.—We assume the "uniformity of nature."

THE MATERIAL FALLACIES OF
INSUFFICIENT EVIDENCE

The *Post Hoc* Fallacy

In most circumstances an argument will be incorrect if it has this form or a variation of it:

When *A* occurs, *B* occurs.
Therefore *A* causes *B*.

Just the fact that *B* occurs when *A* occurs, is not good grounds for concluding that *A* causes *B*, though the fact that when *A* occurs *B* occurs would be relevant in establishing whether or not *A* causes *B*. Incorrect arguments with this pattern are called *post hoc* fallacies or *post hoc, ergo propter hoc* (after this, therefore because of this) fallacies. *Post hoc* fallacies are also called *false cause* fallacies. *Post hoc* fallacies, however, are just one kind, though the most common kind, of false cause fallacies. Consider this simple example of a *post hoc* fallacy:

When Rodger Babson, whose prediction of the great stock market crash brought him renown, became ill with tuberculosis, he returned to his home in Massachusetts rather than follow his doctor's advice to remain in the West. During the freezing winter he left the windows open, wore a coat with a heating pad in back, and had his secretary wear mittens and hit the typewriter keys with rubber hammers. Babson got well and attributed his cure to fresh air. Air from pine woods, according to Babson, has chemical or electrical qualities (or both) of great medicinal value.[10]

As we can see, in the above passage Babson made this inference:

When I returned to the freezing winter of Massachusetts (*A*), I was cured of tuberculosis (*B*).
Therefore the properties of a freezing winter in Massachusetts (*A*) caused the tuberculosis cure (*B*).

[10] Cf. Martin Gardner, *op. cit.*, p. 97.

This argument is incorrect. The reason is not good grounds for affirming the conclusion. The fact that when *A* happened, *B* happened, does not thereby provide good grounds to conclude that *A* causes *B*.

Our last example has to do with a claim made by a Dr. Melvin Page in his book called *Degeneration—Regeneration*. It is his view that milk is good for babies but is dangerous for adults. He claims that, taken by adults, milk is the frequent cause of colds, sinus-trouble, colitis, and, most important, cancer. One reason he gives for his view is that in Wisconsin more people die of cancer per capita than in any other state, and more milk is drunk in Wisconsin than in any other state. If Dr. Page made this inference:

More milk is drunk and more people die of cancer in Wisconsin than in any other state.
Therefore milk drinking is a cause of cancer,

then this would clearly be a *post hoc* fallacy. It is interesting to note that in Wisconsin people tend to be long-lived, perhaps because they drink so much milk. And cancer is a cause of death in later years.[11]

The Fallacy of Special Pleading

Often we find that there are reasons for and reasons against certain propositions. When someone argues for such a proposition and gives only the reasons—or only some of the reasons—which support the proposition, ignoring the reasons against, he is committing the *fallacy of special pleading*.

This fallacy is committed in this argument:

We should legalize gambling in the state of Nebraska because, first, it would provide a rich new source of revenue; second, it would encourage tourists to come spend their money here; and third, it would cost us nothing to get these new moneys, just the passing of a law.

This argument fails to take into account all the reasons for not legalizing gambling in Nebraska, for example, that among the "tourists" would be those people who live on gambling, that another vice would be publicly sanctioned for revenue, that the law enforcement agencies would have to be supplemented. Thus this argument is an instance of the fallacy of special pleading. To avoid this fallacy, the arguer would have to consider both sides of the issue and show, if possible, that the stronger case can be made for legalizing gambling.

Consider this second example of special pleading:

[11] Cf. Gardner, *op. cit.*, p. 222.

All religions have incorporated masses of fables and superstitions; have been created by the weak and ignorant; have been maintained by the enlightened for selfish political ends; have, at one time or another, been used by vested interests to oppose social reform and scientific progress. Thus we say with Voltaire, *"Ecrasez l'infame!"*

All the statements in the reasons are true. But we are reminded only of the bad aspects of religion.

The Fallacy of Hasty Generalization

We are all acquainted with generalizations which have, for example, this form: All *A* is *B*. Often we justify such generalizations by collecting evidence. Sometimes we come to such generalizations by being struck by some particular instance where an *A* is *B*; and, from this alone, conclude that all *A* is *B*. When someone argues from such a particular instance, and from that instance alone, and no effort is made to determine that this instance is representative of all *A*'s, this arguer commits the fallacy called the *fallacy of hasty generalization*. An argument of this kind is incorrect. Merely the fact that an instance of *A* is *B* is not good grounds to conclude unless other things are true, that all *A* is *B*. We are all acquainted with these familiar examples of this fallacy:

Every American young person should serve a hitch in the Peace Corps, for it certainly did a world of good for Flossie Snail.

When I was young I worked thirty hours on a job while going to college, so no boy should worry about where he will find money for his college education.

I tell you, Irish workers are no good! The two I hired drank and sang bawdy ballads all the time.

As can be seen, these generalizations have been inferred from one particular case which has made a strong impression on the arguer.

As noted above, to infer that all *A* is *B* from one instance of *A* being *B* is fallacious unless the *A* is known to be representative of all *A*'s. Often in science, for example, from a single careful experiment with a substance one can properly conclude something about all substances of that kind. However, great care is taken in such cases to be sure that the substance is representative of all such substances. But even when such care is not taken, it is evident that a single instance would be considered in determining whether all *A*'s are *B*; and thus the reason in such an incorrect argument is relevant to determining the truth of the conclusion.

A less obvious example is found in the following:

What is the object or idea which the word "good" stands for? Philosophers for hundreds of years have been looking for this object so they could discover the "'nature" of it. Well, if we are properly tough-minded we will face the fact that there is no such object. There are horses and stones which "horse" and "stone" stand for, but no object corresponding to "'good." Thus it is only reasonable to conclude that this search is hopeless because "good" is a word without any meaning.

This can be regarded as a hasty generalization. The arguer has inferred that what is true of such words as "horse" and "stone" (that there are objects which these words denote) is true of all words, including the word "good." Since he has not shown that words like "'horse" are representative of all words, this is an instance of the hasty generalization fallacy.

The Fallacy of Opposition [12]

When an argument takes this form:

1. the enemy (or opponent) supports X, so we should oppose X,
   or
2. the enemy (or opponent) opposes X, so we should support X,

it is incorrect. That your enemy supports X is often relevant to affirming that you should oppose X (and vice versa), but if this is taken as the only reason, then the argument is incorrect. We will call this type of incorrect argument the *fallacy of opposition*.

Let us consider the first form (1). As will be seen, what is said of this applies to the second form. In order to infer that you should oppose X from the fact that your enemy supports X, at least these four conditions need to be fulfilled: (a) Your enemy must be supporting something which is in his interest. If someone consistently uses an argument of the above form, this implies that he supposes his enemy's judgments as to his own interests are infallible. (b) You must have distinguished between what your enemy supports and what he only appears to support. At least these two conditions must be fulfilled in order to conclude that you should oppose X, for if your enemy supports something which he thinks is in his interest but is not, or supports something which is not in his interest but he wishes to give the impression that it is, then it would not follow from the fact that he supports X that you should oppose X. (c) You must know why he supports X. Your enemy's purpose might be such that if you oppose X, you help him to achieve his purpose in supporting X. If this were so, then the inference from "He supports X" to "I should oppose X" would obviously not be correct. (d) Finally, your

---

[12] This is a fallacy which is not traditional. The authors formulated it.

enemy must support something which is wrong. For if your enemy supports something which is right, it obviously would not follow that you should oppose it.

Consider this example taken from an anti-Communist talk:

In fact, it is clear that the Communists long ago made plans to avail themselves of a strong fifth column in our midst which will provide the leadership to start a civil war in this country. The trouble in our southern states has been fomented almost entirely by the Communists for this purpose. It has been their plan, gradually carried out over a long period with meticulous cunning, to stir up such bitterness between whites and blacks in the South that small flames of civil disorder would inevitably result. They could then fan and coalesce these little flames into one great conflagration of civil war, in time, if the need arose. The whole slogan of "civil rights," as used to make trouble in the South today, is an exact parallel to the slogan of "agrarian reform" which they used in China. And the Communists, who are pulling innocent and idealistic Americans into promoting this agitation for them, have no more real interest in the welfare of the Negroes and no more concern about the damage they actually do to our colored population, than the Chinese Communists had with regard to the welfare of the Chinese peasants.

(ROBERT WELCH, *The Blue Book*) [13]

Some would conclude from this that we should not support school integration, sit-in demonstrations, freedom riders, the efforts of the NAACP, bus boycotts, and the like. In order, then, for those who draw this conclusion to avoid the fallacy of opposition, at least (a), (b), (c), and (d) must be fulfilled. Are they? Let us examine each:

(a)   If integration efforts in the South, even though temporary disorder resulted, would strengthen this country and elevate us in the eyes of other nations, rather than help lead to civil war, then there would be reason to believe that in making these efforts one would *not* be helping the Communists. If this is true, then to draw the above conclusion—we should not support integration efforts—from the above reason would be fallacious.

(b)   Suppose the Communists want us to believe that they support the integration efforts in order to "fan the flames of disorder into a civil war, if the need arose," when in reality they do not support the efforts. Perhaps for propaganda reasons they like the South just as it is. If this were true, the argument would be fallacious.

(c)   Suppose the Communists in the United States and elsewhere champion integration efforts and other popular issues because they reason that this is the way to capture the support of the masses. If this were so, then to oppose integration efforts because the Communists support

13 Robert Welch, *The Blue Book,* p. 29.

them would be to help them in achieving their aims in supporting integration efforts. For if their reasoning is right, then opposing them would leave them as the only champions of such popular issues and thus would give them their sought-after mass support.

(d) Some would argue that even though the Communists support the integration efforts and even though such efforts lead to civil disorder, nevertheless segregation is wrong and should be fought unless, of course, it would lead to a "great conflagration of civil war." If this is true, then to infer that we should oppose integration because the Communists support it would be fallacious.

To avoid the fallacy of opposition, one must not oppose or support X *merely* for the reason that his enemy supports or opposes X. Before drawing any conclusions, one should seek additional reasons, for example, he should ask if (a), (b), (c), and (d) are fulfilled.

In the *Communist Manifesto* is found a ten-point program under which capital will be taken from those who have it, once the workers get control of the government. And once the government owns the means of production and is run by the proletariat, the next step is Communism. If one were to argue that we should be against the ten points since the Communists see them as the way, and perhaps the only way, to achieve Communism, then the opposition fallacy would be committed because (d) would not be fulfilled. For among the ten points are to be found free education for all children, a progressive income tax, and a more equal distribution of population over the country. Most would say that these are three things which we should have. The other seven points most would say we should not have. And it should be noted that the *Manifesto* says *all* ten points are *necessary* to bring on Communism.

A variation of the opposition fallacy often occurs in an argument having the following form: Mr. A supports what my enemy supports, so he is my enemy; or, Mr. A opposes what my enemy opposes, so he is my enemy. All of what has been said about the opposition fallacy also applies here. J. Edgar Hoover, in a report to the Senate Internal Security Subcommittee, made a statement which applies especially to arguments of this form and which provides a summary of the general discussion:

Because Communism thrives on turmoil the Communist Party is continuously attempting to exploit all grievances—real or imagined—for its own tactical purposes. It is, therefore, almost inevitable that, on many issues, the party line will coincide with the position of many non-Communists. The danger of indiscriminately alleging that someone is a Communist merely because his views on a particular issue happen to parallel the official party position is obvious. The confusion which is thereby created helps the Communists by diffusing the forces of their opponents.

Unfortunately, there are those who make the very mistake the Communists are so careful to avoid. These individuals concentrate on the negative rather than on the positive. They are merely against Communism without being for any positive measures to eliminate the social, political, and economic frictions which the Communists are so adroit at exploiting.

These persons would do well to recall a recent lesson from history. Both Hitler and Mussolini were against Communism. However, it was what they stood for, not against, that history has judged.

EXERCISES II

Follow the directions given on page 34 for the exercises at the end of the first section. For four, however, substitute fallacies of insufficient evidence.

1.   Well, I know a woman who had ten thousand dollars under her mattress and wore a mink coat to collect her social security benefits. I tell you we must stop handing out money. We must do away with social security.

2.   Why is it that when the Congress is considering appropriations, Khrushchev, or whoever is the Kremlin leader, stirs up a crisis like Berlin? The answer is clear! Khrushchev is trying to bankrupt the United States of America.

3.   It is reported that at the 1956 Republican Convention someone from the platform reported that he had recently seen President Eisenhower and he did not look well. Instantly, as the story goes, a delegate jumped up and cried: "Washington drinks floridated water, that's the trouble with Ike!"

4.   To fail children who do poorly upsets them and disturbs class morale. The only thing to do, therefore, is to promote everyone.

5.   I doubt the loyalty of the editors of the *Wall Street Journal*. They print the same stories which the Communist press uses to discredit capitalism in the eyes of the world. For example, on April 5 the *Journal* carried the story of the indictment by a federal grand jury in Boston of three milk companies on charges of fixing prices and rigging bids on New England milk sales.

6.   DOCTOR: "You drink two hot scotches every night, don't you?"
   MARK TWAIN: "Yes I do, but I only drink them as a preventive of toothache.—I've never had the toothache!"

7.   It's wrong to "delegate authority" to the Socialists in our federal government to control our hospitals and doctors and thus lower the quality of our medical care.

It's wrong to deprive the aged (and eventually all Americans) of their freedom of choice of hospital and physician.

It's wrong because the Communists want it. In the March 12, 1961, issue of *The Worker* under "A First Step to Medical Care for the Aged" Communists were told that the Kennedy Medicare Bill should have their support.

It's wrong because it is a foot in the door toward socialized medicine and the Socialists admit it. The chairman of the Socialist Party's Committee in

Medical Economics, R. W. Tucker, said on Dec. 1, 1960, of the Forand Bill, a forerunner of the King-Anderson Bill, "Once the bill is passed, this nation will be provided with a mechanism for socialized medicine capable of indefinite expansion in every direction until it includes the entire population." This statement is from the Socialist publication *New America.*

8. As a relative newcomer to Upper Sandusky I would like to express pleasure about the garbage service. No list of special rules, no complaints about extra pick up, just excellent service. I am familiar with the municipal collection in five cities, larger and smaller than Upper Sandusky. The collection service in these cities is not as good and the cost is higher.

This is a good illustration of a small business operating under a free enterprise atmosphere. It is this way of life that built this country, and it is confusing to me why so many people are trying to socialize it. Let's maintain an atmosphere of free enterprise so that more people will have an opportunity to give better service at lower cost and make a profit on top of it.

I did not realize that in such a thing as garbage service, private business could be so superior to a governmental operation. If this is true here, how true it must be with the many hundreds of businesses that various levels of government are in. Private individuals or businesses could do these things better, at less cost, and with a profit.—Incentive is the thing!

Little people in big government building giant empires can only result in higher taxes, poorer service, and eventual chaos.

9. The health department in one city ordered all tattoo parlors closed because tattooing is a possible contributor to the spread of hepatitis, a liver ailment. Tattoo parlors may be transmitting serum hepatitis directly into the blood stream through dirty needles and dyes. The health department said it traced 32 cases of hepatitis—and one death—to tattooing in the last three years.

Brother James, a tattoo artist, responded with this argument: "I think tattoos do the city good. How many guys has the FBI caught from tattoos? How many people have we helped by covering up scars?"

10. In December 1960 the 81 Communist parties of the world, acting on a Moscow directive, placed the job of discrediting and muzzling anti-Communists at the top of their objectives for 1961.

On Feb. 25 the *Peoples World,* the official organ of the Communist party on the west coast, opened fire on the Birch Society. *Time* magazine of March 10, in attacking the same society, used some of the same wording as the Communist organ. Can we have any doubt any longer about *Time* magazine?

THE FALLACIES OF AMBIGUITY

When ambiguity of the language is the basis for the incorrectness or invalidity of an argument, then the argument is classed as a fallacy of ambiguity. In such arguments the reasons are irrelevant to the truth or falsity of the conclusion.

The Fallacy of Equivocation

Many words are ambiguous, that is, they can have two or more meanings. For example, the word "fallacy" can mean: (a) an incorrect argument; (b) the ability to deceive, as in "the fallacy of the senses"; and (c) a widespread, mistaken opinion, as in "the fallacy that the Soviets are stupid." When a word is used (often unknowingly) in a context in different senses, it is said to be used equivocally. The *fallacy of equivocation* occurs when in an argument a word or phrase which is essential to the argument is used in different senses. This fallacy occurs in this example:

The existence of a power above nature is implied in the phrase "law of nature," which is constantly used in science. For whenever there is a law, there is a law giver, and the law giver must be presumed capable of suspending the operation of the law.

In this argument the word "law" is used in two different ways. In "law of nature" in the first sentence, "law" means the formulation in words of relationships which have been found to exist in the world. In the second sentence where we find "for whenever there is a law, there is a law giver," "law" means a rule of conduct set down by some authority. If either sense of "law" were used throughout the argument, we would have patently false or absurd statements. Thus if we substituted the first sense of "law," the second sentence would read: "For whenever there are formulations in words of relationships which have been found to exist in the world, there is a law giver. . . ." This, as we can see, is false. Similarly, if we substituted the second sense of "law," the first sentence would read: "The existence of a power above nature is implied in the phrase 'a rule of conduct set down by some authority of nature' which is constantly used in science." And this is absurd. This provides a good test for determining whether an argument contains an equivocation. Take the word or phrase which is believed to be used equivocally, provide a paraphrase of it or of what is believed to be one of its uses, and substitute this paraphrase throughout the argument. If this results in either patently false statements or absurdities, then the argument is an instance of the fallacy of equivocation.

Not all equivocations in arguments are so obvious. Consider this paraphrase of a United States senator's argument:

Our enemy at this time is not exclusively military. He is far more—he is a political enemy, he is an economic enemy, he is a subversive enemy. The military leader, therefore, in order to perform the duties to which he is sworn, has the responsibility of informing, not only his troops, but the American public concerning the total nature of the Communist menace. For in doing so he is carrying out his oath to defend the Constitution of the United States against all enemies, foreign and domestic.

If we make explicit the steps in the argument, we have this:

(a) The military is pledged to defend our country against all enemies, foreign and domestic.

(b) Our enemy at this time is not exclusively military but political, economic, etc.

(c) Thus the military should defend against the political and economic threats of our enemy.

(d) To educate the American public to the political and economic threats is to defend against these threats of our enemy.

(e) Thus the military leaders should educate the American people to the political and economic threats of our enemy.

This argument is incorrect because the phrase "defend against all enemies" is used equivocally. The first use of the phrase is found in (a). Traditionally, the phrase "to defend our country against all enemies," as it appears in the pledge, is understood to mean something like: "To do battle against the attacking military forces of every one of our country's enemies." And, of course, this is what the United States military is trained and prepared to do. In (c) and (d) is found the second use of the phrase. There the phrase is used to cover those things, whatever they might be, which will stop all our enemy's activities, political and economic as well as military. If we use the first sense of "defend against all enemies" throughout the argument, then (c) and (d) turn into these absurd statements: (c) The military should militarily battle the political and economic threats to our country; and (d) To educate the American public to the political and economic threats is to militarily battle these threats of our enemy. If we use the second sense of the phrase throughout the argument, then (a) becomes the false statement: The military is pledged to do those things, whatever they might be, which will stop all our enemy's activities, political and economic as well as military. What makes this argument persuasive is that this double use of the phrase is not apparent.

Many examples of *ignoratio elenchi,* accident, and converse accident can be regarded as fallacies of ambiguity—specifically, fallacies of equivocation. It is the ambiguity of language which often accounts for the misunderstanding of an accepted general rule or principle which is involved in accident fallacies and for the misunderstanding of some view or statement which is involved in the *ignoratio elenchi.* If, of course, we consider the fallacy of equivocation to be an argument where a key word or phrase shifts its meaning in the course of the argument, then these three fallacies would not be fallacies of equivocation. For, first, views or statements are involved in these arguments. And, second, the key statement is generally not repeated with a shift in meaning as the arguments appear or are written. However, they can be so formulated that it can be seen that a sentence has two different meanings in the arguments. For example, the first example in the discussion of the fallacy of accident could be rewritten:

We hold that all men have a right to express their opinion. Therefore a judge should have the right to express his political opinion in the courtroom since he is a man and all men have a right to express their opinion.

As we can see "all men have a right to express their opinion" in the first sentence means something different (as it is an accepted principle in our country) from what it means in the last sentence. The sentence in this case is being used equivocally.

The Fallacy of Amphiboly

When a phrase or sentence has two meanings (or more) as a result of the awkward construction of the phrase or sentence, it is said to be amphibolous. The English textbook example of an amphibolous sentence is:

Clara Schumann was too busy to compose herself.

(Clara Schumann here is understood to be the music-composing wife of the composer Schumann.) As we can see, the awkward grammatical structure of the sentence leads to these two interpretations: (a) Clara Schumann was too busy to pull herself together emotionally; and (b) Clara Schumann was too busy to compose music, as her husband did.

The *fallacy of amphiboly* can be illustrated in this way. Suppose that Aunt Pooh dies and leaves a will in which she bequeaths a hundred dollars to be shared by her cousins Eliza and Daisy. The will reads:

I hereby bequeath one hundred dollars to Eliza Singleton and Daisy Singleton.

As we can see, this is amphibolous. Now suppose Eliza and Daisy's lawyer argues:

Since Aunt Pooh in her will said, "I hereby bequeath one hundred dollars to Eliza Singleton and Daisy Singleton," each cousin should have one hundred dollars.

This is an instance of the fallacy of amphiboly. An amphibolous sentence is employed in an argument, and a sense is given to the sentence which is different from the intended sense.

Not only a sentence but a group of sentences can be awkwardly put together so that two or more senses can be gotten from the collection. For example, this ad for a time was found in some magazines:

A survey shows many doctors take the fast, pain-relieving ingredients in Brand X. In fact, 3 out of 4 doctors recommend this same type relief to their patients.

This paragraph is amphibolous since it could be understood in two ways: (a) three out of four doctors recommend Brand X and (b) three out of four doctors recommend a number of drugs which also happen to contain ingredients found in Brand X. If someone concluded from reading this ad (a) that three out of four doctors recommend Brand X, he would be mistaken and this would be an instance of the fallacy of amphiboly, since this ad should be understood in sense (b).

A humorous example of awkwardly constructed paragraphs is the following letter of appreciation:

I would like very much to thank both our Walhalla police department and Mayor Snuff for resuming police escorts for funeral processions. It is very definitely a worthwhile function of our police department.

Being one of the first to receive this service, I would like you to know it was very much appreciated.

I was escorted to the edge of the city. The officer then got out and stood at attention until the procession had passed, a very thoughtful and impressive gesture.

To conclude that this was a letter from the dead would be to commit an amphiboly fallacy.

The Division and Composition Fallacies

The *fallacy of division* is committed when someone argues that something which is true only of the whole is also true of its parts taken separately. Consider these examples of this fallacy:

Ice cream tastes sweet, so all the ingredients must taste sweet.

Ice cream tastes sweet, but, obviously, it does not follow from this that each ingredient taken separately tastes sweet. For example, salt does not taste sweet.

Walhalla University produces the best Ph.D's in the country. So Archie Van Dyke, who recently got his degree from the school, must be an excellent man.

The graduates of the best universities are generally excellent, but to infer that a particular graduate is excellent merely from the school's excellence would be an incorrect inference.

The *fallacy of composition* consists in reasoning from what is true only of the parts of some whole to what is true of the whole. The following are both composition fallacies:

Since each of the ingredients of ice cream does not especially taste good, it follows that ice cream doesn't especially taste good.
A, B, C, D, . . . are all star players, so we can easily have the best team and win the pennant by composing our team of them.

Two things should be kept in mind in connection with the fallacies of composition and division. First, the fallacy of composition should not be confused with the hasty generalization fallacy. When one reasons erroneously from what is true about some single entity to what is true about all such entities, this is the hasty generalization fallacy. When one reasons erroneously from what is true about each of the parts of some whole to the whole itself, this is the fallacy of composition. In the last two examples above, someone reasons from what is true of *each* of the ingredients and what is true of *each* of the players. Second, sometimes when one reasons from what is true of the whole to what is true of each part and vice versa, no error is committed. Consider, for example, these two inferences:

The car is brand new, so the parts of the car are new.
Each citizen wants Lord Privy Seal to be elected Prime Minister, so the nation wants Privy Seal to be elected Prime Minister.

The reason that composition and division fallacies are classified as fallacies of ambiguity is that many can be regarded as involving words or phrases whose meaning shifts. Many of these fallacies can be regarded as using the verb "to be" equivocally. We can distinguish the distributive use of the verb and the collective use. For example, in:

Volkswagens are low priced,

the verb "to be" is used distributively. We are saying here that each and every VW is low priced. However, in this example:

Volkswagens are plentiful,

we are using the verb collectively. We are not saying that each and every VW is plentiful but that VW's as a class or group are plentiful. Often it will be found that in a division fallacy the verb is used collectively in the premisses, then distributively in the conclusion, while in a composition fallacy the order is reversed.

The Fallacy of Accent

Sometimes we can change the meaning of a sentence by accenting some word or phrase. Consider this sentence taken from Jevons' logic book: [14]

The study of logic is not supposed to communicate a knowledge of many useful facts.

It is clear how we are to understand it. Logic, among a number of things, will help to determine when an inference is correct (or valid) and when it is incorrect (or invalid), but it will not provide information about the world, as chemistry, for example, does. But we can accent certain words or phrases and change the meaning. For example, we can say:

The study of logic is not *supposed* to communicate a knowledge of many useful facts.

This gives the impression that, though logic is not supposed to communicate many useful facts, it does. Or consider our saying this:

The study of logic is not supposed to communicate a knowledge of *many* useful facts.

Here it sounds as if logic will communicate some useful facts but not many.

The fallacy of accent is committed whenever a statement is accented in such a way as to change its meaning, and is employed in an argument. Suppose, for example, someone used this argument:

The famous logician Jevons, to take one example, didn't know that logic is a formal discipline and that to know the propositions in logic is to know nothing about the world. For in his logic book he said: "The study of logic is not supposed to communicate a knowledge of *many* useful facts."

It is supposed that this is spoken; otherwise we would have a misquotation and not a fallacy of accent.

Quoting out of context, which can be regarded in many of its instances as a fallacy of relevance, is often classed as a kind of accent fallacy. For to quote out of context is in a way to accent some sentence or sentences by neglecting the sentences which surround them. We shall describe this fallacy and consider two somewhat different examples of it.

Sometimes when a statement is removed from its spoken or written context, it may be regarded by many as meaning something different or having an import which is different from what it has in the spoken or written context. When such a statement is employed in an argument in

14 William Stanley Jevons, *Lessons in Logic* (London and New York: The Macmillan Company, 1907), p. 175.

such a way that its import or meaning is changed by not supplying the context, and in such a way that its altered import or meaning figures in a reason relevant to the conclusion, the *fallacy of quoting out of context* occurs.

Suppose a movie critic wrote:

The movie is flawless except for bad acting, a bad plot, and bad photography.

A dishonest promoter of the film, let us suppose, advertises the film indicating that the movie critic wrote "The movie is flawless. . . ." Since the reviewer's opinion is employed as a reason for seeing the film, this argument is implicit:

The movie critic wrote "The movie is flawless . . . ," and that is a good reason for seeing the film.

In this example the phrase out of context quite obviously takes on a radically differing meaning. Since it is then employed in an argument, the fallacy of quoting out of context is committed.

The second example of quoting out of context is a bit different from the first. In early sixties many newspapers demanded that direct action be taken to remove Castro's Communist government from Cuba. They cited the Monroe Doctrine in support of such actions. The provision of the doctrine cited was: "an interposition" by a European power in the Western Hemisphere would be the "manifestation of an unfriendly disposition toward the United States." What many of these papers did not tell their readers is that there was more to the message to Congress in 1823 which bears the name "The Monroe Doctrine." The doctrine not only warned Europe to keep its hands off this hemisphere; it went on to assure Europe that we would not meddle in its affairs: "Our policy in regard to Europe is not to interfere in the internal concerns of any of its powers; to consider the government *de facto* as the legitimate government for us; to cultivate friendly relations with it. . . . It is our duty to remain the peaceful and silent, though sorrowful, spectators of the European scene." In this example a phrase from the doctrine is employed to support the conclusion that direct United States action should be taken to remove the Communist government in Cuba. If, however, the complete statement of what is called the Monroe Doctrine had been brought to the reader's attention, the doctrine could not have been used to support the conclusion since the United States, in becoming a world leader, has itself violated the doctrine. Thus the phrase by itself seems to be a good reason for the conclusion, whereas in the context it is not. In the first example the phrase out of context took on a different sense, while in this example the import of a phrase changes when the phrase is out of context.

EXERCISES III

For these exercises, follow directions given on page 34 for the exercises at the end of the first section, employing the fallacies discussed in this section.

1. Senator Snort can be trusted to do what is right, for he is a member of the majority, and the majority may be trusted to do what is right in the long run.

2. Chocolate syrup, olives, and sliced pineapple are all delicious. How much more delicious would be a mixture of all three of them.

3. Since each atom is completely determined as to its position or motion by the unchanging laws of nature, and since man's body consists entirely of atoms, his body too must be completely determined as to its position and motion by the very same laws.

4. The composite American housewife, according to the United States census of 1960, has 3.8 children. You look like an average United States housewife, Mrs. Ogmore-Pritchard. Therefore you can expect your marriage to yield three children and, after a decent interval, eight tenths of another child. May all your troubles be little ones!

5. As creators, women are superior to men since men can only create works of art, science, or philosophy, whereas women can create life.

6. DANCING MASTER: When a man has made some blunder, whether in his family affairs, or in government, or in generalship, don't we always say: "So-and-so has made a false step in such a matter"?

M. JOURDAIN: Yes, we say that.

DANCING MASTER: And taking a false step, can that result from anything else than not knowing how to dance?

M. JOURDAIN: That's true.

(MOLIERE, *Le bourgeois gentilhomme*)

7. Our country is a free nation "under God." Perhaps those who object to our setting aside, by law, a day to honor Him would prefer the kind of freedom found in a country "under Khrushchev."

We pass laws to safeguard our possessions from those who would take them from us; one of our most valuable possessions is our Sundays—our family days of rest and worship.

God in His holy wisdom created the Sabbath as a gift for us, a gift of one day a week from the toils and cares of this world. Are we going to let some men in their rush toward all-out commercialism take it away from us?

8. With the awesome destructiveness of the H-bomb now a reality, it is inevitable that military considerations should overshadow all others. What should we do with the bomb? How should we as a nation husband it? The answers to these questions lie in the hands of the men who know best, who have first hand experience in weaponry—the military.

9. Marx and Engels pursued their activities in the prerevolutionary period (we have the proletarian revolution in mind), when developed imperialism did not yet exist, in the period of the proletarians' preparation for a revolution, in

the period when the proletarian revolution was not yet a direct, practical inevitability. Lenin, however, the disciple of Marx and Engels, pursued his activities in the period of developed imperialism, in the period of the unfolding proletarian revolution, when the proletarian revolution had already triumphed in one country, had smashed bourgeois democracy and had ushered in the era of proletarian democracy, the era of the Soviets.

That is why Leninism is the further development of Marxism.

(JOSEF STALIN, *What Is Leninism?*)

10. Wilbur Mills, Chairman of the House Ways and Means Committee, has stubbornly refused to permit the medical aid for the aged bill to get out of his committee. This bill would help about fifteen million people in their twilight years. Mills says he opposes Communism, but in real fact he is using the same tactics which the Communists use—refusal to let others vote. We criticize Communists for not holding free elections. But what do we do? We hold elections, then let a handful of men stymie the results of those elections. These men employ the same tactics as the Communists!

11. Improbable events happen almost every day, but whatever happens almost every day is probable. Improbable events, therefore, are probable events.

12. Sir, you unfortunately display ignorance of the religious views of Thomas Jefferson when you call him an agnostic or atheist. The following quotation from the Jefferson Memorial should clearly illustrate this ignorance: "I have sworn upon the altar of God, eternal hostility against every form of tyranny over the mind of man."—Strange language for an atheist or agnostic!

The quote from the Jefferson Memorial is fragmented. The complete quote, from Jefferson's letter to Dr. Benjamin Rush, is as follows: "They [the clergy] believe that any portion of power confided to me, will be exerted in opposition to their schemes. And they believe rightly: for I have sworn upon the altar of God, eternal hostility against every form of tyranny over the mind of man."

EXERCISES IV

Follow the directions given earlier and indicate the fallacies, selecting from *all* those discussed.

1. What prompted the Supreme Court of 1954 in desegregating schools to cast aside the accumulated wisdom of earlier courts and to veer off into the tangled underbrush of sociology where even the best legal bloodhounds lose the trail of law? The explanation is obvious. It is that the Court succumbed to pressures which persuaded the Justices that a desegregation decision could perform a highly useful function in the realm of international relations and enhance the position of the U.S. in its dealings with the non-white nations of the world.

(W. D. WORKMAN, *The Case for the South*) [15]

[15] W. D. Workman, *The Case for the South* (New York: Devin-Adair, 1960).

2.   In *The Merchant of Venice,* the Duke tells Shylock that he should be merciful and not demand by law that he get his bond (a pound of Antonio's flesh). To this he replies:

> You have among you many a purchased slave
> Which, like your asses and your dogs and mules,
> You use in abject and in slavish parts,
> Because you bought them: shall I say to you,
> Let them be free, marry them to your heirs?
> Why sweat they under burthens? let their beds
> Be made as soft as yours and let their palates
> Be season'd with such viands? You will answer
> "The slaves are ours": so do I answer you:
> The pound of flesh, which I demand of him,
> Is dearly bought: 't is mine and I will have it.

3.   Marx held that economic change determines the intellectual, cultural, religious, and political forms of any society. The proof which he gives is taken from history. He shows that an economic change occurred at a certain time and then later a change took place in ideas.

4.   A strong team of Japanese mountain-climbers was given permission by the native government to climb Manaslu, one of the great peaks of the Himalayas. In 1954 the team arrived in the village of Sama, escorted by more than four hundred porters. The villagers attacked the party with sticks and stones so violently that the porters dropped their loads and fled. What was the reason for the violence? The villagers explained that "heathen Japanese," scouting for the climb the year before, had desecrated their holy mountain, and afterwards the gods had loosed a great avalanche, which destroyed a lamasery and killed three priests. It was admitted that the avalanche came six months after the visit of the exploring party, but no villager doubted the connection.

(Taken from STUART CHASE's *Guides to Straight Thinking*) [16]

5.   The story is told that when Lincoln was a young lawyer in one of his first cases, his opponent was an experienced trial lawyer who knew most of the fine legal points. The day was hot and Lincoln slumped in his chair while the case went against him. When the lawyer took off his coat, however, Lincoln noticed that he was wearing one of the new shirts of the 1840's which buttoned up the back. When his turn came his plea was brief: "Gentlemen of the jury, because I have justice on my side, I am sure you will not be influenced by this gentleman's pretended knowledge of the law. Why, he doesn't even know which side of his shirt ought to be in front!"

6.   Our government insures freedom of religion. Now one can easily find a hundred authorities who say Communism is a religion, that it has its deities, rituals, doctrine, commandments, and so forth. It is therefore un-American to lay a ban on Communist activities. It violates freedom of religion. Furthermore

---

[16] Stuart Chase, *Guides to Straight Thinking* (New York: Harper, 1956), p. 76.

it is unconstitutional, for the First Amendment reads: "Congress shall make no law respecting an establishment of religion, or prohibiting the free exercise thereof."

7. From an antiprohibition manual: In dry Kansas the annual divorce rate is 2.36 per thousand, whereas in wet North Carolina it is only .75 per thousand. In dry Kansas there are more murders in proportion to the population than in wet New York or wet New Mexico. In dry Kansas there is a smaller proportion of savings bank depositors than in wet Louisiana, Alabama, Kentucky, or Wyoming. Nail the prohibitionist down to facts. Does he propose to ruin the country?

8. American democracy is being threatened by a new, enormous, and insidious power—the military-industrial complex. As evidence for this I quote former President Eisenhower in his Farewell Address of January 17, 1961: "We must guard against the acquisition of unwarranted interference, whether sought or unsought, by the military-industrial complex." At other times he said that the military-industrial complex is "a very serious matter . . . a very difficult thing to get out of after you've once got into it—no matter how intelligently you went in." If this is not enough, Senator Ralph E. Flanders, the Vermont Republican, said on the Senate floor: "It is not only that we are sacrificing to defence our standard of living and the free independence of our economic life, we are sacrificing our freedom itself. We are being forced to shift the American way of life into the pattern of the garrison state."

9. Jonathan Swift, in his short essay entitled *A Modest Proposal,* argues that since the children of the poor Irish are so numerous and have created such a burden on the economy and society with their extreme poverty, there should be something done to eliminate the problem. He proposes that the English could well profit from taking these children from their parents and shipping them to England to be slaughtered as food for the English table. After all, Swift reasons, both countries would be better off in many ways. England would be relieved of its food shortage, and the aristocracy would be given a new type of table delicacy. The Irish would no longer be burdened with these hungry infants who most often before the age of twelve are well versed in the art of theft.

10. DEAR FELLOW ALUMNUS:

As a Brownstone graduate you are a discerning person. We, your former classmates and Brownstone rooters to the end, want your help now. Certain visionary academic minds have prevailed on the trustees to drop football from the Brownstone program, on the absurd grounds that athletics—those very sports that helped build our college, our country, and our character—are harmful to Brownstone. These dreamy professors forget that there is more to Americanism than stoop-shouldered and nearsighted scholarship. What will a nation of flabby scholars be able to do when Russia attacks? Perhaps tomorrow! We shall need strength and competitive energy as well as learning. We shall need, that is, the Brownstone halfbacks and tackles! This shows how irrational their scheme is. It plays directly into Red hands! You don't find the Russians cutting down on sports.

These weary old men argue that football tends to draw both money and student interest away from studies. But haven't we Brownstone men done well for ourselves in the past? Do we want our sons to be feeble bookworms or well-balanced men like the founders of this country? Washington himself was an athlete, not a library-haunter. Do your bit against these dreamers!

Write or telegraph the trustees! Tell them you don't want to see the old Brownstone pennant dragging in the dust with no one to defend it on the gridiron! Renew that old aggressive Brownstone spirit, and push it to new glories! [17]

> J. B. "Socko" Squidleigh
> Class of '40

11. An animal psychologist, Dr. W. T. James, in Athens, Georgia, found out after ten years of experiments that timid dogs go hungry while the aggressive dogs grow fat. "Dr. James has been placing dogs of various temperaments in a run. At the end of the run is a food box from which only one dog can eat at a time. The timid dog will cower in a corner, while the aggressive type moves straight ahead. Two of the domineering type promptly start fighting until the superiority of one is established. If a top, middle and underdog are in the run at the same time, the top dog proceeds to eat his fill. Occasionally the middle-class dog, out of frustration and rage over his secondary position, will take out his spite on the underdog."

> (*The New York Times*, Oct. 21, 1950)

12. When Joe McCarthy appeared before the Watkins Committee, which was considering censure of his conduct as a U.S. Senator, Edward B. Williams was his counsel. Here is a report of Williams' defense: "When McCarthy's offenses were considered one by one, it turned out that there were very few for which no Senatorial precedent could be found. Had he been inexcusably arrogant and bullying in his treatment of General Zwicker? Indeed, he had been—and to many others besides—but he was not the first man to abuse his power in this way. Williams found an instance, only a few days before the censure hearings, in which Prescott Bush, of Connecticut, had been accused of similar discourtesies in the course of a one-man hearing on public housing. Why not censure Bush along with McCarthy? Had McCarthy given out classified information? He had, but he was not alone in this; a member of the Select Committee, Edwin Johnson, had, only a few years back, been widely criticized for giving out classified facts on hydrogen weapons on a television program. Had McCarthy called Senator Flanders 'senile'—yes, but Senator Flanders had compared McCarthy with Hitler; which is worse, to be senile or a Hitler? It was true that McCarthy had urged government employees to give information directly to him whether or not some 'bureaucrat had stamped it secret,' but was this so different from the action of Watkins himself in signing a committee report that urged 'employees in the executive branch . . . to turn over

---

[17] This argument was created by Professor Harry Nielsen of the University of Notre Dame and is used here with his permission.

to committees of Congress any information which would help the Committees in their fight against subversion'?"

(RICHARD H. ROVERE, Senator Joe McCarthy) [18]

13. These states are among those whose standard of living is the highest: the United States, Canada, Australia, New Zealand, and England. It is to be noted that all these states are democracies. This raises the question whether they are prosperous because they are democratic or democratic because they are prosperous. Is prosperity the economic reward earned by those who organize their government democratically, or is democracy a political luxury which only the richer members of the international family can afford? Since all these states began and developed at a time when they were not democratic, it is therefore true that they are democratic because they are prosperous.

14. Through the long months of debate on the question of medical care for the aged, the American Medical Association has been shouting "Socialism!" at the King-Anderson bill, the Kennedy Administration's approach to the problem.

This charge was attacked recently by Senator Oren E. Long of Hawaii, who pointed out that King-Anderson is the truly conservative approach. Then he added:

"Let me say this to those who give out with the cry of 'socialism':

"If ever there was a proposal based on sound American thinking, this is it.

"It is based not on European practice, not on the ideas of Bismarck, or Marx, or Lenin, but on the reasoning of that most conservative of great Americans, the godfather of the Republican Party, Alexander Hamilton.

"Does that surprise you? Let me explain. At the very beginning of our government, Hamilton, always alert to protect the taxpayer, had a problem. It involved young America's sailors. Leaving home on their ships, healthy and hearty, many returned ill with scurvy, racked with strange diseases or suffering from injuries.

"Inevitably they wound up in the big ports of our young nation dependent for medical care on the local taxpayers—on local relief—on a kind of Kerr-Mills setup. To Hamilton—a businessman if ever there was one—this made no sense whatsoever. Moreover, it set a dangerous precedent for other groups in the population.

" 'So,' Alexander Hamilton said, 'why should we not charge these sailors a very small part of their wages when they are healthy and employed to pay for their own care when they are sick and injured?' It made sense to our 100-percent American forebears. The Congress enacted it into law in 1798, thus providing a system of self-financing care for merchant seamen and, at the same time, originating our U.S. Public Health Service.

"It remains today, in 1962, the same safe, sane, conservative American answer to a great American problem."

(Taken from The Californian, January 1962)

15. In my study of physics I have found that the temperature of a body is the mean kinetic energy of the molecules of that body. Now, as we all know, molecules cannot be said to possess a temperature. So it follows that it is out of ignorance that we say that fire is hot and ice is cold. Things only *appear* to have temperature; in *reality* things are without temperature.

16. There is a view I came across in my ethics class which is called "psychological hedonism." According to this view, all men act with the intention of maximizing their pleasure. This might be true for some or many men but not for all men. This is easily proved. For example, I did a good deed yesterday and my only aim in doing this was to do something good for another person.

17. Resumption of atmospheric nuclear testing by the United States is being urged as a result of the recent tests by Russia. I favor a postponement of such testing.

It is a continuation of the arms race. Arms races since 650 B.C. have numbered 1,656. They have resulted in 1,640 wars. The sixteen occasions which did not result in war resulted in economic collapse.

Tests would increase the hazard to health from fallout. The people who study the effects of radiation from fallout feel that there is harm to health. The disagreement is on the degree of harm.

Is testing in the national interest? No, the United States has nuclear striking capabilities that are superior to the Soviets', even after the Russian tests. In addition, we must recognize that if the United States also begins atmospheric testing, it will bring despair to the world.

18. The upsurge of Communism, we are informed, is, in part at least, due to the failure of the Church. Specifically, we are told, it is the irrelevance of so much of the nineteenth-century Christianity to the urgent problems of modern industrial mass society that has driven large masses to look elsewhere for salvation and meaning in life; Communism has gained its strength from its ability to fill the spiritual vacuum which the failure of Christianity has produced.

Such is the familiar argument; if taken seriously, however, it leads to some rather extraordinary conclusions. The U.S., the Netherlands, the Scandinavian countries, even Britain, seem to be singularly free from Communist infection; are we to conclude, therefore, that Christianity and the Church are particularly relevant in these countries, in contrast, let us say, to Christianity and the Church in Italy or France where Communism is a powerful mass force?

(WILL HERBERG, "Communism, Christianity and the Judgment of God") [19]

19. FRIENDS AND FELLOW CITIZENS: I stand before you tonight under indictment for the alleged crime of having voted at the last presidential election, without having a lawful right to vote. It shall be my work this evening to prove to you that in thus voting, I not only committed no crime, but, instead, simply exercised my citizen's rights, guaranteed to me and all United States

[19] Will Herberg, "Communism, Christianity, and the Judgment of God," in *The National Review,* January 16, 1962, p. 22. Used by permission.

citizens by the National Constitution, beyond the power of any State to deny. . . . The Preamble of the Federal Constitution says:

"We, the people of the United States, in order to form a more perfect union, establish justice, insure *domestic* tranquillity, provide for the common defense, promote the general welfare, and secure the blessings of liberty to ourselves and our posterity, do ordain and establish this Constitution for the United States of America."

It was we, the people; not we, the white male citizens; nor yet we, the male citizens; but we, the whole people, who formed the Union. And we formed it, not to give the blessings of liberty, but to secure them; not to the half of ourselves and the half of our posterity, but to the whole people—women as well as men. And it is a downright mockery to talk to women of their enjoyment of the blessings of liberty while they are denied the use of the only means of securing them provided by this democratic-republican government—the ballot.

For any state to make sex a qualification that must ever result in the disfranchisement of one entire half of the people is to pass a bill of attainder, or an *ex post facto* law, and is therefore a violation of the supreme law of the land. By it the blessings of liberty are for ever withheld from women and their female posterity. To them this government has no just powers derived from the consent of the governed. To them this government is not a democracy. It is not a republic. It is an odious aristocracy; a hateful oligarchy of sex; the most hateful aristocracy ever established on the face of the globe. An oligarchy of wealth, where the rich govern the poor, an oligarchy of learning, where the educated govern the ignorant, or even an oligarchy of race, where the Saxon rules the African, might be endured; but this oligarchy of sex, which makes father, brothers, husband, sons, the oligarchs over the mother and sisters, the wife and daughters of every household—which ordains all men sovereigns, all women subjects, carries dissension, disorder and rebellion into every home of the nation.

Webster, Worcester and Bouvier all define a citizen to be a person in the United States, entitled to vote and hold office.

The only question left to be settled now is: Are women persons? And I hardly believe any of our opponents will have the hardihood to say they are not. Being persons, then, women are citizens; and no State has a right to make any law, or to enforce any old law, that shall abridge their privileges or immunities. Hence, every discrimination against women in the constitutions and laws of the several states is today null and void, precisely as is every one against Negroes.

(SUSAN B. ANTHONY, speech delivered in 1873 on woman's right to the suffrage)

20. In an historic decision, the California Supreme Court ruled in People *vs.* Love that a prosecutor may not tell a jury that capital punishment is an established deterrent to crime.

Associate Justice Marshall F. McComb wrote one of the dissenting opinions. Wrote McComb:

"In my opinion, it is a matter of common knowledge that the death penalty is a deterrent because:

"(a) Christians and Jews from the beginning of recorded history have recognized that the death penalty is a deterrent to murder.

"This is demonstrated by the fact that, according to the account contained in the Old Testament (see New American Catholic Edition, The Holy Bible, 1950), the Lord spoke to Moses and said: 'He that striketh and killeth a man; dying let him die.' (Leviticus 25, verse 17.)

"(b) In the early history of the western states of the United States of America, including California, the death penalty was imposed by the early settlers to stop the rustling of cattle. It is a matter of common knowledge that in the early days of this state the apprehension and hanging of cattle rustlers reduced, and almost stopped, the theft of cattle.

"(c) In the early history of San Francisco, law enforcement broke down and chaotic conditions prevailed. A group of citizens, known as the Vigilantes, undertook to restore order. To do this, they apprehended criminals and after trial promptly executed the guilty parties. Order was restored, and the civil authorities assumed control again. Clearly fear of the death penalty was the basic reason for the restoration of order."

(Taken from *The Californian,* February 1962)

21. Others, again, are distressed because materialism offers them no prospect of a future life. This, again, if it is a fault, is the fault of Nature and not of the philosopher who describes Nature. But there seems nothing so very terrible about it, to one who looks at the facts calmly. . . . as it happens, we are partially dying from the day we are born. I do not allude to the fact that the matter of which our bodies are composed is continually changing, so that after a year or two we are composed of altogether different material substance. I refer more to mental changes. The mind which we possessed at the age of three is dead and gone; and at the age of seventy a man bears less resemblance to himself at three than he does to other men of seventy. The mind has radically changed, the body is entirely different; the child is effectively gone as much as if it were dead. . . . Why then do we not bemoan the spiritual death of our childhood as much, or more, than we do the anticipated death of old age? By all reasonable standards, the loss of youth is more regrettable than the loss of an old and decrepit body and mind. It is, on the whole, true that youth is spent in the pursuit of pleasure, while old age is spent in the avoidance of pain. Yet men fear far more the ultimate extinction of life than they do the onset of old age.

(HUGH ELLIOT, *Modern Science and Materialism*) [20]

22. British historian Arnold Toynbee believes that the stimulation of personal consumption through advertising is un-Christain ("I cannot think of any circumstance in which advertising would not be an evil"), and last year ad-

---

[20] Hugh Elliot, *Modern Science and Materialism* (London: Longmans, Green, 1919), pp. 208–209.

vanced the ridiculous proposition: "The destiny of our Western civilization turns on the issue of our struggle with all that Madison Avenue stands for more than it turns on the issue of our struggle with Communism."

. . . In the most effective rebuttal any adman has yet made to Arnold Toynbee, William Bernbach wrote: "Mr. Toynbee's real hate is not advertising. It is the economy of abundance. . . . If Mr. Toynbee believes a materialistic society is a bad one (and I am not saying he is wrong in that belief), then he owes it to mankind to speak out against such a society and not merely against one of the tools that is available to any society."

In fact, as Historian Toynbee should know, taste and cultivation have historically reached their heights in prosperous societies. By helping to produce mass prosperity, advertising has at least indirectly helped to raise the general level of taste in the U.S.—a development that, in turn, has been mirrored in advertising itself. Even its critics concede that advertising has come a long way since the days when national magazines were littered with ads for nostrums that purported to cure everything from consumption to lost manhood, and when a U.S. soapmaker could bugle: "If we could teach the Indians to use SAPOLIO, it would quickly civilize them." Today most ads, if not 99 44/100% of them, strive for both taste and believability. And, assuming a continued increase in U.S. affluence and cultivation, tomorrow's advertising should be even more sophisticated and tasteful.

Whatever the state of American culture, all signs are that advertising will always be a conspicuously visible part of it. Fascinated as it is with the business of finding ways to live, the U.S. public wastes little time worrying about whether advertising may be damaging to its collective psyche. It is unlikely that the citizenry will ever take the step some admen seem to yearn for and pass a national vote of thanks to advertising for its part in enriching U.S. life. But it is equally unlikely that the public will ever be suborned out of its unemotional recognition of the adman for what he is: a highly effective salesman without whose efforts the world would be a far more primitive and less pleasant place.

(*Time,* October 12, 1962) [21]

23. There is an incredible amount of empty space in the universe. The distance from the sun to the nearest star is about 4.2 light years, or 25×10^{12} miles. This is in spite of the fact that we live in an exceptionally crowded part of the universe, namely the Milky Way, which is an assemblage of about 300,-000 million stars. This assemblage is one of an immense number of similar assemblages; about 30 million are known, but presumably, better telescopes would show more. The average distance from one assemblage to the next is about 2 million light years. But apparently they still feel they haven't elbow room, for they are all hurrying away from each other; some are moving away from us at the rate of 14,000 miles a second or more. The most distant of them so far observed are believed to be at a distance from us of about 500 million

21 *Time,* Vol. LXXX, No. 15, October 12, 1962, p. 87. Courtesy TIME; copyright Time Inc. 1962.

light years, so that what we see is what they were 500 million years ago. And as to mass: the sun weighs about 2×10^{27} tons, the Milky Way about 160,000 million times as much as the sun, and is one of a collection of galaxies of which about 30 million are known. It is not easy to maintain a belief in one's own cosmic importance in view of such overwhelming statistics.

(BERTRAND RUSSELL, *The Impact of Science on Society*) [22]

24. Here they [the laws of thought] are:
   (a) The law of identity affirms that *A* is *A,* or that every event and every judgment is identical with itself.
   (b) The law of contradiction affirms that *A* cannot both be *A* and not be *A*.
   (c) The law of the excluded middle affirms that everything must be either *A* or not *A*.

. . . In the hands of some of his [Aristotle's] followers the three principles have taken on a grim finality, inflexible and absolute. The law of identity, rigidly interpreted, does not allow for changes in *A* through time, or for the differing meanings which can be attached to *A*. "A rose is a rose," but a rose in June is not identical with the same rose in September, so far as color, scent, and structure go. Webster's recent college dictionary gives the word "science" six different meanings, ending up with Christian Science. To say that "science is science and let's have no more nonsense about it" is a non-sensical statement. To which meaning do you refer? The law of identity, inflexibly interpreted, runs head on into the "one-proper-meaning super-stition," which modern students of communication and language most prop-erly condemn.

The laws of contradiction and excluded middle, in the hands of some Aristotelians, have congealed into a mental fixation where an event must be either black or white, with no room for shades of gray. So interpreted, the law of contradiction says that nothing can be both "good" and "bad," both "poisonous" and "beneficial." But such drugs as arsenic, belladonna, curare, can be beneficial in small doses, though lethal in large. And what about a friend of mine who has an allergy for fresh eggs, and becomes deathly ill if he eats one?

The third law, that of the excluded middle, rigidly interpreted, supports the slogan that "those who are not with us are against us." Applied to American foreign policy today, such thinking would throw all the neutral nations, like India and Burma, into the Communist camp—a pretty dis-astrous line to take.

(STUART CHASE, *Guides to Straight Thinking*) [23]

[22] Bertrand Russell, *The Impact of Science on Society* (New York: Columbia University Press, 1951), pp. 13–14. Copyright 1951 Columbia University Press, New York. Used by permission.
[23] Stuart Chase, *Guides to Straight Thinking* (New York: Harper, 1056), pp. 16–17.

25. I can now give a large number of different proofs for the existence of things outside of us, each of which is a perfectly rigorous proof; and . . . at many other times I have been in a position to give many others. I can prove, now, for instance, that two human hands exist. How? By holding up my two hands, and saying, as I make a certain gesture with the right hand, "Here is one hand," and adding, as I make a certain gesture with the left, "and here is another." And if, by doing this, I have proved *ipso facto* the existence of external things, you will all see that I can also do it now in numbers of other ways: there is no need to multiply examples.

(G. E. MOORE, "Proof of an External World") [24]

26. After we came out of church, we stood talking for some time together of Bishop Berkeley's ingenious sophistry to prove the nonexistence of matter, and that everything in the Universe is merely ideal. I observed that though we are satisfied that his doctrine is not true, it is impossible to refute. I never shall forget the alacrity with which Johnson answered, striking his foot with mighty force against a large stone till he rebounded from it, "I refute it thus."

(BOSWELL, *Life of Johnson*)

EXERCISES V

Consider again the incorrect arguments found in the exercises in the first chapter and indicate what fallacies of those discussed in this chapter are to be found in those arguments.

[24] G. E. Moore, "Proof of an External World" in *Philosophical Papers,* pp. 145–146, © George Allen and Unwin Ltd., 1959. Used by permission of George Allen and Unwin Ltd. and The Macmillan Company.

Chapter Three

DEFINITIONS

In this chapter two aspects of words as they are used in everyday discourse will be first considered. These aspects are: first, ordinary words are not used in accordance with strict rules, and, second, ordinary words are so used that they lack definite boundaries. Next, verbal disputes will be considered. And, last, methods and types of definitions will be discussed.

TWO ASPECTS OF ORDINARY WORDS

Exact Definitions

Consider this list of everyday words as they are used in the indicated sentences and phrases:

building (The building is finished.)
shoe (There is a shoe on the road.)
college (He goes to college.)
broom (She swept with the broom.)
lie (He told me a lie.)
theatre (The theatre opens at noon.)
child (She's my only child.)
language (no written language)
mountain (They climbed the mountain.)
intelligent (He is intelligent.)

crying (The baby's crying.)
game (Let's play a game.)
embrace (Embrace me.)
joke (Tell us a joke.)
fox (the fox and the crow)
purchase (Purchase soap.)
author (the book's author)
river (the Nile river)
ball (There's his ball.)

As we all know there are a number of things, objects, which we call buildings. There are a number of things, objects, which we call shoes; there are a number of things, activities, we call games; there are a number of things, statements, we call jokes; and so on. In short, we can point out examples (by using the word "this," by describing examples, and so forth) of things (objects, behavior, persons, actions, statements, and the like) which are X or not X (where "X" stands for any of the above words). We will call this characteristic of the above words *denoting*. That is, to say that "X" *denotes* means, according to this convention, that we can point out examples of things which are X or not X.

All the words in the above list denote existing things. That is, there exist things which are called mountains, foxes, and so forth. There are, however, some words which denote but do not denote any existing thing. For example, the words "gorgon" and "phlogiston" do not denote any existing thing. There are also words which do not denote, for example, the words "if," "not," "this," "meaning," and "Sir Alfred Zot."

Now let us suppose the word "A" only denotes five objects—that is, at a given time only five objects in the world are called "A." Let us also suppose that there is a set of characteristics—C_1, C_2, and C_3—common to these five objects. And let us suppose further that these three characteristics by convention are related to the word "A" in this way: if any object is called "A," or would be called "A," then it must have C_1, C_2, and C_3; and if any object has or would have C_1, C_2, and C_3, then it is or would be called "A." In a word, C_1, C_2, and C_3 are what justify our calling certain objects "A's."

In this imagined situation, the word "A" is so used that this statement is true:

1. An object is called "A" if and only if it has C_1, C_2, and C_3.

For C_1, C_2, and C_3 are the sufficient conditions for calling objects "A," and C_1, C_2, and C_3 are all necessary conditions for calling objects "A." We will call (1) an *exact definition* for "A." Since (1) is a true report of how "A" is used in this imagined situation, (1) is an exact *reportive* definition for "A."

Exact Definitions and Our Everyday Words

Can exact definitions be provided for the words in our list as they are used in everyday discourse? For example, is there a conjunction of characteristics common to all objects which we call "building" which is so related to this word, that if an object has it, then it is called a building, and if an object lacks one or more of the characteristics included in it, the object is not called a building? This is a factual question, but it is not an easy one to answer. One way to begin is to consider some *supposed* exact definitions for these words as they are used in everyday discourse. Consider, for example, this supposed exact definition for "building":

A thing is called a "building" if and only if it is a structure built to shelter things.

Is this true? No. There are some things which are structures used to shelter things which we do not call "buildings," for example, bird houses. In addition, certain structures like the Jefferson Memorial are called "buildings," but they are not used to shelter things. Consider this supposed exact definition for "shoe":

A thing is called a "shoe" if and only if it is a covering for the human foot, having a thick and somewhat stiff sole.

Is this statement true? We know that horseshoes, for example, are objects which people call "shoes," so this statement is false. But let us limit the denotation to things worn by people. Is this statement with this restriction true? As we know, slippers, galoshes, and sandals are things covering the foot having a thick and somewhat stiff sole, but they are not called "shoes." In addition some things are called "shoes" which do not have a thick and somewhat stiff sole, for example, moccasins, wooden shoes, and so on. Other attempts could be made to provide exact definitions, but they would end in failure. Even if the denotations were restricted in various ways, in all likelihood an exact definition could not be provided, unless of course the denotation were so restricted that the proposed definition would be true in virtue of the restriction. The conclusion we draw from this is that exact definitions cannot be provided for the words in our list and others like them as they are used in everyday discourse.

From our inability to provide exact definitions for such words, it should not be concluded that we can never give exact reportive definitions for words. In some contexts a word might be so used that such a definition can be given. For example in geometry the word "triangle" is used in accordance with this rule:

Something is to be called a "triangle" if and only if it is a plane figure bounded by three straight lines.

In such a context this statement would be true:

A thing (figure) is called a "triangle" if and only if it is a plane figure bounded by three straight lines.

That is, an exact definition can be provided for the word "triangle" as it is used in the context of geometry. To consider another example:

In this chapter we are using the phrase "exact definition" in accordance with this rule:

A definition for a word, *"X"*, will be called an "exact definition" if and only if it gives the conjunction of characteristics each of which is necessary and which together are the sufficient conditions for calling something *"X."*

Thus an exact definition could be given for "exact definition" as it is used in the context of this book.

In everyday discourse words like those in our list are not used in accordance with strict rules. This explains why exact definitions cannot be given for these words as they are used in everyday discourse. Only in contexts—for example, in science, legal documents, and technical papers—where precision is important and words are used in accordance with explicitly stated rules or implicit rules can exact definitions be provided.

But this raises some problems: If in everyday discourse we do not follow strict rules, how do we know when to and when not to call a thing a "building," "shoe," "child," "author," or something else? In addition, if we do not follow strict rules in our use of words in everyday discourse, then how is it that we can understand each other?

Paradigm Examples

The solution to these problems can be introduced by considering how we come to understand the meanings of the words we use. To do this means that we must first notice how children learn the language.

Children often learn the meanings of words by just picking them up. This process commonly involves the child's noticing the things called *X* by his parents and others, and his calling these things *X* himself, with success. He then calls these things and things like them *X*. For example, the child notices that the long-handled object with a brush on the end used for sweeping is called a "broom." He then calls this object in his home "broom" and he calls objects outside his home brooms if they are similar to the object in his house. Children are also told, for example, "ball," as the parent points to a ball. Children sometimes ask what a word means. In this case we generally do one of three things. We explain the word by means of an example. If the child asks, for example, what the meaning of the word "game" is, we sometimes point out some clear-cut example of a game he is familiar with and tell him this and similar things are called games. A second thing we do is to describe a clear-cut example of a thing denoted by the word (*X*), and add that this and similar things are called *X*. For example, if we were asked what "intelligence" means, we might call to mind a person who is clearly intelligent, describe his abilities, and say that he and persons like him are intelligent. The third way to explain the meaning of a word is to provide a dictionary definition. The nature of such definitions will be discussed in the next section.

These five ways of coming to understand the meaning of words all involve what are called *paradigm examples*. A paradigm example for a word, say "X," as we will use the term and as it is often used, is a clear-cut case of a thing which is called X—that is, a thing about which there is no dispute as to whether it is an X. When the child picks up the meaning of words like "broom" or is told that something is a broom, the things called brooms in his surroundings are, generally, such paradigm examples. In general, most of the words which the child does pick up are used to refer to paradigm examples since these are the most common uses. In answering requests for the meaning of a word, we ordinarily point to paradigm examples or describe them. Most nonsynonym dictionary definitions, as we will argue, provide us insofar as it is possible with the descriptions of the paradigm examples that people commonly have in mind when they use the word—that is, they cite the characteristics which distinguish these things from other things.[1]

We can now answer the first problem. We know when, and when not, to call a thing a "building," "shoe," "child," and the like, because we have become acquainted with the paradigm examples of the things conventionally denoted by these words, and we know that these and similar things are denoted by these words.

The way many words are used in everyday discourse can be illustrated in this way, with X standing for any such word:

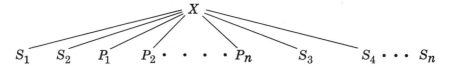

The letter "P" indicates paradigm examples. "S" indicates things similar to the paradigm examples.

The second problem—how is it that people can understand each other—is answered in this way: We have learned the use of most everyday words in connection with the same paradigm examples (qualitatively

---

[1] The respects (e.g., shape, color, use, or such-and-such behavior) in which a paradigm case is taken as different from other things are usually made clear to us or the learner by the general circumstances. Knowledge of the general circumstances guides us in making up the list of characteristics which distinguish a paradigm example from other things. Similarly, the respects in which A needs to resemble or be "similar" to the paradigm example (called an X) in order to be called an X are commonly made clear by the general circumstances.

the same, not numerically the same, of course). Thus when we speak of buildings, brooms, and books we mean the same thing. If someone asked what we mean, we would point out or describe the same paradigm examples or we would describe the distinguishing characteristics of the same examples. Of course people often use words which are learned in connection with common paradigm examples in ways different from their common way. If they were asked what they mean by the word in question, they would not cite or describe the paradigm examples. When this happens, what the person means is generally shown by the context. For example, if someone spoke of the hood of a car as a "bonnet," after returning from an auto race, the circumstances and the verbal contexts would most likely make clear that he was referring to the hood of a car.

For many words and phrases there is nothing which can be identified as the common meaning. These words are learned or picked up in connection with a variety of examples. Thus when people using such words are asked what they mean different examples would be pointed out, described, and so forth.[2] For example, words like "conservative," "moderate," and "liberal" are today, in our society, used in this way. When these words are used, how do we understand each other? Often, here again, the context makes clear what someone means. For example, "liberal" often is used to mean someone who supports the program of Northern Democrats. However, sometimes the speaker or writer himself will not understand what he means when he uses a word, for example, when he characterizes someone as a liberal or as a conservative.

It was said earlier that often if the context does not make clear what someone means by a word we can ask what he means. In such cases one can make clear the meaning of the word by giving a paradigm example or by stating the distinguishing characteristics of the things denoted. The first way is illustrated in this example:

At one time the United States was negotiating with Russia over a cease-fire in the war in Laos. Part of the first meeting of President Kennedy with Khrushchev was spent in an attempt to agree to terms for the cease fire. Here it was important that Kennedy and Khrushchev make adequately clear the meanings of their proposals. For this purpose Kennedy made Khrushchev give paradigm examples, for instance, examples of what he meant by "neutral nation" and "having a cease fire."

The second way and the first way are illustrated in this example:

SENATOR SNORT: There have been just wars.
CONSTITUENT: How can killing others ever be right?

---

2 Within particular groups there can, of course, be paradigm examples—that is, clear-cut cases of X which no member would dispute.

SENATOR SNORT: Let me make my meaning clear. When I said that there have been just wars I meant there have been wars where one side had a very good legal justification for war, for example, the Poles were justified in resisting the Nazis.

The senator made adequately clear what he meant by giving examples and stating how he was using the phrase "just war"—that is, by stating the distinguishing characteristics of the things denoted by the phrase.

Criteria and Our Everyday Words

Dictionary definitions report how words are commonly used at some point in time. They generally report how these words are used by the educated. From time to time, however, we find a definition which can be regarded as a statement of how a word should be used in light of old conventions rather than a true report of how it is commonly used.

Formulating dictionary definitions for such words as "building," "shoe," and "game" involves noticing the things people commonly refer to when they use these words and stating the characteristics these things have which distinguish them from other things. For example, in formulating a reportive definition for the word "broom," we noticed that man-made objects with long handles which have brushes on the end and which are used for sweeping are commonly called brooms. These are the characteristics which in general are taken as distinguishing the objects commonly called brooms. Dictionary definitions (in giving one of the senses of a word, if it has more than one sense) describe the characteristics which distinguish the paradigm examples of things called X from other things of the same kind. Often such descriptions are a composite of these features connected by "or's." As noted earlier, not all denoting words, in everyday discourse, are so used that there is such a thing as a common paradigm example or examples; for example, the words "propaganda," "aggression," and "freedom" are so used that there is no common paradigm example or examples. In a sense, then, these words cannot be defined, since there is no common use to report. As we have seen, the particular context often shows how these words are used, and people can always stipulate how such words are to be understood when they use them.

Let us suppose that this is a dictionary definition for "B":

"B" means an object with characteristics C_1, C_2, and C_3.

If this is a *good* dictionary definition, as we will use the word "good," then it would follow that generally when people use "B" in certain sentences, they have in mind or they mean objects with C_1, C_2, and C_3. Now let us suppose that this is a good dictionary definition for "shoe" as the word is used in "He has a size eight shoe":

"Shoe" means an object which is a covering for the human foot, having a thick and somewhat stiff sole.

It would follow that generally when someone speaks of a "shoe" as in "He has a size eight shoe," he has in mind an object which:

S_1 is a covering.
S_2 is used on the human foot.
S_3 has a thick and somewhat stiff sole.

It will be helpful to introduce here the technical term "criteria." A characteristic or characteristics which, when present in something, constitute in ordinary circumstances a justification for calling that something X, is called a *criterion* for "X." [3] S_1, S_2, and S_3 together would be a criterion for the application of the word "shoe." That is, ordinarily if an article of clothing has S_1, S_2, and S_3 we call it a shoe. Generally, for ordinary words, there are, as we will point out in a moment, more than one criterion. Thus we can speak of the *criteria* for a word.

To take some other examples, consider the words "broom" and "intelligent." Let us suppose that this is a good dictionary definition for "broom" as the word is used in "She swept the floor with the broom":

"Broom" means an object which is used for sweeping and which consists of a long stick with a brush on one end.

If a household object had these characteristics:

B_1 it has a long handle
B_2 it has a brush on one end
B_3 it is used for sweeping,

in ordinary circumstances, we would call it a broom. Consider this dictionary definition for the word "intelligent" as used in "He is intelligent":

[3] This use of "criterion" should be distinguished from a common use of the word to refer to a test to determine whether something is X. For example, the appearance of an egg when placed before a light source is often called the criterion for telling whether the egg is good. The fact that a beef steak has a thick layer of fat is often spoken of as a criterion for the steak being tender. Here again the thick layer of fat is a test or a reliable indication that the steak is tender. It is the frequently observed concomitance of thick layers of fat and tenderness which in large part leads us to use the presence of thick layers of fat as a "criterion."

Our treatment of criteria is for words and not *necessarily* for statements, though to give criteria for "X" is ordinarily to give criteria for the truth of such statements as "This such-and-such is X."

These considerations do not apply to words for feelings and mental acts, such as the words "pain" and "anger," though there are criteria for saying someone is in pain or is angry—that is, there are characteristics (what a person says and does) which constitute, in ordinary circumstances, a justification for our saying someone is in pain. What we say is intended to have application to the words in our list and words like them.

"Intelligent" means possessing the ability to learn quickly, to understand difficult material, and to cope with new situations.

Here, again, if a person had these characteristics:

I_1 the ability to learn quickly
I_2 the ability to understand difficult material
I_3 the ability to cope with new situations,

we would, in ordinary circumstances, call him intelligent.

We will call characteristics which by themselves or with others act as criteria for a word "C-characteristics." There are several things which should be noted about C-characteristics and ordinary words: First, the above C-characteristics are not the only ones used with the words "shoe," "broom," and "intelligent." There are articles of clothing, household objects, and persons which we call "shoes," "brooms," and "intelligent" which lack one or more of the characteristics mentioned above. But the things which come to mind here have *other* C-characteristics. For example, if in ordinary circumstances an article of clothing:

S_1 is a covering
S_4 is made of wood
S_2 is used on the human foot,

we would call it a shoe. Or if an article of clothing

S_1 is a covering
S_2 is used on the human foot
S_5 has a tissue-thin, rigid sole,

we would call it a shoe. In turn, if a household object had these characteristics:

B_4 has a short handle
B_2 has a brush on one end of the handle
B_3 is used for sweeping,

or if an object:

B_1 has a long handle
B_2 has a brush on one end
B_5 is used by witches for riding,

we would, in ordinary circumstances, call these objects brooms. And if, for example, a person:

I_4 knows a great deal
I_5 is highly perceptive
I_6 can quickly relate ideas,

we would, in ordinary circumstances, call him intelligent. In short, words like "shoe," "broom," and "intelligent" are used in connection with a cluster of characteristics which act as criteria. B_1-B_5 would be part of the cluster for "broom" as it is used to refer to household objects. I_1-I_6 would be part of the cluster for "intelligent," and so on. If some part of this cluster is exemplified in a thing, in ordinary circumstances, this provides a sufficient condition to use the word. How much of the cluster needs to be exemplified varies with the word and context. Furthermore, ordinarily we can only give a more or less full inventory of the characteristics which make up a cluster.

Second, if we used a word to refer to a thing which lacks all of the characteristics in a cluster or most of them, then we would say that the word has a second meaning. For example, we call the part of the brake in an automobile which presses on the wheel to retard its motion a "shoe." Though these shoes have some of the characteristics which make up the cluster connected with the first sense of "shoe," they lack enough to warrant our saying that "shoe" has two meanings. Thus in a dictionary we find that "shoe" has these two different meanings (and others, of course): (a) a covering, used on the human foot, which has a thick and somewhat stiff sole, and (b) the part of the brake in an automobile which presses on the wheel to retard its motion. The word "broom" is used to denote a certain kind of shrub of the pea family. Here again these shrubs lack many of the characteristics found in the man-made objects denoted by "broom." Thus we say that "broom" has at least two meanings. Notice that in this sense of "different meaning" we would *not* say that "intelligent" used to refer to a person with I_1, I_2, and I_3 has a meaning different from "intelligent" used to refer to a person with I_4, I_5, and I_6. The same would hold for "broom," "shoe," and the other words when used to refer to one thing with part of the cluster of C-characteristics and to another thing with a different part of the cluster. To employ a metaphor at this point, most ordinary words are used to denote things which are part of the same family. There are strong resemblances between each of the different things denoted by the word. To say these words do *not* have different meanings is to stress the fact that things denoted strongly resemble one another in virtue of sharing some part of the cluster of C-characteristics.

Third, all of us know how to use the words found in the list and words like them. We can generally tell the difference between things which are X and those which are not X. *If* called upon, we can usually describe roughly the characteristics which distinguish the paradigm examples of X from other things of the same kind. But not all of us have paid attention to the ways in which the things we refer to by some of these words differ from other things. We know how to use these words because we are acquainted with the paradigm examples and know that these examples and things like them are referred to by the words. But in many cases, we have never stopped to consider what characteristics distinguish these paradigm examples from other things. But lack of such knowledge does not ordinarily impede our knowing how to use the words. For example, in speaking of "laws" in science people often mean statements like Galileo's law—whenever a body falls freely, it has a constant acceleration, or "D equals $\frac{1}{2}\ AT^2$"—and they have never noticed how Galileo's law and statements like it differ from other general statements. To consider another kind of example, we generally know when to characterize someone as deceiving himself, as being hypocritical, intellectually indecisive, stupid, indulging in wishful thinking, or living in a fool's paradise. And yet most of us have never stopped to consider those characteristics which distinguish self-deception from wishful thinking, and so on.

Fourth, for some words (X) no characteristic which serves with others as criteria for "X" is pervasive. Consider, for example, the word "game" as it is used in "Let's play a game." And consider this good definition of the word:

"Game" means a diversion of the nature of a contest, played according to rules, and decided by superior skill, strength, or good fortune.

None of these characteristics is pervasive. There are some activities we call games which lack in turn each characteristic. For example, not all games are diversions—the Olympic Games, for example, are not. Folk games are not contests. Children's games are not always played according to rules. The way the word "game" is used can be represented by this schema where the capital letters stand for criteria-characteristics:

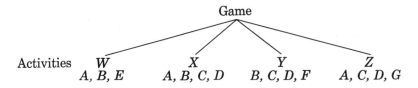

Fifth, for most of the words in our list, no characteristics which act as criteria are fundamental conditions for the use of the word. The word "game" is a clear-cut example of a word which is not used in connection with a fundamental C-characteristic, since, as we have seen, no characteristic is pervasive. An example of a word which is used in connection with a fundamental C-characteristic would be the word "lying" as it is used to refer to communication. The fundamental characteristic here would be making a statement one knows to be false. If an instance of behavior resembled in every way those paradigm cases we call lying, but lacked the characteristic of someone's making a statement he knows to be false, we would, it seems, not call it lying. If we did, and for some reason we might, then we would regard the word as having two different meanings, in the sense that "broom" has two different meanings when used to refer to man-made objects and to pea shrubs. What is here meant by saying a characteristic is *fundamental* is this: If the absence of C_1, even with the presence of any other characteristics, would lead us to say the thing in question is not X or that "X" has a different meaning when used to refer to it, then C_1 is fundamental. Often what controls our saying "X" has the "same meaning" when C_1 is missing is the fact that the absence of C_1 does not affect the thing's strong resemblance to the members of the "old family." In turn, what often controls our saying "X" has a "different meaning" is that the absence of C_1 breaks down the resemblance between the thing in question and the members of the old family. As we have said, no one of the characteristics which act as criteria for the words in our list is fundamental. That is, having more or less specified the cluster of characteristics for any of these words (X), we can imagine or in time we might come upon things which would lack one of these particular characteristics, and yet the resemblance would still be strong enough with what we now call X so that we would say that "X" has the same meaning if used to refer to these things.

Sixth, often criteria are added to other criteria of words when, for example, there is found to be an invariable connection between things called or said to be X and some particular characteristic or characteristics. For example, in some contexts, melting at 327°C. is a criterion for a substance being lead; or in some contexts, having a constant acceleration is a criterion for a thing being a free falling body. Sometimes a criterion (or criteria), say C_1, for a word is (or are) fundamental in contrast with other criteria for the word, say C_2 and C_3, because C_1 was the first and for a time the only criterion. The others were added to it because, for example, things with C_1 were found to be invariably connected with C_2.

We will end this part of the discussion by summarizing and by adding a few additional remarks. (a) In some contexts words are used in connection with a conjunction of C-characteristics all of which are necessary (because strict rules are laid down and followed). Exact reportive definitions can be provided for these words. In mathematics, science, philosophy, in contexts where clarity is important, and so on, we find words used in this way. (b) Most ordinary words are used in everyday discourse in connection with paradigm examples and things which resemble these examples. The characteristics which distinguish these paradigm examples from other things make up a cluster of C-characteristics. For many words no single characteristic is fundamental. (c) For some words one or more of the characteristics are fundamental.

Not all denoting words fall into these three classes. For example, (d) some words are so used that there is no common paradigm example, nor is there a common set of C-characteristics which people have in mind when they use the words. Today "democracy," "conservative," "un-American," "'freedom," and so on are words like this. These words are repeatedly used in different ways; thus there is no common cluster of C-characteristics to be reported. (e) There are some words which have no C-characteristics, for example, "red," "pain," "sweet," and "loud," as they are used to report our sense experiences. It makes no sense to say that if something has such-and-such characteristics, then we call it "red" or "pain," though there are criteria for saying, for example, "He is in pain." Such words are sometimes called *simple words*. (f) There are some words for whose use we cannot state C-characteristics, but we can give characteristics which justify our use of these words when they are applicable to a thing. Such words as "graceful," "majestic," "forceful," are like this. They are not simple words, for we can justify their use in a particular context. On the other hand, we cannot give a set of characteristics such that, if a thing had them, then in ordinary circumstances we would call it graceful, forceful, and so on.[4]

EXERCISES I

Make an attempt at giving exact definitions for the words in the list at the beginning of this chapter. Indicate in what ways the definitions fail to be exact definitions.

EXERCISES II

Cite a paradigm example for each of the following words:

1. itch (He has an itch.)
2. table (Set the table.)
3. work (Men work five days a week.)
4. city (The city continues to grow.)
5. dachshund
6. widow
7. college
8. war (Will the U.S.A. and the U.S.S.R. go to war?)
9. poverty (Many Americans live in poverty.)
10. laws (This is a country ruled by laws, rather than by men.)

EXERCISES III

Indicate the C-characteristics of the paradigm examples selected for the words above.

[4] There are paradigm cases, though, for such words.

EXERCISES IV

Indicate two or more meanings for each of the following words.

1. conservative	7. laws	13. patriot
2. liberal	8. work	14. imperialism
3. propaganda	9. nationalism	15. table
4. superstition	10. sin	16. war
5. un-American	11. philosophy	17. satellite
6. aggression	12. progressive	

EXERCISES V

Select five words and for each word cite different sets of *C*-characteristics which would justify our use of the word to denote a thing ("different sets" in the sense that at least *one* characteristic differs).

EXERCISES VI

Mention five words which are like the word "game"—that is, no characteristic which serves alone or with others as a criterion is pervasive.

EXERCISES VII

Using the six categories found in the summary, (a) through (f), classify the following words. If a word falls in none of these categories, then classify it as "none of these."

1. Romantic (as it is used to refer to the period of literature)
2. Charles de Gaulle
3. hot
4. giraffe
5. while
6. logic
7. sin .
8. happiness
9. elegant
10. right act
11. Euclidian triangle
12. grandmother
13. complex
14. crime

Connotation

The word "connotation" is often used to refer to the personal associations that a person comes to attach to a word. Consider this amusing example:

A little girl, having recently learned to read, was spelling out a political article in the newspaper. "Father," she asked, "what is Tammany Hall?" And her father replied in the voice usually reserved for the taboos of social communication, "You'll understand that when you grow up, my dear." Acceding to this adult whim of evasion, she desisted from her inquiries; but something in Daddy's tone had convinced her that Tammany Hall must be connected with illicit *amour,* and for many years she could not hear this political institution mentioned without experiencing a secret nonpolitical thrill.[5]

In this example, "Tammany Hall" had the connotation of illicit *amour* for this person. For many people in the United States, "communist," is associated with or connotes a doer of evil while "capitalist" in Soviet Russia has a similar connotation.

Logicians use the word "connotation" in a different way. For some logicians the connotation of a word is the set of characteristics which constitute the sufficient and necessary conditions for applying the word. In this sense of "connotation," only words used in accordance with strict rules [class (a)] have connotations. Words which fall into classes (b) through (f) would have no connotations. Some logicians use the word "connotation" to refer to what is given in a dictionary definition like those examined above, what is given when someone explains the meaning of a word by citing those characteristics commonly found in the things referred to by the words, or what one gives when he explains what he means by a word by citing characteristics of the things he is referring to. In this sense of "connotation" all the words in the groups above, except simple words, would have connotations.

Words Lack Definite Boundaries

If we again consider the list of words in the first section (see page 66) we will find that there are things or we can imagine things which are such that we would not know whether to call them "X" or "not-X." And this uncertainty would not be the result of lack of knowledge about the thing in question. There are things we can imagine which we would not know whether to call "building," "broom," "game," and so on. For example, is the Statue of Liberty a building? Is a dust mop used for sweeping a broom? Is a job in some industrial organization which is a diversion, a contest, played according to rules, and decided by superior skill, strength, or good fortune a game? No further knowledge about the Statue of Liberty, a dust mop, or this job would help us to settle this uncertainty.

[5] Margaret Schlauch, *The Gift of Tongues* (New York: The Viking Press, 1942).

The fact that we are able to find things for a word (X) which are such that we do not know whether to call them "X" or "not-X" can be illustrated schematically as follows:

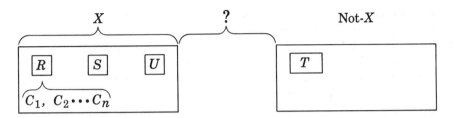

In this schema, $C_1, C_2, \ldots, C_n$ are the characteristics of the clear-cut paradigm case of the kind of thing called "X." Spreading out from the right of R are other things which resemble R closely enough so that they are called X. T lacks all the characteristics $C_1, C_2, \ldots, C_n$, so it is a clear-cut case of something which is not-X. But in the question mark area there are things which have some of the characteristics of those things called "X" but lack enough of these characteristics so that they clearly do not fall into the X group or the not-X group. It is this feature which creates our uncertainty. Even with simple words there might be cases where we would be uncertain whether to call a color red or not-red, a taste sweet or not-sweet, and so forth. When it is said that a word (X) *lacks definite boundaries,* what is meant is that there are things which are such that we are uncertain (not as a result of lack of knowledge) whether to call them X or not-X.

In the question mark cases, there simply has not been any good reason or motivation to make a decision as to whether these things are X's. It is not that a (more-or-less) arbitrary decision cannot be made—it just has not been made. No convention has been adopted. A good reason to adopt such a convention would be, for example, to avoid constant misunderstandings.

Ambiguity, Vagueness, and the Two Aspects of Ordinary Language

The two aspects of everyday discourse which we have been interested in are:

1. We cannot provide exact definitions for ordinary words since they are not used in accordance with strict rules.
2. Ordinary words lack definite boundaries.

What is the relation of (1) and (2) to the ambiguity of words and the vagueness of words?

Ambiguity

Sometimes when it is said that a word is ambiguous, what is meant is that the word has two or more meanings. For example, to say that the word "game" is ambiguous, in this sense, is to say that the word has at least these two meanings: a diversion of the nature of a contest . . . and wild birds, fish, or animals. . . . In this sense of "ambiguous," a word may not be used in accordance with strict rules and may lack definite boundaries and yet may not be ambiguous. For example, suppose at one time the word "broom" were only used to denote things which consist of a long stick with a brush on one end and which are used for sweeping, and things like this. The two aspects, (1) and (2) above, would be true of the word "broom" at this time. But, as we can see, the word would not be ambiguous in this first sense. A word could also be ambiguous in this first sense and lack (1) and (2). For example, in one formal system a word could be used in one way while in another formal system the word could be used in another way. Thus whether a word is ambiguous in this first sense is independent of whether (1) and (2) are true of the word.

Logicians commonly use "ambiguous" in a different way. Ambiguity in this second sense is relative to context. To say that a word is ambiguous means that in a certain context it can be understood in at least two ways. Often we do not give enough clues as to how we are using a word, with the consequence that what we say is ambiguous to others. For example, we can imagine a context where someone might say that he wants to go to the bank and we would not know whether he wants to go to the river bank or the People's Bank. Or, to consider a more relevant example, to say "A *knows* the criteria for '*X*'" is ambiguous, since "know" can either mean that A knows how to use "*X*" or that A knows the characteristics which distinguish the paradigm examples of things called "*X*" from other things. Sometimes we ourselves do not fully understand what we say. For example, a student might say that morality is relative without knowing what he means by "relative" and "morality"—he just repeats what he has heard from a source he respects. It is quite obvious that a word can be ambiguous in the first sense above and be used in a context where it is not ambiguous in the second sense.

But can a word which is not used in accordance with strict rules and which lacks definite boundaries be unambiguous in this second sense? A word which is such that (1) and (2) are true of it can be used in a context where it is quite clear how it is to be understood. Our everyday discourse, in fact, is generally like this. Our words are such that (1) and (2) are true of them; nevertheless our statements on the whole are not ambiguous. For example, we might have occasion to say "The garden is

covered with weeds." And if we said this, what we meant would be perfectly clear even though such words as "garden" and "weeds" lack definite boundaries and are not used in accordance with strict rules. Generally, our ordinary discourse is unambiguous because people have the
same paradigm examples in mind, or the context shows the characteristics of the things referred to.

Vagueness

Often when we say a word is vague we mean that in a given context
it is not clear what is meant by the word. That is, it is not that the word
can be understood in one or more ways, but rather it is not clear how
it would be understood at all. Some people think that "cultural lag" as
it is used in the context of sociology is such a word. "Un-American,"
"tough minded," and "soft on Communism" would be, or often are,
other examples. And sometimes when people use the words "progress"
and "complex" what they mean is vague. Vagueness in this sense is independent of (1) and (2).

Sometimes when we say that a word is vague we mean that the word
does not indicate adequately the number, amounts, degrees, and so on of
something. For example, if we wanted to know someone's height because
we are interested in buying him a pair of trousers for Christmas, and
we are told that he is a tall man, we would say that "tall" is vague. It
does not indicate what we need to know in order to purchase the trousers. On the other hand, if we wanted to know who we are supposed to
meet at the airport and are told that he is a tall man, has black hair,
and so forth, "tall" would not in this context be called vague. As
we can also easily see, vagueness in this sense is independent of (1)
and (2).

Commonly, when logicians say that a word is vague they have in mind
a property of its use which is independent of its use in a context. To say
that a word is vague means that there are situations in which we cannot
decide whether to apply the word, and this indecision is not due to lack
of information about the subject matter. To say a word is vague in this
third sense is the same as to say that it lacks definite boundaries. This
naturally raises the question: What is the relation between (1) and (2)?
If a word is not used in accordance with strict rules, then it would be
vague in this third sense. On the other hand, if a word is used in accordance with strict rules, then it may or may not be vague. In formal
systems, words used in accordance with strict rules are not vague. But in
some other context one might use a word in accordance with a strict
rule such that this is true:

A thing is called X if and only if it has C_1, C_2, and C_3.
And yet there may be cases where we cannot decide whether some-

thing which has C_2 and C_3 has C_1. If this were so, then we would be un-decided whether to call the thing X, and this indecision would not result from lack of knowledge about the thing.

EXERCISES VIII

First, imagine a paradigm case of a thing denoted by each word and a par-adigm case of a thing not denoted by each word. Then for each word imagine a thing which is such that we would hesitate in calling it X or not-X.

1. horse (People still ride horses.)
2. offensive weapons (Missiles are offensive weapons.)
3. magazine (*Time* is a weekly magazine.)
4. rain (It is raining.)
5. war (Two nations are at war.)
6. luxuries (Americans enjoy many luxuries.)
7. disturbing the peace (He was arrested for disturbing the peace.)
8. fanatic (He's a fanatic.)
9. religion (There are many religions of the world.)
10. spoon (Put the spoons on the table.)

EXERCISES IX

In light of the discussion of the two aspects of our ordinary words, criticize the following arguments and statements:

1. Since the term "luxury" is a vague term, that is, since you cannot draw a line between those things which are luxuries and those things which are not luxuries, there is no real distinction between luxuries and things which are necessities. So stop looking that way at my new three-speed electric comb.

2. The only adequate way to explain the meaning of a word is by giving an exact definition. We cannot give exact definitions for most of our ordinary words, so we cannot make adequately clear what we mean.

3. The question is constantly debated in this assembly whether some coun-try is an aggressor in some action. It is evident that we can never come to an agreement as things stand. I propose we appoint an impartial committee made up of members from both the East and the West and from neutral countries to find out what aggression *is,* so we can settle all of these disagreements.

4. We cannot define a word without using other words. But we must un-derstand the meaning of the words used in the definition. This can be done only by using still other words which in their turn will have to be defined, and so on. Thus it is theoretically impossible really to define a word.

5. Definitions are neither true nor false.

6. They tell me that we cannot provide exact definitions for most of our words because we don't use them in accordance with strict rules. Well, this is our fault. We should do something about it. Just think how clear our statements

would be if our language was set straight. Just think of the misunderstandings which could be avoided.

7. Vagueness can be reduced, but it is impossible to eliminate it.

8. As we all know, there are a number of acts which we speak of as "just." There must be something in common in all these acts since we say they are all just. If we could find out what this is, then we could tell whether any act is just by seeing if it has that which just acts have in common. Philosophers have always wanted principles to tell just acts from unjust acts. Why don't they just work together and find out what this common characteristic (or characteristics) is!

9. Now, I continued, if two things, one large, the other small, are called by the same name, they will be alike in that respect to which the common name applies. Accordingly, insofar as the duality of justice is concerned, there will be no difference between a just man and a just society.

(PLATO, *The Republic*)

10. Words are poor instruments for the communication of thoughts. Although dictionaries give what may be called the official meaning of a word, no two people who use the same word have just the same thought in their minds. Words are ill-fitting garments for the thoughts they clothe.

11. "I don't know what you mean by 'glory,'" Alice said.

Humpty Dumpty smiled contemptuously. "Of course you don't—till I tell you. I meant 'there's a nice knock-down argument for you!'"

"But 'glory' doesn't mean 'a nice knock-down argument,'" Alice objected.

"When *I* use a word," Humpty Dumpty said, in rather a scornful tone, "it means just what I choose it to mean—neither more nor less."

"The question is," said Alice, "whether you *can* make words mean so many different things."

"The question is," said Humpty Dumpty, "which is to be master—that's all."

Alice was too much puzzled to say anything; so after a minute Humpty Dumpty began again. "They've a temper, some of them—particularly verbs: they're the proudest—adjectives you can do anything with, but not verbs—however, *I* can manage the whole lot of them! Impenetrability! That's what *I* say!"

"Would you tell me please," said Alice, "what that means?"

"Now you talk like a reasonable child," said Humpty Dumpty, looking very much pleased. "I meant by 'impenetrability' that we've had enough of that subject, and it would be just as well if you'd mention what you mean to do next, as I suppose you don't mean to stop here all the rest of your life."

(LEWIS CARROLL, *Through the Looking-Glass*)

12. SOCRATES: What is piety, and what is impiety?

EUTHYPHRO: Piety is doing as I am doing; that is to say, prosecuting anyone who is guilty of murder, sacrilege, or of any other similar crime . . . and not to prosecute them is impiety. . . .

S: But . . . I would rather hear from you a more precise answer, which you have not as yet given, my friend, to the question, What is "piety"? When asked, you only replied, Doing as you, charging your father with murder.

E: And what I said was true, Socrates.

S: No doubt, Euthyphro; but you would admit that there are many other pious acts?

E: There are.

S: Remember that I did not ask you to give me two or three examples of piety, but to explain the general idea which makes all pious things to be pious. Do you not recollect that there was one idea which made the impious impious, and the pious pious? . . . Tell me what is the nature of this idea, and then I shall have a standard to which I may look.

(PLATO, *Euthyphro*)

13.   . . . the meaning of the term will be what is common to the various examples pointed out as meant by it.

(C. I. LEWIS, *Mind and the World Order*)

14.   The purpose of Newspeak was not only to provide a medium of expression for the world-view and mental habits proper to the devotees of Ingsoc, but to make all other modes of thought impossible. It was intended that when Newspeak had been adopted once and for all and Oldspeak forgotten, a heretical thought—that is, a thought diverging from the principles of Ingsoc—should be literally unthinkable, at least so far as thought is dependent on words. Its vocabulary was so constructed as to give exact and often very subtle expression to every meaning that a Party member could properly wish to express, while excluding all other meanings and also the possibility of arriving at them by indirect methods. This was done partly by the invention of new words, but chiefly by eliminating undesirable words and by stripping such words as remained of unorthodox meaning, and so far as possible of all secondary meanings whatever. To give a single example. The word *free* still existed in Newspeak, but it could only be used in such statements as "This dog is free from lice" or "This field is free from weeds." It could not be used in its old sense of "politically free" or "intellectually free," since political and intellectual freedom no longer existed even as concepts, and were therefore of necessity nameless. Quite apart from the suppression of definitely heretical words, reduction of vocabulary was regarded as an end in itself, and no word that could be dispensed with was allowed to survive. Newspeak was designed not to extend but to *diminish* the range of thought, and this purpose was indirectly assisted by cutting the choice of words down to a minimum.

(GEORGE ORWELL, *1984*) [6]

Would Newspeak prevent heretical thoughts? Would it make *impossible* the concept of political or intellectual freedom? How would you go about stripping words of unorthodox meaning? In what way are thoughts dependent on language?

[6] From *Nineteen Eighty-Four* by George Orwell. Copyright 1949. Used by permission of Secker and Warburg Ltd. and Brandt and Brandt (New York).

15. It is a rather curious fact in philosophy that the data which are undeniable to start with are always rather vague and ambiguous. You can, for instance, say: "There are a number of people in this room at this moment." That is obviously in some sense undeniable. But when you come to try and define what this room is, and what it is for a person to be in a room, and how you are going to distinguish one person from another, and so forth, you find that what you have said is most fearfully vague and that you really do not know what you meant.

(BERTRAND RUSSELL, *The Philosophy of Logical Atomism*) [7]

16. In everyday language it very frequently happens that the same word has different modes of signification, and so belongs to different symbols—or two words that have different modes of signification are employed in propositions in what is superficially the same way.

Thus the word "is" figures as the copula, as a sign for identity, and as an expression for existence; "exist" figures as an intransitive verb like "go," and "identical" as an adjective; we speak of *something,* but also of *something's* happening.

(In the proposition, "Green is green"—where the first word is the proper name of a person and the last an adjective—these words do not merely have different meanings: they are *different symbols.*)

In this way the most fundamental confusions are easily produced (the whole of philosophy is full of them).

In order to avoid such errors we must make use of a sign-language that excludes them by not using the same sign for different symbols and by not using in a superficially similar way signs that have different modes of signification: that is to say, a sign-language that is governed by *logical* grammar—by logical syntax.

(LUDWIG WITTGENSTEIN, *Tractatus Logico-Philosophicus*) [8]

17. A definition of a concept (of a possible predicate) must be complete; it must unambiguously determine, as regards any object, whether or not it falls under the concept (whether or not the predicate is truly assertible of it). Thus there must not be any object as regards which the definition leaves in doubt whether it falls under the concept; though for us men, with our defective knowledge, the question may not always be decidable. We may express this metaphorically as follows: the concept must have a sharp boundary. If we represent concepts in extension by area on a plane, this is admittedly a picture that may be used only with caution, but here it can do us good service. To a concept without sharp boundary there would correspond an area that had not

[7] Bertrand Russell, "The Philosophy of Logical Atomism," reprinted in *Logic and Knowledge* by Bertrand Russell, edited by Robert C. Marsh (New York: Macmillan, 1956), p. 179; originally published in *The Monist* (1918).

[8] Ludwig Wittgenstein, *Tractatus Logico-Philosophicus,* Trans. D. F. Pears and B. F. McGuinness (London: Routledge and Kegan Paul, 1961), p. 29. © Routledge and Kegan Paul Ltd., 1961. Used by permission of Routledge and Kegan Paul.

a sharp boundary-line all round, but in places just faded away into the background. This would not really be an area at all; and likewise a concept that is not sharply defined is wrongly termed a concept.

(GOTTLOB FREGE) [9]

VERBAL DISPUTES

Extending the Use of Words

Since our everyday words lack definite boundaries, there will be times when we will be uncertain whether a word should be applied. Sometimes we will have good reasons to extend the use of the word and sometimes we will not. Sometimes we will judge that something in the question mark area so strongly resembles our paradigm cases for a certain word that the word should be *extended* to cover this instance, and there will be times when the resemblance is so weak that we will decide not to extend the word, and so on.[10]

Such a judgment is made in an amusing way in *Alice in Wonderland*. Alice swallows a morsel of the left hand side of a mushroom and grows an immense length of neck. Her head goes into a tree where she encounters the Pigeon. Here is part of their conversation:

"And just as I'd taken the highest tree in the wood," continued the Pigeon, raising its voice to a shriek, "and just as I was thinking I should be free of them at last, they must needs come wriggling down from the sky! Ugh, Serpent!"

"But I'm *not* a serpent, I tell you!" said Alice. "I'm a—I'm a—"

"Well! *What* are you?" said the Pigeon. "I can see you're trying to invent something!"

"I—I'm a little girl," said Alice, rather doubtfully, as she remembered the number of changes she had gone through, that day.

"A likely story indeed!" said the Pigeon, in a tone of the deepest contempt. "I've seen a good many little girls in my time, but never *one* with such a neck as that! No, no! You're a serpent; and there's no use denying it. I suppose you'll be telling me next that you never tasted an egg!"

"I *have* tasted eggs, certainly," said Alice, who was a very truthful child; "but little girls eat eggs quite as much as serpents do, you know."

[9] Gottlob Frege, *Translations from the Philosophical Writings of Gottlob Frege*, Peter Geach and Max Black, trans. (London: Blackwell) p. 159.

[10] Resemblance between X and Y is not the only reason we have to call Y by the same name as X. The fact that X and Y stand in the same relation to A might be a good reason, the fact that X and Y are caused by the same A might be a good reason, and so on. See J. L. Austin's "The Meaning of a Word," *Philosophical Papers* (Oxford, 1961). But we will ignore these cases in this chapter.

"I don't believe it," said the Pigeon; "but if they do, why, then they're a kind of serpent: that's all I can say."

In this example, the Pigeon considers the fact that Alice has a long, snakelike neck and eats eggs enough to extend the word "serpent" to cover Alice. Alice feels that the differences between a serpent and Alice in her strange state are great enough not to extend the use of "serpent" in this way.

Often we hear political liberals called "socialists." What prompts this seems to be this: Socialists (a) desire federal welfare legislation which would provide inexpensive medical care for everyone, unemployment compensation, old age retirement under social security, and the like. Socialists also (b) desire to remove concentrations both of poverty and of great wealth from among the people. Socialists (c) want government planning in the operation of the economy. Traditionally, political liberals also want (a), (b), and (c). This similarity has led to liberals being called socialists, even though socialists want, for example, (d) government ownership of the means of production. What we see here is an extension of the word "socialist." The similarity in (a), (b), and (c) has led people to extend the word. Some people, of course, feel that with (d) missing, the similarity is not sufficiently strong to extend the use of the word in this way.

Word-Extension Disputes

From time to time people find themselves in disagreements which are not over some matter of fact. Often the disputers are unaware of this and regard their dispute as a factual dispute. When a disagreement is not a factual dispute but hinges on the use of a word or phrase, this is called a *verbal,* or *semantic,* dispute. When the dispute hinges on whether a word is to be extended or not to be extended we will call it a *word-extension dispute.*

Such a word-extension dispute is illustrated in this often quoted passage from William James: [11]

Some years ago, being with a camping party in the mountains, I returned from a solitary ramble to find every one engaged in a ferocious metaphysical dispute. The *corpus* of the dispute was a squirrel—a live squirrel supposed to be clinging to one side of a tree-trunk; while over against the tree's opposite side a human being was imagined to stand. This human witness tries to get sight of the squirrel by moving rapidly around the tree, but no matter how fast he goes, the squirrel moves as fast in the opposite direction, and always keeps the tree between himself and the man, so that never a glimpse of him is caught. The

[11] William James, *Pragmatism* (London: Longmans, Green, 1907), p. 43.

resultant metaphysical problem is this: *Does the man go round the squirrel or not?* He goes round the tree, sure enough, and the squirrel is on the tree; but does he go round the squirrel? In the unlimited leisure of the wilderness, discussion had been worn threadbare. Every one had taken sides, and was obstinate; and the numbers on both sides were even. Each side, when I appeared therefore appealed to me to make it a majority.

This is a verbal dispute, for there is no disagreement in facts. William James thought this verbal dispute could be resolved in this way:

Mindful of the scholastic adage that whenever you meet a contradiction you must make a distinction, I immediately sought out and found one, as follows: "Which party is right," I said, "depends on what you *practically mean* by 'going round' the squirrel. If you mean passing from the north of him to the east, then to the south, then to the west, and then to the north of him again, obviously the man does go round him, for he occupies these successive positions. But if on the contrary you mean being first in front of him, then on the right of him, then behind him, then on his left, and finally in front again, it is quite obvious that the man fails to go round him, for by the compensating movements the squirrel makes, he keeps his belly turned towards the man all the time, and his back turned away. Make the distinction, and there is no occasion for any further dispute. You are both right and both wrong according as you conceive the verb 'go round' in one practical fashion or the other."

Although one or two of the hotter disputants called my speech a shuffling evasion, saying they wanted no quibbling or scholastic hair-splitting, but meant just plain honest English "round," the majority seemed to think that the distinction had assuaged the dispute.[12]

James, as we can see, believes that if two senses of "going round" are distinguished, "there is no occasion for any further dispute." For the one party is using the phrase in one way, thus what they say is true; and the other party is using it in another way, and what they say is also true. The two senses of "going round" are, as we can see:

1. passing from the north of something, to the east, then to the south, then to the west, and then to the north again;
2. being first in front of something, then to the right, then behind, then to the left, and finally in front again.

Now James' solution is open to question. For one thing his solution implies that one party *meant* (2) by "going round." But would anyone mean this by "going round"? If they did, then a man sitting on a couch can go around a man in a spinning swivel chair. A more realistic way to look at this dispute is as a word extension dispute. As we ordinarily use the phrase "going round," both (1) and (2) occur. The squirrel-tree-man situation is an unusual case. It is a case which falls in the question

12 *Ibid.*, pp. 43–44.

mark area discussed in the section Words Lack Definite Boundaries (see pages 80–81). (1) is true in this situation but (2) is not. One party thought the presence of (1) even with (2) missing was enough to extend the use of "going round."

In the James example nothing important rests on whether "going round" is extended. However, word extension disputes are often quite important. For example, in 1933 a United States District Court considered the question whether James Joyce's *Ulysses* was pornographic. In this case a great deal rested on whether the book was to be included in the class of pornographic literature. If the court decided it was pornographic, the book could neither be printed nor admitted into the United States. The presence of dirty words in *Ulysses* and the preoccupation with sex in the thoughts of the characters are what led those who instituted the suit to claim that it was pornographic. The decision that the Hon. John M. Woolsey made was that *Ulysses* is not pornographic, for commonly, if a piece of literature is pornographic, there must be the desire by the author to exploit the obscene. In addition, the judge said that *Ulysses* was not obscene within the legal definition of obscene (tending to stir the sex impulses or to lead to sexually impure and lustful thoughts). This decision easily gives rise to the convention that in order for a book to be pornographic there must be the desire on the part of the author to exploit the obscene, and he must have some success in doing this.

Definition Disputes

Sometimes a dispute hinges on whether a word has (or should have) one meaning or another meaning. This kind of verbal dispute is clearly different from one which concerns whether a word should be extended. We will call this kind of verbal dispute a *definition dispute*.

The first kind of definition dispute (whether a word *has* one meaning or another) is illustrated in this fictitious example:

UTAH JENKINS: President Johnson was not impeached because to impeach a President is to find him guilty of a crime while in office and, as we know from reading our American history books, he was found not guilty.

UTAH WATKINS: President Johnson was impeached, though you are of course correct in saying that he was not found guilty of any crime, for to impeach a President is not to find him guilty of something but merely to charge him with a crime or misbehavior in office.

The disagreement here is over what it means to impeach a President. Utah J. says it means one thing while Utah W. says it means another. There is a clear meaning for this word in this context, which can be found in a dictionary. Utah W. is correct.

The second kind of definition dispute (whether a word should have one meaning or another) is illustrated in this example:

When a tree falls in the wilderness with nobody around, will there be a sound?
JOHNNIE CRACK: No, there is no sound because no one is there to hear it.
FLOSSIE SNAIL: Of course there is a sound, regardless of whether anyone is there to hear it.

Frequently, this dispute is represented as involving no disagreement either in fact or over the use of a word. "Sound" is said to have two meanings: (a) the physical cause—the waves in the air, and (b) the auditory sensation—the experience of hearing the sound. Johnnie is thinking of sense (b), Flossie of sense (a). Now in some cases of this dispute this might be all it comes to, but generally this is not true. Is the word "sound" ordinarily used in either sense? As we ordinarily use the word, we do not hesitate to speak of the noise which things make when no one is around: "Can you imagine the deafening sound that rocket made when it hit?" Furthermore, the word "sound" had uses long before anyone knew about waves in the air. What we have here is not a disagreement as to facts, of course, but neither do we have no disagreement. For some reason (for example, he has been reading Berkeley), Johnnie thinks that "sound" should be used in sense (b), whereas Flossie disagrees and for some reason (for example, she has been reading elementary physics books) believes that this would be a mistake and that "sound" really should be used in sense (a).

Pseudo-disputes

A verbal dispute can be of the kind James imagined the squirrel-tree-man dispute to be. That is, sometimes a dispute is resolved by showing that the two parties are using some key word or phrase in different ways. Consider this example of such a dispute which we will call a *pseudo-dispute*:

A: Our government must abandon its policy of containment or peaceful coexistence and adopt the policy of total victory.
B: I can see the folly of containment and peaceful coexistence; we should do what we can short of war to push back Communism, but to wage a nuclear war against the Russians to achieve total victory is absolute insanity.

Generally when politicians speak of "total victory" they mean activities, short of any kind of traditional or nuclear war, which will result in fundamental changes in existing Communist controlled countries. Supposing that this is what A means, we can see that there is no dispute of any kind between A and B. The supposed difference springs from B's not understanding what is meant by "total victory" as A uses the phrase.

It will be helpful if we close this section with a clear-cut example of a factual dispute:

A grocery store each week puts a coupon in its newspaper advertisement which is redeemable on Saturday for one silver dollar. Each week they change the day in which the ad appears. One Saturday Tommy Tubman and his wife prepare to go shopping. Tommy tells his wife that the coupon is to be found in Monday's paper; Mrs. Tubman insists that it is in Tuesday's paper. It turns out that the coupon is in Sunday's paper, which they used to wrap the garbage.

EXERCISES X

Which of the following items can be regarded as involving a verbal dispute? Indicate the type of verbal dispute found. It might be that some are verbal disputes of a kind different from the three distinguished in this chapter.

1.   A: Snort is a conservative. He always opposes bills that would improve the working man's life.

B: Snort is no conservative. Conservatives want to keep things as they are, whereas Snort is forever proposing to make this or that change.

C: He is a conservative, though, because he has written several articles for *Fortune* magazine. On top of that he's a Republican. What more proof could you want?

2.   A: Man hasn't progressed at all in 2,000 years—still the same old sinner, more plagued by guilt than ever.

B: Of course he has progressed. Look at our blessings: TV, wonder drugs, satellites, space travel, modern art, etc.

A: But progress is movement toward redemption. It does not consist in sinking deeper into the muck of this world.

C: No, progress consists actually in finding ways to enjoy the most agreeable form of misery—physical comfort.

3.   I have no doubt that the First Amendment—Congress shall make no law . . . abridging the freedom of speech and the press—intended that there would be no libel or defamation law in the United States, just absolutely none. My view is, without exception, that freedom of speech means that you shall not do something to people either for the views they have or the views they express or the words they speak or write.

DISPUTER: But surely the Bill of Rights doesn't grant absolute freedom of speech and press. The Bill of Rights doesn't nullify libel and slander laws. In addition, it doesn't or shouldn't cover the peddlers of filth, those advocating the violent overthrow of the government, the one who spills security secrets, etc.

4.   A: It is impossible to negotiate agreements with the Soviet Union. They will never concede to us anything which we can accept, and we will never concede to them anything that they want.

B: Of course it is possible to negotiate. Negotiation isn't an interchange in which one side wins and the other side loses. True negotiation is an interchange that leads to an agreement in which each side gains more than it gives up.

5. . . . a man's earnings are his property as much as his land and the house in which he lives. . . . It has been the fashion in recent years to disparage "property rights"—to associate them with greed and materialism. This attack on property rights is actually an attack on freedom. It is another instance of the modern failure to take into account the whole man. How can a man be truly free if he is denied the means to exercise freedom? How can he be free if the fruits of his labor are not his to dispose of, but are treated, instead, as part of a common pool of public wealth? Property and freedom are inseparable: to the extent government takes the one in the form of taxes, it intrudes on the other.

(BARRY GOLDWATER, *The Conscience of a Conservative*) [13]

DISPUTER: When we speak of "freedom" in a democratic context we have in mind the freedom of the general public. If a few are allowed to accumulate great wealth while a great many are left with very little, then freedom *is* granted to a few but denied to the many. Since without some "property" the many cannot exercise their freedom, if we are interested in freedom, then the government should tax so as to distribute the wealth.

6. A: Slavery was never legally abolished. The Thirteenth Amendment, which abolished slavery, was "ratified" in the Southern states at the point of the bayonet. The Republican Party in 1867 passed the Reconstruction Act. This divided the South into five military districts, imposing martial rule, and made ratification of the Fourteenth Amendment the price for restoration of civil government and full rights in the union.

B: Stop talking this foolishness. Whether or not they were blackmailed, they still ratified it, and so it was quite legal. It was disgraceful but legal.

7. Let us focus attention on one method of federal interference—one that tends to be neglected in much of the public discussion of the problem. In recent years the federal government has continued, and in many cases has increased, federal "grants-in-aid" to the States in a number of areas in which the Constitution recognizes the exclusive jurisdiction of the States. These grants are called "matching funds" and are designed to "stimulate" state spending in health, education, welfare, conservation or any other area in which the federal government decides there is a need for national action. If the States agree to put up money for these purposes, the federal government undertakes to match the appropriation according to a ratio prescribed by Congress. Sometimes the ratio is fifty-fifty; often the federal government contributes over half the cost.

There are two things to note about these programs. The first is that they are *federal* programs—they are conceived by the federal government both as

[13] Barry Goldwater, *The Conscience of a Conservative* (Shepherdsville, Kentucky: Victor Publishing Co., 1960) pp. 61–62. © Copyright 1960, Victor Publishing Company, Inc. Used by permission of the Victor Publishing Co.

to purpose and as to extent. The second is that the "stimulative" grants are, in effect, a mixture of blackmail and bribery. The States are told to go along with the program "or else." Once the federal government has offered matching funds, it is unlikely as a practical matter, that a member of a State Legislature will turn down his State's fair share of revenue collected from all of the States. Understandably, many legislators feel that to refuse aid would be political suicide. This is an indirect form of coercion, but it is effective nonetheless.

(BARRY GOLDWATER, *The Conscience of a Conservative*) [14]

DISPUTER: "Matching funds" is not "a mixture of blackmail and bribery." "Blackmail" is extortion by intimidation, especially by threats of public exposure. To bribe is to reward someone in an important position with the view of inducing him to do something for you. The "matching funds" program of the federal government involves none of this.

8. Were the students involved in "sit-in" demonstrations in Louisiana "disturbing the peace"?

A: Yes, they were, for the Louisiana statute under which the sixteen were convicted defines "disturbing the peace" as "engaging in a fistic encounter, or using insulting language, or appearing in an intoxicated condition, or holding an unlawful assembly, or commission of any other act in such manner as to *unreasonably disturb or alarm the public*." The students conducted themselves in such a manner that their actions might well have led to disturbing and alarming the public. In the environment of a segregated community the mere presence of a Negro at a white lunch counter might inflame some people as much as fisticuffs would in other places.

B: You are wrong! There has to be outwardly boisterous or unruly conduct in order to charge a defendant with "unreasonably disturbing or alarming the public."

9. A lumberman is asked by a passerby, "How long have you had *that* axe?"

"For about ten years now. Had the handle changed three times and the blade twice."

"But then you haven't had *that* axe for ten years."

10. PHILOSOPHER: A doubt about the reality of what we are sensing is easily raised, since there may even be a doubt whether we are awake or in a dream. How can you determine whether at this moment we are sleeping, and all that we sense are dream images, or whether we are awake? The resemblance between waking experience and dream experience can be at times quite astonishing!

JOE: Of course we can know when we are awake! Are you telling me that I could be asleep at this moment?

11. A: It takes about eight minutes for the sun's light to reach us, and it takes much longer in the case of the other stars. It is quite possible, for example, that that star which we are looking at ceased to exist eight minutes ago. This only brings to light the not often recognized fact that what we are seeing is not the star but what it looked like about eight minutes ago.

[14] *Ibid.,* pp. 26–27. Used by permission.

B: Nonsense! Let's face it, it sounds paradoxical, but if that star ceased to exist eight minutes ago what we are seeing is an object which doesn't exist. Let's be tough-minded.

C: Enough of those virile adjectives. It is all quite simple. Science has found out that we are *really* seeing sensations in the mind which are caused by the star which no longer exists.

12. A: Dr. Jekyll and Mr. Hyde were the same person who merely changed his physical appearance.

B: No, they were two persons who inhabited the same body—the body of course changed its appearance.

13. In 1954 Harry A. Jones, sixty-six, of Long Beach, California, was found by his wife, slumped over his desk. She called a doctor. The doctor could find no pulse, no heart beat, nor any sign of breath. Jones was pronounced dead and an ambulance was called to take him to the mortuary. On the road the blankets began to move, causing the driver a very bad moment. Mr. Jones "came back to life" and made a full recovery. Was he dead?

A: Of course he wasn't dead. He didn't "come back to life" for he never left life. He is alive and was alive; the doctor must have made a mistake.

B: But he was dead. The doctor found no pulse, no heart beat, and no breath. If this is true of someone, then we say he is dead. No, he was dead. This was a true resurrection.

14. What is the nature of the issue in the following passage? How does Christ settle it?

Then some Sadducees came forward. They are the people who deny that there is a resurrection. Their question was this: "Master, Moses laid it down for us that if there are brothers, and one dies, leaving a wife but no child, then the next should marry the widow and carry on his brother's family. Now, there were seven brothers: the first took a wife and died childless; then the second married her, then the third. In this way the seven of them died leaving no children. Afterwards the woman also died. At the resurrection whose wife is she to be, since all seven had married her?" Jesus said to them, "The men and women of this world marry; but those who have been judged worthy of a place in the other world and of the resurrection from the dead, do not marry, for they are not subject to death any longer. They are like angels; they are sons of God, because they share in the resurrection."

(Luke 20: 27-36)

15. A: The government in 1962 seized 5,400 Giant Economy Size jars of Grandma's instant coffee. Their reason: It was discovered that the *Economy* jar costs the American housewife 1.9 cents per ounce more than the ordinary six ounce jar of the same coffee. This is false advertising.

B: No, it isn't. Time is money, don't you know! Just think of the time that's saved by buying the giant jar. It saves the housewife a trip or two to the store. Also it's cheaper at current garbage-disposal rates to throw away three big jars than five little ones.

16. During Prohibition two young men ran through the Elks Convention train at a quick stop selling "cold tea" at five dollars a pint. After the train

started the Elks discovered that what they had bought was cold tea. Was this false advertizing?

A: No. They announced that they were selling cold tea and it was cold tea. How can this be called false advertizing?

B: It was false advertizing. In those circumstances anyone saying that he was selling cold tea at five dollars a pint would be understood to be selling whisky, so it was false advertizing.

17. On August 24, 1962, 23 Cuban refugees shelled Havana with 20 mm shells from two 36-foot motorboats. These Cubans were living in and came from Miami. Should they be indicted under the Neutrality Act, which reads that it is a crime for a group to launch "a military expedition or enterprise" from the United States against a country with which the United States is at peace?

A: Yes. They launched a military attack and the United States is not at war with Cuba.

B: No. We are not certain that these boats did not touch down at some Carribbean island en route to Havana, in which case they wouldn't have departed from the United States. Also does shooting up the Havana waterfront with 20 mm cannon constitute a military expedition? No. It is a symbolic act.

C: No. Twenty-three men are not a group, much less a military expedition. Shooting does not make a military expedition. In addition, if the United States is on bad terms with the country to which the nongroup goes, we are not at peace with it, although we may not be at war either.

D: Yes. What would you have said if Canadian refugees had shelled Quebec or Toronto?

METHODS AND TYPES
OF DEFINITIONS

In this section some methods of defining and some types of definitions will be considered.

Methods of Defining

The three most common methods by which we can explain the meaning of a word are definitions by synonym, example, and analysis.[15] Let us consider each of these methods of defining words.

Definition by synonym

When we provide a word with the same meaning in response to the question "What does X mean?" we employ a *definition by synonym*.

---

[15] Another method of explaining the meaning of a word—and there are many more methods—is by use of an implicit definition. This method is explained in Chapter Fourteen, first section (see page 294).

For example, someone who asks what "banal" means can be given this answer: "Banal" means "trite," "commonplace," "insipid." Each of these words is a synonym for "banal." If it were asked what "insipid" means, a definition by synonym would be: "Insipid" means "lifeless." When one gives a definition by synonym, "*X*" means "*A*," the statement is made that the word "*X*" is used in the way in which the word "*A*" is. Definitions by synonym are sometimes criticized on the grounds that there are no synonyms in a language—there are no words which are used in exactly the same way as are other words in the same language. This could be true, and yet such definitions can still be an effective way to explain the meaning of a word. However, when in a definition by synonym it is asserted that "*X*" is used in the way in which the word "*A*" is, this is not to be understood to mean in "exactly the same way" but rather "close enough so that the difference can be ignored."

Definition by example

If we were in the Chicago Natural History Museum and someone asked "What does 'troika' mean?" we could point to a troika. This is an example of the method of explaining the meaning of a word by example. If Khrushchev had explained what he meant by a "neutral nation" by giving Poland as an example, then this would be an example of explaining the meaning of a word by example. Often such a definition can be given by describing the example. When the example is not described or is not mentioned but is called to the learner's attention by some physical means, for example, pointing, this is called the *ostensive* method of teaching the meaning of a word. It is the method of defining a word which dispenses with words except for the word being defined. Pointing to the troika in the first example is an instance of the ostensive method of defining. Such a definition—"troika" means (pointing)—is called an *ostensive definition*. Thus when one either points to an example, names an example or describes an example of a thing denoted by "*X*," this is *defining by example*.

Simple words such as "blue," "loud," "sweet," and "pain" cannot be explained by the method of definition by synonym or analysis (discussed next). Such words are commonly spoken of as *indefinable words*. Now these can be defined by use of ostensive definition; thus what is meant by calling them "indefinable" is that they are not defined by the methods of synonym or analysis. To define "blue" ostensively we point to something; to define "pain" ostensively we can pinch someone.

Some logicians have questioned the adequacy of ostensive definitions. They have pointed out that ostensive definitions are ambiguous (second sense), and they have said that this ambiguity can be resolved only by adding some descriptive phrase to the ostensive definition. For example if you pointed to a desk to explain the meaning of the word "desk" you would add: "The word 'desk' means this article of furniture." It is of course true that often an ostensive definition is ambiguous and can be variously interpreted. That is, if you point to a desk to explain the meaning of the word "desk" to a child, the child might think you are pointing to the material of which the desk is made. But it is not true that this ambiguity can be resolved only by adding some descriptive phrase to the ostensive definition. Generally, the circumstances remove this ambiguity. For example, the circumstances in which a child asks what a desk is are likely to be such that the child knows a piece of furniture is being talked about.

Definition by analysis

The definitions of "game," "building," "shoe," and "broom" above were all examples of what are called *analytic* definitions. Whenever we explain or state the meaning of a word not by using synonyms or examples but by indicating the kind of thing denoted and the characteristics which distinguish it from other such things, we employ an *analytic definition*. In the case of dictionary definitions, as we have argued, the distinguishing characteristics of the common paradigm examples are described, or, as it can also be put, the characteristics which are commonly the criterion for the application of the word are set down.

Aristotle's famous dictum of definitions *by genus and differentia* is an example of the method of definition by analysis. In defining by genus and differentia, say, the word "broom," we give the name of the largest class to which the thing belongs (genus)—in this case "objects"—and indicate those characteristics which distinguish the objects called brooms from other objects (the differentia)—in this case "a long stick with a brush on the end which is used for sweeping."

Some writers have thought that definition by analysis is the only adequate way to define a word, even though there are other ways which are effective (for example, definitions by synonym and example). If "adequate" here means that definition by analysis is the only way to make clear the meaning of a word, then this claim for this method of defining is mistaken. But definition by analysis has one virtue (and perhaps this is what is being stressed when it is said that it is the only adequate way to define a word): If a definition by analysis is a good one and is successful, then not only does one know how to use a word—what things generally to call X and what things not to call X, and so forth—but also his attention is called to those characteristics which on the whole distinguish the paradigm example or examples. As we have seen in the section Criteria and Our Everyday Words (see pages 75–76), often we use words without ever stopping to enumerate such characteristics.

Types of Definitions

Exact definitions

An exact definition is a definition which states the conjunction of characteristics each of which is necessary and which together are sufficient for the use of a word. Such definitions cannot be provided for words as they are used in everyday discourse. If ordinary words were used in accordance with strict rules, then they could be provided. Exact definitions can be provided in those contexts where a strict rule is followed.

Lexical or dictionary definitions

Dictionary definitions report how a word is used. Generally analytic definitions are employed. Such definitions state the distinguishing characteristics of common paradigm examples. Analytic definitions are not the only method employed in dictionaries to explain the meaning of a word. Often synonyms are used and even, at times, ostensive definitions (pictures and diagrams). Analytic definitions in dictionaries can be good (accurate) or bad (inaccurate). If they in fact state the distinguishing characteristics of the things people have in mind when they use a word in one of its senses, then they are good, or, as it is sometimes put, accurate. And of course synonym and ostensive dictionary definitions can be accurate or inaccurate. It should be noted that generally verbal disputes of the second type are settled by lexical definitions unless the dispute is about a word like "conservative," in which case there is no good lexical definition.

Stipulative definitions

In the last section it was said that verbal disputes which hinge on the extension of a word or phrase will be called "word-extension disputes." This is an example of a stipulative definition for the phrase "word-extension disputes." At the beginning of this chapter it was said that the word "thing" would be used to denote objects, behavior, statements, processes, activities, and so on. This is a rather vague stipulative definition for "thing" as it is used in this chapter. It is easy to find many other examples in these chapters. When in a legal document we find such statements as:

"Hospital" means a legally constituted and operated institution having organized facilities for the care and treatment of sick and injured persons, including facilities for diagnosis and major surgery, and providing twenty-four hour nursing service and medical supervision

we have a stipulative definition. In the formal and material sciences stipulative definitions are often used. For example, Galileo defined "uniform motion" as motion in which the distances traversed by the moving particle during any equal intervals of time are equal. From time to time we find it necessary to make clear how we are using some word or phrase. When we do this we employ a stipulative definition. Senator Snort did this in an earlier example. Bertrand Russell does this in the following passage in reply to the question "What is your definition of fanaticism?": [16]

> I should be inclined to say that a man is a fanatic if he thinks some one matter so overwhelmingly important that it outweighs anything else at all. To take an example, I suppose all decent people dislike cruelty to dogs, but if you thought that cruelty to dogs was so atrocious that no other cruelty should be objected to in comparison, then you would be a fanatic.

The immense value of stipulative definitions should be obvious from these examples. Their use in this chapter results in a greater precision and economy. In legal documents such definitions make clearer the boundary lines of certain key words. In the case of Galileo this kind of definition in part enables him to formulate laws which relate what he calls uniformly accelerated motion to distance and time. And, as is quite clear, stipulative definitions served to make clear what the senator and Bertrand Russell meant.

Stipulative definitions, unlike lexical definitions, are neither accurate nor inaccurate (or true or false in any sense). They are proposals or announcements of intentions. Any method for giving a definition can be employed in stipulative definitions. It should also be noted that verbal disputes of the third type are generally settled by stipulative definitions.

Theoretical definitions

These questions are sometimes asked:

What is justice?
What is knowledge?
What is truth?
What is beauty?
What is good?

What is light?
What is heat?

[16] *Bertrand Russell Speaks His Mind* (New York: Bard Books, 1960), p. 117. Copyright © 1960 by The World Publishing Co. All rights reserved. Used by permission of The World Publishing Company.

The first group of questions, as they are raised in the context of philosophy, appear to be requests for exact definitions of the words "justice," "knowledge," "truth," and so forth. If we regard such questions in this way, then no answers can be given these questions. For words like "justice," "truth," and so forth are so used that even good lexical definitions cannot be provided. There are no *common* paradigm examples, nor is there for each word a common set of characteristics which acts as the criterion for its application. However, it is doubtful that when people ask such questions they are asking for exact definitions or, for that matter, for lexical definitions. Socrates, for example, in Plato's *Republic* asks "What is justice?" and "What is the definition of justice?" It seems that this question is not to be understood as a request for an exact or lexical definition but is to be understood as a request for the *nature* of justice. And in turn, to ask for the "nature" of justice is to look for a standard by which we can judge whether an act is just. To ask for the nature of truth is to ask for a standard or standards by which we can judge whether statements are true. Perhaps it is an illusion to believe that there are such standards or that one can search for them as Socrates did, but this seems to be the way to understand these "What is ———?" questions.

The question "What is light?" or "What is heat?" as it comes in the context of physics is not a request for a lexical definition of the word "light" or the word "heat." Rather, the request is being made for the set of statements which will explain the phenomena connected with light and heat. In a word, the question is to be understood as a request for a theory. When a question is a request for a theory, whether it be in ethics, epistemology, science, and so on, such a question is a request for a *theoretical definition*. The answer would be the theoretical definition.

Persuasive definitions

When a writer or speaker, in order to persuade us to accept certain ideas, does not report how a word is used, but rather gives a definition which *appears* to report what the word means, he is generally said to be giving a *persuasive definition*. C. L. Stevenson was the first to describe and name this activity. He points out that frequently the words so defined are highly emotional words like "honesty," "patriot," "democracy," "freedom," "scientific," and "moderate"; and "atheist," "communists," "immature," "radical," and "un-American." Words like those in the first group are sometimes called *honorific* words. Most people, in our country at least, regard having these traits as a desirable thing. For example, what one person may mean by "moderate" to another might be "radical," yet most agree that being moderate is a desirable thing. Words like those in the second group are called *pejorative* words. Most people agree that to be immature is undesirable, though people often do not agree in what they mean by "immaturity." As it is sometimes put, the first group of words are hurrah-words while the second are boo-words. It should be noticed that these words would fall into group (d) of the classification on page 77 (paragraph 3). That is, such words are so used that there are no common paradigm examples in our society, nor are there sets of characteristics which commonly act as criteria for the words. Of course in context it is often clear what someone means by these words. Stevenson also points out that words like "true" and "really" are often the sign of a persuasive definition. Let us now consider some examples of persuasive definitions.

Imagine a social group, a business community, or college where some men who have great personal power freely express their opinions on important matters. Imagine, in addition, that in an alarming number of instances their opinions are mistaken. Someone who sees this and wishes this situation changed takes the opportunity to say in their presence: "Honesty is not merely expressing your opinion but expressing your opinion after having tried to the best of your ability to find the truth."

Is this what we mean by "honesty"? There are a number of uses of the word "honesty." "Honesty" is a class (d) word. But in our imagined situation the speaker's statement *appears* to be a definition (it has, for example, the form of a definition). And it is in part the fact that it has this appearance that makes it possible for the speaker to achieve his end. For honesty, along with the other virtues, is what most people want to possess. Even some of those who are dishonest, cowardly, and hateful do not think they are; rather they think of themselves as honest, courageous, and kind. Thus, if one wants someone to take great care in coming to his opinions prior to uttering them, he might say, as in the above situation, "Honesty is not merely. . . . " If the hearer thinks this is a definition, then he cannot very well object to what is said. Consequently, this statement could affect his thinking and actions.

The term "art" is used in many ways, but most agree that it is desirable to have one's work called art. Tolstoy in *What is Art?* sets out to "correctly define art." He writes, "art is a human activity, consisting in this, that a man consciously, by means of certain external signs, hands on to others feelings he has lived through, and that other people are infected by these feelings, and also experience them." He then distinguishes "real art" from "counterfeit art" by saying that real art "transmits the feeling flowing from love of God and man or merely the simple feelings uniting all men." Tolstoy is attemping to influence the reader. He presents what might appear to many to be lexical definitions of "art" and "real art." At the end of the fourth book of the *Republic* Plato gives a long string of persuasive definitions. He says that to say a state is wise means that the rulers have knowledge of " . . . the best possible conduct of the State as a whole in its internal and external relations." To say a state is courageous means that the soldiers of the state act fearlessly from right convictions. To say a state is just means each citizen is "performing the function in the community for which his nature best suits him." Neither Tolstoy nor Plato is reporting the use of the words. They are trying to influence the reader to accept certain standards and ideals. They are using persuasive definitions.

Real and nominal definitions

When someone describes how a word is used, as in a lexical definition, or sets down how he is using or will use a word, as in stipulative definitions, such definitions are definitions of words. These are often called *nominal definitions*. There are, however, a number of thinkers who believe there is another kind of definition, namely, definitions of *things*. Such definitions are called *real definitions*. In a real definition the interest does not lie in how a word is used, but in describing "the real nature" or "essence" of the thing(s) denoted by the word. Thus to be interested in a real definition of shoe is not to be interested in how the word "shoe" is used but rather to be interested in "the real nature" of a shoe. Many feel that when Plato asked questions like "What is justice?" he did not want a nominal or theoretical definition but rather thought that the word "justice" denoted something (a universal) and wanted to know "the real nature" of that something (which "participates" in instances of just acts). G. E. Moore in his famous *Principia Ethica* begins his book by asking for a definition of good, and it is clear that he is looking for a real definition. This can be seen in this passage:

What, then, is good? How is good to be defined? Now, it may be thought that this is a verbal question. A definition does indeed often mean the expressing of one word's meaning in other words. But this is not the sort of definition I am asking for. Such a definition can never be of ultimate importance in any study except lexicography. If I wanted that kind of definition I should have to consider in the first place how people generally used the word "good"; but my business is not with its proper usage, as established by custom. I should, indeed, be foolish, if I tried to use it for something which it did not usually denote; if, for instance, I were to announce that, whenever I used the word "good," I must be understood to be thinking of that object which is usually denoted by the word "table." I shall, therefore, use the word in the sense in which I think it is ordinarily used; but at the same time I am not anxious to discuss whether I am right in thinking that it is so used. My business is solely with that object or idea, which I hold, rightly or wrongly, that the word is generally used to stand for. What I want to discover is the nature of that object or idea, and about this I am extremely anxious to arrive at an agreement.

Many philosophers think it is a mistake to believe that words refer to nonmaterial objects in a world of ideas or in the mind. Thus it is a mistake to believe that one can state the real nature or essence of these things. In addition many find it difficult to understand what it means to talk of "the real nature" or "essence" of something, say a shoe, unless to ask for the essence of a shoe is to ask for the distinguishing characteristics of the paradigm cases of things called shoes, in which case we have a request for a lexical analytic definition. But our interest is not in considering the cases for and against real definitions, rather we are interested in seeing what is meant by the distinction real/nominal definitions.

EXERCISE XI

(1) Which of the following offer a definition of some term? (2) What *method* or methods are used in the following to explain the meaning of a word (definition by synonym, analysis, example, or other method)? (3) Do you find any examples of the *types* of definitions discussed (exact, lexical, stipulative, theoretical, persuasive, nominal, and real definitions)?

1. A liberal is a man who cultivates the skills that make freedom operational. He is always a man on special assignment.

(MAX ASCOLI, editor and publisher of *The Reporter* magazine)

2. The root difference between the Conservatives and the Liberals of today is that Conservatives take account of the *whole* man, while the Liberals tend to look only at the material side of man's nature. The Conservatives believe that man is, in part, an economic and animal creature; but that he is also a spiritual creature with spiritual needs and spiritual desires. What is more, these needs and desires reflect the *superior* side of man's nature, and thus take precedence over his economic wants. Conservatism therefore looks upon the enhancement of man's spiritual nature as the primary concern of political philosophy. Liberals, on the other hand—in the name of a concern for "human beings"—regard the satisfaction of economic wants as the dominant mission of society. They are, moreover, in a hurry. So that their characteristic approach is to harness the society's political and economic forces into a collective effort to *compel* "progress." In this approach, I believe they fight against Nature.

(BARRY GOLDWATER, *The Conscience of a Conservative*) [17]

17 Goldwater, *op. cit.*, pp. 10–11. Used by permission.

3. I think sin is something that it is positively good to punish, such as murder, not only because you want to prevent murder, but because the murderer deserves to suffer.

(Bertrand Russell Speaks His Mind) [18]

4. "Fabian Socialists," the general explained to the senators, could be more or less defined as "some of those to the left who seem to appear at various times, usually anonymously, and who are not in the records of Mr. Hoover as are the card-carrying Communists, who sometimes raise questions as to where we are going or where they would like us to go."

5. Every truly civilized and enlightened man is conservative and liberal and progressive.

A civilized man is conservative in that his deepest loyalty is to the Western heritage of ideas which originated on the shores of the Mediterranean.

Because of that loyalty he is the indefatigable defender of our own constitutional doctrine, which is that all power, that all government, that all officials, that all parties, and all majorities are under the law—and that none of them is sovereign and omnipotent.

The civilized man is a liberal because the writing and the administration of the laws should be done with enlightenment and compassion, with tolerance and charity, and with affection.

And the civilized man is progressive because the times change and the social order evolves and new things are invented and changes occur.

(WALTER LIPPMANN in a speech to the Women's National Press Club in
Washington)

6. True cynics—"those canine philosophers," as St. Augustine called them —are very rare, and true hypocrites are even rarer. Cynicism requires a disbelief in the possibility of sincerity, and most men, at least in our kind of society, find it necessary to insist upon their own sincerity. As for hypocrisy, one cannot practice it without acknowledging the fact to oneself; to be a hypocrite, a man must *see* a hypocrite whenever he faces a mirror. And such is the human capacity for self-deception that almost every sinner born of woman has some device for convincing himself that his base acts serve in some perspective some sort of good.

(RICHARD H. ROVERE, *Senator Joe McCarthy*) [19]

7. You said just now that the government in 1933 gave a lot of work to the unemployed. It is a great mistake to believe this. It is false. Oh yes, the men built roads and planted forests and things like that. But I don't call that

work. Real work, *real* employment, doesn't have to be invented. It doesn't need any government to create it. It springs naturally from the economy.

8. "I was complaining to a friend of mine who is in the Defense Department about the industrial-military complex the other day," [Congressman John] Lindsay says. "He said he had heard a lot of vague talk about this sort of thing, but he just wished someone would come up with one concrete example. I told him I could give him two.

"Last year the Justice Department brought in a bill which would have given it the power to fire any employee of a defense contractor whom it judged a security risk. The Pentagon, of course, testified for it. And then every Congressman got a letter from the largest association of defense contractors urging him to vote for the Industrial Security Bill. And this would have been the first law ever written in the United States which would have given the government the power to fire people in private industry.

"Then we were debating the raise in the debt limit from $306 billion to $308 billion. One Congressman took the floor to report that the chairmen of the boards of mighty corporations had called to ask him to vote to raise the debt. They freely admitted that the Pentagon had called and told them that, if the debt limit wasn't increased, they wouldn't get paid. 'All right,' my friend conceded; 'you win.'"

Gerald Ford, a Grand Rapids Republican, was the first Congressman to inject the fact of corporate pressure for a higher national debt into the debate.

"I mentioned Chrysler," says Congressman Ford. "And right away five or six other members asked me to yield so they could tell the same story about calls from their districts."

(MURRAY KEMPTON, "The Adult Congressman") [20]

9. The true definition of each thing involves nothing and expresses nothing but the nature of the thing defined.

(SPINOZA, *Ethics*)

10. A definition is "a rule for mutual transformation of words in the same language."

(CARNAP, *The Unity of Science*)

11. Happiness is an activity of soul in accordance with virtue in a complete life.

(ARISTOTLE, *The Nicomachean Ethics*)

12. A leading member of several nationalist groups has defined American Nationalism as "an awareness that the United States is at least potentially a great, powerful, and superior nation." Bertrand Russell defines nationalism in this way: " . . . nationalism is not a single world-wide system, but is a

[20] Murray Kempton, "The Adult Congressman" in *The New Republic*, April 6, 1963, pp. 11–12. Copyright © 1962, by Harrison-Blaine Inc. Used by permission of *The New Republic*.

different system in each nation. It consists essentially in collective self-glorifica-
tion and in a conviction that it is right to pursue the interests of one's own
nation however they may conflict with those of others."

And here is another definition: "The Nationalist opposes the belief that
the world is one, that all human beings are "brothers" in the broadest sense,
and that all men everywhere in the world must cooperate with each other and
live together in peace under world law."

13. Turning to the Jews who had believed him, Jesus said, "If you dwell
within the revelation I have brought, you are indeed my disciples; you shall
know the truth, and the truth will set you free." They replied, "We are
Abraham's descendants; we have never been in slavery to any man. What do
you mean by saying, 'You will become free men'?" "In very truth I tell you,"
Jesus said, "that everyone who commits sin is a slave. The slave has no permanent standing in the household, but the son belongs to it for ever. If then
the Son sets you free, you will indeed be free."

(John 8: 31-36)

14. Philosophy is a battle against the bewitchment of our intelligence by
means of language.

(WITTGENSTEIN, *Philosophical Investigations*)

William James was once asked to define philosophy and he replied, "Just
words, words, words!"

Philosophy is the body of highest truth, the organized sum of science; the
science of which all others are branches.

(*The Century Dictionary*)

15. WOODROW WYATT: Lord Russell, what is philosophy?

LORD RUSSELL: Well, that's a very controversial question. I think no
two philosophers will give you the same answer. My own view would
be that philosophy consists of speculations about matters where exact
knowledge is not yet possible. That would only be my answer—not
anybody else's.

WYATT: What's the difference between philosophy and science?

RUSSELL: Well, roughly, you'd say science is what we know and philosophy is what we don't know. That's a simple definition and for that
reason questions are perpetually passing over from philosophy into
science as knowledge advances.

WYATT: Then when something is established and discovered it ceases
to be philosophy and becomes science?

RUSSELL: Yes, and all sorts of questions that used to be labelled philosophy are no longer so labelled.

(*Bertrand Russell Speaks His Mind*) [21]

[21] *Bertrand Russell Speaks His Mind* (New York: Bard Books, 1960), p. 9.
Copyright © 1960, by The World Publishing Company. All rights reserved.
Used by permission of The World Publishing Company.

16. "Network" means anything reticulated or decussated, at equal distances, with interstices between the intersections.

(SAMUEL JOHNSON)

17. We will use the word "and" to conjoin two sentences to make a single sentence which we call the *conjunction* of the two sentences. For example the sentence:

Goldwater loves Rockefeller and Rockefeller loves Goldwater,

is the conjunction of the sentences "Goldwater loves Rockefeller" and "Rockefeller loves Goldwater." We will use the sign '·' for conjunction. Thus the conjunction of the above two sentences is written:

Goldwater loves Rockefeller · Rockefeller loves Goldwater.

The rule governing the use of '·' is: the conjunction of two sentences is true if and only if both sentences are true.

18. Some philosophers have I think doubted whether there are such things as other philosophers have meant by "sense-data" or "sensa." And I think it is quite possible that some philosophers (including myself, in the past) have used these terms in senses such that it is really doubtful whether there are any such things. But there is no doubt at all that there are sense-data, in the sense in which I am now using that term. I am at present seeing a great number of them, and feeling others. And in order to point out to the reader what sort of things I mean by sense-data, I need only ask him to look at his own right hand. If he does this he will be able to pick out something (and, unless he is seeing double, *only* one thing) with regard to which he will see that it is, at first sight, a natural view to take that that thing is identical, not, indeed, with his whole right hand, but with that part of its surface which he is actually seeing, but will also (on a little reflection) be able to see that it is doubtful whether it can be identical with the part of the surface of his hand in question. Things *of the sort* (in a certain respect) of which this thing is, which he sees in looking at his hand, and with regard to which he can understand how some philosophers should have supposed it to *be* the part of the surface of his hand which he is seeing, while others have supposed that it can't be, are what I mean by "sense-data."

(G. E. MOORE, "A Defence of Common Sense") [22]

EXERCISES XII

The following is an article, which appeared in the *New Republic* April 23, 1962, and a letter criticising the article. (1) State exactly the views criticised and the criticism. (2) Who is right?

[22] G. E. Moore, "A Defence of Common Sense" in *Philosophical Papers* (London: George Allen and Unwin Ltd., 1959 and New York: Macmillan, 1959), p. 54. Copyright George Allen and Unwin Ltd., 1959. Used by permission of George Allen and Unwin Ltd. and The Macmillan Company.

1. "It Ain't Right"

Since, in his letter of justification to *The New York Times,* the editor of Webster's Third New International Dictionary, Philip G. Gove, twice cites word usage in *The New Republic* as authority, it is ungracious to suggest that the dictionary's compilers have abandoned a function indispensable in any advanced society, that of maintaining the quality of its language. If that language is primitive, vague and illogical, so will the thought be. Until now, Americans have gone to Webster's International to learn, for example, that "bimonthly" means once in two months rather than twice a month, for which the word is "semimonthly."

Now, however, Dr. Gove has written that a dictionary "should have no traffic with . . . artificial notions of correctness or superiority. It should be descriptive and not prescriptive." The new edition bases its definitions simply on current usage, refusing to distinguish good from bad. Thus if the ignorant use "bimonthly" to mean twice a month, then that becomes a new meaning, even though the consequent ambiguity makes the word useless. So the language is allowed to degenerate.

The function hitherto performed by Webster's International in the U.S. (as by the Oxford English Dictionary in Britain) is so vital that we dare not allow it to lapse for long. Some other company of lexicographers will sooner or later have to take it up. A new discriminating dictionary of the American language, bringing the old Webster's up to date, will be increasingly needed as the old gradually becomes both obsolete and unavailable. The production of such a dictionary will require large financial resources as well as intelligence and long labor. Our great foundations could not spend money in the service of our society and the English-speaking world in general more constructively than by supporting such an undertaking.[23]

2. Sirs:

In your attack on Webster's *Third New International Dictionary·* ("It Ain't Right," April 23), you start off by saying that if a language is "primitive, vague and illogical," the thought of its speakers will be that way too. Maybe you'll say more about all this. Linguists swear they've never found a "primitive, vague and illogical" language, but everybody knows he can't trust a bunch of sneaking professionals. You may have stumbled on something big. Why don't you just up and name a primitive language and say what makes it primitive? If you do, you'll make a reputation for yourself; and *until* you do, the dirty linguists are likely to say you're only another amateur, talking through your hat. The dictionary-maker, you say, has to keep his language good so that thought will be possible. When you've finished telling what you mean by a good language and a bad language (and be clear and logical, remember—not primitive), you can get on with the explanation of how an unabridged dictionary can make people talk the way its editors want them to.

Take you, for example. In almost 30 years you didn't learn anything about your own favorite, the *Second International.* If you had learned anything about it, you would have known that its editors set out, like that bolshevik Gove, to record "the usage that now prevails among the educated and cultured people to whom the language is vernacular," and you would have known better than to choose an example like *bimonthly* to bless the *Second* and damn the *Third*. Didn't you ever look up any of the other *bi*words? Here's the definition of *biweekly* in the *Second*: "Occurring or appearing every two weeks; fortnightly; also, semi-weekly." Some people would like to hear you argue that the editor of the *Third* is a newfangled scoundrel because he says a dictionary "should be descriptive and not prescriptive." Just a bit more than a hundred years ago, the Dean of Westminster said the same thing in the essay that got the *Oxford English Dictionary* going. A dictionary, said the Dean, is "an inventory of the language," and a lexicographer "is an historian of it, not a critic." And the Dean wasn't saying anything new. Sam Johnson himself said in his big way that he did not "form, but register the language," that he did not "teach men how they should think, but relate how they have hitherto expressed their thoughts."

The sense "twice a month" for the word *bimonthly* is new, you say, and "the consequent ambiguity makes the word useless. So the language is allowed to degenerate." Drag yourself away from *Webster's Second* long enough to look at the *Oxford*. You'll find *bimonthly* in the filthy sense as early as 1864, *bidural* "twice a day" from 1854, *biquarterly* "twice a quarter" from 1884, *biweekly* from 1865, *biwinter* from 1884, *biyearly* from 1879; and while you're on the *bi*-kick you might look up *biannual*, too. As the *Third International*—repeat, *Third*—says under the first prefix *bi-*, people often disapprove of these uses "because of the likelihood of confusion"; but the ignorant don't use such words at all, and yet there they stand in the *Oxford*. When you scurry back to Webster's *Second*, be ready for a shock; because you're going to find *biannual, bidural, biquarterly, biweekly, biwinter,* and *biyearly,* all in their wrong meanings.

(JAMES SLEDD, Evanston, Illinois) 24

24 Used by permission of Mr. Sledd.

Chapter Four

USES OF LANGUAGE

THREE COMMON USES
OF SENTENCES

Traditionally, three uses of language have been discussed in informal logic. There are many more, but let us begin by considering these three common uses first. These uses of language have been called informative, expressive, and directive. When a sentence is used to express a matter of fact it is said that a statement of fact is thereby made—or that the sentence is used informatively.[1] When a sentence is used to express emotions, it is said to be used expressively; and when a sentence is used to command or request, it is said to be used directively.

Here are examples of the informative use of language:

1. "The Eiffel Tower is the tallest structure in Paris"—as uttered by a Paris guide.

   "Some Democratic Senators do not support Kennedy's domestic program"—from an analysis of the relationship between Kennedy and Congress.

   "Lead melts at 327°C."—as uttered by a student in a laboratory after performing experiments with lead.[2]

---

[1] We will use the word "statement" to refer to what is said in using a sentence to express what is true or false. A sentence not used to make a statement might be used to express a command, a request, an emotion, and so on.

[2] Let us suppose that "lead melts at 327°C." is not used here to express a definition or part of one.

112

Language is used expressively in the following examples:

> **2.** "Poor thing"—as uttered by a mother on finding that her baby has been stung by a bee.
>
> "How perfectly divine"—as uttered by one woman in the presence of another woman as they see the Mona Lisa in a gallery.

Language is said to be used directively in these two episodes:

> **3.** "Love your enemies and pray for your persecutors . . ."—as uttered by Christ (Matthew 5:45).
>
> "Please pass the salt"—as uttered by a boy at the dinner table.

How can we tell that language is used differently in the above examples? One answer would be this: We can just see that the sentence "The Eiffel Tower is the tallest structure in Paris" in the indicated context is used to assert a matter of fact, and is not used as the sentences "Poor thing" or "Love your enemies" are. In turn, we can easily see that the sentence "Love your enemies" is used as a command, while "Lead melts at 327°C." is not, and so on.

But there is another way to tell that a sentence in one context is used differently from a sentence in another context. Certain questions can sensibly be asked in connection with one use of language but cannot sensibly be asked in connection with another use of language. For example, consider this question:

> Is it factually true or false? [3]

This question can sensibly be asked of the statement that some Democratic senators do not support Kennedy's domestic program. That is, we can sensibly ask: Is it factually true that some Democratic senators do not support Kennedy's domestic program? It is, of course, true that some Democratic senators do not support his program; and if someone should doubt this, then one could easily show him that it is true. But to ask this same question of "Poor thing" as uttered by the mother or "Please pass the salt" as uttered by the boy at the table would be to ask a senseless question. In turn, there are certain questions which go with "Love your enemies" as uttered by Christ, which could not sensibly be asked in connection with the assertion that some Democratic senators do not support the Kennedy domestic program. For example, we can ask of the command:

> Should I obey it or not?
>
> Does it demand too much?
>
> Is it possible?

> [3] To make this a bit clearer: a statement (X) is factually true or false, as the phrase "factually true or false" is used in this chapter, if observations can be described which would constitute good grounds for affirming X or denying X.

Such questions cannot, in the same sense, sensibly be asked of "Poor thing" as uttered by the mother or "Lead melts at 327°C." is uttered by the student in the laboratory. Similarly, with the expression of emotion —"Poor thing"—the question can be asked:

Is it genuine or not?

And this cannot be asked, in the same sense, of the command "Love your enemies" or of the statement "The Eiffel Tower is the tallest structure in Paris."

These observations suggest the second way to tell whether a sentence is being used differently from another sentence. This way can be expressed as follows: A sentence S_1 is used differently from S_2 if the same question—a question with the same meaning—can sensibly be asked of what is expressed by one sentence but not of what is expressed by the other sentence. If the same questions can sensibly be asked of what is expressed by both S_1 and S_2, then they are used in the same way.

There are two aspects of this criterion which need clarification. First, when "questions" are spoken of, this term is to be understood to cover questions which deal with general matters such as truth and falsity, obeying and not obeying—not questions addressed to any particular subject matter, for example, "Which senators are Democrats?"

Second, the phrase "questions with the *same meaning*" is used in stating the criterion. Why is this? Sometimes the same questions—"same" in the sense of having the same words—can express *different* questions. For example,

Is it true?

can be asked of both "Love your enemies" as used by Christ and "The Eiffel Tower is the tallest structure in Paris" as used by the guide. But though the same question—that is, the same group of words—is asked, the question expressed is different in the two cases. To ask "Is it true?" of "The Eiffel Tower is the tallest structure in Paris" means "Is it factually true?" or "Is the Eiffel Tower the tallest structure in Paris?" But to ask "Is it true?" of "Love your enemies" is to ask "Should I obey it?" or "Does he really want us to do that?" Thus the same group of words is used to express two different questions in the two cases. To determine whether a question in some context has a different meaning from the same question (same group of words) used in another context, one can paraphrase the questions, or ask them in different words—as was done with "Is it true?"

What exactly does it mean to say that "S_1" is used in a certain context informatively, "S_2" is used in a certain context expressively, and "S_3" is used in a certain context directively? First, notice that there are differences between the examples of language use within each of the above groups (1), (2), and (3). For example, there are differences between the way language is used in group (3):

"Love your enemies"—as uttered by Christ.
"Please pass the salt"—as uttered by the boy.

The first we call a command, the second a request. The difference can be brought out by noticing that in connection with such a command we can ask:

By what authority does he say this?

but this cannot sensibly be asked of the request. Why then are both classified as directive use? The answer, in part, is that they have certain common features. First, they differ in the same way from the examples of informative use and expressive use. That is, they differ in the same way in the sense that those questions which can be sensibly asked of the examples of informative use and expressive use cannot be sensibly asked of either this command or this request. And, second, we can ask of both: Should I obey it?

To avoid certain confusions it will prove useful to stipulate the following: If we can ask of what is expressed by S, (a) Is it factually true? but not (b) Should I obey it?, then S is to be classed as an instance of the informative use. If we cannot ask (a) of what is expressed by S but can ask (b), then S is to be classed as directive use. If we cannot ask (a) or (b) of what is expressed by S, but S can be replaced by a natural expression of emotion, then S would be classed as expressive use. Other criteria could be employed for this classification. For example, it could be stipulated that if S is used like those sentences in group (1), then it is to be classed as informative; if S is used like those sentences in group (2), then it is to be classed as expressive; and if S is used like those sentences in group (3), then it is to be classed as directive. If these criteria were adopted, then, as one consequence, some sentences could be so used that we would be inclined to say they fall into one or more classes. For example, consider this use:

"The nurse will take you to the operating room"—uttered by a doctor before his patient in the presence of the nurse.

It closely resembles the clear-cut examples of commands or orders and it resembles the examples of language used informatively. But given the above criteria this use of language is to be classed neither as informative nor as directive.

In the preceding examples of the three uses of language we have been considering, we find different sentences. It is interesting to note that the same sentence (that is, the same group of words) can be used informatively, expressively, and directively. Consider this simple sentence: It is raining. And recall these familiar situations:

4. The Waldo family has for some time been planning a Memorial Day picnic. It would have been their first picnic that year. It is raining an all-day rain. Billy Waldo is the first one up and he sees the rain. The rest of the family is awakened by Billy running into the bedrooms and saying, "It is raining."
5. Billy goes out on the porch and is soon joined by most of the family. Humphrey, his older brother, mutters disconsolately, "It is raining."
6. Billy at breakfast hears his friend Utah Jenkins calling him. Billy jumps up and glances at his father. Mr. Waldo says sternly, "It is raining." Billy goes and tells Utah he cannot come out.

In (4) the sentence "It is raining" is used in such a way that we can ask "Is it in fact raining?" In (5) the sentence "It is raining" is used in place of a natural expression of emotion such as a sign of disconsolation. The sentence in (6) is used like the sentence "You cannot go out" might be used in these circumstances.

FORM, PURPOSE, AND EFFECT

It is important to distinguish the *use* to which language is put from:
1. the grammatical structure of the sentence
2. the purpose or purposes of the user of the sentence
3. the effect the use of language might have.

Let us consider each of these.

The Grammatical Structure

English grammar books commonly divide sentences into these four classes: declarative, interrogative, imperative, and exclamatory. It would be a mistake to identify these grammatical forms with use. For example, it would be a mistake to identify informative use with declarative sentences, expressive use with exclamatory sentences, and directive use with interrogative and imperative sentences. It can easily be seen that this would be a mistake. For example, interrogative sentences can be used informatively and expressively. Consider these sentences:

1. Isn't it true that we could have torn down the Berlin Wall without triggering a conflict if we had acted immediately after the wall was put up?
2. What is that?

We can imagine contexts where (1) would be used informatively and where (2) would be a spontaneous expression of, say, fear rather than a request for information. In turn, declarative sentences can be used expressively and directively. Consider:

3. It is raining;
4. I would like some more water.

(3) uttered by someone in a family standing on the porch on the rainy morning of their Memorial Day picnic would, as we have seen, be like a moan or sigh of disappointment. (4), as we know, is often used as a command.

The Purpose

It would also be a mistake to identify the use to which a sentence is put with the purpose or purposes of the language user. For example, consider this statement: "The United States now has 500 times more nuclear striking power than the U.S.S.R."—uttered in a talk comparing United States and Soviet military strength. And think of the different purposes people might have in making this statement. One man might say this because he merely wants to state a fact. He might, for example, be a historian. Another man might make this statement in order to bring about a tougher foreign policy. Another might say this to persuade the Russian leaders that they need to increase their arms productions. Or a man might say this to arouse our sense of well-being. We can easily imagine many, many other purposes. To take another example, consider the earlier example of directive discourse: Love your enemies. Christ's purpose in saying this was to provide instruction concerning the conduct of our lives. But we can imagine purposes other than this one which someone might have in giving this command. For example, some government official might say this with the purpose of keeping peace and order. A politician might say this to win the church vote. In some cases language is used expressively without the user uttering it for any purpose—it comes as naturally as a cry of pain or a laugh. Thus the use to which a sentence is put is not to be identified with the purpose (or purposes) of the user of the sentence.[4]

The Effect

The use to which language is put should also be distinguished from the effect that using the language might have. For example, if someone

---

[4] One can, for example, use language informatively and do it intentionally (immediate purpose) with the (mediate) purpose, say, of producing some action. "Purpose" in the above text means remote purpose.

presented to an audience the reasons why the United States and the U.S.S.R. cannot agree on a plan for disarmament, we could easily imagine the following different effects: some hear it and go to sleep; some question it and spend time next day in the library checking it; some become emotionally upset. A simple request like "Pass the hominy" might bring any number of different reactions. Clearly the effect language has cannot be identified with its use.

THE COUNTLESS USES
OF SENTENCES

How many different uses of language are there? Ludwig Wittgenstein, a contemporary philosopher, raises this question and provides this answer: [5]

But how many kinds of sentences are there? Say assertion, question, and command?—There are *countless* kinds: countless different kinds of uses of what we call "symbols," "words," "sentences"; and this multiplicity is not something fixed, given once for all; but new types of language, new language-games, as we may say, come into existence, and others become obsolete and get forgotten. . . .

Review the multiplicity of language-games in the following examples, and in others:

Giving orders, and obeying them—
Describing the appearance of an object, or giving its measurements—
Constructing an object from a description (a drawing)—
Reporting an event—
Speculating about an event—
Forming and testing a hypothesis—
Presenting the results of an experiment in tables and diagrams—
Making up a story; and reading it—
Play-acting—
Singing catches—
Guessing riddles—
Making a joke; telling it—
Solving a problem in practical arithmetic—
Translating from one language into another—
Asking, thanking, cursing, greeting, praying.

His answer is that there are *countless* uses of language.

In Wittgenstein's list, contexts are indicated in which we use language. If sentences were imagined which could appropriately be used in each

[5] Ludwig Wittgenstein, *Philosophical Investigations* (New York: Macmillan, 1953), p. 11.

context (or if we examined the use to which sentences are put in actual contexts), it would be evident that some of these uses of language could be classified as informative, expressive, or directive and some could not. Let us consider two examples of language used differently from those presented in the three groups of the first section.

"Greeting" is found at the end of Wittgenstein's list. Imagine this use of language:

"How are you?"—uttered by a woman to a friend she sees as she is leaving church.

Of this use of language it could not sensibly be asked:

Is it factually true or false?
Should I obey it?

In addition, to utter the sentence "How are you?" in this context is not obviously to express something which could be replaced by a natural expression of emotion. Thus "How are you?" used in this way is not language used informatively, expressively, or directively. This sentence, by the way, in another context might be used directively. For example, a doctor might ask the question "How are you?" of a patient after an operation. Furthermore, questions can be imagined which sensibly go with the greeting "How are you?" which cannot be sensibly asked of the statement "The Eiffel Tower is the tallest structure in Paris," the command "Love your enemies," and so on. For example, it can be asked of the greeting:

Is it warm or not?

Near the middle of Wittgenstein's list we find "making up a story." As an example of language used in this context, consider this selection:

"It was Apollo, Son of Zeus and Leto, who started the feud, when he punished the King for his discourtesy to Chryses, his priest, by inflicting a deadly plague on his army and destroying his men"—the first sentence of Homer's *The Iliad*.

Clearly language is used here in a way different from those examples of informative, expressive, and directive use considered in the first section. Also, this is clearly not a greeting. What questions can be imagined which can sensibly be asked here but which cannot be asked, in the same sense, of the other examples so far considered?

Other examples of different uses of language can easily be brought to mind. For example, one which is employed often in this book is the use of language in an argument. None of the questions so far considered— for example, "Is it factually true or false?" and "Should I obey it or not?" —can sensibly be asked of an argument. As we have seen, such questions as the following can sensibly be asked of arguments:

Is it valid or invalid?
Is it correct or incorrect?
Is it fallacious or not?

Enough has been said to show that language is used in different ways and that there are countless uses.

THE VALUE OF DISTINGUISHING
SENTENCE USES

The value of distinguishing sentence uses is that it helps us to avoid confusing one use with another. However, that such confusions can occur is not obvious. In this section we will examine some arguments which can be regarded as involving the confusion of one use of sentences with another. Such arguments are obviously incorrect. Good grounds have not been provided for the conclusion since the reasons involve mixing one language use with another (in a way similar to confusing the meaning of words in fallacies of equivocation). We will call incorrect arguments of this kind instances of the *use-mixing fallacy*. Since such fallacies are the product of the ambiguity of the language, use-mixing fallacies can be classed among the fallacies of ambiguity.

Consider this first example of use-mixing:

Christ commanded us to love our enemies. But I can't find one shred of evidence that this is true. And no one else can produce the facts which will show that it is true. Thus it is false; I can't believe what is false, and I can't follow what I don't believe.

This intentionally ludicrous example is an argument in which the directive use of language has been confused with the informative use of language. The arguer believes that it makes sense to ask for evidence to show that the command is true. He also concludes that the command is false since there is no evidence.

A second example of the use-mixing fallacy is found in this argument:

H: That cloud looks like a badminton shuttlecock.
W: Oh, I think it looks like George Washington's nose.
U: Well, one of you must be wrong since it cannot look like both a shuttlecock *and* a nose.

In this example U has confused the "look-like" or "appearance" statements of H and W with a statement like: "X is a badminton shuttlecock" and "X is George Washington's nose." Clearly, the same X cannot be both a shuttlecock and a human nose, but, as is equally clear, the same X can appear to be or look like both a badminton shuttlecock and

George Washington's nose (to different persons or to the same person). U has confused language used to report appearances with statements like "X is such-and-such." (Since the appearance statements above indicate how something looks to a normal observer or one who is not "aspect-blind" to what is to be seen here, both uses of language can be classed as informative.)

This next example is generally regarded as containing a use-mixing fallacy:

It is foolish to dispute about matters of taste. Obviously it is silly, for example, to debate whether light meat is better than dark meat. Whoever said *"de gustibus non est disputandum"* was right. Why, then, don't people stop debating whether some book is better than another or whether some music is better than other music. All we can say about a book or piece of music is that some people like it or that some people do not like it.

In this argument esthetic judgments are regarded by the arguer as mere judgments of taste like "light meat is better than dark meat." But are esthetic judgments like this? For example, is the sentence:

"War and Peace is a better novel than *Gone with the Wind"*—uttered by a literature professor to his class,

used in the same way as:

"Light meat is better than dark meat"—uttered in the course of a turkey dinner?

There are interesting similarities between them. For example, one cannot sensibly ask of either judgment:

Is it factually true or false?

That is, in certain respects they both differ from examples of the informative use of language. On the other hand, the test proposed in the first section for whether S_1 is used differently from S_2 is to see whether certain questions can sensibly be asked of what is expressed by one sentence but not of what is expressed by the other sentence. It is quite proper to ask, for example,

What reasons do you have?

in connection with esthetic judgments like *"War and Peace* is a better novel than *Gone with the Wind,"* whereas this question cannot sensibly be asked of a mere judgment of taste. Thus the use to which language is put in esthetic judgment differs from the use to which language is put in statements which express mere matters of taste.

Classifications (such as classifying language as being used informatively, expressively, or directively) can sometimes lead to confusions and even to use-mixing arguments. For example, someone having noticed that language can be used in these three ways might draw the erroneous conclusion that all language is used in one of these three ways or is a combination of these three uses. In a word, he might fail to see that there are countless uses of language. This in turn might lead to the following argument:

> People from time to time make moral judgments. Just the other day I heard someone make the judgment: "It is wrong to execute a man for a crime he didn't commit." Now when you make a moral judgment you are not using language informatively, for we do not say that such judgments are factually true or false. If moral judgments were true or false, there would be no disagreement about them once men saw what the facts are. But, as we all know, there is disagreement in moral matters among reasonable men. On the other hand, a moral judgment like "It is wrong to execute a man for a crime he didn't commit" is not language used directively. The one who makes the judgment is making a *judgment* and is not, ordinarily, commanding or requesting something. Therefore moral judgments must be language used expressively. Moral judgments are thus nothing but expressions of feelings and emotions.

Many feel that it is a mistake to identify moral judgments with expressions of emotion like "Poor thing" and "How perfectly divine." For one thing, reasons can be and are given for moral judgments, whereas one cannot sensibly give reasons for expressions of emotion. If a use-mixing fallacy is committed here, then what accounts for this mistake is the belief that all language must fall into one of these three classes: informative, expressive, or directive.

Another danger in such classifications is that differences among the uses of language within a class might be overlooked. Let us illustrate the danger. It was stipulated in the first section that if it can sensibly be asked of what is expressed by S "Is it factually true or false?" then (with one other slight requirement) S is to be classed as being used informatively. Following this criterion one could classify, for example, this use of "I have a headache" as informative:

> "I have a headache"—uttered by a patient in response to the doctor's question, "Why are you here?"

Now nothing is wrong with doing this. But classifying this use of "I have a headache" with statements like "The Eiffel Tower is the tallest structure in Paris," might well obscure the differences between them and this, in turn, could produce this argument:

> When someone uses language informatively, as in "Some Democratic senators do not support Kennedy's **domestic** program," it could turn out that he is mistaken in his judgment. Now **when someone** makes the claim that he has a headache, he is using language **informatively**, since what he says is either true or

false. Consequently, he might be mistaken in the same way. It is thus possible for a person to think he has a headache and not really have one.

One difference which is ignored here is that while the question:

Am I mistaken?

can sensibly be asked of this example of the informative use of language, it cannot be sensibly raised in connection with "I have a headache" as used above. In a word, a use-mixing fallacy has been committed.

SUMMARY

A sentence S_1 is used differently from S_2 if the same question—a question with the same meaning—can sensibly be asked of what is expressed by one sentence but not of what is expressed by the other sentence. Employing this criterion, we have distinguished a number of different uses of language.

To avoid certain confusions the classification of informative, expressive, or directive is to be understood in this way: If we can sensibly ask of what is expressed by S, (a) Is it factually true? but not (b) Should I obey it? then S is to be classed as an instance of the informative use. If we cannot ask (a) of what is expressed by S but can ask (b), then S is to be classed as directive use. If we cannot ask (a) or (b) of what is expressed by S, but S can be replaced by a natural expression of emotion, then S would be classed as expressive use.

When an argument is incorrect because it involves the confusion of one use of language with another, it is an instance of the use-mixing fallacy.

EXERCISES I

First, classify these examples using the following categories: informative use, expressive use, directive use, and none of these. Second, employing the criterion for S_1 being used differently from S_2, indicate which sentences are used differently. Justify your answers.

1. How blest are those of a gentle spirit; they shall have the earth for their possession.

(Matthew 5:5)

2. Goodbye, we've had a wonderful time.
3. I pronounce you man and wife.
4. We are such stuff as dreams are made of, . . .

(SHAKESPEARE, *The Tempest*)

5. Henry the Fifth is outnumbered five to one in the approaching battle. Before the battle he prays his men will forget the odds.

> O God of battles! steel my soldiers' hearts;
> Possess them not with fear; take from them now
> The sense of reckoning . . .

(SHAKESPEARE, Henry V)

6. A body immersed in a fluid is acted upon by an upward force equal in magnitude to the weight of the fluid displaced.

7. Rule Britannia!

8. Hurrah! Hurrah!

9. The surest way to corrupt a youth is to instruct him to hold in higher esteem those who think alike than those who think differently.

(NIETZSCHE)

10. William Faulkner's books are superior to Ernest Hemingway's.

11. Russia has told the United States that it will withdraw, by March 15, "several thousand" of the 17,000 Soviet troops and technicians in Cuba.

12. Go jump in the lake!

13. Go to the store and buy a dozen eggs.

14. I feel sick deep down inside.

15. I prefer Scotch to bourbon.

16. Means do not justify ends.

17. It looks as if the stick is bent.

18. "I do"—as uttered in the course of the marriage ceremony.

19. Before leaving them and going into the stormy night, the enraged King Lear says to his daughters Goneril and Regan:

> You unnatural hags, I will have such revenges on you both
> That all the world shall—I will do such things,—
> What they are yet I know not, but they shall be
> The terrors of the earth. You think I'll weep;
> No, I'll not weep. I have full cause of weeping,
> But this heart shall break . . .
> Or ere I'll weep. O fool! I shall go mad.

(SHAKESPEARE, King Lear)

20. . . . and Gibraltar as a girl where I was a Flower of the mountain yes when I put the rose in my hair like the Andalusian girls used or shall I wear a red yes and how he kissed me under the Moorish wall and I thought well as well him as another and then I asked him with my eyes to ask again yes and then he asked me would I yes to say yes my mountain flower and first I put my arms around him yes and drew him down to me so he could feel my breasts all perfume yes and his heart was going like mad and yes I said yes I will Yes.

(JAMES JOYCE, Ulysses) [6]

---

[6] From *Ulysses*, by James Joyce. Copyright 1914, 1918 and renewed 1942, 1946 by Nora Joseph Joyce. Reprinted by permission of Random House, Inc. and The Bodley Head Ltd.

21. "Well, now after such a confession I believe that you are sincere and good at heart. If you do not achieve happiness, you must always remember that you are on the right path and try not to stray from it. Above all, run from lies, all lies, and especially from self-deception. Watch over your lies and examine them every hour, every minute. Avoid, too, a feeling of aversion towards others, and towards yourself: what seems to you bad in yourself is purified by the very fact that you've noticed it in yourself. Avoid fear, too, though fear is only the consequence of every sort of lie. Never be afraid of your own cowardliness in attaining love, and do not be too much afraid of your bad actions, either. I'm sorry I cannot say anything more comforting to you, for, compared with romantic love, active love is something severe and terrifying." [7]

22. Gulliver's last voyage is to the island of the Houyhnhnms. He says of his life with them:

I enjoyed perfect health of body, and tranquillity of mind; I did not feel the treachery or inconstancy of a friend, nor the injuries of a secret or open enemy. I had no occasion of bribing, flattering, or pimping to procure the favour of any great man or of his minion. I wanted no fense against fraud or oppression; here was neither physician to destroy my body, nor lawyer to ruin my fortune; no informer to watch my words and actions, or force accusations against me for hire; here were no gibers, censurers, backbiters, pickpockets, highwaymen, housebreakers, attorneys, bawds, buffoons, gamesters, politicians, wits, splenetics, tedious talkers, controvertists, ravishers, murderers, robbers, virtuosos; no leaders or followers of party and faction; no encouragers to vice, by seducement or examples; no dungeon, axes, gibbets, whipping-posts, or pillories; no cheating shopkeepers or mechanics; no pride, vanity, or affectation; no fops, bullies, drunkards, strolling whores, or poxes; no ranting, lewd, expensive wives; no stupid proud pedants; no importunate, overbearing, quarrelsome, noisy roaring, empty, conceited, swearing companions; no scoundrels, raised from the dust for the sake of their vices, or nobility thrown into it on account of their virtues; no lords, fiddlers, judges, or dancing-masters.

(JONATHAN SWIFT, *Gulliver's Travels*)

23. Well, Chaerephon, as you know, was very impetuous in all his doings, and he went to Delphi and boldly asked the oracle to tell him whether—as I was saying, I must beg you not to interrupt—he asked the oracle to tell him whether anyone was wiser than I was, and the Pythian prophetess answered, that there was no man wiser. Chaerephon is dead himself; but his brother, who is in court, will confirm the truth of what I am saying.

Why do I mention this? Because I am going to explain to you why I have such an evil name. When I heard the answer, I said to myself, What can the god mean? and what is the interpretation of his riddle? for I know that I have no wisdom, small or great. What then can he mean when he says that I am the wisest of men? And yet he is a god, and cannot lie; that would be against his nature. After long consideration, I thought of a method of trying the question.

I reflected that if I could only find a man wiser than myself, then I might go to the god with a refutation in my hand. I should say to him, "Here is a man who is wiser than I am; but you said that I was the wisest." Accordingly I went to one who had the reputation of wisdom, and observed him—his name I need not mention; he was a politician whom I selected for examination—and the result was as follows: When I began to talk with him, I could not help thinking that he was not really wise, although he was thought wise by many, and still wiser by himself; and thereupon I tried to explain to him that he thought himself wise, but his enmity was shared by several who were present and heard me. So I left him, saying to myself, as I went away: Well, although I do not suppose that either of us knows anything really beautiful and good, I am better off than he is,—for he knows nothing, and thinks that he knows; I neither know nor think that I know. In this latter particular, then, I seem to have slightly the advantage of him. Then I went to another who had still higher pretensions to wisdom, and my conclusion was exactly the same. Whereupon I made another enemy of him, and of many others beside him.

(PLATO, *Apology*)

24. Still I have a favor to ask of them. When my sons are grown up, I would ask you, O my friends, to punish them; and I would have you trouble them, as I have troubled you, if they seem to care about riches or anything, more than about virtue; or if they pretend to be something when they are really nothing,—then reprove them, as I have reproved you, for not caring about that for which they ought to care, thinking that they are something when they are really nothing. And if you do this, both I and my sons will have received justice at your hands.

(PLATO, *Apology*)

EXERCISES II

Provide examples for each of the items in Wittgenstein's list (p. 118). Attempt a classification, using new categories, when necessary.

EXERCISES III

Which of the following involve mistaking one use of language for another? Analyze each in the manner in which the arguments are treated in the text.

1. I tell you Utah lies. He hardly ever tells the truth. Why only yesterday he promised to take me to see the new laundromat, but today when I reminded him he just sat indifferently watching Bullwinkle.
2. On reflection we can all see that we can never know any proposition which expresses a matter of fact—for example, bread nourishes—to be true.

For there is no contradiction in denying such propositions. Thus we make a mistake whenever we say we know some matter of fact.

3. "How can one think what is not the case? If I think that King's College is on fire when it is not on fire, the fact of its being on fire does not exist. Then how can I think it? How can we hang a thief who doesn't exist?" [8]

4. He's a liar, I tell you, and I can prove it. When I saw him last, he said that he intended to come to this meeting, and as we all know, he is not here.

5. Junior told me that this picture he drew is a picture of me, his father; but obviously he is not telling the truth because it doesn't at all look like handsome me.

6. You said you dreamt that the President appointed you Secretary of Health, Education, and Welfare. But are you sure? Couldn't you have forgotten what he appointed you? Maybe even he was kidding you.

7. What do you mean you are *certain* that the window is open in the next room. You are certain that $2 + 3 = 5$, but not that the window is open.

8. I heard our philosophy professor, of all people, say the other day that a machine cannot think. And do you know he hasn't examined a single machine! That just shows you that we haven't yet shaken off the Middle Ages. Go tell the Dean!

9. We don't know what we wish until our wish is fulfilled. So Risby contradicted himself when he said, "I wished to eat an apple, but a pear has satisfied me."

10. MARGARET LU: So long. I've had a wonderful time. (To her companion Flora Su) My, I'm glad we left—those people are such bores!

FLORA SU: If that is so, why did you say you had a wonderful time? Why aren't you a truthful person like me? I would have said, "So long. I've had a dull time."

11. Our accumulated knowledge and experience has shown us that the principle "Love your neighbor as yourself" is as established as the principle that bodies expand when heated. Today for anyone to deny this is to oppose facts.

12. As a result of my research, I have found that all statements which express matters of fact can, in principle, be verified—or at least partially verified —by observations which would make such statements probably true or false. If a statement which is represented as expressing a matter of fact cannot in principle be verified, then it is clear, as we can all see, that the statement is literally nonsensical. Now, none of the statements which appear in works of fiction can be verified, so we can safely conclude that they are literally nonsensical.

13. All esthetic judgments which have the form "X is beautiful" clearly assert matters of fact. As we all know, assertions of matters of fact—in short, propositions—can be verified or falsified directly or indirectly by *a person* making the proper observations or experiments. Esthetic judgments cannot be publicly verified. Thus esthetic judgments must, as we can see, refer to *feelings*. To say that X is beautiful is thus, on proper analysis, nothing more than a

---

[8] Ludwig Wittgenstein, *The Blue Book* (Oxford: Basil Blackwell, 1958), p. 31.

proposition which asserts that such-and-such a person has such-and-such a feeling (the peculiar "esthetic feeling") in the presence of X.

14. SALESMAN: That table, Mrs. Ogmore-Pritchard, is a lovely dark brown.
MRS. O-P: It looks black. Let's take it near the window. Oh, yes, it is
brown.
LISTENER: What are her grounds for saying it looks black if the table
is brown? Either she must have seen something which is black or else
her judgment is quite arbitrary. Now her judgment isn't arbitrary,
so she sees something which is black. Now, as we know, nothing in the
area is black; thus what she sees must be located in a place different
from the place where we find tables, [and so on].

EXERCISES IV

Invent some arguments which involve confusing one use of language with
another.

THE INFORMATIVE USE OF
LANGUAGE AND
NONSENSE UTTERANCES

Here are some clear cut examples of language used informatively:

1. New York has the largest population of any city in the world.
2. The Declaration of Independence was signed in 1763.
3. This logic book is a little under four hundred pages in length.

Contrast this use of language with these utterances:

4. The mome raths outgrabe.
5. Saturday is in bed.
6. Snodgrass left his grin behind when he went home.

Of each of the first statements it can be asked: Is it true or false? and,
clearly, each statement is false. With the second group this question cannot sensibly be asked. Why is this? The reason is that the utterances
cannot be either true or false, for they are nonsense utterances, sentences
without meaning. Here is one way to bring out this difference: The fact
that Tokyo has the largest population of any city makes (1) false. The
fact that the Declaration of Independence was signed in 1776 makes (2)
false. And the fact that this book is over four hundred pages makes
(3) false. If these states of affairs were different—if, say, New York were
the largest city—then (1) would be true. Now no states of affairs could
make either (4), (5), or (6) true or false. In sentence (4) the words have

been given no meaning. In (5) Saturday (the last day of the week) can neither be in bed nor not be in bed because it makes no sense to use "bed" and "Saturday" in this way. Snodgrass in (6) cannot leave his grin or take it with him (in the sense in which one can take with him something he could leave).

Sometimes informative statements are spoken of as "nonsense." In fact the word "nonsense" is used in a number of different ways. It will be useful at this point to review some of the uses of this word in preparation for the discussion of fallacies which follows.

Here are five ways in which the word "nonsense" is used in everyday conversation.

1. A: The Washington Senators will win the Pennant in 1964.
   B: Nonsense.
2. A: The problem of over-population can be solved by sending large portions of the population by rocket to settle the Moon and Mars.
   B: Nonsense.
3. An English instructor responds to a carelessly written essay which violates many composition rules: "This is nonsense."
4. Child: What does the word "nonsense" mean?
   Father: Do you hear those noises baby sister is making? That's nonsense.
5. Child: What does the word "nonsense" mean?
   Father: Listen to this poem by Lewis Carroll:

   'Twas brillig and the slithy toves
     Did gyre and gimble in the wabe:
   All mimsy were the borogoves,
     And the mome raths outgrabe.

   That's nonsense.

In the first example what is being called nonsense is a statement which is implausible, farfetched, unlikely to happen, or out of the question. In the second example what is being called nonsense is a foolish idea. A confused and muddled presentation is being called nonsense in (3). Meaningless babble is called nonsense in (4). In the last example what is being called nonsense is a deliberate putting together of words which have been given no meaning in such a way that the resulting sentences have the rhythm, sound, and proper-sounding syntax of regular poetry.

Another use of the word "nonsense" is brought to our attention in another well-known masterpiece of nonsense, Edward Lear's "The Jumblies." Here is the first stanza:

6. They went to sea in a sieve, they did;
     In a sieve they went to sea:
   In spite of all their friends could say,

On a winter's morn, on a stormy day,
  In a sieve they went to sea.
And when the sieve turned round and round,
And everyone cried, "You'll all be drowned!"
They cried aloud, "Our sieve ain't big;
But we don't care a button, we don't care a fig:
  In a sieve we'll go to sea!"
Far and few, far and few,
  Are the lands where the Jumblies live;
Their heads are green and their hands are blue;
  And they went to sea in a sieve.

There are at least two aspects of this verse which lead us to speak of it as nonsense. The first is the idea of going to sea in a sieve. Sieves do float, at least momentarily, if the holes are small, the sieve is light, and the water is calm; but these conditions are not apparently met in the poem. So we speak of this as nonsense. Here the sense of "nonsense" seems to be similar to (1). The second aspect of this stanza we would characterize as nonsense is the response of the friends. When the sieve is in the water and is turning around, they tell those who are going to the islands of the Jumblies: "You'll all be drowned." Now such a warning would be appropriate if the trip were being taken in something which floated, but since this condition is missing here, it is absurd to give such a warning. We are inclined to say that the circumstances or context in which such a warning can be given are missing here. Similarly, we might characterize as nonsense the utterance "Close the door" made in the presence of a closed door which everyone sees is closed. We are inclined to say this is nonsense because the proper circumstances are missing for making the command "Close the door." The sentence "Close the door" might be uttered but the command could not be given. We will call this the sixth use of the word "nonsense." [9]

Four rarer uses of nonsense are brought out in the following:

7. "The earth has existed for one million years" has sense.
   "The earth has existed for five minutes" is nonsense.
8. "I believe that he is not an automaton," just like that, so far makes no sense.
9. The supposition that there can be in a small town a clean shaven barber who shaves only those and all those who do not shave themselves is nonsense.
10. G. E. Moore recognized a kind of nonsense involved in saying: "The cat is on the mat, but I don't believe it."

[9] See J. L. Austin's superb William James Lectures, *How to Do Things with Words* (London: Oxford University Press, 1962) for a careful treatment of this kind of nonsense ("misapplications") and other kinds of nonsense that result when linguistic acts go wrong.

In (7) the word "nonsense" is being used to express the fact that we cannot easily imagine those conditions in which one seriously would say, "The earth has existed for five minutes." In (8) to characterize the sentence as nonsense is to stress that this is an unusual sentence and no context has been described in which we might have used the sentence "I believe that he is not an automaton." We could, of course, easily imagine a number of situations where we might use this sentence. For example, we might use the sentence to point out that someone always behaves like a human being, that is, is kind, honest, generous, and so forth. Or we may want to stress the fact that he does not perform his job "inhumanly"— that is, unthinkingly, slavishly, coldly (without regard for the feelings of others), mechanically, stupidly, and the like. His manner is impersonal, and this can give one the impression that he is an "automaton"; but, in fact, he deeply sympathizes with others in their troubles, so I believe that he is not an automaton. The feature of (9) which leads us to say that the supposition is nonsense is the fact that two contradictory propositions can be deduced from the supposition (see chapter on Paradoxes.) J. L. Austin says (10) is like saying "I promise to do X, but I do not intend to do X." The act of informing is defeated by saying "I don't believe it." (10) is not like (9). (10) is "self-stultifying" rather than self-contradictory.[10]

CONTEXT AND CATEGORY-MIXING

There is an eleventh use of the word "nonsense" which will occupy our interest for the remainder of this chapter. To illustrate this use of "nonsense" consider this last stanza of Carroll's poem "Sylvie and Bruno":

> He thought he saw a Rattlesnake
> That questioned him in Greek:
> He looked again, and found it was
> The Middle of Next Week.

In this stanza someone sees the middle of next week and mistakes it, at first, for a rattlesnake. We say that this is nonsense. What is it which is being called nonsense here? Notice first that we could imagine some circumstances in which someone might meaningfully use the phrase "see the middle of next week." For example, a fortune-teller might use these words. Thus in saying the phrase is nonsense we are not saying it is babble as in (4) or words without meaning as in (5). Also we can imagine circumstances in which this phrase would make sense, so what we have in mind in speaking of it as nonsense is different from (7). The phrase

10 *Ibid.*, pp. 48–52.

implies no contradiction, a context is provided, and it is not self-stultifying.

But what then are we emphasizing when we say the phrase "seeing the middle of next week" as it is used above is nonsense? First, the word "seeing" is used as it is used in "seeing a rattlesnake"—that is, as it is used in connection with objects. This is brought out by noticing that he "looked again" and mistook it for a rattlesnake. Second, the middle of next week is not such an object—that is, the phrase "the middle of next week" is not used to denote objects as is the word "rattlesnake." Third, in the poem the middle of next week is treated as such an object.

What is being called "nonsense" here can be put in either of two ways: First, regarding the phrase "the middle of next week" as a name for an object in the way in which the word "rattlesnake" or the phrase "the mayor of the city" are names for objects is what is being called nonsense. Second, using the word "see" in the way it is used with names for objects with a phrase which is not the name of an object is what is being called nonsense. When a word or phrase is intentionally (as in Carroll's poem) or unintentionally regarded or treated in some linguistic context as like a phrase of a different category—for example, when a phrase which is not the name of an object is regarded as a name of an object— we call this *category-mixing*. When a word or phrase is misused as "see" is in our example, we will call this *context-mixing*. The above example can be regarded as containing category-mixing, context-mixing, or both.

CONTEXT- AND
CATEGORY-MIXING FALLACIES

When an argument contains an utterance which we would characterize as nonsense because of category-mixing or context-mixing, we will call such an incorrect argument a *category-mixing fallacy* or a *context-mixing fallacy*.

To illustrate these fallacies, consider this passage from *Through the Looking-Glass:*

ALICE: Would you—be good enough—to stop a minute—just to get one's breath again?

WHITE KING: I'm *good* enough, only I'm not *strong* enough. You see, a minute goes by so fearfully quick. You might as well try to stop a Bandersnatch!

We can put what the White King says in this way:

A minute goes by very fast.
Therefore, I'm not strong enough to stop it.

This argument can be regarded as either a context-mixing fallacy or a category-mixing fallacy (or both). The phrase "I'm not strong enough to stop it" is being used by the White King as it is used in connection with moving objects such as automobiles. But a minute is not such an object—that is not how we use the word "minute." Thus "I'm not strong enough to stop a minute" contains a misuse of "I'm not strong enough," in the sense in which "see" is misused in the "Sylvie and Bruno" example; and the argument is an instance of a context-mixing fallacy. In addition, the White King can be regarded as having made the mistake of thinking that the word "minute" denotes an object as does say, the word "automobile" or the word "stone."

Suppose someone—let us call him Willie—failed to notice an important difference between these two sentences:

Nobody is in the auditorium.
Utah Jenkins is in the auditorium.

Willie correctly notes that if the second is true, then something is in the auditorium. But he mistakenly thinks that if the first is true, then, similarly, something is in the auditorium. This leads him to reason:

Something is in the auditorium, since the first sentence is true. I cannot see the something, so it is invisible; I cannot feel or hear it, so it is an invisible, undetectable thing.

He has mistakenly construed "nobody" in the first sentence to be like the name "Utah Jenkins" in the second sentence. This is category-mixing. He also misuses the phrases "invisible," "cannot see," and so forth. Thus both fallacies are again committed.

We would not say that Willie's utterance—I cannot see, feel or hear nobody—or the White King's utterance—I'm not strong enough to stop a minute—are false. Since they both involve context-mixing, or category-mixing, they are nonsense in the way in which "seeing the middle of next week" is nonsense.

Not all context-mixing fallacies are also category-mixing fallacies. (Category-mixing fallacies are actually a variety of context-mixing fallacies.) Many of the examples of fallacies considered in the fourth section (see pages 120–123) which arise from confusing one use of language with another can be classed as having nonsense (context-mixing) premises, but they cannot be classed as instances of category-mixing. Recall, for example, the first example of use-mixing considered in that section.

Christ commanded us to love our neighbor as ourselves. But I can't find one shred of evidence that this is true. And no one else can produce the facts which will show that it is true. Thus it is false; I can't believe what is false, and I can't follow what I don't believe.

The words "facts" and "evidence" are misused. They are used in connection with the directive use of language in the same way as they are used in connection with the informative use of language.

A second example of an argument containing context-mixing but not category-mixing is found in this example:

All of us are continually interested in whether one particular man is more virtuous than another or whether men of some particular group or society are more virtuous than men of another group or society. But a matter which has a very pertinent bearing on these considerations has generally been overlooked. How does man stand up to other creatures in terms of virtue? Recently I have had the rare opportunity to study closely the effects that wolf-parents had on two lovely six year old girls, recently rescued, who were reared by these wolf-parents. On the basis of my examination I found that the children were entirely free from sin and had, in fact, no interests to speak of except, perhaps, in raw meat. Not only does this show that wolf-parents do not teach their charges anything bad, but it makes clear that such things as pride, envy, lying, avarice, sloth, and the like are missing from the psychological make-up of wolves. Thus in terms of virtue it is clear that wolves, and perhaps many other animals, are more virtuous than men. . . .

The argument, here, is, in summary:

Wolves do not teach the humans they rear anything bad; wolves do not act from pride, do not lie, and so on. Therefore wolves are more virtuous than men.

The arguer supposes that it makes sense to speak of wolves as having or not having pride, teaching or not teaching their "charges" bad things, and so on. But it makes no sense to use these phrases and words in the context of talking about wolves as if they had the sense they have in the context of talk about humans. The argument is thus an instance of context-mixing.

NONSENSE AND THE METAPHORICAL USE OF LANGUAGE

When two things are compared without the use of the words "like," "as," "similar," or "same," we have, roughly speaking, a *metaphor*. Here is a sample of a simple metaphor:

1. "He is a tiger"—uttered by A about B.

"Tiger" is being used metaphorically. A person is being compared in some respect to a tiger. Generally, in the context in which this sentence would appear, it would be clear in what way a person is being compared with a tiger. Often, though, to say someone is a tiger means that he is scrappy, high-tempered, and the like—or fierce or courageous (as in T. S. Eliot's "Christ the Tiger"). The *literal meaning* of a word most often is the dictionary sense or senses of the word. The literal meaning of the word "tiger" is: a large animal of the cat family having a coat striped with black. When a word is used metaphorically, as "tiger" is used in (1), it is not to be understood in its literal sense. If it were, then (1) would be false, whereas (1) is true or false depending on whether the person is or is not scrappy, high-tempered, and so on.

What we have called "context-mixing" needs to be distinguished from the metaphorical use of language. Consider, for example, this metaphor:

2. The fog comes on little cat feet. (SANDBURG)

It makes sense to say of animals and of those things which closely resemble animals that they have or do not have feet. But it is a misuse of language to say of a fog that it has feet. It thus looks as if (2) is a case of context-mixing. But "little cat feet" is used metaphorically. The following considerations make this clear. First, "little cat feet" in (2) is not to be understood in one of its literal senses, specifically, the feet of a cat. Or, as we can put it, "little cat feet" is not being used in (2) in the way it is used in the context of animals and other things with legs. Second, in (2) certain aspects of a fog are compared with a cat. The fog is like a cat, in that the fog moves in so slowly that one almost does not know it is moving in, or the fog comes in silently and unobtrusively. Third, (2) can be in a limited way reexpressed in nonmetaphorical language. Instead of saying "The fog comes on little cat feet" we could say "The fog comes in silently and unobtrusively," and so forth. It is true that this paraphrase loses, among a number of things, the imagery associated with the metaphor—a picture of the fog as a kind of creeping animal. Often language is selected because of the imagery it produces. The loss of such things as imagery is in part, what leads us to say that a metaphorical statement can be in a *limited way* reexpressed in nonmetaphorical language. In contrast with (2), in our first example of context mixing—I see the middle of next week—the word "see" is to be understood in one of its literal senses, no comparison is being made, and a reexpression cannot be given.

SUMMARY

The word "nonsense" is used in many ways. The use of the word which is the concern of this chapter is its use to characterize an utterance like: "I saw the middle of next week but mistook it at first for a rattlesnake." Context-mixing—misusing the word "see"—and category-mixing—regarding the phrase "the middle of next week" as a name like "the mayor of the city"—create the nonsense in such cases. Thus the context-mixing fallacy and the category-mixing fallacy occur when arguments contain utterances which can be analyzed as instances of context-mixing and category-mixing. All category-mixing can also be regarded as context-mixing, for category-mixing is a subclass of context-mixing.

EXERCISES I

Each of the following examples contains a use of language which is called nonsense or might be called nonsense. Classify the examples, as far as possible, using the categories discussed plus "none of these."

1. "My neighbor can beat Sonny Liston."
"Nonsense."

2. "The Federal Government should not meet the needs of the people; rather it should extend freedom and not do violence to the United States Constitution."
"Nonsense."

3. Bentham said: "Rights of man, nonsense; imprescriptible rights of man, nonsense on stilts."

4. Baron von Munchhausen is supposed to have told a story about words which froze before crossing the Volga River and were not heard on the other side until a thaw released them.

5. Mother, when I was born, how did you know that I was really Cosmo and not some other boy?

6. Everyone could be automatons even though they behave and speak in the usual way.

7. An infinitely long row of trees would be simply one which does not come to an end.

8. A French politician once wrote that it was a characteristic of the French language that in it words occur in the order in which one thinks them.

(LUDWIG WITTGENSTEIN, *Philosophical Investigations*) [11]

9. "This body has extension." To this we reply: "Nonsense."

(LUDWIG WITTGENSTEIN, *Philosophical Investigations*) [12]

10. Dowsing is nonsense.

11. . . . . a society which in peacetime attributes the highest importance to the satisfaction of consumer wants—in which people are taught to believe that a great range of goods is essential for existence and elementary happiness—will, in the event of a national emergency, divest itself of these attitudes as simply

[11] Ludwig Wittgenstein, *Philosophical Investigations* (New York: Macmillan, 1953), p. 108.
[12] *Ibid.*, p. 90.

and naturally as a man removes his nightshirt on arising. Needs so carefully nurtured will be forgotten. As a result, the capacity that supplied the goods can quickly be made available to the common effort. Having come to believe, like the people of Hamburg, that a given standard of living is minimal, and having been brought to this conclusion by the efforts of the world's most capable propagandists and persuaders, supported increasingly by the nation's most competent psychologists, they will divest themselves of this misconception effortlessly and unreluctantly and reduce their standard of living as required.

Patently this is nonsense. . . .

(JOHN KENNETH GALBRAITH, *The Affluent Society*) [13]

12.   The sun was shining on the sea,
          Shining with all his might:
       He did his very best to make
          The billows smooth and bright—
       And this was odd, because it was
          The middle of the night.

       The Walrus and the Carpenter
          Were walking close at hand;
       They wept like anything to see
          Such quantities of sand;
       "If this were only cleared away,"
          They said, "it would be grand!"

       "If seven maids with seven mops
          Swept it for half a year,
       Do you suppose," the Walrus said,
          "That they could get it clear?"
       "I doubt it," said the Carpenter,
          And shed a bitter tear.

(LEWIS CARROLL, "The Walrus and the Carpenter")

13.   He then led me to the frame, about the sides whereof all his pupils stood in ranks. It was twenty foot square, placed in the middle of the room. The superficies was composed of several bits of wood, about the bigness of a die, but some larger than others. They were linked together by slender wires. These bits of wood were covered on every square with paper pasted on them, and on these papers were written all the words of their language, in their several moods, tenses, and declensions, but without any order. The professor then desired me to observe, for he was going to set his engine at work. The pupils at his command took each of them hold of an iron handle, whereof there were forty fixed round the edges of the frame, and giving them a sudden turn, the whole disposition of the words was entirely changed. He then commanded

---

13 John Kenneth Galbraith, *The Affluent Society* (Boston: Houghton Mifflin Co., 1958), p. 168. Copyright © 1958 by John Kenneth Galbraith. Used by permission of Houghton Mifflin Co. and John Kenneth Galbraith.

six and thirty of the lads to read the several lines softly as they appeared upon the frame; and where they found three or four words together that might make part of a sentence, they dictated to the four remaining boys who were scribes. This work was repeated three or four times, and at every turn the engine was so contrived that the words shifted into new places, as the square bits of wood moved upside down.

Six hours a day the young students were employed in this labour, and the professor showed me several volumes in large folio already collected, of broken sentences, which he intended to piece together, and out of those rich materials to give the world a complete body of all arts and sciences; . . .

(JONATHAN SWIFT, Gulliver's Travels)

"Nonsense."

EXERCISES II

Which of the following can be regarded as involving context-mixing? Which involve category-mixing? Defend your answer. If any item can be more appropriately analyzed as involving use-mixing, and thus context-mixing, do this.

1. "Who did you pass on the road?" the King went on, holding out his hand to the Messenger with some hay.

"Nobody," said the Messenger.

"Quite right," said the King: "This young lady saw him, too. So of course Nobody walks slower than you."

(LEWIS CARROLL, Through the Looking-Glass)

2. Man is indeed one of the weakest of God's creations. Just think, for thousands of years no one has been able to count to infinity. I imagine it will take those computers to do it.

3. ADAM: What should I call this animal?

EVE: Call it a horse.

ADAM: Why a horse?

EVE: It looks like a horse, doesn't it?

(MARK TWAIN)

4. Why can't my right hand give my left hand money? My right hand can put it into my left hand. My right hand can write a deed of gift and my left hand a receipt.

(LUDWIG WITTGENSTEIN, Philosophical Investigations) [14]

The answer is simple: Some people have stingy right hands. Now, take mine, for example. . . .

5. One of the most amazing hypotheses of Charles Fort, founder of the

---

[14] Wittgenstein, *op. cit.*, p. 94.

Fortean Society, was that humanity was *owned* by higher intelligences who visited earth occasionally to check on their charges. According to Fort, ". . . something now has a legal right to us, by force, or by having paid out analogues of beads for us to former, more primitive, owners . . . all this has been known, perhaps for ages, to certain ones upon this earth, a cult or order, members of which function like bellwatchers to the rest of us, or as superior slaves or overseers, directing us in accordance with instructions received—from Somewhere else. . . ."

(Taken from MARTIN GARDNER, *Fads and Fallacies in the Name of Science*) [15]

6. X: I can easily walk 64 miles an hour.

   Y: That's impossible!

   X: It's easy. The B and O Rocket travels a smooth 60 miles an hour. I'll get on the train and when it is going this speed, I'll walk four miles an hour toward the engine. Thus I'll be walking 64 miles an hour.

7. When you go to heaven and are with the saints you do not go to a "place" in the sense of a physical place, but you go to a divine place. Those who see difficulty in the notion of "heaven" continually overlook this distinction.

8. Are actions good because God commands them or does He command them because He is good? Actions cannot become good just because someone, even God, commands them, so He must command them because He is good. Thus, God too follows certain standards and maxims.

9. In the fourth century A.D. a churchman wrote an essay on what he called "the heretical doctrine of the globular form of the earth." The argument to show the falsity of the heretical doctrine was contained in this question: "Is it possible that men can be so absurd as to believe that there are crops and trees on the other side of the earth that hang downward and that men have their feet higher than their heads?"

10. There is at least one thing we know about material objects: They cannot be in several different places at the same time. A table, for example, cannot be both here and over there simultaneously. There are, of course, things which can be in several places at once. The same shape or the same color can be both here and over there simultaneously. There is thus a very great difference between material objects and such things as colors and shapes.

11. What is the object or idea which the word "good" stands for? Philosophers for hundreds of years have been looking for this object so they could discover the "nature" of it. Well, if we are properly tough-minded we will face the fact that there is no such object. There are horses and stones which "horse" and "stone" stand for, but no object corresponding to "good." Thus it is only reasonable to conclude that this search is hopeless because "good" is a word without any meaning.

12. We say "Children are lively." Now children must exist in order to have the property of being lively. So when we say "The Furies are fictitious," unless

[15] Martin Gardner, *Fads and Fallacies in the Name of Science* (New York: Dover, 1957).

in some way Furies exist, they could not have the property of being fictitious. But it sounds odd to say that fictitious objects "exist" as children do, so they must "exist" in a mode different from the way things like children exist. Fictitious objects thus have a special nonempirical mode of real being.

13. Have you ever noticed that for words which name objects, like "table," "stone," and "pencil," we can in each case replace the word in sentences with a phrase like "the thing with P_1, P_2, . . . ," where P names properties. What does the word "thing" name in such phrases? It is that in which the properties inhere—a substratum—for, after all, properties just can't exist by themselves; they must exist in something. Thus when we use words which name objects, like "table," this denotes a substratum in which particular properties inhere.

14. But though our thought seems to possess this unbounded liberty, we shall find, upon a nearer examination, that it is really confined within very narrow limits, and that all this creative power of the mind amounts to no more than the faculty of compounding, transposing, augmenting, or diminishing the materials afforded us by the senses and experience. When we think of a golden mountain, we only join two consistent ideas, *gold,* and *mountain,* with which we were formerly acquainted. A virtuous horse we can conceive; because, from our own feeling, we can conceive virtue; and this we may unite to the figure and shape of a horse, which is an animal familiar to us. In short, all the materials of thinking are derived either from our outward or inward sentiment: the mixture and composition of these belongs alone to the mind and will. Or, to express myself in philosophical language, all our ideas or more feeble perceptions are copies of our impressions or more lively ones.

(DAVID HUME, *An Enquiry Concerning Human Understanding*)

15. It is melancholy, and at first sight perplexing, that, although both intelligence and imagination enable men to find new means of satisfying their desires and indulging their impulses, neither has so far increased the happiness of human beings, or even enabled it to maintain the level which it had reached when apes first became men. Consider for a moment the comparison of two typical individuals: one, a monkey in a tropical forest, swinging from branch to branch in skillful gymnastics, gathering bananas and coconuts and indulging unrestrainedly every impulse of pleasure or fury that the moment may bring; the other, an employee in a city firm, living in a dismal suburb, waked by an alarm clock long before he has any impulse to leave his bed, breakfasting hastily, harassed throughout the day by fear of the displeasure of superiors, and returning wearily in the evening to familiar monotony. Can you honestly maintain that the man is happier than the monkey?

(BERTRAND RUSSELL, *Human Society in Ethics and Politics*) [16]

[16] Bertrand Russell, *Human Society in Ethics and Politics* (London: Allen and Unwin, 1954) pp. 175–176.

Chapter Five

ANALOGY

THREE USES OF ANALOGY

When two things are compared with respect to their structure or elements this is an *analogy*. For example,

Running the government is like running a farm,

is an analogy. The analogy suggests that in some respects the job of running the government is similar to the job of running a farm. The respects in which the two are similar are usually shown by the context in which the analogy is offered. For example, in a discussion of the size of the public debt this analogy might be offered to suggest that the economic problems or goals of the government and the farm are similar. When two things are compared with respect to some quality such as intensity, brightness, loudness, beauty, and the like, by use of the words "like," "as," "similar," or "same," this is traditionally called a *simile*. A simile is found in this line: [1]

I could hear the whistling of trains, which, now nearer and now farther off, punctuating the distance like the note of a bird in a forest. . . .

Here the whistling of a train is said to be like the note of a bird, and the two sounds are being compared.

In this chapter we will not be interested in similes. We will be interested, rather, in three ways in which analogies are used—the use of analogies to illustrate or explain, the role of analogies in suggesting hy-

[1] Marcel Proust, *Swann's Way*, C. K. Scott Moncrieff, trans. (New York: Modern Library, 1928), p. 4. Copyright 1928 by The Modern Library, Inc. Used by permission of Random House, Inc. and Chatto and Windus Ltd.

potheses, and their use in arguments. The first use is illustrated in this passage: [2]

I feel that there is much to be said for the Celtic belief that the souls of those whom we have lost are held captive in some inferior being, in an animal, in a plant, in some inanimate object, and so effectively lost to us until the day (which to many never comes) when we happen to pass by the tree or to obtain possession of the object which forms their prison. Then they start and tremble, they call us by our name, and as soon as we have recognized their voice the spell is broken. We have delivered them: they have overcome death and return to share our life.

And so it is with our own past. It is a labour in vain to attempt to recapture it: all the efforts of our intellect must prove futile. The past is hidden somewhere outside the realm, beyond the reach of intellect, in some material object (in the sensation which that material object will give us) which we do not suspect. And as for the object, it depends on chance whether we come upon it or not before we ourselves must die.

The second use is illustrated in this passage:

If a light ray traveling through space is like a wave traveling in the water, then it should bend around objects as waves bend around objects in the water.

In this passage an analogy is used argumentatively: [3]

My critics seem to think that, if you have once advocated a certain policy, you should continue to advocate it after all the circumstances have changed. This is quite absurd. If a man gets into a train with a view to reach a certain destination and on the way the train breaks down, you will not consider the man guilty of an inconsistency if he gets out of the train and employs other means of reaching his destination. In like manner, a person who advocates a certain policy in certain circumstances will advocate a quite different policy in different circumstances.

The analogy in the first example is between our past and the soul as the Celts regarded it. The analogy is made to bring to our attention aspects of remembering. The analogy in the second example is between a beam of light and a wave in water. The supposition is made that they are similar, and a hypothesis is drawn from the supposition, namely the hypothesis that light bends around objects. In the last example, Russell is defending himself against the charge that he is inconsistent in changing his policy views. He meets this charge by employing an analogy. He

[2] *Ibid.*, p. 61. Used by permission of Random House, Inc. and Chatto and Windus Ltd.

[3] Bertrand Russell, *Common Sense and Nuclear Warfare* (New York: Simon and Schuster, 1959), p. 90. Copyright 1959 by George Allen and Unwin Ltd. Used by permission of George Allen and Unwin Ltd. and Simon and Schuster, Inc.

argues that there are certain similarities between a man taking a trip and someone advocating certain policies, and as there is no inconsistency in the man on the trip changing his plans if conditions change, so there is no inconsistency in changing one's policy if world conditions change. He is using the analogy to support the claim: there is no inconsistency in changing one's policy if world conditions change. In short, he is using the analogy argumentatively.

EXPLANATORY ANALOGIES

Some explanatory analogies are good and some are poor. It would be difficult and tedious to indicate the many ways in which an explanatory analogy could be poor. So we will touch on some of the ways. And we will touch on the ways in which explanatory analogies, as they come up in common contexts, for example, everyday conversations, ordinary arguments, and politics, are poor.

To begin, consider this example of a good explanatory analogy: [4]

We do, each year, provide some aid for others. But first we have a prayerful discussion of whether or not we can afford the sacrifice. The question is, indeed, inescapable, since production keeps wants abreast of itself. Elsewhere in the world, however, it is our vast well-being and not the urgency of our need which is evident. The nineteenth-century plutocrat who devoted his energies to expanding his already considerable income; who was led by his competitive position in the plutocracy to live on a suitably ostentatious scale; who found, as a result, that his income was never entirely adequate; who came to the aid of the poor only after a careful consideration of their worth, his ability to spare from his needs and the realistic likelihood of revolt and disorder if he abstained; and who believed withal that God inspired his enterprise and generosity and often said so, was not in all respects an attractive figure. Thus with nations.

In this passage the economist John Galbraith is comparing our nation and its foreign aid with a nineteenth-century plutocrat. The purpose of this comparison is to help us see what we look like as a nation in respect to foreign aid. There are at least three aspects of this analogy which make it good. First, the elements in the behavior of the nineteenth-century plutocrat said to be analogous to elements in the behavior of our nation are analogous. That is, we as a nation are devoted to expanding our wealth, which is already very great; many live ostentatiously; there is universal agreement that our gross national product is

[4] John Kenneth Galbraith, *The Affluent Society* (Boston: Houghton Mifflin Co., 1958), p. 179. Copyright © 1958 by John Kenneth Galbraith. Used by permission of Houghton Mifflin Co. and John Kenneth Galbraith.

not expanding fast enough; we generally aid another country only if it is in our national interest; and we believe that this aid is a sign of great generosity. Second, the analogy achieves its purpose. It gives us a vivid, quite accurate look at ourselves in regard to these aspects of foreign aid. And third, generally no one would be misled by the analogy to think something is true of our nation which is not true. For example, few would think we as a nation are paying taxes to some great power, as the plutocrats did to the government. Or, few would be led to believe from reading this passage that our nation will grow old and die, as was the case with the nineteenth-century plutocrat. The elements found in the plutocrat's life which are dissimilar to our nation do not readily come to mind and lead us to think that something is true of our nation which is not true.

Thus a good explanatory analogy fulfills the following criteria:

1. The elements said to be similar are similar.
2. The analogy is successful—it achieves what it sets out to achieve.
3. The dissimilar elements are not generally misleading.[5]

Consider next this explanatory analogy: [6]

Such mutual demonstrations between nations have undoubtedly been far commoner, from the beginning, than all-out fighting—even, one supposes, in the days when rocks and clubs were the deadliest weapons. Combative and willful as our species may be, all-out fighting among its own members has been rather the exception than the rule. Like the pigeons, however, the nations of mankind have been able to afford it because their weapons were less than absolute. Now, however, they have at last moved out of the pigeon class and joined the rattlesnakes, which can kill each other with one bite. Today the United States and the Soviet Union, in their great contest, could kill each other with one bite. Like the rattlesnakes, however, they now show an instinctive inhibition against biting, an inhibition distinctly greater than ever before.

What is the behavior we observe in Berlin today? Is it not that of the two snakes who push against each other, head to head, but never bite? Both sides use tear-gas bombs freely, but never the nuclear bombs that each also has.

Is this a good explanatory analogy or a poor one? A case, it appears, can be made for its failing the first criterion. We read: "Like the rattlesnake, however, they now show an instinctive inhibition against biting. . . ." Is there an instinctive inhibition which prevents war between the United States and Soviet Russia like the instinctive inhibition which prevents

---

[5] Explanatory analogies are used in science, for example, Rutherford's picture of the atom as a miniature solar system. Different criteria are employed to evaluate these.

[6] Louis J. Halle, "Is War Obsolete?" in *The New Republic*, April 2, 1962, p. 14. © 1962 by Harrison-Blaine Inc. Used by permission of *The New Republic*.

the rattlesnakes from biting each other? The analogy does help us to see the radical difference between total nuclear war and wars of the past. Thus it fulfills the second criterion. In relation to the third criterion would some be misled by the analogy? Perhaps some might be led to believe erroneously that there is a certain instinctive force which prevents the possible outbreak of total nuclear war.

Consider this explanatory analogy:

There has been a lot of talk about the President's tax-cut proposal and his idea that it would spur revenues even though we would have a bigger deficit. This just doesn't make sense. Only those professors cut off from the world in their academic cloisters could think up such a thing. But let's talk sense. From my own practical background I can tell you that the fiscal problems of government are just like those of a business. Increased expenses and reduced revenues will kill the government in the same way that it would kill a business. This kind of arithmetic just doesn't work out for government just as it doesn't work for business.

Does this fulfill the above criteria for a good explanatory analogy? First, are the elements said to be similar similar? Most contemporary economists would argue that given the economic situation in the United States today, the government is not like a business in the sense that increased expenses and reduced revenues would kill it. In fact, they argue that such things are necessary to avoid increased unemployment and a slow economic growth rate. But the analogy does fulfill the second criterion. It does give us a vivid picture of the way some look at tax reduction and deficit spending. But it appears to fail the third criterion. Such an analogy can easily mislead some into thinking that things which are true of business are true of government. For example, on hearing the above, some might be led to think that governments might be unable to pay their debts in the way that businesses are often unable to pay their debts.

ANALOGIES WHICH
SUGGEST HYPOTHESES[7]

When someone supposes that X is analogous to Y, and draws a consequence from this which is to be tested, the analogy plays a role noted above. We will call such analogies *hypothesis-suggesting analogies*. There are many instances in science and in other areas where analogies have

[7] The role of analogy in formulating theories, and in suggesting applications and alterations of theories is an important one. For a good discussion of this see Ernest Nagel's *The Structure of Science*, Chapters Five and Six.

suggested hypotheses to be tested. For example, Darwin's theory of natural selection was suggested by analogy. Robert Malthus held that human life increases at a faster rate than food production, and thus some men cannot escape from starvation. Darwin on his voyage in the *Beagle* noticed how species vary from island to island. What explains these modifications? The surroundings? The will of the organisms? In answer to this question Darwin wrote:

> In October, 1838, that is fifteen months after I had begun my systematic enquiry, I happened to read for amusement Malthus on Population, and being well prepared to appreciate the struggle for existence which everywhere goes on from long continued observation of the habits of animals and plants, it at once struck me that under these circumstances favorable variations would tend to be preserved, and unfavorable ones to be destroyed. The result of this would be the formation of a new species. Here then I had at last got a theory by which to work.

It occurred to Darwin that what Malthus said was true of men was analogous to other animals—that is, animals, like men, must have checks on their multiplication. If this is so, then with animals the fittest must survive (favorable variations) and the inferior do not survive (unfavorable variations). And if this were true, then this would explain the formation of new species. As we can see, from this analogy this hypothesis was suggested: The fittest survive and the inferior do not survive.

ARGUMENTATIVE ANALOGIES

When an analogy is used argumentatively it has this form or a variation of it:

X has certain elements *A, B,* and *C.*
Y also has elements *A, B,* and *C.*
But X has *D.*
Therefore Y has *D.*

Variations are created by considering in such an argument more individuals, more or less elements, and so forth. Let us now consider three examples of analogical arguments. Each of these arguments has the above form or a variation of it.

Thomas Reid's often quoted example of an analogical argument is the first example: [8]

1. . . . we may observe a very great similitude between this earth which we inhabit, and the other planets, Saturn, Jupiter, Mars, Venus, and Mercury.

---

[8] Thomas Reid, *Essays on the Intellectual Powers of Man* (Essay I, Chapter 4) (London: Macmillan, 1941), p. 36.

They all revolve round the sun, as the earth does, although at different distances and in different periods. They borrow all their light from the sun, as the earth does. Several of them are known to revolve round their axis like the earth, and, by that means, must have a like succession of day and night. Some of them have moons that serve to give them light in the absence of the sun, as our moon does to us. They are all, in their motions, subject to the same law of gravitation, as the earth is. From all this similitude, it is not unreasonable to think that those planets may, like our earth, be the habitation of various orders of living creatures. There is some probability in this conclusion from analogy.

As can be seen, the argument is:

The earth revolves around the sun (A), borrows all its light from the sun (B), revolves on its axis (C), and is subjected to laws of gravitation (D).

Saturn (S), Jupiter (J), Mars (M), Venus (V), and Mercury (E) have A and D, and some have B and C.

The earth is inhabited by living creatures (I).
Therefore there is some probability that S, J, M, V, and E are inhabited by living creatures.

For the second example let us phrase Russell's argument in the first section so that it would have a form like the above:

2. A man on a trip makes his travel plans in accordance with existing circumstances (for example, transportation and weather).

A man who advocates a certain policy formulates his policy in accordance with existing circumstances (for example, the balance of international power).

When conditions change, the man on a trip changes his plans and is not inconsistent in doing this.

Therefore when conditions change, a man who advocates a certain policy changes his policy and is not inconsistent in doing this.

Consider next this example:

3. If a doctor is justified in deceiving a sick patient, if there is no harm in telling the children about Santa Claus, if a stage manager in case of fire behind the scenes ought to deceive the audience so as to avert a panic, then it is only logical to conclude that there is no wrong in cribbing at an exam.

Here the argument has this form:

X deceives (A).
Y deceives (A).
Z deceives (A).
W deceives (A).
It is justifiable (B), for X, Y, and Z to deceive.
Therefore, it is justifiable (B) for W to deceive.

As can be seen, an analogical argument can show considerable variation on the basic form.

EVALUATING ANALOGICAL ARGUMENTS

Traditionally, six criteria have been provided to help determine whether an analogical argument is good. To understand these criteria, one must keep in mind the basic form indicated in the last section. Here are the six traditional criteria:

1. The greater the number of entities having A, B, C, and D, the stronger the conclusion. Thus if in addition to entity X, we had said that Z and W have the elements, then the conclusion, Y has D, would be strengthened.

2. The greater the number of elements shared by X (and other entities if any are mentioned) and Y, the stronger the conclusion. If X and Y did share not only elements A, B, and C, but also F and E, then the conclusion would be strengthened.

3. The argument is strengthened in direct proportion to how weak the conclusion is. (a) To say Y probably has D is to draw a weaker conclusion than to say Y has D. (b) When one can talk about degrees of D, to say Y has D to some degree or other is a weaker conclusion than to say Y has D to exactly the degree that X has. (c) In addition, if the conclusion is merely that Y has D and not that Y has D plus other elements, say E, which X has, then it is weaker in this form than in the other.

4. As the dissimilar elements between X and Y increase, the conclusion is weakened. There have to be *some* dissimilar elements between X and Y or else it would not be an *analogical* argument. But if there are, say, ten dissimilar elements rather than, say, one or two, then the argument is weakened.

5. If elements A, B, and C are thought to cause or lead to D, then as one increases the number of entities in the premises with dissimilar elements between them, the conclusion is strengthened. If X, Z, and W differ in most respects except for having A, B, C, and D, then the supposition that A, B, and C cause or lead to D is strengthened, and hence the conclusion is strengthened.

6. The conclusion is strengthened when A, B, and C have a causal or determining effect for D.

Let us now consider again the three analogical arguments introduced in the fourth section, and let us attempt to apply the above criteria to determine whether they are good analogical arguments.

Do all six criteria have an application to Reid's analogical argument (1)? To say that a criterion has an application means that the argument in fulfilling the criterion is strengthened or weakened (depending on the criterion). To say that a criterion has no application means that whether or not the analogy fulfills the criterion is irrelevant to strengthening or weakening the argument.

The first criterion *seems* to have an application to the argument. If we were to discover that another planet, say Pluto, has *I* (life), then the argument would be:

(4)   The earth has *A* (revolves around the sun), *B* (borrows all its light from the sun), *C* (revolves on its axis), *D* (is subjected to laws of gravitation).
Pluto has *A, B, C,* and *D.*
Saturne (*S*), Jupiter (*J*), Mars (*M*), Venus (*V*), and Mercury (*E*) have *A, B, C,* and *D.*
The earth and Pluto have *I* (life).
Therefore *S, J, M, V,* and *E* have *I.*

This argument appears to be a stronger argument than (1). The reason for this is that on the basis of current knowledge, *A, B, C,* and *D* are clearly not factors which are sufficient or near sufficient for the existence of life. However, if it were true that Pluto has life, this would most likely result in our revising our views about what is sufficient or near sufficient for life. And it would seem that the direction these revisions would take would make *A, B, C,* and *D* factors which are somewhat nearer a sufficient condition; and thus would make (4) a stronger argument than (1). (Since it is uncertain how we would react to finding life on Pluto, it is not clear that the first criterion is applicable. This is why the word "seems" is used.)

The second criterion, with a qualification, has an application in evaluating the analogy (1). For, as can be seen, if there were certain elements other than *A, B, C,* and *D* which earth and other planets had in common (for example, atmosphere, water, and similar temperature), the conclusion would be strengthened. But it should be noticed that the elements would all have to be *relevant* to life (this is the qualification). The increase of just any elements would not strengthen the conclusion. (The above six criteria do not help us in determining which elements are relevant in an analogy. This is one serious shortcoming in these rules for appraising analogical arguments.) The third criterion is also useful in evaluating the analogy. As (1) stands, the argument is quite weak because the conclusion is that the planets "probably have" life. If it read, say, "They possibly have life," the analogy would be stronger. Criterion four also has application. In order for the dissimilar elements to weaken the analogy, they would all obviously have to be relevant to life. For example, the differences in temperature, lack of water, and so on would be relevant dissimilar elements which would weaken the analogy, whereas the difference in size would be an irrelevant element which would neither weaken nor strengthen the conclusion. Since there are so many relevant dissimilar elements between the earth and the other planets, the analogy, following the fourth criterion, is weaker than would be an analogy where the relevant elements are not dissimilar. The last two criteria also have application to the analogy. If A, B, C, and D cause life or have a determining effect on life, then the conclusion is certainly strengthened.

In summary, knowing some of the relevant elements, we can judge that the analogy is weak in terms of the second and fourth criteria. The analogy is also weak in terms of the third criterion; and since A, B, C, and D are not the causes of life the analogy is weak in terms of the last two criteria. Consequently, in relation to the traditional criteria, the analogy is indeed a poor analogical argument.

It will not be necessary to go through analogical arguments (2) and (3) of the last section in the manner we did with (1). For, as we would find if we went through the list of criteria, none of them, except the fourth criterion, have an application to (2) and (3). For example, if the man on the trip in (2) shared or did not share any additional elements with the man who advocates a certain policy, it would be irrelevant to the strength of the conclusion. Or, for another example, a weakened conclusion would be irrelevant to the strength of (3). Even the application of the fourth criterion is open to question in connection with (2) and (3). (2) is generally regarded as a good analogy and (3) as a patently poor one. With (2), even if the dissimilar elements were increased (if this makes sense), as long as the essential similarity remains, the analogy remains strong. This essential element can be expressed in this way: travel plans and policy are contingent on circumstances (and this similar contingency, by the way, is the substance of the analogy). In turn, in (3), no matter how many dissimilar elements there might be, the analogy is poor as long as this one exists: what justifies the deception in the doctor's case and in others is missing in the case of a deception on exams.

What we learn from all this is that the six traditional criteria were formulated with examples like (1) in mind and not with ones like (2) and (3). Thus the criteria are limited in their range of usefulness.

Are there, then, other criteria which can be employed widely in appraising analogical arguments as good or poor? This author thinks not. One learns to spot poor analogies by acquiring a nose for it, so to speak. This ability is developed by studying analogical arguments. A teacher or a book will help one to see in what way certain examples of analogical arguments are poor or strong. With practice and help the student will develop this nose. At the risk of using a poor explanatory analogy, we can say that this process of getting the nose is similar to the way one learns to tell whether a work of art is of merit or not.

SOME POOR ANALOGICAL ARGUMENTS

Since practice is important in acquiring the capacity to evaluate analogical arguments, we will consider some examples of poor analogical arguments in this section. And we will give a criticism of each one.

A humorous example of a poor analogical argument is found in *Alice in Wonderland:*

"But I don't want to go among mad people," Alice remarked.

"Oh, you can't help that," said the Cat: "we're all mad here. I'm mad. You're mad."

"How do you know I'm mad?" said Alice.

"You must be," said the Cat, "or you wouldn't have come here."

Alice didn't think that proved it at all: however, she went on: "And how do you know that you're mad?"

"To begin with," said the Cat, "a dog's not mad. You grant that?"

"I suppose so," said Alice.

"Well, then," the Cat went on, "you see a dog growls when it's angry, and wags its tail when it's pleased. Now *I* growl when I'm pleased, and wag my tail when I'm angry. Therefore I'm mad."

Notice that this is an example of an analogical argument which runs: since a dog has *A, B,* and *C,* and since I don't have *A* and I don't have *B,* then I do not have *C.* We might call it a negative analogical argument. The argument, of course, is ridiculous, because there is no connection between not having *A* (barking when angry) and *B* (wagging tail when happy) and not having *C* (sanity).

A more serious example is found in this statement suggested by a newspaper editorial:

The Attorney General sent federal marshals into Alabama when gangs of whites attacked the so-called "Freedom Riders." In Chicago, at the same time, gangs of Negroes attacked and beat at least eighteen whites in connection with integration of a residential area.

We ask the Attorney General: Do you plan to send federal marshals into Chicago? Are you going to protect those innocent citizens? Are you going to send a personal representative to Chicago to insure the civil rights of those white victims as you sent a representative to Alabama? You demanded that the

Governor of Alabama and the Alabama police protect the "Freedom Riders."—
What about those white victims in Chicago?

The logic of the situation is clear.

The argument is that since the situation in Chicago is like Alabama, and since the Attorney General sent federal marshals and a personal representative to Alabama, and demanded that the governor provide protection, he should do one or all of these things in Chicago. What makes this argument poor is that the situations differ in at least one important respect. In Alabama the officials are charged with not having enforced certain laws in an area where the federal government also has jurisdiction. In Chicago this was not true, since these laws were enforced by local officials. Once this difference is brought out, it can be seen that the conclusion of the argument loses its support.

The next example is taken from Freud's *Moses and Monotheism:* [9]

In legends which glorify heroes, such as Sargon of Agade, Cyrus, and Romulus, we find certain common features such as the fact that the hero is the son of parents of the highest station, most often the son of a king. Moses is a legendary hero. Therefore this is reason for its being true that Moses was a son of parents of the highest station, i.e., a son of an Egyptian Pharaoh.

This argument has several weak points, but let us consider the major one. To do this, let us assume that in many stories of legendary heroes the hero is the son of parents of the highest station (a dubious assumption). In addition, let us suppose that there are any number of similarities between the story of Moses and each of these stories (also a dubious assumption). Even assuming that both are true, there seems no reason why Moses' being born of parents of the highest station should or should not be connected with this cluster of supposed common elements.

To conclude this section, here are three poor analogical arguments. [10]

We frown on people who live off the labors of others, without themselves producing anything. But isn't this precisely what engineers do? They don't work on any assembly lines. They chatter with one another about formulas and blueprints. But do they produce anything? Never. We ought to frown on engineers. Here comes one now. Let's frown.

So you object to our ad showing a hand holding a razor and shaving what is supposed to be a piece of sandpaper to which our shave cream has been applied. So it is true that we don't use sandpaper but a piece of plexiglass over which sand has been applied lightly. But no one objects to the use of cardboard sets to represent Western saloons or an actor's drinking tea instead of the beverage called for by the script!

[9] Sigmund Freud, *Moses and Monotheism* (New York: Knopf, 1939).
[10] The first and third examples were created by Professor Harry Nielsen of the University of Notre Dame and are used here with his permission.

College students shouldn't have to take anything but practical courses. After all, life is no literary tea. It's a hard-fought game. Suppose a football coach spent half his time teaching football, and the other half teaching the squad about flowers and Chinese pottery. What kind of team would you get? That's why I say: Forget the arts and literature. Take business and science. Get ready for the hard scrap ahead.

Briefly, what stands out in the first is that what gives the appearance of an important similarity between engineers and people who live off the labor of others is that we would say of each that "they do not produce anything." But on reflection one can see that when we say this of engineers we mean something different from what we mean when we say this of the others. This argument contains an equivocation of the phrase "they do not produce anything." The second is poor because, obviously, the cardboard sets and tea are not a sham concocted to sell a saloon or a liquor. In the last, though life is "a hard-fought game" for some, for others it is not. For everyone, however, it is unlike football in that there is more to it than just doing a job well and achieving the goals which come from doing the job well. In addition, some jobs require a knowledge of the arts, as do some of the "battles" that must be fought.

CRITICISM BY LOGICAL ANALOGY

An interesting and proper application of analogical arguments is found in what are called criticisms by logical analogy. Such a criticism is found in the following passage from Orwell's *Coming Up For Air*.[11]

Father was always a bit sceptical of this story, and of the new flying machines, otherwise he believed everything he read. Until 1909 no one in Lower Binfield believed that human beings could ever learn to fly. The official doctrine was that if God had meant us to fly He'd have given us wings. Uncle Ezekiel couldn't help retorting that if God had mean us to ride He'd have given us wheels, but even he didn't believe in the new flying machine.

What we have here is someone showing that an argument is incorrect by producing another argument which is essentially like the first but which more clearly displays its incorrectness. This is called *criticism by logical analogy*. The first argument in the above passage is, as we can see:

If God had meant us to fly, he would have given us wings.
We have no wings.
Therefore God does not mean for us to fly.

11 George Orwell, *Coming Up For Air* (New York: Harcourt, Brace, 1950).

The second argument which is essentially similar to it and displays the incorrectness of it is:

If God had meant us to ride, he would have given us wheels.
We do not have wheels.
Therefore God does not mean for man to ride.

It is supposed that even one who would present the first argument would see the weakness of the second argument, especially if he owns an automobile.

Consider, finally, this second excellent example of a criticism by logical analogy: [12]

Thus we have had the controversy whether Pope was a *poet,* not whether he was a good poet or a bad one, but whether he was a poet at all. The disputants, or some of them, claimed a right to define poet, and decided that none but verse makers of a certain goodness (to be settled by themselves) were poets. They might just as well have decided, on their own authority, that none but men of a certain amount of reasoning power were men. Had they done this last, as long as they fixed the amount at a figure which included themselves under the name, nobody would have thought they materially altered the extent of the term; it is not easy to see why they have rights so arbitrary, over words the objective definitions of which are nearly as well fixed as that of man.

SUMMARY

An explanatory analogy (for example, an explanatory analogy as it comes up in a debate or a discussion) is good when it fulfills these three conditions:

The elements said to be similar are similar.

The analogy is successful.

The dissimilar elements are not generally misleading.

If an explanatory analogy fails to fulfill one of these conditions, it is poor.

The traditional rules for evaluating argumentative analogies are limited in their application. The ability to see a poor argumentative analogy and to see where it goes wrong is like the ability to see what works of art are of merit. It is an ability that comes not through the application of general rules but through practice and experience.

Often argumentative analogies are poor. There is, however, one effective and proper use of argumentative analogies, namely, criticism of an argument by logical analogy. When a criticism of an argument is made by constructing another argument which is essentially similar to the first

[12] Augustus De Morgan, *Formal Logic* (London: Open Court, 1926), p. 285.

but which is obviously incorrect, then this is a criticism by logical analogy.

EXERCISES

Classify each of the following as an explanatory, hypothesis-suggesting or argumentative analogy or none of these. Evaluate each of the explanatory and argumentative analogies as good or poor. Do you find any criticisms by logical analogy?

1. What!, art mad? A man may see how this world goes with no eyes. Look with thine ears. See how yond Justice rails upon yond simple thief. Hark, in thine ear. Change places and, handy-dandy, which is the Justice, which is the thief? Thou hast seen a farmer's dog bark at a beggar? . . . And the creature run from the cur? There thou mightst behold the great image of authority. A dog's obey'd in office.

(SHAKESPEARE, *King Lear*)

2. Franklin D. Roosevelt in his acceptance speech in 1932 said, "Revenue must cover expenditures by one means or another. Any government, like any family, can for a year spend a little more than it earns. But you and I know that a continuation of that habit means the poorhouse."

3. It is no more necessary for there to be two political parties than that a man should have two heads.

4. The Hatter opened his eyes very wide on hearing this; but all he *said* was "Why is a raven like a writing-desk?"

"Come, we shall have some fun now!" thought Alice. "I'm glad they've begun asking riddles—I believe I can guess that," she added aloud.

"Do you mean that you think you can find out the answer to it?" said the March Hare.

"Exactly so," said Alice.

"Then you should say what you mean," the March Hare went on.

"I do," Alice hastily replied; "at least—at least I mean what I say—that's the same thing, you know."

"Not the same thing a bit!" said the Hatter. "Why you might just as well say that 'I see what I eat' is the same thing as 'I eat what I see!' "

"You might just as well say," added the March Hare, "that 'I like what I get' is the same thing as 'I get what I like!' "

"You might just as well say," added the Dormouse, which seemed to be talking in its sleep, "that 'I breathe when I sleep' is the same thing as 'I sleep when I breathe!' "

"It *is* the same thing with you," said the Hatter, and here the conversation dropped. . . .

(LEWIS CARROLL, *Alice in Wonderland*)

5. . . . unless something other than the continued arms race is undertaken by governments, it only postpones a war. After all, before 1914 there were crises very similar to the crisis that we've had in the policy of brinkmanship, and those crises didn't lead to war until 1914, and people thought, "Oh, well, if we keep the armaments equal on the two sides, there won't be war." But it wasn't so, and I'm afraid that may happen again. . . .

. . . Everybody remembers that Nobel, who invented the Nobel peace prize and was a very keen advocator of peace, was also the inventor of dynamite. He thought dynamite made war so horrible that there never would be another war. Well, it didn't work out that way, and I'm afraid it may be the same with the H-bomb.

(Bertrand Russell Speaks His Mind) [13]

6. I think there ought to be no rules whatever prohibiting improper publications. . . . I think prohibitions immensely increase people's interest in pornography, as in anything else. I used often to go to America during Prohibition, and there was far more drunkenness than there was before, far more, and I think that prohibition of pornography has much the same effect. Now, I'll give you an illustration of what I mean about prohibitions. The philosopher Empedocles thought it was very, very wicked to munch laurel leaves, and he laments that he will have to spend ten thousand years in outer darkness because he munched laurel leaves. Now nobody's ever told me not to munch laurel leaves and I've never done it, but Empedocles who was told not to, did it. And I think the same applies to pornography.

(Bertrand Russell Speaks His Mind) [14]

7. . . . the obvious *logical* impossibility of re-enacting a given happening in the past does not prove that historical explanations for it are not testable, and therefore incapable of being objectively grounded. Were this argument correct, a strictly analogous argument would prove that no decisions by courts of law concerning the guilt of defendants accused of some deed could possibly be based on objective evidence. However, although legal trials sometimes do result in mistaken decisions, it would be an absurd exaggeration to claim that every litigation terminates in a miscarriage of justice, or even that the correctness of a court's conclusion is just a matter of chance.

(ERNEST NAGEL, *The Structure of Science*) [15]

8. A man of the ruling class put this question to him: "Good Master, what must I do to win eternal life?" Jesus said to him, "Why do you call me good? No one is good except God alone. You know the commandments: 'Do not

13 *Bertrand Russell Speaks His Mind* (New York: Bard Books, 1960) p. 129. Copyright © 1960 by The World Publishing Company. All rights reserved. Used by permission of The World Publishing Company.

14 *Ibid.,* p. 56. Used by permission.

15 From *The Structure of Science* by Ernest Nagel, pp. 581–582. © 1961, by Harcourt, Brace and World, Inc., and reprinted with their permission and that of Routledge and Kegan Paul.

commit adultery; do not murder; do not steal; do not give evidence; honour your father and mother'." The man answered, "I have kept all these since I was a boy." On hearing this Jesus said, "There is still one thing lacking: sell everything you have and distribute to the poor, and you will have riches in heaven; and come, follow me." At these words his heart sank; for he was a very rich man. When Jesus saw it he said, "How hard it is for the wealthy to enter the kingdom of God! It is easier for a camel to go through the eye of a needle than for a rich man to enter the kingdom of God."

(Luke 18: 18–26)

9. And now, Athenians, I am not going to argue for my own sake, as you may think, but for yours, that you may not sin against God by condemning me, who am his gift to you. For if you kill me you will not easily find a successor to me, who, if I may use such a ludicrous figure of speech, am a sort of gadfly, given to the state by God; and the state is a great and noble steed who is tardy in his motions owing to his very size, and requires to be stirred into life. I am that gadfly which God has attached to the state, and all day long and in all places am always fastening upon you, arousing and persuading and reproaching you. You will not easily find another like me, and therefore I would advise you to spare me.

(PLATO, Apology)

10. Yes, it certainly is possible [for communism and capitalism to learn to live side by side in the world together]. It's only a question of getting used to each other. Now take the . . . Christians and the Mohammedans. They fought each other for about six centuries, during which neither side got any advantage over the other, and at the end of that time some men of genius said: "Look, why shouldn't we stop fighting each other and make friends?" And they did, and that's all right, and just the same thing can happen with capitalism and communism as soon as each side realizes that it can't gain the world.

(Bertrand Russell Speaks His Mind) [16]

11. Hymie Shorenstein was the large, rotund leader of the Brownsville district of Brooklyn, New York, many years ago, when that community was still solidly Jewish. . . . One year—so the well-worn story goes—as the politicians divided up the local nominations, it was given to Shorenstein to choose a Democratic candidate for judge as his share of the patronage. The candidate so named thereupon contributed heavily to Shorenstein for campaign expenditures and watched the campaign's progress well into October—but could see no posters blazoning his name on walls, no organization working, no parades or demonstrations. Worried about his chances, the candidate marched into the anteroom of Boss McCooey one afternoon to complain about Shorenstein's sloth. There he met Shorenstein himself, also waiting to see McCooey; and when Shorenstein asked why his candidate was there, the candidate unburdened himself of his fears. "Ah," replied Shorenstein, "you're worried? Listen. Did you ever go down to the wharf to see the Staten Island Ferry come in? You ever watch it, and look down in the water at all those chewing-gum wrappers, and the banana peels, and the garbage? When the ferryboat comes into the wharf, automatically it pulls all the garbage in too. The name of your ferryboat is Franklin D. Roosevelt—stop worrying!"

(THEODORE H. WHITE, *The Making of the President 1960*) [17]

12. "He received us politely. When I started explaining that the Church often had to make the best of a bad business in order to avoid worse evils, he interrupted me. 'The theory of the lesser evil may be valid in a political society, but not in a religious society,' he said to me. I tried not to argue with him on an abstract level, because the worst heresies are capable of seductively insinuating themselves into abstract discussions. So I replied: Imagine what would happen if the Church openly condemned the present war. What persecutions would descend on its head! You will never imagine what Don Benedetto replied. 'My dear Don Girasole,' he said, 'can you imagine John the Baptist offering Herod a concordat to escape having his head cut off? Can you imagine Jesus offering Pontius Pilate a concordat to avoid crucifixion?' "

(IGNAZIO SILONE, *Bread and Wine*) [18]

13. The men who argue in favor of unrestricted national freedom do not realize that the same reasons would justify unrestricted individual freedom. I will not yield to Patrick Henry, or anyone else, in love of freedom, but if there is to be as much freedom in the world as possible, it is necessary that there should be restrictions preventing violent assaults upon the freedom of others. In the internal affairs of states this is recognized: murder is everywhere made illegal. If the law against murder were repealed, the liberty of all except murderers would be diminished, and even the liberty of murderers would, in most cases, be short-lived, since they would soon be murdered. But, although everyone, except a few anarchists, admits this as regards the relations of an individual to his national state, there is immense reluctance to admit it as regards the relations of national states to the world at large.

(BERTRAND RUSSELL, *Has Man a Future?*) [19]

14. According to William James, "medical materialism" is a kind of argument. It is this kind of argument: since there are organic causes for religious states of mind, religious opinions are mistaken. James wrote:

Modern psychology, finding definite psycho-physical connections to hold good, assumes as a convenient hypothesis that the dependence of mental

[17] Theodore H. White, *The Making of the President 1960* (New York: Atheneum, 1961) p. 49.
[18] Ignazio Silone, *Bread and Wine,* Copyright, 1937, by Harper and Row, Publishers, Incorporated. Used by permission.
[19] Bertrand Russell, *Has Man a Future?* (London: George Allen and Unwin, 1961).

states upon bodily conditions must be thoroughgoing and complete. If we adopt the assumption, then of course what medical materialism insists on must be true in a general way, if not in every detail: Saint Paul certainly had once an epileptoid, if not an epileptic seizure; George Fox was an hereditary degenerate; Carlyle was undoubtedly auto-intoxicated by some organ or other, no matter which—and the rest. But now, I ask you, how can such an existential account of facts of mental history decide in one way or another upon their spiritual significance? According to the general postulate of psychology just referred to, there is not a single one of our states of mind, high or low, healthy or morbid, that has not some organic process as its condition. Scientific theories are organically conditioned just as much as religious emotions are; and if we only knew the facts intimately enough, we should doubtless see "the liver" determining the dicta of the sturdy atheist as decisively as it does those of the Methodist under conviction anxious about his soul. When it alters in one way the blood that percolates it, we get the Methodist, when in another way, we get the atheist form of mind. So of all our raptures and our drynesses, our longings and pantings, our questions and beliefs. They are equally organically founded, be they religious or of non-religious content.

(WILLIAM JAMES, The Varieties of Religious Experience)

15. To those who continue to peddle the Communist line that 10,000 Communists in this country of 180 million are of little or no consequence, may I remind them that at the time Russia was taken over, less than one-seventh of 1 per cent of the people in that unhappy country were Communists. Poland had only 4 per cent. When Castro seized Cuba and took it behind the Iron Curtain, there were only a handful of Communists pulling the strings. Even today in Czechoslovakia, which has the largest percentage of Communists in any country in the world, we find only 11 per cent.

From this it should be obvious to the least informed that the 10,000 Communists in this country are a great danger.

16. And in truth, I am quite willing it should be known that the little I have hitherto learned is almost nothing in comparison with that of which I am ignorant, and to the knowledge of which I do not despair of being able to attain; for it is much the same with those who gradually discover truth in the sciences, as with those who when growing rich find less difficulty in making great acquisitions, than they formerly experienced when poor in making acquisitions of much smaller amount.

(RENE DESCARTES, A Discourse on Method)

17. It is rather odd that emphasis upon the merits of one's own nation could be considered a virtue. What should we think of an individual who proclaimed: "I am morally and intellectually superior to all other individuals, and, because of this superiority, I have a right to ignore all interests except my own"? There are, no doubt, plenty of people who *feel* this way, but if they proclaim their feelings too openly, and act upon it too blatantly, they are thought ill of. When, however, a number of such individuals, constituting the population of some area, collectively make such a declaration about themselves, they are thought noble and splendid and spirited. They put up statues to each other and teach school-children to admire the most blatant advocates of the national conceit.

(BERTRAND RUSSELL, *Common Sense and Nuclear Warfare*) [20]

18. [In very early Greek philosophy] Fire was held to be a distinct entity on a par with the other three [earth, air, water]. We now know that it is not itself an entity of any kind, but is a manifestation of a certain chemical process, as for instance, the oxidation of carbon, in the course of which the carbon particles give forth light and heat. There is nothing whatever present in a flame except these molecules undergoing chemical change; yet, to an uneducated eye, the flame seems to be a distinct entity, differing altogether from a mere collection of chemically active material particles.

We may interpret the existence of mind in a precisely analogous manner. All that really exists is the material particles of the substance of the nervous system. When these particles enter upon a certain kind of chemical activity, the effect is to suggest the existence of some new kind of elusive non-material entity called mind. But this entity has no more real existence than has fire. In each case we have to do exclusively with molecules undergoing disintegration or combination. This chemical activity suffices in itself to account for the whole of the phenomena flowing from the center of activity, and the belief in any additional independent entity is a fallacy which itself can be expressed and explained in physico-chemical terms. The flames of fire flash out swiftly in all directions and vanish again, to reappear instantly in a closely similar form. So, too, the ideation or emotion of the individual may open up new avenues of mind for a brief moment, as they travel on to a new position. In each case the fluctuations of form are due to the constantly changing area of chemical activity; and just as the fire maintains for short periods a relative constancy of size and shape, so the mental content of an individual is apt to remain for a time at about the same value of intensity, and fastened to the same subjects of attention. At times the fire burns low; at other times it bursts forth into exuberant activity. The accuracy of the analogy is due to the fact that both phenomena are based upon the same foundation; the one is a manifestation from organic matter, and therefore immeasurably more complex as to its chemistry.

(HUGH ELLIOT, *Modern Science and Materialism*) [21]

19. Mankind are so much the same, in all times and places, that history informs us of nothing new or strange in this particular. Its chief use is only to discover the constant and universal principles of human nature, by showing men in all varieties of circumstances and situations, and furnishing us with materials from which we may form our observations and become acquainted with the

20 Bertrand Russell, *Common Sense and Nuclear Warfare*, pp. 78–79. Copyright 1959 by George Allen and Unwin Ltd. Used by permission of George Allen and Unwin Ltd. and Simon and Schuster, Inc.

21 Hugh Elliot, *Modern Science and Materialism* (London: Longmans, Green, 1919) pp. 196–197.

regular springs of human action and behavior. These records of wars, intrigues, factions, and revolutions, are so many collections of experiments, by which the politician or moral philosopher fixes the principles of his science, in the same manner as the physician or natural philosopher becomes acquainted with the nature of plants, minerals, and other external objects, by the experiments which he forms concerning them.

(DAVID HUME, *An Enquiry Concerning Human Understanding*)

20. For his doctoral dissertation at Gottingen, Young produced a thesis on sounds and the human voice, a subject which he connected up with his earlier work on optics by suggesting that both sound and light were wave vibrations, colours being analogous to notes of different frequencies. It was generally accepted that sound consisted of wave vibrations in the air along the direction of the sound beam, and Young presumed that light consisted of similar longitudinal vibrations in a luminiferous ether which pervaded all space, as Huygens had done before him. He pointed out that light from a weak source travelled just as fast as that from an intense source, a fact which could be accounted for more easily by the wave theory of light than the particle theory. It was well known that two sets of sound waves or water waves could interfere with one another, and Young performed an experiment in which two light beams were allowed to overlap and interfere, producing alternate light and dark bands where one beam reinforced or cancelled out the other. From the separation of the bands, and the dimensions of the apparatus, he was able to calculate the wave-lengths of the light vibrations, showing them to be of the order of a millionth of a metre or so. Since the wave-lengths of the light vibrations were very small compared with the size of visible objects, Young pointed out that light would travel in straight lines and could cast sharp shadows. He was aware that light beams did bend round the edges of opaque objects to some degree, producing shadows with coloured edges and other interference effects which had been studied by Grimaldi and others during the seventeenth century, and Young instanced such phenomena as evidence for the wave theory of light.

(S. F. MASON, *Main Currents of Scientific Thought*) [22]

21. My second maxim was to be as firm and resolute in action as I could, and to follow out my most doubtful opinions, when once I had settled upon them, no less steadily than if they had been thoroughly assured. In this I would imitate travelers lost in a wood; they must not wander about turning now to this side, now to that, and still less must they stop in one place; they must keep walking as straight as they can in one direction, and not change course for slight reasons, even if at the beginning their choice was determined perhaps by mere chance; for in this way, even if they do not arrive just where they wish, they will at least finally get somewhere where they will probably be better off than in the middle of a wood. Similarly, it often happens in life that action brooks no delay; and it is a sure truth that, when we cannot discern the most correct opinion, we must follow the most probable. And even if we can observe no more likelihood in one than another, we must settle upon some opinion, and consider it afterwards in practice not as doubtful but as perfectly true and certain; for our ground for settling upon it really is of this sort. This maxim could henceforth set me free from all regrets and remorse that usually trouble the consciences of those weak and stumbling characters who let themselves set out on some course of action as a good one and then in their inconstancy decide afterwards that it is bad.

(DESCARTES, *Discourse on the Method*) [23]

22. Let us suppose, however, that Berlin is right in thinking that if we really did come to believe in a thoroughgoing determinism, the meanings of our moral discourse would be altered. What would this assumed fact establish? It is pertinent to recall comparable situations in other domains of thought, where the meanings associated with various linguistic expressions were modified as a consequence of the adoption of new beliefs. Thus, most educated men today accept the heliocentric theory of planetary motions, but although they continue to employ such terms as "sunrise" and "sunset," they do not use them with the same meanings those terms had when the Ptolemaic theory was dominant. Nevertheless, some of the distinctions these terms codified when they were associated with geocentric ideas are not without foundation even today, since in many contexts of observation and analysis it is not incorrect to describe the facts by saying that the sun rises in the east and sinks in the west. We have evidently learned to use such language to express distinctions that are still correct, without committing ourselves to other distinctions that depend entirely on accepting the geocentric theory.

Accordingly, and by parity of reasoning, if in agreement with Berlin's supposition we really came to believe in determinism, we would not therefore have to ignore the distinction between those acts described in current language as "freely chosen" and those acts which are not, or between those traits of character and personality over which an individual has effective control and those over which he does not. In any event, moreover, when as a result of the assumed change in belief the shifts in the meanings of currently used expressions are completed, it would still be the case that certain types of conduct are affected by praise and blame and other types are not, that men are able to control and modify by suitable discipline some of their impulses but not others, that some men by making an effort can improve the quality of their performances while other men are unable to do so and so on. In short, our ordinary moral language with its associated customary meanings, as well as our differential capacities for various kinds of actions, would survive in considerable measure a general acceptance of the deterministic thesis. To deny this is to subscribe to the hardly credible assumption that merely by adopting a belief in deter-

---

[23] Descartes, *Discourse on the Method*, in *Philosophical Writings*, Elizabeth Anscombe and Peter Geach, trans. (London: Nelson, 1954), pp. 25–26.

minism men would be transformed into creatures almost unrecognizably different from what they were before this change in their theoretical convictions.

(ERNEST NAGEL, *The Structure of Science*) [24]

[24] From *The Structure of Science* by Ernest Nagel, p. 604. © 1961, by Harcourt, Brace and World, Inc. and reprinted with their permission and that of Routledge & Kegan Paul.

Chapter Six

DILEMMAS AND
PARADOXES

In this chapter we will consider two closely related special types of argument called "dilemmas" and "paradoxes." Though our interest in these arguments is somewhat different from our interest in arguments up to this time, their consideration and appraisal is of importance. Dilemmas are commonly encountered arguments and are especially apt to be misleading and, at times, even dangerous. Paradoxes are important not only because they expose puzzling aspects of language but also because of their great historical importance in exposing certain misconceptions which were regarded as central to logic and mathematics.

WHAT IS A DILEMMA?

What is a dilemma? As we use the word "dilemma" in everyday language, it is often a synonym for "predicament." In logic, however, the word is customarily used to refer to a particular kind of argument. This kind of argument is found in this example: [1]

During the Civil War, James Mason and John Slidell were Confederate commissioners to Britain and France. Learning that they had left Havana for England on the British ship *Trent,* Union Captain Wilkes stopped the *Trent* and removed them. Wilkes' action was contrary to international law. The British government demanded that the U.S. release the prisoners and apologize for

---

[1] Henry Steele Commager, *The Blue and the Gray* (New York: Bobbs-Merrill Company, 1950), p. 529.

Wilkes' action. "Lincoln and Seward were in a dilemma. If they did not satisfy Britain they might find themselves with another war on their hands. If they did, public opinion—which had made a hero of Wilkes—would be outraged."

Written out fully, the argument which Commager calls a dilemma would look like this:

If we satisfy Britain, then the United States public will be outraged.
If we do not satisfy Britain, then there might be war.
Either we satisfy Britain by releasing the prisoners and apologizing for Wilkes' action, or we do not satisfy Britain.
Therefore, either the United States public will be outraged or there will be war.

The argument has this *form:*

1. If *A,* then *B.*
   If *C,* then *D.*
   Either *A* or *C.*
   Therefore either *B* or *D.*

The first two premisses are called *conditional,* or *hypothetical,* statements. The third premiss is called a *disjunctive* statement. A dilemma is said to be *constructive* when it has this form. It is said to be *destructive* when it has the following form:

2. If *A,* then *B.*
   If *C,* then *D.*
   Either not-*B* or not-*D.*
   Therefore either not-*A* or not-*C.*

The conclusion of a dilemma can be either a disjunctive statement, as in (1) and (2), or a singular statement, as in the following:

3. If *A,* then *B.*
   If *C,* then *B.*
   Either *A* or *C.*
   Therefore *B.*

A *complex* dilemma is one which has a disjunctive conclusion. A *simple* dilemma has a singular conclusion.

Most of the examples which we will consider in this chapter will be complex constructive dilemmas. An example, however, of a complex destructive dilemma is:

4. If Congress is not in a state of anarchy, then it does have leadership.
   If Congress does not block the President, then it does not have leadership.
   Either Congress has leadership or it does not have leadership.
   Therefore either Congress is in a state of anarchy or it is blocking the President.

An example of a simple constructive dilemma is:

5. If Congress is active, then it is harmful to the country.
   If Congress is not active, then it is harmful to the country.
   Congress is either active or not active.
   Thus, in any case, what Congress does will be harmful to the country.

THE VALUE OF THE DILEMMA

The value of a dilemma is that if it correctly represents the situation (which, as we will presently see, the *Trent* dilemma does not), it states the alternatives confronting someone and the consequences which must be faced. Or, we might say, the value of a realistic dilemma, one which correctly represents the situation, is that it represents the situation in a neat, rigorous way. But, as we will see, most dilemmas are not realistic. However, before turning to the criticism of dilemmas, let us examine a dilemma which comes close to being realistic.

Marx, in *Das Kapital,* maintains that there are certain irreversible laws operating in history. One of the consequences of these dialectical laws is that Capitalism will shatter and out of it will come Communism. Communism can emerge *only* from Capitalism. Russia was one of the first countries where the ideas of Communism flourished. Yet Russia at that time was a backward country, ruled by the Tsar, and would take many years to catch up to the stage Marx calls "Capitalism." In 1881 a member of the Populists in Russia wrote to Marx and asked for his support in their movement. Marx was in a dilemma. If he encouraged the movement, then this would conflict with his theory. If he did not encourage it, then perhaps the strongest Communist movement would die or be taken over by other idealogies.

This dilemma, it would seem, correctly represents the situation, for (a) the disjunctive premiss is exhaustive, that is, Marx must either encourage the Populists or not encourage them, there is no third alternative, and (b) both hypothetical statements are true. When a dilemma satisfies these two conditions, then we will call it a *realistic dilemma*.

APPRAISING A DILEMMA

Not all dilemmas are realistic. That is, as it can now be put, one or both of the above conditions—(a) and (b)—for a realistic dilemma are not fulfilled. Often when a dilemma is unrealistic an unfortunate situation develops. For an unrealistic dilemma can give the appearance of realistically representing the situation when it does not, and thus make it appear that the alternatives stated are all that are open and that the consequences stated *must* be faced.

The *Trent* case illustrates this danger. The dilemma makes it appear that Lincoln and Seward must prepare either for war with England or for an outraged United States public. You can imagine that such a belief might have serious consequences. But it is not true that these are the only alternatives facing them, for the dilemma is not realistic. On examination we can see that it violates the first condition (a). (There is a way in which we might understand "satisfy" so that the argument violates the second condition and not the first.) Recall the disjunctive premiss: Either we satisfy Britain by releasing the prisoners and apologizing for Wilkes' action or we do not satisfy Britain. This does not exhaust the alternatives open. It is not true that the only choice open is to release the prisoners and apologize for Wilkes' action or not to do this. Obviously, one possibility would be to release the prisoners but not apologize for Wilkes' action. Seward, in fact, avoided the consequences of the dilemma by avoiding the stated alternatives. Seward did not apologize, but congratulated England on at last adopting the principles of international law for which the United States had long contended, and then he had Mason and Slidell shipped off to England. There was no war, nor were the people in the United States enraged.

This way of avoiding a dilemma or of criticizing a dilemma—finding that the disjunctive premiss is not exhaustive—has traditionally been called *slipping between the horns of the dilemma.*

In an elegant passage Socrates presents a dilemma which can be criticized by slipping between the horns:

Let us reflect in another way, and we shall see that there is great reason to hope that death is good; for one of two things—either death is a state of nothingness and utter unconsciousness, or, as men say, there is a change and migration of the soul from this world to another. Now if you suppose that there is no consciousness, but a sleep like the sleep of him who is undisturbed even by dreams, death will be an unspeakable gain. For if a person were to select the night in which his sleep was undisturbed even by dreams, and were to compare with this the other days and nights of his life, and then were to tell us how many days and nights he had passed in the course of his life better and more pleasantly than this one, I think that any man, I will not say a private man, but even the great king .will not find many such days or nights, when compared with the others. Now if death be of such a nature, I say that to die is gain; for eternity is then only a single night. But if death is the journey to another place, and there, as men say, all the dead abide, what good, O my friends and judges, can be greater than this? If indeed when the pilgrim arrives in the world below, he is delivered from the professors of justice in this world, and finds the true judges who are said to give judgment there, Minos and

Rhadamanthus and Aeacus and Triptolemus, and other sons of God who were righteous in their own life, that pilgrimage will be worth making. What would not a man give if he might converse with Orpheus and Musaeus and Hesiod and Homer? Nay, if this be true, let me die again and again.

(PLATO, *Apology*)

Socrates presents us with a simple dilemma which can be put in this way:

When we die we either have an undisturbed sleep or have the great pleasure of being with certain people.
If we have an undisturbed sleep, then this is a gain.
If we are with these people, then this is the greatest gain. Thus death is a gain.

Certain Christian theologians, for example, would most likely criticize this dilemma by slipping between the horns. That is, they would argue that the only alternatives if we die are not undisturbed sleep and visiting people; there is, they would argue, at least a third alternative—the possibility of hell. Others might criticize the first hypothetical premiss. For example one might argue that in comparison with the joys and delights of life, an undisturbed sleep is little gain.

The above dilemma taken from the passage in the *Apology* can, as we have said, be criticized by arguing that the first hypothetical premiss is false. This way of criticizing a dilemma—arguing that one or both of the hypothetical premisses are false—is traditionally called *taking the dilemma by the horns*. The following example can be formulated so as to be criticized in this manner.

During the Berlin crisis in 1961 an editorial appeared in a newspaper which in substance argued: Mobilization can't be wrong. If the United States mobilization calls the Soviet bluff, then it merely brings out the fact that the Soviets do not intend to go to war over Berlin. On the other hand, if the Soviets are planning to initiate a war of conquest in order to spread their slavery over the world, then it is essential to mobilize. In both cases mobilization is either worth it or essential; thus no error can be made in mobilizing now.

In this form the dilemma violates the second criterion for being realistic —it is not true that both the "if-then" statements are true. For though the second is true, the first might not be. If the Communists do not intend to initiate a war over Berlin, then it does not follow without question that mobilization will call their bluff. Mobilization might make them go to war from fear or for self-defense. Since this is possible, the conclusion which really *follows* is that mobilization will either call their bluff, be essential, *or provoke war*. This does, of course, conflict with the conclusion which is drawn in the editorial.

How is this next dilemma to be criticized?

Years ago the question whether Adam had a navel was a discussed problem. It is a problem because, the argument goes, if Adam did not have a navel, then he was an imperfect human being. And God would have created something imperfect. On the other hand, if he did have a navel, then it had no use, and God would have created something without a purpose.

Most readers will find this dilemma amusing. But it is interesting to note that in 1944 a subcommittee of the House Military Affairs Committee opposed the distribution of *The Races of Mankind* to soldiers. One of the reasons was that "Adam and Eve are depicted with navels." [2] One cannot slip between the horns of the dilemma, for the "either-or" statement is: either Adam had a navel or he did not. Whenever the "either-or" statement has the form *"A or not-A,"* as this one and others that we have examined have, then if *"A"* is being used in the same way in both its occurrences, the "either-or" statement is invulnerable to criticism. If the conclusion that God creates things either imperfect or without purpose is to be avoided, then one must take the dilemma by the horns. Cases, it seems, can be made for the falsity of both "if-then" statements. For example, one might argue that the first is false. If Adam did not have a navel, it does not follow that he was an imperfect human being but only that he was different. A child has an "imperfection" when in developing he fails to develop as other children do. Adam did not develop at all, so, it seems, it is incorrect to speak of his difference as an "imperfection."

Three famous cold-war dilemmas follow. Are they realistic?

In 1948 the Russians violated treaty rights when they accomplished the political division of Berlin during the time of the airlift. In 1961 they again violated Western rights by constructing a wall closing off their sector. Such actions occasioned this dilemma: If the West takes action to stop these things it will lead to war. If the West retreats and lets the Russians go ahead with such things, then this has the effect of overexciting them, of pushing them to redouble their pressure, and, finally, of facilitating and hastening a war.

Any kind of war will inescapably lead to the obliteration of the human race. But if war is to be avoided, then this can happen only through nonresistance to Communism. Since a Communist victory would not be so great a disaster as the extinction of human life, it is best to accept Communism.

Either we risk a nuclear disarmament with Russia or the arms race between the United States and Russia continues. If we do not have 99.9 per cent guarantees on Russian disarmament, then this involves certain risks. On the other hand, if we continue the arms race other countries will join in and eventually some of the bombs will go off.

[2] Cf. Bergen Evans, *A Natural History of Nonsense* (New York: Vintage Books, 1959), p. 8.

To treat these dilemmas properly one needs to have knowledge about the total cold-war situation at the time the dilemmas were stated. And, obviously, not many people have this knowledge. However, certain apparent weaknesses in these dilemmas can be indicated. In the first the "either-or" statement—either we try to stop such actions or we do not— is exhaustive. But it appears that one can take the dilemma by the horns. Would action of a certain sort which might stop these things, lead to war? Perhaps tearing down the wall might have consequences not in our interest, but are there other ways that we could take action to stop such things? Some might also question whether the second "if-then" is true. The second dilemma can be put in this way:

If there is any kind of war, then this will lead to the extinction of human life.
If there is to be no war, then we must not resist Communism.
Either there will be war or there will not be war.
Therefore we either obliterate the human race or accept Communism.

Regarding the argument in this form, one would direct criticisms against the "if-then" statements, and the one which appears to be the weakest is the second. The last dilemma contains a suspicious "either-or" statement: Either we accept a risky disarmament or continue the arms race. Is this exhaustive?

THE COUNTERDILEMMA

When one responds to a dilemma by constructing another dilemma which is essentially like the first but which has a conclusion which opposes the conclusion of the first, he is meeting a dilemma in a way traditionally called rebuttal by a *counterdilemma*. It should be kept in mind that such a rebuttal does not establish that the original dilemma is unrealistic.

The easiest way to construct a counterdilemma is as follows: Suppose we have:

If A, then B.
If C, then D.
Either A or C.
Therefore either B or D.

A counterdilemma can be constructed by changing the position of the B's and D's and negating them in this way:

If A, then not-D.
If C, then not-B.
Either A or C.
Therefore either not-D or not-B.

For example consider our first dilemma in section one:

1. Either we satisfy Britain by releasing the prisoners and apologizing for Wilkes' action, or we do not satisfy Britain.
   If we satisfy Britain, then the United States public will be outraged. If we do not satisfy Britain, then there might be war.
   Therefore, either the United States public will be outraged or there will be war.

The counterdilemma constructed along the above lines would be:

2. Either we satisfy Britain by releasing the prisoners and apologizing for Wilkes' action, or we do not satisfy Britain.
   If we satisfy Britain, then there will not be a war.
   If we do not satisfy Britain, then the United States public will not be outraged.
   Therefore either there will not be a war or the United States public will not be outraged.

One classic example of such a counterdilemma occurs in the story of the Athenian mother and her son who wanted to go into politics. The mother, who did not want him to go into politics, argued:

3. If you act justly, men will hate you; and if you act unjustly, the gods will hate you; but you must either act justly or unjustly. So in either case you will be hated.

The son replied:

4. Mother, by your own argument I *should* go into politics. For if I am just, the gods will love me, and if I am unjust, men will love me. So in either case I will be loved.

Notice that in neither (1) and (2) nor in (3) and (4) do the conclusions contradict each other. In fact the conclusions of (1) and (2) can *both* be true, as can the conclusions of (3) and (4). What a counterdilemma does is to emphasize the opposite aspect of the situation. In many choices there is something good and something bad in each alternative. (1) and (3) bring out the bad aspects of such a situation, whereas (2) and (4) bring out the good aspects of such a situation.

Not all counterdilemmas have conclusions which are compatible with those of the corresponding dilemmas. The classic example of such a dilemma and counterdilemma is provided in this example:

During the fifth century B.C. a young Greek named Eulathus wanted to become a lawyer, so he went to the famous teacher Protagoras. Not being able to pay Protagoras at the time, Eulathus arranged to pay his teacher after he won his first case. For some reason Protagoras later brought suit against Eulathus for the money, and was able to get the case into court. He pleaded his own case. Eulathus also pleaded his case. Protagoras presented his side in the form of a dilemma: "If Eulathus loses this case, then he must pay me (by the judgment of the court); if he wins this case, then he must pay me (by the terms of the contract). He must either lose or win this case. Therefore Eulathus must pay me."

Eulathus offered in his defense this counterdilemma: "If I win this case, I shall not have to pay Protagoras (by judgment of the court); if I lose this case, I shall not have to pay Protagoras (by the terms of the contract, for then I shall not yet have won my first case). I must either win or lose this case. Therefore I do not have to pay Protagoras."

It is a good exercise to ask what *should* be the judgment of the judge, and how would this judgment be supported? The judge's judgment must involve a criticism of one or both dilemmas. How are the dilemmas to be criticized? In both cases the "either-or" statements are exhaustive, so the weakness is to be found in the "if-then" statements. One possible solution is to argue that the trial is *about* the payment arrangement—whether the arrangement has been violated. Thus *this* case, the one being tried, should not be considered as one falling under the terms of the arrangement. Thus Protagoras' second "if-then" statement is false. The judgment, since the contract has not been violated, should be, naturally, that the contract has not been violated, and thus Eulathus need not pay. (But if, by the way, Eulathus should win a case—one, of course, not about the arrangement—in the future, then he should pay by the terms of the arrangement.)

SUMMARY

A dilemma is realistic when (a) the disjunctive premiss is exhaustive and when (b) the two hypothetical premisses are true. There are three ways to criticize a dilemma: first, take the dilemma by the horns—that is, show that one of the hypothetical premisses is false; second, slip between the horns—that is, show that the disjunctive premiss is not exhaustive; and third, construct a counterdilemma. This third way does not establish that the original dilemma is unrealistic. Most often it emphasizes the good in alternatives which involve some good and some bad. When a dilemma is realistic it provides a concise, orderly representation of some situation.

EXERCISES

Each of the following passages contains a dilemma. If the item is not already in an explicit dilemma form, then rewrite it so it will be. Pick out those dilemmas which are not realistic. Criticize them by either taking them by the horns or slipping between the horns.

1. Either it is right to kill another human being or it is not right. If it is right, murder is not a crime and should not be punished. If it is not right, there is no justification for putting anyone to death—this would only multiply wrongs. Therefore in either case capital punishment cannot be defended.

2. Either I am fated to pass this course or I am not. If I am fated to pass, I shall do so whether I do the work or not. If I am not fated to pass, I shall not pass, no matter what I do. So why study?

3. If God is benevolent, then He desires to prevent the suffering of helpless human beings. If He is omnipotent, then He has the power to prevent such suffering. The fact that helpless human beings are suffering all over the world proves either that God does not desire to prevent such suffering or that He is unable to do so.

4. In the coming phase of Russo-American relations, we are faced with a choice: either deliver our bombs and wipe out their strong points, or else prepare to knuckle under completely to increasing Soviet pressure.

5. SOCRATES: I know, Meno, what you mean; but just see what a tiresome dispute you are introducing. You argue that a man cannot inquire either about that which he knows or about that which he does not know; for if he knows, he has no need to inquire; and if not, he cannot; for he does not know the very subject about which he is to inquire.

(PLATO, *Meno*)

6. The South Vietnam affair is an ugly little undeclared peripheral war to which we now seem irrevocably committed. It carries nothing but grief, no matter what happens. If we don't give aid, Southeast Asia may go over like falling dominoes. If we continue aid, we have a president, Ngo Dingh Diem, on our neck who won't institute the basic reforms necessary to create a stable and popular government.

7. A country cannot have full liberty and full equality, for if individual liberty is pushed too far, it creates opportunities for the ruthless and the strong and tends to breed inequalities; if, on the other hand, equality is carried to its fullness, it ends in uniformity and stifles freedom.

8. The dilemma of modern armaments is that the will to use nuclear weapons is indispensable as a deterrent to nuclear and perhaps major conventional aggression; yet if the United States were to exercise its will and use anything like its full arsenal of nuclear weapons it would destroy the very things it was fighting to save.

9. In Shakespeare's *Julius Caesar,* Brutus, a good man, is led by Cassius and the circumstances to believe that Caesar might declare himself king, become a tyrant, and destroy democratic Rome. He cannot let a tyrant destroy his beloved Rome. Since it seems to him that there is no way to kill Caesar's potential tyranny without killing Caesar, Caesar must be stopped by death. On the other hand, how can his death be justified since he has not yet committed any act of actual tyranny? In addition, Caesar is Brutus' friend.

10. Construct the dilemma which the secret agents tried to put Jesus in:

The lawyers and chief priests wanted to lay hands on him there and then, for they saw that this parable was aimed at them; but they were afraid of the people. So they watched their opportunity and sent secret agents in the guise of honest men, to seize upon some word of his as a pretext for handing him over to the authority and jurisdiction of the Governor. They put a question to him: "Master," they said, "we know that what you speak and teach is sound; you pay deference to no one, but teach in all honesty the way of life that God requires. Are we or are we not permitted to pay taxes to the Roman Emperor?" He saw through their trick and said, "Show me a silver piece. Whose head does it bear, and whose inscription?" "Caesar's," they replied. "Very well then," he said, "pay Caesar what is due to Caesar, and pay God what is due to God." Thus their attempt to catch him out in public failed, and, astonished by his reply, they fell silent.

(Luke 20: 19-26)

11. After the Confederate loss at Chattanooga, and with Lee's army entrenched around Petersburg, the Confederate generals in the West and South held a council to decide what could be done to prevent their losing the war. General Clebourne, a foreign-born, Irish general, proposed that the army could be enlarged by offering Negro slaves their freedom for serving in the army. His argument was something like this: If the war is to be won and the South to become an independent nation, then the Negroes must be freed so as to have the necessary army. If the war is lost, the slaves will be freed because of Lincoln's Emancipation Proclamation. Therefore let's try to win the war and free the slaves. (When Jefferson Davis heard of this proposal he ordered that it not even be discussed—it conflicted with Southern pride, honor and tradition.)

12. It may be said, for instance, that, if voluntary actions be subjected to the same laws of necessity with the operations of matter, there is a continued chain of necessary causes, preordained and predetermined, reaching from the original cause of all to every single volition of every human creature. No contingency anywhere in the universe; no indifference; no liberty. While we act, we are, at the same time, acted upon. The ultimate Author of all our volitions is the Creator of the world, who first bestowed motion on this immense machine, and placed all beings in that particular position, whence every subsequent event, by an inevitable necessity, must result. Human actions, therefore, either can have no moral turpitude at all, as proceeding from so good a cause; or if they have any turpitude, they must involve our Creator in the same guilt, while he is acknowledged to be their ultimate cause and author. For as a man, who fired a mine, is answerable for all the consequences whether the train he employed be long or short; so wherever a continued chain of necessary causes is fixed, that Being, either finite or infinite, who produces the first, is likewise the author of all the rest, and must both bear the blame and acquire the praise which belong to them. Our clear and unalterable ideas of morality establish this rule, upon unquestionable reasons, when we examine the consequences of any human action; and these reasons must still have greater force when applied to the volitions and intentions of a Being infinitely wise and powerful. Ignorance or impotence may be pleaded for so limited a creature as man; but those imperfections have no place in our Creator. He foresaw, he ordained, he intended all those actions of men, which we so rashly pronounce criminal. And we must therefore conclude, either that they are not criminal, or that the Deity, not man, is accountable for them.

(DAVID HUME, *An Enquiry Concerning Human Understanding*)

WHAT IS A PARADOX?

The word "paradox" is used in a number of ways in everyday language. Often it is used to denote something which is merely surprising. Another interesting use of the word is to refer to the incompatibility of two actions or intentions rather than of two statements. When an action for which one may have good reasons, tends to defeat or nullify another action for which one may also have good reasons, the attempt to carry out *both* actions is sometimes said to be paradoxical. Here is an example:

Sen. Paul Douglas, Illinois Democrat, pointed to the paradox of the states-righters weakening the states' authority by refusing to deal adequately with urban problems.

"It is very interesting," he said, "that those who complain most about federal encroachment in the affairs of the states are most often the very ones who deny to the urban majorities in their states the opportunity to solve their problems through state action. Until the state legislatures have been reformed, the plea for federal action will remain strong and just."

Another common use of the word "paradox" which is close to the one we will be interested in is found in this example:

These polls have surprised even the most ardent Kennedy booster, who notes the paradox of rising Kennedy popularity and growing conservative strength.

The paradox is this: Both

The popularity of Kennedy (a liberal) is rising.

and

There is growing conservative strength.

are true but are apparently—or almost—incompatible.

In this chapter we are interested in what are called *logical* paradoxes. In a logical paradox, in contrast with the Kennedy paradox, the two statements do not merely *appear* to be incompatible, but they *are* incompatible, that is, they are contradictory. And, in addition, they are apparently both true. Each is backed by an argument which seems correct.

There are, however, distinguishable types of logical paradoxes, some of which are trivial from the point of view of logic, and some of which are of great importance. Some are important because, as W. V. Quine says: [3]

> The argument that sustains a paradox may expose the absurdity of a buried premiss or of some preconception previously reckoned as central to physical theory, to mathematics or to the thinking process. Catastrophe may lurk, therefore, in the most innocent-seeming paradox. More than once in history the discovery of paradox has been the occasion for major reconstruction at the foundation of thought.

Thus in addition to providing some impetus to the study of logic because of its intrinsic interest, the logical paradox has a great deal of theoretical importance. In this chapter, some of the simpler logical paradoxes and one or two more important and complicated ones will be discussed.

TWO CLASSICAL
LOGICAL PARADOXES

One of the most ancient paradoxes, and one of the best known, is that of Zeno concerning an imagined race between the fleet-footed Achilles and a somewhat slower moving tortoise. The paradox is this: Suppose Achilles is given a handicap of one hundred yards. The gun (or arrow) goes off at time T, and Achilles speeds one hundred yards in a flash. But when he reaches the starting point of the tortoise, the tortoise, of course, is not there, having moved a short distance beyond. Let's say this is at time $T + T_1$. Achilles continues in pursuit of the tortoise, and at time $T + T_1 + T_2$ comes to the spot the tortoise was at $T + T_1$. The tortoise, of course, is not there. Achilles continues in pursuit of the tortoise and at time $T + T_1 + T_2 + T_3$ comes to the spot the tortoise was at $T + T_1 + T_2$. The tortoise, of course, is not there. Achilles continues in pursuit, and so on, and on. The point of Zeno's argument is that Achilles never catches up with the tortoise.

Here, two statements,

1. Achilles will catch up to the tortoise since Achilles can run faster than the tortoise

and

2. Achilles will not catch up to the tortoise since . . . (Zeno's argument)

[3] W. V. Quine, "Paradox," *Scientific American*. April, 1962, pp. 84 ff.

which are incompatible are each strongly supported by arguments. Now we know something must be wrong with Zeno's argument. The trick is to find the fallacious step. One common (but not universal) description of the fallacious step is this: To say that Achilles *never* catches the tortoise implies that the race continues for an infinitely long time. But, as modern mathematics shows, it does not. The sum of the (infinite number of) time intervals we described (that is, $T_1 + T_2 + T_3 \cdots$) is finite, not infinite. Therefore Achilles must catch the tortoise in a finite length of time. Zeno's argument *seems* to establish that Achilles will never catch the tortoise because it just *seems* that $T_1 + T_2 + \cdots$ should add up to an infinitely long time.

Suppose there is a clean shaven barber in a small town who shaves only those and all of those who do not shave themselves. If this is the only barber in town, who shaves the barber? Clearly, either (a) someone shaves him or (b) he shaves himself.

Suppose (a) is the case. The objection to (a) is that the *barber* is supposed to shave all those who do not shave themselves, so someone else could not shave him.

Suppose (b) is the case. The objection to (b) is that the barber does *not* shave those who shave themselves, so he cannot shave himself.

The resolution of this paradox is sometimes explained in the following way: From an assumption—there is such a barber—one is able to deduce a contradiction—he is shaved but he cannot be shaved. Thus our assumption that there could be such a barber is false.[4] The difficulty is that in describing the working conditions of the barber we unwittingly make them impossible, thereby eliminating the possibility of such a barber. Thus, from an apparently innocent account of his working conditions we come to the surprising but true conclusion: "There is no such barber."

FALSIDICAL AND VERIDICAL PARADOXES

In Zeno's argument, a false result was obtained through a faulty argument—namely, that Achilles would never catch the tortoise. Arguments like Zeno's which purport to establish a false and absurd conclusion—thus creating a paradox—have been called "falsidical" paradoxes; and arguments like the barber paradox, which establish a surprising but true conclusion, are called "veridical" paradoxes.

---

[4] This form of argument is called a *reductio ad absurdum*. Cf. page 237 for a discussion of this form of argument.

Here is another example of a paradox which, like the barber's paradox, is veridical. We are asked to imagine a town of which the only residents are those mayors, and all those mayors, who do not reside in towns of which they are the mayors. In this town, no one wanted to be elected mayor. For where would the mayor live? He could not live in the town, for the residents of the town were only mayors who did *not* live in the towns of which they were mayors. He could not live anywhere else because *that* town was the residence of all mayors not residing in the towns of which they were mayors. The (true) conclusion is that there could be no mayor of such a town.

THE LIAR'S PARADOX

One of the most famous paradoxes is derived from a letter of St. Paul. Paul was writing a letter to a man named Titus in Crete, warning Titus of the "many unruly and vain talkers and deceivers." "One of themselves," wrote St. Paul, "even a prophet of their own, said, the Cretians are always liars, evil beasts, slow bellies." He added, "This witness is true." The Cretian prophet was Epimenides, and the difficulty with the statement of Epimenides is this: Suppose some one asked Paul, "Was Epimenides telling the truth?" Obviously, Epimenides was either telling the truth or lying. Suppose Epimenides was telling the truth. If *he*, a Cretian, was telling the truth, he was telling a lie. Suppose Epimenides was lying. If he was lying, what he said—"Cretians always lie"— is false and (so the argument goes) Cretians always tell the truth. But if Cretians always told the truth, this Cretian could not be lying.

This is indeed peculiar—if a man always lies, he cannot say that he does without becoming involved in a paradox.[5] The argument connected with the second supposition, however, is faulty [see number (1) of the exercises], so we do not have, as yet, a paradox.

We can tighten the argument in this way. Consider the sentence:

(1) This sentence is false.

and the question:

Is the sentence on the line of this page which begins with (1) true or false?

Again there are two possibilities, both of which lead to a contradiction. If the sentence is true, what it says must be the case—but what is the

---

[5] What St. Paul said is clear enough. One would not think that Epimenides was referring to what he was saying as a lie—unless one were a logician looking for trouble.

case, then, is that it is false. So if it is true, it is false. If the sentence is false, it is true. So if it is false it is true. This is, now, a genuine paradox—the arguments against each possible alternative seem to be conclusive. In this case we cannot assume that there can be no such sentence as (1) as we assume that there can be no such barber or no such mayor as described in the previous paradoxes. A more subtle analysis is needed to remove the sting of this paradox.

One can question whether it makes sense to talk of a sentence which *refers* to itself. People often refer to sentences as being false, and in so doing might very well utter (1). Suppose, for example, that a witness to an accident was reading a newspaper account of the accident. Noticing a false statement, he might point to it and say to his neighbor, "This sentence is false." This situation, clearly, is one that makes sense, but our description of (1) as a sentence which refers to itself, seems to impute to the sentence powers (of referring) that only people possess. It is true that we speak of such and such a word as referring to Thirty-second degree Masons, or we speak of so and so's speech as referring to the farm problem; but what is meant by these expressions is that people use such and such a word to refer to Thirty-second degree Masons, and in so and so's speech, *he* referred to the farm problem.

Most proposals for the solution of the liar paradox block, in one way or another, the self-referring powers of the sentence, and it seems clear that this is where the difficulty lies.[6]

ANTINOMIES

The liar paradox, along with the paradoxes which are discussed below, is called an "antinomy," to distinguish it from the veridical and falsidical paradoxes. The distinguishing characteristic of an antinomy is that a contradiction is produced through accepted and traditional modes of reasoning, so that the resolution of the paradox can only be brought about by a revision of the reasoning process that results in a contradiction. Some of the most startling and revolutionary theories in the sciences and in mathematics have come about because of the need to change traditional modes of thinking—that is, because an antinomy arose from the results of different experiments, theorems, and so forth. One example, in the rather amazing branch of mathematics called set theory, is the discovery that although there is an infinite number of integers, there are even more real numbers. The traditional ideas about infinity as a num-

[6] See A. N. Whitehead and Bertrand Russell's solutions, *Principia Mathematica* (London: Cambridge), p. 10.

ber underwent drastic changes when the mathematician Cantor proved that there are numbers greater than the number of integers.[7]

The contemporary logician and philosopher Bertrand Russell showed that another antinomy follows from a long accepted method of constructing sets, or classes of objects. In the early investigations of class logic (see Chapter Fifteen) it was assumed that there is always a class whose members conform to any arbitrarily formulated conditions. For example, if the desired condition is that the members be satellites of the earth in 1549, the class of satellites of the earth in 1549 is the desired class. If the condition that the satellites be made of green cheese is added to the previous condition, the required class is the empty class, or null class. Any class exists so long as the conditions under which something is a member of the class can be specified. Many branches of mathematics involve class logic, and it has been discovered that this long-accepted method of constructing classes is also involved in these branches of mathematics. Because Russell showed that indiscriminate construction of classes may lead to an antinomy, the proofs of some basic theorems are now regarded with some suspicion.

Russell's antinomy concerns the self-membership of a class. Classes of some objects, for example, the class of logic books, are not members of themselves. That is, the class of logic books is not a logic book—it has no pages, no exercises, and no price. The class of freshmen at old Peuw U. is not itself enrolled at Peuw U., although each freshman is. The class of Misses America has only one dimension—the number of members. But some classes are members of themselves. Consider the class (A) of all classes that have more than two members. The class of astronauts is a member of A since there are more than two astronauts, and the class of rhubarb pies and the class of lost marbles are both members of A since there are more than two rhubarb pies and more than two lost marbles. So A must belong to A—it must belong to itself. If A were *not* a member of itself, A would not be the class of *all* classes with more than two members. There is no difficulty in allowing A to be a member of itself.

Now, consider the class (B) of all the classes which are not members of themselves—such as the classes of logic books, freshmen, Misses America, and so forth—and the question: Is B a member of itself? It either *is* a member of itself or is not a member of itself. If B *is* a member of itself, it is a class which *is not* a member of B, since B has as members only those classes which are not members of themselves. If B *is not* a member of itself, it is a class which *is* a member of B, since B is the class of those classes which are not members of themselves.

---

[7] See E. Kamke, *Theory of Sets* (New York: Dover, 1950), p. 10.

Each alternative—*B* is a member of itself and *B* is not a member of itself—yields a contradiction, so we must conclude that neither alternative is true. This situation is similar to those of the barber and of the mayor—that is, each alternative (for example, the barber shaves himself or he does not) yields a contradiction. In the cases of the barber and of the mayor, we assumed that the derived contradictions meant that there could be no such barber and no such mayor. And in the case of class *B*, the correct conclusion is that there can be no such class. Russell's paradox is an antinomy, however, and the others are not, since it has been held obvious for a long time that any class exists so long as the conditions under which something is a member of the class are specified. No such habits of thinking supported the existence of the barber or mayor, so these paradoxes are not called antinomies. Russell showed, at any rate, that in logic [8] and mathematics care must be exercised in the construction of classes.

EXERCISES

1. It was mentioned in the text that there is an error in the following argument:

Suppose Epimenides was lying. If he was lying, what he said—"Cretians always lie"—is false and Cretians always tell the truth. But if Cretians always told the truth, this Cretian could not be lying.

What is the error?

2. Instructors sometimes say that all generalities are false. If you were looking for (logical) trouble, could you show that a paradox arises from that statement?

3. If an adjective itself possesses the property denoted by it, it is called autological. Thus "polysyllabic" is polysyllabic and so is autological. "Short" is short and so is autological. A heterological adjective is one which does not possess the property denoted by it. Thus "long" is not long, "precious" is not precious, and so each of these adjectives is heterological. But what about "heterological"? Is it heterological or autological?

4. There is a bibliography in the Library of Congress which lists all bibliographies which do not list themselves. Does it list itself?

5. In a certain army camp, the commanding officer listed a Class A blackout as a surprise blackout in which the men cannot know more than twenty-four hours beforehand that the blackout will occur. One Saturday he announced that a Class A blackout would be held the following week (supposing the week begins Saturday at midnight). One of the men objected that the blackout could not be held without violating the "surprise" condition. For suppose the blackout was scheduled for Saturday night, the last night of the week. The men

---

[8] Russell discovered the antinomy that bears his name in 1901 in the work of the German logician Gottlob Frege.

would know Friday morning that the blackout must be Saturday night, since that was the last night it could be held. This means that they would know *more* than twenty-four hours beforehand when the blackout was to occur. Thus the blackout could not be held Saturday night. But it could not be held Friday night either, since on Thursday, the men would know that since Saturday is out, the blackout must be Friday night. They would again know more than twenty-four hours beforehand when the blackout would occur. So Friday night is out. Reasoning in this way for each night back to Sunday, the men convinced the commanding officer that the Class A blackout was impossible. Can you find an error in their reasoning?

6. Here is Russell's version of a paradox he attributes to G. G. Berry, a librarian. How should this paradox be classed?

The numbers of syllables in the English names of finite integers tends to increase as the integers grow larger, and must gradually increase indefinitely, since only a finite number of names can be made with a given finite number of syllables. Hence, the names of some integers must consist of at least nineteen syllables, and among these there must be a least. Hence, "the least integer not nameable in fewer than nineteen syllables" must denote a definite integer; in fact, it denotes 111,777. But "the least integer not nameable in fewer than nineteen syllables" is itself a name consisting of eighteen syllables: hence, the least integer not nameable in fewer than nineteen syllables can be named in eighteen syllables, which is a contradiction."

(WHITEHEAD and RUSSELL, *Principia Mathematica*, p. 12)

7. A body cannot really move. For a moving body must be either in the place where it is or in the place where it is not; now, it is absurd that a body can be where it is not, and if it moves, it cannot be in the place where it is. Therefore it cannot move at all. Resolve this.

8. It is impossible to define a word. For you cannot define any word until you can define "define." Resolve this.

9. Consider an arrow that is shot from a bow to a target. During its flight, the arrow changes its position (if you will allow me to state the obvious) for it starts in one place, ends in another, and passes through an enormous number of others on the way. Consider any one of these places, say the one exactly midway between the bow and the target. The arrow cannot *stay* in that place for any length of time, no matter how small; for the arrow is constantly moving during the flight, and therefore *changes* its position during every interval of time. The arrow must, therefore, be at that place (the half-way mark) only for an *instant*.

At this instant, the arrow is at a perfectly definite place, for a body cannot be in two places at once. And that place is exactly filled by the arrow at that instant or, to put the matter in another way, the space occupied at the instant is of exactly the same dimensions as the arrow itself. But doesn't this mean that the arrow must be *at rest* at that instant? For, at that instant, it is confined to a space exactly equal to it—at that time, it has no room in which to be moving. And (as we have seen) the arrow is not in that position for any length of time—it has, at that instant, *no time* in which to be moving.

If this seems strange, consider the following comparison. After the arrow has reached the target, I pick it up, and hold it, once again, at the halfway mark. This time, there is no doubt that the arrow is motionless. But the first time the arrow was in *exactly the same condition* at the instant it was passing through the halfway mark. Both times, the arrow *exactly fits* the place in question. So the arrow must have been at rest the first time, just as it is the second time.

You still think motion is something more than being *at* different places at different times? Then consider the following comparison. First, I shoot the arrow from bow to target in the normal way. During the flight, the arrow passes through each definite position in the path at some definite instant. Next, suppose that after the arrow has been retrieved, some contrivance (a machine, if you like) now makes the arrow occupy again each of the places previously occupied—and *exactly one minute later* than the corresponding instant. (So that if it was at *P* at *t* minutes after noon, the first time, it is brought to *P* again at *t* + 1 minutes after noon the second time.) I suggest that there would be no conceivable way of distinguishing the second episode from a real "flight." No observation that could possibly be made the second time could show that the arrow was not behaving in exactly the same way as it did the first time. Hence, it was at rest at each instant both the first time and the second.

I began by talking about the place at the halfway mark. But what I have said clearly applies to every place passed during the flight. The arrow is at rest at every instant of the flight; so, although it is at different places at different times, it is always motionless.

(MAX BLACK, "The Paradox of the Arrow") [9]

Resolve this.

10. Here is a paradox due to P. E. B. Jourdain. On one side of a card is written "The sentence on the other side of this card is false" and, of course, on the other side is written "The sentence on the other side of this card is true." Is either of the sentences true or false? What kind of a paradox is this?

[9] Max Black, "The Paradox of the Arrow," in *Problems of Analysis* (Ithaca, New York: Cornell University Press, 1954), pp. 133–134. Copyright 1954 by Cornell University. Used by permission.

FORMAL LOGIC

Chapter Seven

VALIDITY

In this part of the book our primary interest is in the logical appraisal of deductive arguments. Methods will be introduced to distinguish valid deductive arguments from invalid deductive arguments.

DEDUCTIVE ARGUMENTS

Consider this example of a simple deductive argument:

1. The house has a basement and an attic.
    Therefore the house has a basement.

Clearly, if the premiss is true then the conclusion is true. If someone would assert the premiss and deny the conclusion he would utter a contradiction—the house has a basement and it does not have a basement. When such a relation exists between a conclusion and the premisses, the premisses are said to *entail* or *imply* the conclusion. A *deductive argument,* as we will use the phrase, is one which is presented as having premisses which entail the conclusion.[1]

Consider next this argument:

2. If Mrs. Ogmore-Pritchard is going to the play, then she will not visit Mr. Ogmore-Pritchard who is in the hospital recovering from fatigued ear drums.

---

[1] A nondeductive argument, as we use the phrase, is an argument which is not presented as having premisses which entail the conclusion. The premisses are presented as providing justification, evidence and support for the conclusion; good grounds, or a good case for affirming the conclusion, and so on.

187

Mrs. Ogmore-Pritchard is going to the play.
Therefore she will not visit Mr. Ogmore-Pritchard.

This argument is also a deductive argument. The premisses are presented as implying the conclusion, and, in fact, do imply the conclusion. For if someone asserts:

If Mrs. Ogmore-Pritchard is going to the play, then she will not visit Mr. Ogmore-Pritchard. . . .
Mrs. Ogmore-Pritchard is going to the play.

then he will contradict himself if he concludes that Mrs. Ogmore-Pritchard will visit her husband. This would amount to saying that she will not visit her husband and she will visit him.

THE VALIDITY OR INVALIDITY
OF A DEDUCTIVE ARGUMENT

We have said that a deductive argument is one presented as having a conclusion which is such that its denial contradicts the premisses. From time to time a deductive argument appears to be such that the conclusion is related in this way to the premisses, when actually the premisses and conclusion are not related in this way. When, in fact, it would be a contradiction to affirm the premisses and, at the same time, to deny the conclusion, the argument is a *valid* deductive argument. Thus, in a valid argument, the premisses imply the conclusion. When it turns out that there is not this relation between the premisses and the conclusion the argument is an invalid deductive argument. Both (1) and (2), as we have seen, are valid deductive arguments.

Many deductive arguments appear to be valid when they are actually invalid—just as many nondeductive arguments appear to be correct when they are actually fallacious. For example, the following deductive argument is an invalid argument, but to some it may appear to be valid:

3. If Moses was an Egyptian, then he would have been raised in an Egyptian family.
   Moses was raised in an Egyptian family.
   Therefore Moses was an Egyptian.

On inspection, one can see that this argument is invalid, for no contradiction results from asserting the premisses and denying the conclusion. It might be true that Moses was not an Egyptian even though the premisses were true.

Examine the following deductive arguments; which are valid?

4. Moses was either raised in an Egyptian family or a Jewish family.
    He wasn't raised in a Jewish family.
    Therefore he was raised in an Egyptian family.
5. If Moses had been an Egyptian, then he would have had an Egyptian name.
    Moses was not an Egyptian.
    Therefore he did not have an Egyptian name.
6. If natural laws cannot be suspended, then the Red Sea cannot have been parted.
    The Red Sea was parted.
    Therefore natural laws can be suspended.

(4) and (6) are valid, but (5) is invalid. The reader will find it profitable to see for himself that it would be a contradiction to affirm the premises of (4) or (6) and to deny the conclusion. In many cases, however, the validity of a deductive argument is not as obvious as it is in (4) and (6) and some method is needed to determine whether these arguments are valid or not.

In Part I the procedure in learning how to tell incorrect arguments from correct arguments was this: A representative sample of those kinds of incorrect arguments often found in everyday situations was presented. These arguments were classified under such categories as "equivocation fallacies," "opposition fallacies," and "the fallacy of special pleading." In studying these classifications and in classifying other examples given in the exercises, one develops the ability to detect an incorrect argument. Of course, everyone in the course of his life develops this ability to some extent; but like other abilities, it is improved and refined by study and instruction. One also learns the difference between valid and invalid arguments in the course of his life—or, more precisely, in learning the language he speaks. Deductive arguments, however, differ from nondeductive arguments in that it is possible to find criteria of validity which are exact and which (generally) can be applied mechanically. There are no such criteria for the correctness of nondeductive arguments. In the following chapters some of these criteria will be introduced—after techniques of symbolizing arguments have been introduced.

LOGICAL FORM

If each of the statements in the Ogmore-Pritchard argument is replaced as follows: 'P' for "Mrs. O-P is going to the play," and 'Q' for "Mrs. O-P will not visit Mr. O-P" then the argument can be written:

7. If P, then Q.
    P.
    Therefore Q.

Such replacement of statements reveals what will be called the *form* of the argument. But it is important to note that, in fact, no argument has a unique, single form. Rather, each argument has different forms, since there are always different ways to replace the statements (and, as we will see, other expressions) of a given argument. Often, however, one way of replacing the statements (or other expressions) of an argument has a particular interest to the logician. (7) is an example. For notice that if we now replace '*P*' and '*Q*' with any arbitrarily selected statements the resulting argument will also be a valid argument. For example, replacing '*P*' with "Green apples grow on green trees" and '*Q*' with "Red apples grow on green trees," we have

8. If green apples grow on green trees then red apples grow on green trees.
   Green apples grow on green trees.
   Therefore red apples grow on green trees.

This argument is also valid. If the premisses are affirmed and the conclusion denied a contradiction results. Similarly, if we replace '*P*' by "My instructor was correct" and '*Q*' by "David Hume wrote a book about germanium," we have

9. If my instructor was correct, then David Hume wrote a book about germanium.
   My instructor was correct.
   Therefore David Hume wrote a book about germanium.

Again it is evident that (9) is valid, even though the second premiss and the conclusion are false. The conclusion would not be false if the premisses *were* true. *If* the premisses are true and *if* the argument is valid, the conclusion will necessarily be true.

Now suppose "If Mrs. O-P is going to the play, then she will not visit Mr. O-P . . ." is replaced by '*P*' and "Mrs. O-P is going to the play" is replaced by '*Q*'. Then, replacing the conclusion of "Mrs. O-P will not visit her husband" by '*R*', we have another form of (2);

10. *P*.
    Q.
    Therefore *R*.

And now if '*P*' is replaced by "Green apples grow on green trees," '*Q*' is replaced by "Red apples grow on green trees" and '*R*' is replaced by "Pears grow on green trees," we have a series of statements

11. Green apples grow on green trees.
    Red apples grow on green trees.
    Therefore pears grow on green trees.

which no longer resembles a valid argument. Thus, the method of replacing the statements in (2) which results in (10) is uninteresting since
replacing the letters of (10) by arbitrary statements does not *invariably*
yield valid arguments. (11) is, of course, invalid.

We will be interested only in those methods of replacing the statements of an argument which will preserve the validity or invalidity of
the argument—that is, those methods which leave intact those words or
phrases in the argument which are essential to the validity or invalidity
of the argument and which are sufficient to show the validity of it. These
words and phrases will be referred to, for convenience, as the form of
the argument, even though, as was mentioned, to speak of the form of
an argument may be misleading. Thus, (7) is the form of (2), not (10).
The form of (2)—the Ogmore-Pritchard argument—involves the use of
the words "if . . . then . . . ," ("and"), and "therefore" in a certain
order:

7. If P then Q.
    (And) P.
    Therefore Q.

All this shows that the validity of this argument rests on the form of the
argument. All deductive arguments, if they are valid, are valid by virtue
of the fact that they possess such a form.

To show why an argument is invalid, however, is a more complicated
matter. Let us call an argument form [such as (7) and (10)] which is
obtained by replacing the *statements* in an argument by letters a 'form
(S).' Now, we have seen that an argument such as (2) has a number of
forms (S). These may differ in that replacing the letters of one [for example, (7)] by statements arbitrarily selected invariably yields a valid
argument, but replacing the letters of another [for example, (10)] does
not. But we cannot always be certain that there is *no* valid form [2] of an
argument just because we have not found one. For even if it is determined that there is no valid form (S) it may be possible (as we will see
later) to replace various expressions in the argument and find a valid
form which is not a form (S). So when an argument is said to be invalid
because there is no way to replace the statements in it to obtain a valid
form (S), it will be said to be invalid (S). Thus, an argument is invalid
(S) if and only if it does not have a valid form (S). We will, in later chapters, show that valid and invalid forms (S) are readily distinguishable.

In the preceding section it is said that we are interested in introducing techniques to check the validity of deductive arguments. We can now

---

[2] By "valid form" is meant "a form which yields invariably a valid argument
upon replacement of the letters."

say that our first aim is to introduce ways of distinguishing valid forms (*S*) from invalid ones in order to be able to decide whether an argument is valid or invalid (*S*).

CONTINGENT TRUTHS AND LOGICAL TRUTHS

Suppose the Ogmore-Pritchard argument (2) is rewritten in the following way:

12. If it is the case that if Mrs. Ogmore-Pritchard is going to the play then she will not visit Mr. Ogmore-Pritchard; and she is going to the play; then she will not visit Mr. Ogmore-Pritchard.

This rather complicated statement is an example of what is called a *logical truth*. Here are some other examples:

13. Either you have six apples or you do not.
14. If he is a bachelor, he is not married.
15. If he came before noon, then he came before noon.
16. You cannot have arrived before one and after two if you did not leave after you arrived.
17. What is visible can be seen.
18. The square of the hypotenuse of a right triangle is equal to the sum of the squares of the other two sides.

One does not need evidence for the truth of a statement which is a logical truth. All that is necessary is that one understand what is being said. This may be a simple matter, as with (13), or it may involve some work, as with (18). But these statements are true regardless of what is happening, or has happened, in the world.

Many statements which are logical truths are logical truths because of the role of certain kinds of words in the statement. One group of these words is the group of *statement connectives:* "and", "or", "if . . . then . . .", "if and only if", and "not" (which for the sake of convenience will be called a statement connective). These words, and many others, are often used to connect statements; for example, "and" connects two statements in the following:

She turned on the fire and he put the pot on the stove.

(12) and (13) are logical truths just because of the role of the statement connectives which occur in them. Consider (13); if the statement "you have six apples" is replaced by '*P*' and the statement "you do not have six apples" is replaced by 'not-*P*', we have

19. Either *P* or not-*P*.

One can now see that if any statement is put in place of '*P*' and its negation is put in place of 'not-*P*' the result would still be a logical truth. For example:

20. Either Truman was elected president four times or he was not elected president four times.

The statement replacing '*P*' does not have to be true to retain logical truth, clearly. The logical truth of (20) and (13) depends on the fact that they have the same structure—that is, they both resemble (19). Similarly, any statement in which the statement connectives have the same role as they do in (12) will be a logical truth. But the logical truth of (14) through (18) depends not, or not only, on the roles of their statement connectives but also on the meanings of expressions in the statements. Some of these will be considered later.

Logical truths are to be distinguished from what are sometimes called *contingent truths*—statements whose truth is known from evidence. For example, the statement "You have six apples" is a contingent statement. Its truth or falsity depends on (is contingent on) whether the person addressed has six apples. If a contingent statement is denied—if one asserts, for example, "You do not have six apples"—the result is also a contingent statement whose truth or falsity also depends on matters of fact. The negation of a logical truth, however, is a logical contradiction. For example, the negation of (13) is

21. It is false that either you have six apples or you do not.

This is, clearly, a contradiction.

As one might suspect, there is a close connection between the notions of a logical truth and a valid argument. The connection is this: if a valid deductive argument is written as a statement, this statement will be a logical truth. And if the premisses and the negation of the conclusion of a valid deductive argument are written as a single statement, this statement will be a logical contradiction. The Ogmore-Pritchard argument (2) is, as we know, valid. And it has been pointed out that when this argument is written as a single statement, the statement (12) is a logical truth. Also, we know that if the premisses of this argument are asserted along with the negation of the conclusion, the result is a logical contradiction. This amounts to negating (12).

TERMINOLOGY

There is an advantage in keeping to the terminology initiated in Chapter Four. But more explanation is needed. We will use the word "sentence" to refer to what is ordinarily referred to as such. For example, "There are advantages in keeping to a certain terminology" is a sentence and so is "You have six apples." A statement is, roughly, what it is that is said in the utterance of the words of a sentence when what is said is (contingently or logically) true or false. This is also close to what the word "statement" ordinarily means.

Different sentences are often used to say the same thing—that is, make the same statement. For example,

Al is our neighbor.
We are Al's neighbor.
We live next door to Al.

and similar sentences may be used to say the same thing. If A says, "B is my son" and B says, "A is my father," they are saying the same thing, using different sentences.

And, of course, different statements are made by use of the same sentences.

A to B: My father can lick yours.
B to C: My father can lick yours.
C to A: My father can lick yours.

Clearly, sentences and statements are quite different things, and need to be distinguished. Making a statement is an action, necessarily, like using a word, but the idea of a word or a sentence does not include the idea of activity.

We have defined "validity" in terms of the idea of contradiction, but, so far, have said very little about contradictions. Now we can partially remedy this situation.

When someone says, through confusion or in an attempt to introduce confusion, something like, "A low-fat diet is conducive to health" but a moment later says or implies that a low-fat diet is detrimental to health, we ordinarily say that he has contradicted himself or has uttered a contradiction. Notice it is the statements made which are contradictory, not the sentences. We say, moreover, of a statement or series of statements that they constitute a valid or invalid argument, but we do not say these things of a sentence or series of sentences. One may say something contradictory when he utters a series of sentences, but this is just to say that the statements he made are contradictory. That is, the statement made, for example, by using the sentence "A tomato contains more than fifty seeds and less than forty" is contradictory.

It is easy to see why the word "contradictory" does not apply to sentences, and to make it very easy to see, let us consider this pair of sentences;

The car is blue.
The car is not blue.

Let us suppose that Alabaster, in describing his neighbor's new car, uses the sentence "The car is blue." At the same time, Waxhead is in an argument three miles away. In describing another car, Waxhead says, "The car is not blue." Of course they were not contradicting each other. They were not even talking to each other. Yet, if we were to describe a contradiction in terms of sentences, presumably we would have to say that these sentences are contradictory—so Alabaster and Waxhead would be contradicting each other. Clearly, this is very misleading.

There is another point in connection with the idea of a contradiction worth noting here. We do say things like, "Well, the car is blue and it isn't." This might mean, of course, that the color of the car is a faded, dirty blue. Or someone might say of a movie that it was good and not good, meaning, perhaps, that the plot was a good one but the acting was amateurish. Often statements come to mean something other than what it appears they ought to mean. The captured villain always mutters into the microphone, "I'm not talking." These, however, are instances of subtleties of the uses of language which we will henceforth ignore. We will be concerned only with certain portions of the language (such as the statement connectives). In the succeeding chapter we will consider some of the logical subtleties connected with their use. And later we will give an exact definition of "logical contradiction" within the symbolism we develop.

SUMMARY

Our primary purpose in this part of the book is to introduce methods of distinguishing valid arguments from invalid ones. A deductive argument is valid if asserting the premisses of the argument along with the negation of the conclusion results in a logical contradiction. We have seen that an argument is valid because of its form. A valid argument written as a single statement becomes a logical truth.

A deductive argument is valid (to put it another way) and a statement is a logical truth, sometimes because of the role of the statement connectives in the argument. It is this role which is displayed by the form of an argument.

The terms "argument" and "contradiction" are applied to statements or series of statements, not to sentences. Although contradictions are often difficult to identify due to the complex ways in which language is used, it is possible to give a precise definition of a contradiction in the symbolism to be developed.

EXERCISES I

1. Indicate which of the following arguments are deductive arguments and which are not.

2. Indicate the form of each deductive argument by substituting letters for the component statements; and then construct a new argument (not a new form) by replacing the letters with different component statements.

3. Show which deductive arguments are valid by finding the contradiction resulting from affirming the premises and denying the conclusion.

Example: If Gordon Gudd complained that no one should tell someone else when to vaccinate cattle, he will lose all his friends. Since we heard him say this after church, he will certainly lose all his friends.

1. This is a deductive argument.
2. The form of this argument is:

> If *G* then *F*.
> And *G*.
> _____
> So *F*.

(Where G: G.G. complained that. . . . .
F: G.G. will lose his friends.)

3. This is a valid argument, since the following is a contradiction:

If G.G. made this complaint, then he will lose all his friends; and he did make the complaint, so he will not lose his friends.

1. Oscar smokes cigarettes and cigars. So surely he smokes cigars.

2. If we soften in our resolve to stamp out fire, then we shall have betrayed all those who have burned and suffered in the battles with bonfires, campfires, cigarettes, and firecrackers.

3. Either Edgar can pronounce "equivocal" or he is a complete idiot. And since he is not a complete idiot, he can not pronounce "equivocal."

4. If Edgar can pronounce "equivocal," then certainly he can pronounce "equalitarian." He can not pronounce "equalitarian." Therefore he can not pronounce "equivocal."

5. The habitual use of distilled spirits is wholly unnecessary, for they neither fortify the body against the morbid effects of heat or cold, nor do they render labor more easy or productive.

(College of Physicians and Surgeons of Philadelphia, 1790)

6. Either the church buffet will be held Monday, or it will not. It will not be held on Monday (since Rev. Dagnabbit can't come), so it will be held on Tuesday.

7. It is not the case that Rev. Dagnabbit can't come to the buffet Monday and that he has to be in the Hollow on Tuesday. Therefore he can come to the buffet Monday.

8. If Donald Never is a kook, he will show that he is at the buffet. If he shows that he is at the buffet, then he will be sent home. Therefore, if he is not sent home, he is not a kook.

9. If George Good decided to go camping, *or* if George decided to go to the ball game, then he won't be back in time for the buffet. He did not decide to go camping. Thus he won't be back in time for the buffet.

10. The buffet will be at 8:00. If Peter Push can come and if it doesn't rain, the buffet will not be cancelled, so either it will rain or Peter can not come.

EXERCISES II

Which of the following statements are contingent truths, which are logical truths, and which are contradictions?

1. My paternal grandfather had no sons.
2. My paternal grandfather must have had at least one son.
3. My paternal grandfather had one son.
4. Either he came with Aloyce or he did not come with him.
5. Either he came with Aloyce or he came with Alwin.
6. He held up two fingers and said: "We must notice three things."
7. No one can travel thirty miles in three seconds.
8. If $x > y$ then $-y > -x$. ('$x > y$' means 'x is greater than y')
9. The sun must rise in the east.
10. Page eight comes before page thirteen, certainly.

EXERCISES III

Which of the following are contradictory?

1. Jonas invented a dispenser for indispensable objects.
2. The sign on the card said, "Come as you are"; but Gordon decided not to.
3. Jonas also invented a sofa only two feet wide for small apartments.
4. Freud neglected to explore reason directly and challenged the potency of reason in guiding human conduct. But . . . he has an exalted esteem for reason, and . . . in this more crucial respect he is a believer in reason.
5. He said that he was sitting perfectly still.
6. This last club (the Scarlet Knights) is a random assortment of Jersey "sharps" who have been gunning to puncture the records of the city slickers. To do this they were forced to travel to the big town, since the New Yorkers have always known that it is further from New York to New Jersey than from New Jersey to New York.[2]

2 Al Horowitz, "Chess" in *The New York Times,* May 13, 1962.

7. A: Pete has nerves of steel—he's brave.

   B: Pete has no nerves at all—he's courageous.

8. A: Do you know that all meat is nourishing?

   B: I know that very well—I once lived on beans for a week.

   A: All right. Here is a covered dish—are its contents nourishing?

   B: I really don't know.

   A: I'll raise the cover—what are the contents?

   B: Pig's knuckles.

   A: You've now said the following:

   (1) All meat is nourishing.

   (2) I don't know whether the contents of this dish are nourishing.

   (3) The contents of this dish are meat.

   So you've contradicted yourself.

9. You have to go east to get to the South Pole from here.

10. Edgar decided to comb his hair immediately but did not even try to do it.

Chapter Eight

THE STATEMENT
CONNECTIVES

In order to provide methods of testing the validity of deductive arguments whose validity depends on the statement connectives—"not", "and", "or", "if-then", and "if and only if"—it will first be necessary to introduce a symbolism for these connectives. The names of these connectives are, respectively, "negation", "conjunction", "disjunction", "conditional", and "biconditional".

'~' AND ENGLISH "not"

Let us begin our discussion of the connectives we will use in the formal system of symbols with '~'. It will be read "not" because its role in the symbolism is similar to the role of "not" in English. "Not" and '~' are both used to deny or negate a statement. If someone tells us he is passing a course, and we know he is not, we tell him that he is not, usually using "not" to do so. If we represent his statement by '*P*' (that is, let '*P*' be the statement "*X* is passing Biology 16"), then '~ *P*' is the statement "*X* is not passing Biology 16." '~ *P*' is read 'not-*P*', or "it is not the case that *P* (is true)".

Suppose that "*X* is passing Biology 16" is true. Then "*X* is not passing Biology 16" is false. When '*P*' is true, '~ *P*' is false, and if '~ *P*' is true, then '*P*' is false. That is, when "*X* is not passing Biology 16" is true, "*X* is passing Biology 16" is false. Now when someone says "But it isn't true that *X* is not passing Biology 16," he means, often, that *X* *is* passing Biology 16. We adopt this idea and say that '~ (~ *P*)' or '~ ~ *P*'

199

is the same as '*P*'. (We will omit parentheses—which, in the symbolism, serve as punctuation marks—except in cases where their omission might cause confusion.) He *may* mean, however, that it is not certain whether *X* is passing the course—but we have no need to represent this in the symbolism. Just what is meant in situations in which double negatives are used must be learned from the context.

There are in English various techniques and words used in denying or just negating a statement. For example:

1. He is patriotic.
1'. He is unpatriotic.
2. She is modest.
2'. She is immodest.
3. Some went to the party.
3'. None went to the party.

If one had occasion to represent (1) by '*P*', (1') would be '∼ *P*', since "He is unpatriotic" means "He is not patriotic." This holds also for (2) and (2') but not for (3), for in saying "Some did not go" one does not deny "Some went." We often deny a statement in more elaborate ways than by asserting the simple negation of the statement—that is, by inserting the word "not". We deny the truth of a statement, for example, when we say of a statement, "That's absurd!" or "Whatever possessed you to say that?" We express the negation of a statement in various ways, for example, "The view that such and such is untenable." There is in English an indefinitely large number of ways to deny and negate statements, but there is only one way in the symbolism.

There is no point in attempting to devise a symbol to parallel every use of every connective in English. The purpose of devising the symbolism is not to provide an alternative notation for English, but rather to enable us to concentrate on certain very common patterns of argument. It happens that these particular forms or patterns of argument are used almost exclusively in the formal disciplines and are commonly used in everyday life. By adopting the definitions of the formal connectives which will be introduced, it is possible to concentrate on these patterns. So even though some of the connectives introduced share little with their counterparts in English, they have a significant role in formal reasoning as well as an important role in other areas. This will become more apparent.

'·' AND ENGLISH "and"

In the symbolism "and" is represented by '·'. "And" enjoys a relatively uncomplicated role as a statement connective. This is not to claim, however, that the role of '·' is an exact replica of the role of "and". Each of the counterparts of our formal symbols has wider and different uses in English than the symbol has in the symbolism. But the conditions under which we say that a conjunction of two statements:

1. Today is Tuesday and the time is 10:00.
2. I said it and I mean it.
3. Mary is in school and Laurie is playing golf.

is true are fairly standard. We would say of (3) that it is true only in case *both* statements are true. But if Mary is not in school or Laurie is not playing golf, or both, we regard (3) as false. Likewise, in the symbolism, '$p \cdot q$' is to be counted as true when 'p' and 'q' (arbitrary statements) are true and only in case both 'p' and 'q' are true.

There are reasons, however, why this characterization of '·' is artificial.

First, in the study of arguments, we will not be concerned with whether 'p' and 'q' are related in any way. If it were true, (3) would serve as an answer to the question "Where are Mary and Laurie?" There is always a reason, in intelligent conversation, why two statements, or phrases, are conjoined. But 'p' and 'q' are arbitrary, as far as we are concerned.

Second, "and" is not always used in English as a statement connective. For example, "and" is not used in this way in:

4. Mary and Laurie are at school.

But a statement in which "and" is not used as a connective between statements can often be very naturally construed as one in which it is:

4'. Mary is at school and Laurie is at school.

In other cases this construction becomes more and more artificial. Consider:

5. Grant and Lincoln were contemporaries.
6. Two and two make four.

One could, with some manipulation, get

5'. Grant lived from 1822 to 1885 and Lincoln lived from 1809 to 1865.

But there might very well be some question as to whether (5') states exactly what (5) does. (6) could not be rephrased as two statements.

Third, the order in which statements occur is sometimes essential to the sense of the compound statement:

7. She juggled three eggs and broke them into the frying pan.

This loses something if we interpret "and" as connecting two statements and then reverse their order:

7′. She broke the eggs into the pan and juggled three of them.

Often, when the order is essential, it is emphasized in various ways:

7″. She juggled three eggs and then broke them into the pan.

There is often a point in putting one statement before another, and even though the conjunction may still make sense when the order is reversed, the point, of course, is lost.

We will ignore, then, the facts that in English order is often important to the sense of a conjunction; that "and" is used in ways other than as a statement connective; and that the statements with which "and" is ordinarily used have some relevance to each other—that there is some point in grouping them. '$p \cdot q$', then, will mean the same as '$q \cdot p$'; that is, either expression will be true if and only if both 'p' and 'q' are true.

'v' AND ENGLISH "or"

The word "or" is notoriously ambiguous. In some languages there are two words which perform the duties performed by "or" in English. Suppose you are eating dinner and the waitress asks whether you want milk or coffee. If you say "Yes," she will hestiate because you have not replied as she expected you to reply. She meant for you to choose between milk and coffee. But suppose you are being consulted about what drinks to offer on a picnic—either milk or coffee, or cocoa or beer. Then, if you were asked if you wanted milk or coffee, your answer (if you did want to offer these drinks) would properly be "Yes."

(One might wonder how it is that we do not often misunderstand how we are to construe "or". But if we remember that sense is connected with context and use, the answer to how we distinguish between the senses of "or" or any other ambiguous word, is found in the answer to the question as to how contexts are distinguished. This is not so puzzling.)

Before considering some of the complexities of the role of "or" in our language, let us simply describe, in terms of truth and falsity, how 'v' acts in the symbolism. The *only* case in which '$p \lor q$' is false is when both 'p' and 'q' are false. Ed says, "Either John will join me or Joe will and perhaps both will." If John joins him or if Joe does or if both do, we count what Ed says as true. But if neither joins him, he has made a mistake or lied, so what he said is false.

Now consider some examples in which "or" is apparently used in different ways.

8. Either today is his birthday or today is not his birthday.
9. Either today is Tuesday or today is Wednesday.
10. Either a student writes a term paper for this course or the student does not get a grade.
11. He can be identified by his ten gallon hat or he can be identified by his green boots.

Note that both statements in (8) cannot be true, nor can they both be false. (8) is, of course, a logical truth. And it will be counted as true since it would be symbolized as 'p v $\sim p$'. That is, if 'p' is true then '$\sim p$' is false, and if 'p' is false, '$\sim p$' is true; so, in either case, both statements would not be false. Thus (8) would be true in either case. Both statements of (9) cannot be true (but they can both be false, and, in this case, (9) is false). Presumably, the two statements of (10) would not be simultaneously true if (10) were true. That is, it is not the case that a student who finishes a term paper does not get a grade. But (10) is clearly not a logical truth—merely a statement which will be factually true or false.[1] (10) would be false (ordinarily) if a student did not write a term paper but did get a grade *or* if a student did write a term paper but did not get a grade.

For the reasons given, neither (8), (9), or (10) provides an exact parallel to 'p v q'. But (11) does, for both statements of (11) can be true and both can be false, and one or the other can be true while the other is false. Further, in accordance with the interpretation of 'p v q' (11) would be counted as false only if neither statement was true.

Nevertheless, both (9) and (10), as well as (11), will be symbolized as 'p v q' since the role of "or" in them shares essentially the same logical property as the role of "or" in (11)—that is, each would be counted as false if both statements of each were false. Now sometimes an argument will make use of the other feature of (9) and (10). For example:

Either today is Tuesday or it is Wednesday.
It is Tuesday.
Therefore it is not Wednesday.

involves, or makes use of, the fact that today cannot be both Tuesday and Wednesday. We will simply regard these arguments as requiring an additional premiss, or an additional phrase added to the appropriate premiss, to the effect that both alternatives are not to be counted as true. In symbols, the first premiss of the example would be:

$(p$ v $q)$ • $\sim (p$ • $q)$.

[1] (10), of course, may be regarded as a rule, in which case it would be neither true or false.

This would be read

Either 'p' or 'q' is the case, but not both.

(The parentheses serve as punctuation marks.)

'⊃' AND ENGLISH "if-then"

"If-then" also performs various duties in English. For example, consider these uses:

1. If John can recite the first stanza of "The Raven," then he has studied it.
2. If the pipe is not fixed, then the plaster will be ruined.
3. If either you or he has broken the window, and you did not, then he did.
4. If we have a cold spell, then the tomatoes will die.

We could easily increase this list. Note also that (3) is a logical truth and that (2) and (4) and perhaps (1)—depending on how it is interpreted—are learned through experience.

All of these uses have a parallel feature of special interest to us. If we say that one of these "if-then" statements is false, this would mean that the consequent—what follows "then"—is false, while the antecedent—what is between "if" and "then"—is true. Or, to put it another way, if the antecedent of an "if-then" statement is true and the consequent is false, we say that the statement is false. For example, if the pipe is not fixed and if the plaster is not ruined, (2) is said to be false. If (4) is not to be regarded as expressing a universal law of nature (see below), but is meant simply as a statement of fact then, again, if we have a cold spell but the tomatoes do not die (because, for example, they are a hardy variety), then (4) is false. The same considerations apply to (1), but since (3) is a logical truth, the supposition that it might be false is spurious. Nevertheless *if* an antecedent of an "if-then" statement—a conditional—is true and the consequent is false, we say that the conditional is false. This provides some justification for saying (as we will) that to say that a conditional is *true,* is to say that this state of affairs ('p' is true and 'q' is false) does not hold, or that it is false that 'p' is true and 'q' is false—that is, '$\sim (p \cdot \sim q)$'.

Therefore '$p \supset q$', which we now introduce, will mean '$\sim (p \cdot \sim q)$'. And we will symbolize all conditionals similar to (1) through (4) by use of this symbol. Thus, for example, (4) will be symbolized:

$C \supset T$

where 'C' is "we have a cold spell" and 'T' is "the tomatoes will die." There are other ways in which (4) can be stated, for example:

The tomatoes will die if we have a cold spell.
The tomatoes will die in the event of a cold spell.

Each will be rendered '$C \supset T$'.

Obviously the significance of each of the statements (1) through (4) is not completely captured by employing '$\supset$'. For example, '$\sim (p \cdot \sim q)$' is true if 'p' is false. If 'p' is false in '$\sim (p \cdot \sim q)$', then the conjunction of 'p' and '$\sim q$' is false, since '$r \cdot s$' is false if either 'r' is false or 's' is false. If '$p \cdot \sim q$' is false, then its negation, '$\sim (p \cdot \sim q)$', or '$p \supset q$', would be true. But of (1) through (4) we would not say that they are true if their antecedents (the 'p's) are false. For example, if the pipe is not fixed we would not say that (2) is true on *that* account. (2) is true if the pipe is not fixed *and* if the plaster is ruined because of the pipe's not being fixed. Similarly, if we did not have a cold spell we would not suppose that (4) is true because of *this*. (4) is shown to be true by observation of tomato plants in a cold spell and by knowledge about the relation of cold to the life of plants and, in particular, of tomato plants. (1) would not be true if the person cannot recite the first stanza of "The Raven"; rather (1) is true because the 'ability to recite' requires 'study'. Also if the consequent (q) is true in a conditional, the statement is true whether the antecedent is true or false. This too does not accord with our uses of "if-then". Often, if the antecedent is false, we do not judge the statement as being true or false.

If the '$\supset$' does not capture all the significance of our ordinary uses of "if-then", what justifies our translating "if-then" into '$\supset$'? The justification is quite simple. Our purpose in introducing symbols for "and," "not," "if-then", and so forth in this chapter is to aid in developing methods for testing the validity of formal arguments. As we have just seen, the '$\supset$' *does* capture a common feature of some of the various uses of "if-then". Now if this common feature were all that needs to be preserved in symbolism in connection with "if-then" statements in order to test the validity of an argument, then this translation, given our purpose, is fully justified. This common feature is all that needs to be preserved. In the next chapter, the first method will be introduced to test the validity of an argument—truth tables. With a few exceptions (see below), if we take any example of a valid deductive argument containing an "if-then" premiss and if we render this argument into symbols by use of '$\supset$', it will come out valid when tested. On the other hand, if we take any intuitively invalid argument which contains an "if-then" statement and employ the '$\supset$' symbol, the argument will be shown, on testing, to be invalid.

There are uses of "if-then" which lack the common feature just mentioned. For example:

5. If Sen. Chitterlings is elected President in 1964, then the moon is made of blue cheese.

We would *not* ordinarily say that if (5) is true, then it is false that both Chitterlings will be elected and that the moon is not made of blue cheese for we would not, in most contexts, speak of (5) as true or false. (5) would commonly be used as an expression of pessimism about Chitterlings' chances, as a joke, and the like. For example, (5) may mean:

6. It is absolutely impossible for Chitterlings to be elected.

(6) is not, as we can see, an "if-then" statement.

Here is another example of an "if-then" statement which lacks the common feature:

7. If Nixon had won the 1960 election, he would not have written the book *Six Crises.*

This is known as a contrary-to-fact conditional—for obvious reasons. In the case of these conditionals it is understood that the antecedent is, as a matter of fact, false, so that the falsity of (7) could not result from the truth of the antecedent and the falsity of the consequent. The conditions under which such conditionals are true and false is a topic of the philosophy of science.

The last examples to be considered here are known as generalized conditionals. As one could guess, the generalized conditional is a generalized version of the ordinary conditional:

8. If one can recite the first stanza of "The Raven," then he has studied it.
9. If a number is divisible by four, then it is even.

Notice that it makes no sense to speak of the antecedent as being true, since the antecedent is not a factual statement; that is, one cannot say that

One can recite the first stanza of "The Raven."
A number is divisible by four.

are true or false because no particular person or number is being referred to. The consequent, as is easily seen, is also neither true or false. So the truth conditions of the conditional are not applicable to the generalized conditional. Later it will be seen that the generalized conditional must be analyzed into more complex components than whole statements.

In all arguments discussed in the remainder of the book which contain "if-then" statements, the common feature is present. Thus we will symbolize all such statements by using '$\supset$'. Since '$p \supset q$' is defined as '$\sim (p \cdot \sim q)$', '$p \supset q$' is false when and only when 'p' is true and 'q' is false; otherwise it is true.

'≡' AND NECESSARY AND
SUFFICIENT CONDITIONS

In mathematics there is a carefully observed distinction between necessary, sufficient, and necessary and sufficient conditions for some statement to be true. To say that 'p' is a necessary condition for the truth of 'q', in our symbolism, is to say:

1. $q \supset p$

That is, if 'q' is true, 'p' is certainly true since 'p' is necessarily so in order that 'q' may be true. To say that 'p' is a sufficient condition for the truth of 'q' is to say:

2. $p \supset q$

Here we know that if 'p' is true, 'q' must be, since 'p' is sufficient to guarantee the truth of 'q'. Of course, in regard to (1) we can say 'q' is a sufficient condition for the truth of 'p' and in (2) we can say that 'q' is a necessary condition for the truth of 'p'.

A necessary and sufficient condition for the truth of 'q' would be, on the basis of our previous remarks, a statement 'p' such that '$p \supset q$' and '$q \supset p$'. We define the statement connective "if and only if", or '≡', as being this relation—the biconditional—between two statements 'p' and 'q'. So '$p \equiv q$' means '$p \supset q$ and $q \supset p$'. The biconditional statement is true if both 'p' and 'q' are true and if both 'p' and 'q' are false. It is false if either 'p' is true and 'q' false or if 'p' is false and 'q' true, since these conditions would mean that either '$p \supset q$' or '$q \supset p$' is false, and this, in turn, would mean that one of the statements in the conjunction '$(p \supset q) \cdot (q \supset p)$' is false, and this means the conjunction is false. And the conjunction is the same as the biconditional '$p \equiv q$'.

To say that 'p' is *equivalent* to 'q', in the symbolism, is to say simply that both are true or both are false. We read '$p \equiv q$' as "p if and only if q", although it is clear that this reading is subject to the difficulties involved in reading '$p \supset q$' as "If p then q". (Note also that speaking of the truth of 'p' as a necessary or sufficient condition for the truth of 'q' will have a point only if 'p' and 'q'—that is, statements replacing them—are relevant to each other.)

COMPLEX STATEMENTS AND THE
SCOPE OF STATEMENT CONNECTIVES

The *scope* of a connective is, or comprises, those parts of complex statements, such as

1. $p \vee q \cdot r$
2. $\sim p \supset \sim q$

which are controlled by the connective. (1) and (2), as they stand, are ambiguous. They could be either

1'. $(p \vee q) \cdot r$
2'. $\sim (p \supset \sim q)$

or

1". $p \vee (q \cdot r)$
2". $(\sim p) \supset \sim q$

where parentheses are used to indicate the scope of each connective. Thus, in (1') the scope of 'v' is 'p' and 'q', and in (1") the scope of 'v' is 'p' and '$(q \cdot r)$'. The scope of '·' in (1') is '$(p \vee q)$' and 'r', while its scope in (1") is 'q' and 'r'. In (2') the scope of '$\sim$' is '$(p \supset \sim q)$' and the scope of '$\supset$' is 'p' and '$\sim q$'; and in (2") the scope of '$\sim$' is 'p' and the scope of '$\supset$' is '$(\sim p)$' and '$\sim q$'. In

3. $(\sim (p \supset (q \vee r))) \cdot s$

the scope of '$\sim$' is $(p \supset (q \vee r))$, but 's' is not included in its scope. The scope of '·' is '$\sim (p \supset (q \vee r))$' and '$s$'. Clearly, the scope of '$\sim$' includes whatever is in the pair of parentheses following it. In (3) a left parenthesis follows '$\sim$', and its mate is the last but one before '·'.

In the cases of '·', 'v', '$\supset$', and '$\equiv$', the innermost pair of parentheses which encloses them indicates their scope. In

4. $((p \supset (\sim q)) \vee (p \equiv (q \cdot r)))$
    $12 \quad~ 5 \quad 52 \quad 3 \quad~ 4 \quad~ 431$

the pair of parentheses '2' indicates the scope of '$\supset$', '3' indicates the scope of '$\equiv$', '4' indicates the scope of '·', '5' indicates the scope of '$\sim$', and, of course, '1' indicates the scope of 'v'. It is often convenient to drop parentheses when it is not confusing to do so—(4), for example, may be written:

4'. $(p \supset \sim q) \vee (p \equiv (q \cdot r))$.

The connective with the greatest scope will be called the *main* connective. In (4) the main connective is 'v'; in (3) it is '·'.

In English, various methods besides parentheses are used to indicate the scope of the connectives we use—commas, colons, semicolons, periods are used; emphasis is indicated by underlining, voice inflection, shouting, gestures—and often the context enables us to decide what the logical organization of the complex statement is. Saying without any inflection,

    5. It is not true that Harold got dessert and you did.

is to leave open the possibility of understanding what was said in either of two ways—in symbols (read H as "Harold got dessert" and Y as "You did."):

    5'. $\sim (H \cdot Y)$

and

    5''. $(\sim H) \cdot Y$

The scope of '$\sim$' would not be indicated unless one said

    5'. It is not true that you *and* Harold got dessert.

or

    5''. It is not true that Harold got dessert. (But) *You* did.

Often judicious phrasing allows the unambiguous statement of a complicated idea. Thus

    6. If either Mary pops her balloon or Laurie doesn't, and Dierdre lets hers go into the clouds, we will all go home happy.

should be rendered in symbols (in steps):

    6'. *If* ((Mary pops her balloon v $\sim$ (Laurie pops her balloon)) · Dierdre lets hers go into the clouds) *then* (we will all go home happy).

    6''. $((M \text{ v} \sim L) \cdot D) \supset H.$

SUMMARY

In this chapter we introduced five statement connectives: '$\sim$', 'v', '·', '$\supset$', and '$\equiv$'. Generally these will be used to replace "not", "or", "and", "if-then", and "if and only if" in symbolizing statements. The function of these connectives in the symbolism is indicated by the following rules:

    1. '$\sim p$' is opposite in truth value to 'p'.
    2. 'p v q' is false when and only when *both* 'p' and 'q' are false.

3. '$p \cdot q$' is true when and only when *both* 'p' and 'q' are true.
4. '$p \supset q$' is false when and only when 'p' is true and 'q' is false.
5. '$p \equiv q$' is true when and only when 'p' and 'q' have the same truth value.

The exercises which follow are primarily designed to help one acquire a familiarity with these connectives. Some additional instructions are needed to work them. Supposing that 'M', 'L', 'D', and 'H' are all true, what would be the truth value of

$$((M \text{ v} \sim L) \cdot D) \supset H \,?$$

To find out, one must start by finding out the truth value of the formulas with connectives which have the *least* scope and work out from there. The '$\sim$' has the least scope, so '$\sim L$', since all the letters are given as true, is $\boldsymbol{F}$ (that is, false) according to rule (1). The 'v' has the next least scope. Since 'M' is $\boldsymbol{T}$ (that is, true) and '$\sim L$' is $\boldsymbol{F}$, 'M v $\sim L$' is $\boldsymbol{T}$ according to rule (2). '$(M$ v $\sim L) \cdot D$' is $\boldsymbol{T}$ according to rule (3) since:

$$(M \text{ v} \sim L) \cdot D$$
$$\quad\; \boldsymbol{T} \qquad \boldsymbol{T}$$

and, finally, the entire statement is $\boldsymbol{T}$, according to rule (4), since

$$(((M \text{ v} \sim L) \cdot D)) \supset H.$$
$$\qquad \boldsymbol{T} \qquad\;\; \boldsymbol{T}$$

It will be most convenient to work such problems as follows (supposing all the letters are $\boldsymbol{F}$):

$$(A \cdot \sim B) \text{ v } (A \equiv (B \cdot C))$$
$$(F \cdot \sim F) \text{ v } (F \equiv (F \cdot F)) \qquad \text{(assignment)}$$
$$\;\; \boldsymbol{F\ T} \quad\; \boldsymbol{T} \quad\;\;\; \boldsymbol{T} \quad\;\, \boldsymbol{F}$$

The truth value of the statement will be found under the connective with the greatest scope—in this case, the 'v'. As we can see, given the above assignment, the complex statement is $\boldsymbol{T}$.

EXERCISES I

Consider the following statements. Distinguish between those which express logical truths and those which do not; those which express generalized conditionals and those which may be said to express truth functional conditionals; and those which are none of these.

1. If the train is late, we will miss our connection.
2. If the train had been late, we would have missed our connection.
3. If we can start by two o'clock we can catch the train.

4. If the track washed out, the train will be late.
5. If ice is heated to 33°, it melts.
6. If that ice had been heated to 33°, it would have melted.
7. If you will remember, I paid you yesterday.
8. If this is a circle, all radii are equal.
9. If the train doesn't arrive on time, we can catch the bus.
10. If the train is late, it is not early.
11. If we miss the train I'll never speak to you again.
12. If we missed the train, it is your fault.
13. If this had been a circle, the equation would have been easy to find.
14. If we miss this train, I'll be a monkey's uncle.
15. If x is a circle then x has equal radii.
16. I don't know if I'll go.
17. If Ed is disappointed, he doesn't act like it.
18. If Ed agrees, they will be on the two o'clock train.
19. If Grant had not been so reckless, many lives would have been saved.
20. If the phone does not ring, the wire has been cut.

EXERCISES II

In the statements below, distinguish between (a) those in which 'p' and 'q' cannot both be true and (b) those in which 'p' and 'q' may both be true. For each statement in which 'p' and 'q' may (possibly) both be true, describe a situation to which it may apply.

1. Either we are going to get some rain or our neighbors are.
2. Either Harding was the twenty-eighth President or Roosevelt was.
3. Bob or Jack will raise the flag tonight.
4. Bob or Jack will come with me.
5. Bob or Jack is the sole owner of the tavern.
6. Either we get the troops out of the sun or they will get unhappy.
7. Either we get the troops out of the sun, or we don't and we take the consequences.
8. Either he was disappointed or he is a good actor.
9. Either this is ice or I'm badly mistaken.
10. Either Bob was elected president or Jack was defeated for president.

EXERCISES III

Idioms: Express the following in terms of '$\sim$', '$\cdot$', '$\vee$', '$\supset$' (if possible).

1. The mail was late because a dog bit the postman.
2. A dog bit the postman, so the mail was late.
3. The mail is on time if it is sorted on time.
4. The mail is on time, but I forgot to bring it.

5. Only if the dog is hungry will he bite.
6. The dog will bite if he is hungry.
7. Whenever the mail is sorted on time it is delivered on time.
8. Either the dog will bite or he is not hungry.
9. The dog looked at the postman but he didn't bite.
10. The postman was bitten since the dog was hungry.
11. Jack did not faint although Jo did.
12. He is either strong or not.
13. I will go provided that you do.
14. Both Jack and Jill fell down the hill.
15. Both books are too expensive.

EXERCISES IV

A. Put into symbols those statements which are not already in symbols, using the suggested letters to represent the appropriate statements.

B. Suppose A, B, C are true and all the rest of the letters are false. Find the truth value of each.

1. $\sim (A \supset B)$
2. $(A \cdot B) \supset \sim C$
3. Either Ben Rodger will be captain of the gang or Jo Harper will be; if Tom Sawyer decides not to be. (B, J, T)
4. $(A \vee B) \cdot (D \vee F)$
5. $(A \vee B) \supset (D \equiv \sim E)$
6. If Tommy Barnes quits the gang and if Ben quits the gang, then neither Jo nor Huck will leave. (T, B, J, H)
7. $((B \vee D) \vee F) \vee E$
8. $\sim ((A \cdot \sim B) \supset E)$
9. Tom Sawyer is captain if and only if it is not true that either Ben is second captain or Jo is treasurer. (T, J, B)
10. $(A \equiv E) \cdot (\sim (E \equiv B) \cdot F)$
11. If Tommy saw the A-rabs, and if Jo saw the elephants, and if Ben saw the camels, then both Huck and Don Quixote were telling the truth. (T, J, B, H, D)
12. $((A \supset E) \equiv \sim (B \cdot C)) \cdot A$
13. $((A \cdot B) \vee (E \vee A)) \vee (E \cdot F)$
14. Both Jo and Huck saw only a Sunday School primary class; and if Tom asks them again to ambush, then Jo and Huck will not do it. (J, H, T, Ja, Ha)

EXERCISES V

Order the logical connections in terms of least to greater scope: Indicate where two interpretations may be made.

1. $(\sim p) \cdot q$
2. $\sim (p \supset q)$
3. $\sim ((p \supset q) \cdot \sim p) \cdot q$
4. $((\sim p) \supset \sim q) \cdot \sim (p \cdot q)$
5. $(p \equiv \sim q) \supset (\sim q)$
6. $(\sim (p \equiv \sim q)) \supset (\sim ((p \lor q) \supset \sim (p \cdot q)))$
7. $(\sim ((\sim (p \lor q)) \supset q)) \cdot ((\sim q) \supset \sim p)$
8. $(\sim ((((\sim p) \lor q) \cdot r)) \equiv (q \lor r)) \cdot (\sim p)$
9. $p \lor (\sim ((p \lor q) \cdot r) \lor ((\sim q) \cdot r))$
10. $(\sim p) \equiv \sim (((\sim q) \cdot \sim r) \cdot \sim p)$

EXERCISES VI

In (V) determine whether the formulae are true or false given the assignments:

1. Both p and q true
2. p true, q false
3. p false, q true
4. p false, q false
5. p false, q true
6. p false, q true
7. p true, q true
8. p true, q false, r true
9. p false, q true, r true
10. p true, q true, r false

Chapter Nine

TRUTH TABLES

In this chapter we introduce the first technique for testing the validity of deductive arguments which depend on statement connectives for their validity. In the last chapter, we thought of '*P*', '*Q*', and other capital letters as replacements of statements. In this chapter, in order to stress the difference between an argument and its (statement) form, we will call such expressions as '*p*', '*q*', '~ (*p* v *q*)', and so on, *formulae,* and treat '*p*', '*q*', '*r*', and so on, as blanks in which *any* statement may be put. (This was done in the latter part of the last chapter.) Different occurrences of the same letter indicate that the same statement is to be put in these blanks.

TRUTH TABLES FOR THE
LOGICAL CONNECTIVES

In the last chapter the connectives—'~', 'v', '·', '⊃', '≡'—were introduced. The functions of these connectives are given in the following rules:

1. '~ *p*' is opposite in truth value to '*p*'.
2. '*p* v *q*' is false when and only when *both* '*p*' and '*q*' are false.
3. '*p* · *q*' is true when and only when *both* '*p*' and '*q*' are true.
4. '*p* ⊃ *q*' is false when and only when '*p*' is true and '*q*' is false.
5. '*p* ≡ *q*' is true when and only when '*p*' and '*q*' have the same truth value.

214

Each of these rules can be expressed by use of what are called *truth tables*. Consider '∼' and this table:

1.

	p	$\sim p$
1	**T**	**F**
2	**F**	**T**
	(a)	(b)

1 and 2 are the *rows* of the table. (a) and (b) are the two *columns* of the table. In the first column are listed all possible truth values for 'p'. In row 1, where 'p' is given as **T**, '∼ p' is **F**, and in row 2, where 'p' is given as **F**, '∼ p' is **T**. This table gives the function of '∼'. It gives a value to '∼ p' for each possible value of 'p', in accordance with rule (1).

Similarly, the function of '·', in accord with (3), is expressed in this table:

3.

p	q	$p \cdot q$
T	**T**	**T**
T	**F**	**F**
F	**T**	**F**
F	**F**	**F**
(a)	(b)	(c)

All possible combinations of truth values for 'p' and 'q' are given in columns (a) and (b). In column (c) is given the truth value of '$p \cdot q$', given the truth value of 'p' and 'q' on each row—for example, on row 1, given that 'p' is **T** and 'q' is **T**, '$p \cdot q$' is **T**; on row 2, given that 'p' is **T** and 'q' *is* **F**, '$p \cdot q$' is **F**. The table can also be written in this way:

p	·	q
T	**T**	**T**
T	**F**	**F**
F	**F**	**T**
F	**F**	**F**

The functions of the other three connectives are given in these three truth tables:

	(2)			(4)			(5)	
p	v	q	p	⊃	q	p	≡	q
T	**T**	**T**	**T**	**T**	**T**	**T**	**T**	**T**
T	**T**	**F**	**T**	**F**	**F**	**T**	**F**	**F**
F	**T**	**T**	**F**	**T**	**T**	**F**	**F**	**T**
F	**F**	**F**	**F**	**T**	**F**	**F**	**T**	**F**

RELATIONS BETWEEN THE
LOGICAL CONNECTIVES

The first use to which the tables can be put is showing the relation-ships which exist between the connectives.

As was noted in the previous chapter:

'$p \supset q$' is equivalent to "It is not the case that both p and not-q are true", that is, '$\sim (p \cdot \sim q)$'.

"Being equivalent" means here that the two expressions agree in truth value with respect to each possible different combination of truth values for 'p' and 'q'. It can now be shown by using truth tables that this is indeed the case.

For '$p \supset q$' we have this truth table:

4.	p	$\supset$	q
	T	*T*	*T*
	T	*F*	*F*
	F	*T*	*T*
	F	*T*	*F*
	(a)	(b)	(a)

In column (b) is given the truth value of '$p \supset q$' for all possible combi-nations of truth values for 'p' and 'q'. The truth values of '$\sim q$' would be:

q	$\sim q$		$\sim q$
T	*F*		*F*
F	*T*	or	*T*
T	*F*		*F*
F	*T*		*T*

So the truth values for '$p \cdot \sim q$' are:

p	$\cdot$	$\sim q$
T	*F*	*F*
T	*T*	*T*
F	*F*	*F*
F	*F*	*T*
(a)	(c)	(b)

Column (c) indicates the truth values for '$p \cdot \sim q$'. Now that the truth values of '$p \cdot \sim q$' have been determined, the truth values of '$\sim (p \cdot \sim q)$'

can be determined. According to rule (1), the truth values of '~ (p · ~ q)' are just the opposite of '(p · ~ q)'. This is indicated by this table:

~	(p · ~ q)
T	*F*
F	*T*
T	*F*
T	*F*
(b)	(a)

Column (b) gives the truth values for '(p · ~ q)' when it is negated— that is, it gives us the truth values of '~ (p · ~ q)'. This column (b) gives the truth values of '~ (p · ~ q)' for all possible combinations of truth values for 'p' and 'q'. The truth values of '~ (p · ~ q)' (found under the first '~') match the truth values for 'p ⊃ q' on table (4).

When the truth values of two formulae match, the formulae are equivalent. All the steps in the preceding discussion are shown in this one set of tables:

p	q		p	⊃	q		~	(p	·	~ q)
T	*T*		*T*	*T*	*T*		*T*	*T*	*F*	*F*
T	*F*		*T*	*F*	*F*		*F*	*T*	*T*	*T*
F	*T*		*F*	*T*	*T*		*T*	*F*	*F*	*F*
F	*F*		*F*	*T*	*F*		*T*	*F*	*F*	*T*
(a)	(a)		(a)	(b)	(a)		(d)	(a)	(c)	(b)

It turns out that 'p ⊃ q' is equivalent to '~ p v q'. We can now show that they are equivalent by using a truth table like the preceding one. First we fill in the possible truth values for 'p' and 'q'.

p	⊃	q		~ p	v	q
T	*T*	*T*		*F*		*T*
T	*F*	*F*		*F*		*F*
F	*T*	*T*		*T*		*T*
F	*T*	*F*		*T*		*F*
(a)	(b)	(a)		(b)		(a)

We have eliminated the 'p' and 'q' columns to avoid unnecessary notation. One can easily see how to fill in the 'v' column of 'p v q', but certain things need to be kept in mind with '~ p v q'. Earlier, the notion of the *scope* of connectives was introduced. In '~ p v q', the '~' has the least scope. Since the 'v' has the greatest scope, it is the main connective in '~ p v q'. (In '~ (p · ~ q)', the first '~' is the main connective.) Under the main connective will be found the truth value of the whole formula '~ p v q'. Thus we first fill in the value for the connective with the least scope, the '$\sim$', then for the connective with the next greatest scope, the '$\lor$', which is also the main connective in this case. We obtain:

p	$\supset$	q
T	*T*	*T*
T	*F*	*F*
F	*T*	*T*
F	*T*	*F*
(a)	(b)	(a)

$\sim p$	$\lor$	q
F	*T*	*T*
F	*F*	*F*
T	*T*	*T*
T	*T*	*F*
(b)	(c)	(a)

The same truth values are given under the *main* connectives of each, thus the two formulae are equivalent.

The truth values of '$p \equiv q$' and '$(p \supset q) \cdot (q \supset p)$' are also the same, as shown on this table:

p	$\equiv$	q
T	*T*	*T*
T	*F*	*F*
F	*F*	*T*
F	*T*	*F*
(a)	(b)	(a)

$(p$	$\supset$	$q)$	$\cdot$	$(q$	$\supset$	$p)$
T	*T*	*T*	*T*	*T*	*T*	*T*
T	*F*	*F*	*F*	*F*	*T*	*T*
F	*T*	*T*	*F*	*T*	*F*	*F*
F	*T*	*F*	*T*	*F*	*T*	*F*
(a)	(b)	(a)	(c)	(a)	(b)	(a)

In '$(p \supset q) \cdot (q \supset p)$' the '$\supset$' are tied for having the least scope. In these cases, it makes no difference which column of truth values is listed first. The '$\cdot$' is the main connective.

The truth values of '$\sim p \cdot q$' are not the same as that of '$\sim (p \cdot q)$', and thus the two formulae are not equivalent, though they might appear to be equivalent. That they are not equivalent can be shown in this table:

$\sim p$	$\cdot$	q
F	*F*	*T*
F	*F*	*F*
T	*T*	*T*
T	*F*	*F*
(b)	(c)	(a)

$\sim$	$(p$	$\cdot$	$q)$
F	*T*	*T*	*T*
T	*T*	*F*	*F*
T	*F*	*F*	*T*
T	*F*	*F*	*F*
(c)	(a)	(b)	(a)

In '$\sim (p \cdot q)$' the '$\sim$' is the main connective. Clearly, columns (c) and (c) do *not* match.

Another way to determine whether two formulae or statements expressed in symbols are equivalent is by using '$\equiv$'. When two formulae or statements are equivalent, as, say, '$\sim (p \cdot q)$' and '$(\sim p \lor \sim q)$' are, then the truth table for '$\sim (p \cdot q) \equiv (\sim p \lor \sim q)$' will have all *T*'s under the '$\equiv$'. For according to rule (5), '$p \equiv q$' is true when 'p' and 'q' have the same truth value. Thus we have this table:

~	(p	·	q)	≡	(~p	v	~q)
F	*T*	*T*	*T*	*T*	*F*	*F*	*F*
T	*T*	*F*	*F*	*T*	*F*	*T*	*T*
T	*F*	*F*	*T*	*T*	*T*	*T*	*F*
T	*F*	*F*	*F*	*T*	*T*	*T*	*T*
(c)	(a)	(b)	(a)	(d)	(b)	(c)	(b)

In column (d)—the column of the main connective—there are all *T*'s. The equivalence of any two formulae, then, can be tested by joining the formulae with '≡', and seeing what is obtained for the '≡' column on the truth table. If there are all *T*'s, the formulae are equivalent; if there are one or more *F*'s, the formulae are not equivalent.

EXERCISES I

Use truth tables to determine which pairs of formulae are equivalent.

1. ~ (p · q) and (~ p · ~ q)
2. ~ (p v q) and (~ p · ~ q)
3. ~ (p ⊃ q) and ~ (~ p v q)
4. p ⊃ q and (~ q ⊃ ~ p)
5. p ⊃ q and (~ p ⊃ ~ q)
6. p v q and q v p
7. p ⊃ q and p ⊃ (p · q)
8. ~ p ⊃ q and ~ (p ⊃ (p · q))
9. (p ⊃ q) v r and p v ~ q
10. (p ⊃ q) · (q ⊃ r) and ~ (r ⊃ p) · q
11. (p ⊃ ~ q) · (r ⊃ q) and (p ⊃ ~ r)
12. p v (q · r) and (p v q) · (p v r)
13. p · (q v r) and (p · q) v (p · r)
14. p and p v (q ⊃ (r v s))
15. (p · q) · r and (p · r) · q
16. (p v q) v r and (p v r) v q
17. (p v q) v r and r v (q v p)

TAUTOLOGIES, CONTRADICTIONS
AND CONTINGENT STATEMENTS

A second use of truth tables is to determine whether a statement expressed in our symbolism is a logical truth, a logical contradiction, or a contingent statement. Consider the following:

1. John F. Kennedy was the first Catholic President in American history.
2. J.F.K. was not the first Catholic President in American history.
3. Either J.F.K. was the first Catholic President in American history or he was not the first Catholic President in American history.
4. J.F.K. was the first Catholic President in American history, and he was not the first Catholic President in American history.

As was noted in Chapter Seven (1) and (2) are called contingent statements. Whether they are true depends on certain facts. As we all know, (1) is true and (2) is false. But (3) is not true or false because of certain facts. (3) is an example of a logical truth and as we saw in the fourth section of Chapter Seven (see pages 192–193) it is a logical truth which depends on the role of its statement connectives for its truth. For if we replace "J.F.K. was the first Catholic President" with 'P', (3) has the form 'P or not-P'. The truth or falsity of (4), also, does not depend on matters of fact; it is a contradiction. Its logical falsity depends on its connectives, for it has the form 'P and not-P'. If a truth table is constructed for (3)

P	v	$\sim P$
T	T	F
F	T	T
(a)	(c)	(b)

then all the entries in column (c), under the main connective, are T's. If the truth values of a complex statement for all possible values of component statements are T's the statement is a logical truth.

Now, in *general,* a statement can not be judged to be a logical truth, or a logical contradiction, or a contingent statement, by constructing a truth table for it. This is because some statements are logical truths and others are logical contradictions for reasons other than the one we are considering—the role of their statement connectives. For example:

5. If A's grades are lower than B's, and B's are lower than C's, then A's grades are lower than C's.

is a logical truth although its (statement) form is

$(P \cdot Q) \supset R$

which would not be a logical truth by the truth table test (as the reader may verify). Nor would the negation of (5) be a logical contradiction by the truth table test even though the negation of (5) is a logical contradiction. (Later, other tests for logical truth and logical contradictions will be introduced.) In short:

(A) If the truth table test shows a statement to be a contingent statement, it may or may not be one. In these cases we will say that the statement is contingent (*S*). The notation indicates that the statement is contingent relative to the truth table test.

(B) If the truth table test shows a statement to be a logical truth or a contradiction, then it is—but not all logical truths or contradictions can be shown to be such by the truth tables.

These complications do not arise when we are considering formulae, of course. Truth tables can be employed to determine whether the formulae are what we will call *tautologies,* that is, whether the columns under the main connectives of the formulae consist of *T*'s only.

Consider, for example, '*p* ⊃ (*q* ⊃ *p*)'. Is this a tautology? Employing a truth table, we find:

p	⊃	(*q*	⊃	*p*)
T	*T*	*T*	*T*	*T*
T	*T*	*F*	*T*	*T*
F	*T*	*T*	*F*	*F*
F	*T*	*F*	*T*	*F*
(a)	(c)	(a)	(b)	(a)

In column (c), the main connective column, we have all *T*'s; thus '*p* ⊃ (*q* ⊃ *p*)' is a *tautology.*

We can also employ truth tables to determine whether a formula is contradictory or neither a tautology nor a contradiction (there is no special term for formulae corresponding to the term "contingent" used in connection with statements). If a formula has all *F*'s under its main connective, it is a contradiction. If it has a mixture of *T*'s and *F*'s it is neither a tautology nor a contradiction, but contingent (*S*).

Thus statement (4) would have this truth table:

p	•	~*p*
T	*F*	*F*
F	*F*	*T*

and statement (1) would have this truth table:

p
T
F

Statement (4) is a contradiction and the formula '*p* • ~ *p*' is a contradiction. Statement (1) is a contingent statement and the formula '*p*' is neither a tautology nor a contradiction, but contingent (*S*).

The negation of a logical truth or a tautology is a contradiction. Thus if we negate '$p \supset (q \supset p)$', the second example of a tautology, what results, '$\sim (p \supset (q \supset p))$', is a contradiction. This is shown in this table:

$\sim$	$(p$	$\supset$	$(q$	$\supset$	$p))$
F	T	T	T	T	T
F	T	T	F	T	T
F	F	T	T	F	F
F	F	T	F	T	F

All of the entries under '$\sim$', the main connective, are *F*'s.

Finally, consider these two formulae:

$$p \supset p$$
$$p \vee \sim p$$

They are clearly tautologies. If we test them for equivalence, we find:

p	$\supset$	p	$\equiv$	p	$\vee$	$\sim$	p
T	T	T	T	T	T	F	T
F	T	F	T	F	T	T	F

All entries under the '$\equiv$' are *T*'s. Similarly, if we test two contradictions, such as '$\sim (p \vee \sim p)$' and '$p \cdot \sim p$', for equivalence, we find they are equivalent. As a matter of fact, all tautologies are logically equivalent to each other, and all contradictions are logically equivalent to each other.

EXERCISES II

Determine by using truth tables whether the following are tautologies, contradictions, or contingent (*S*) statements:

1. $(p \vee p) \supset p$
2. $p \vee (q \vee r)$
3. $(p \vee \sim p) \supset q$
4. $(p \cdot \sim p) \supset \sim (p \cdot \sim p)$
5. $(p \vee q) \equiv (\sim p \cdot \sim q)$
6. $(p \vee (q \cdot r)) \supset (p \vee q)$
7. $(p \cdot (q \cdot r)) \vee (\sim p \cdot \sim r)$
8. $p \supset (q \supset p)$
9. $p \supset (q \supset (p \cdot q))$
10. $(p \supset q) \equiv (p \cdot \sim q)$
11. $(p \cdot q) \supset (p \vee q)$
12. $(p \vee q) \supset (p \cdot q)$
13. $p \vee (\sim p \cdot p)$
14. $(p \vee \sim p) \cdot (p \supset p)$

15. $r \supset (q \cdot r)$
16. $r \supset (q \text{ v } (r \text{ v } p))$
17. $r \supset (r \text{ v } (q \text{ v } p))$
18. $\sim ((p \text{ v } q) \equiv (q \text{ v } p))$
19. $p \equiv (\sim \sim \sim p)$
20. $\sim \sim (p \cdot \sim p)$

TESTING VALIDITY

The final use for truth tables which will be considered in this chapter is their use in testing whether certain deductive arguments are valid.

Returning to the previous example of a valid deductive argument:

If Mrs. Ogmore-Pritchard goes to the play, then she cannot visit Mr. Ogmore-Pritchard, who is in the hospital.
Mrs. O-P goes to the play.
Therefore she cannot visit Mr. O-P.

If each of the statements is replaced with these letters:

'*P*' for 'Mrs. O-P goes to the play'.
'*W*' for 'She does not visit Mr. O-P'.

then the form of the argument will be:

$$P \supset W$$
$$P$$
$$\therefore \quad W$$

In the fourth section of Chapter Seven (see pages 192–193) we saw that this argument can be written as a statement of this form:

If *p* then *w*, and *p*; then *w*.

or

$((p \supset w) \cdot p) \supset w.$

If we construct a truth table for this form:

((p	$\supset$	w)	$\cdot$	p)	$\supset$	w
T	*T*	*T*	*T*	*T*	*T*	*T*
T	*F*	*F*	*F*	*T*	*T*	*F*
F	*T*	*T*	*F*	*F*	*T*	*T*
F	*T*	*F*	*F*	*F*	*T*	*F*

we find that under the main connective, the second '$\supset$', we have all *T*'s. The statement is thus a logical truth. Those arguments whose validity depends on the statement connectives are logical truths if they are written as single statements. An argument which is invalid by the truth-table test is not necessarily invalid—for its validity may rest on things other than the role of its statement connectives. Thus, we call all arguments which are invalid by the truth table test 'invalid (S)' arguments.

The general procedure is this: rewrite the argument as a single statement—the formula is:

$$\text{(Premiss 1)} \cdot \text{(Premiss 2)} \cdots \text{(Premiss } n) \supset \text{Conclusion.}$$

Construct a truth table and treat '$\supset$' as the main connective. If all T's are entered in the '$\supset$' column, then the argument is valid. If not, then it is invalid (S). Whether or not a group of symbols is an argument or an argument form depends on how the letters are construed: if the letters are just replacements of certain designated statements we may call the group of letters an argument; but if the letters are construed as variables, the letters constitute an argument form.

Consider this valid argument form:

$$p \supset (p \cdot q)$$
$$p$$
$$\therefore q \vee p$$

To test its validity we rewrite it and construct a truth table:

$((p$	$\supset$	$(p$	$\cdot$	$q))$	$\cdot$	$p)$	$\supset$	$(q$	$\vee$	$p)$
T	T	T	T	T	T	T	T	T	T	T
T	F	T	F	F	F	T	T	F	T	T
F	T	F	F	T	F	F	T	T	T	F
F	T	F	F	F	F	F	T	F	F	T

Each of the formulae considered has been constructed of only two variables (p and q). With two variables the truth tables must have four rows. The number of possible combinations of truth values, and thus of rows in the table, for n variables is 2^n. Thus with two variables we have 2^2 or 2×2, which is four possible combinations of truth values, or four rows. If there were three variables, there would be 2^3 or eight rows. It is easy to see that, using truth tables, it becomes cumbersome to work with more than three variables. To determine the validity of this argument form:

$$p \supset q$$
$$q \supset r$$
$$\therefore p \supset r$$

which has three variables, an eight-row table is needed:

$$((p \supset q) \cdot (q \supset r)) \supset (p \supset r)$$

T	*T*	*T*
T	*T*	*F*
T	*F*	*T*
T	*F*	*F*
F	*T*	*T*
F	*T*	*F*
F	*F*	*T*
F	*F*	*F*

None of the exercises (except 13) will employ more than three variables. In the next section we will introduce a short cut method of handling arguments and argument forms with a large number of variables.

EXERCISES III

Determine whether the following arguments are valid. There are a number of statements which the student may find difficult to express in symbolic form. To aid the student in doing this, a number of arguments have been expressed in symbols.

1. It is not true that both the price of gold is fixed and people speculate on the price. People do speculate on the price of gold, so the price of gold is not fixed.

(*G*, *S*)

$(\sim (G \cdot S) \cdot S) \supset \sim G$

2. Either you can reach the roof with the ladder or we need a new ladder. We do not need a new ladder, so you can reach the roof with the ladder. (*R*, *N*)

3. Only actors are good politicians or only clever people are actors. But not all good politicians are good actors, so not all actors are clever people.

(*A*, *P*)

$((A \lor P) \cdot \sim A) \supset \sim P$

4. If Blue is at the top of the batting order, then our team has a chance of winning. But since his slump, he has been batting seventh. Therefore our team doesn't have a chance. (*B*, *T*)

NOTE: In this example, as in some of the following, there are clauses which are irrelevant to the argument.

5. It is false that a snake can curl up but not swim. It is true that it cannot swim, though. So it is true that it can curl up.

(*C*, *S*)

$(\sim (C \cdot \sim S) \cdot \sim S) \supset C$

6. Either it is too late to study or everyone has gone to bed early. Since not everyone went to bed early, it must be too late to study. *(L, B)*

7. If the pool is closed, we can't practice dives, and if we can't practice we'll lose the meet. So if the pool is closed we'll lose the meet. *(C, P, M)*

8. Either the hypothesis will be tested or it will be ignored (by not testing it). And so if it is tested it will not be ignored. *(T, I)*

9. If the pizza is done we will either split it with our roommates or eat it all and get sick. Since we will not share it, we will, therefore, eat it all and get sick. *(P, S, E)*

10. Either Edgar will get his degree in June or he will drop out of school and take a job with his father. If I know him he will not drop out of school and he will, consequently, get his degree. *(D, S)*

$((D \vee S) \cdot \sim S) \supset D$

11. If the high pressure system has moved in, the weather back home is clear and the temperatures are mild. But since the system has not yet moved in, the weather must be cloudy and hot. *(H, W)*

12. Church will start early only if Elder Older is home from the convention, and he will be home from the convention only if he has a lot of will power. Since church is already late, Elder Older has no will power. *(C, H, W)*

13. If the president has the long range interests of the college in mind, he will either obtain money for the psychology laboratory or persuade Dr. Freund to stay another year and raise Dr. Freund's salary. But he won't do any of these things, so, obviously, he is taking a short range view. *(L, M, P, S)*

14. Either the Dirty Sox or the Greenskins will wind up in the cellar but only if Ned Witt keeps hitting. But Ned won't keep up his hitting and the Dirty Sox will win more than the Greenskins, so the Greenskins will wind up in the cellar. *(D, G, N)*

15. Dr. Freund will not speak to Dr. Fiendish only if Dr. Fiendish will not speak to Dr. Freund. And Dr. Fiendish will speak to Dr. Freund unless Dr. Freund will not cut down the tree that is about to fall on Fiendish's garage. Therefore, if Freund cuts the tree down or Freund speaks to Fiendish, Fiendish will speak to Freund. *(Fr, Fi, T)*

16. Unless you fish early in the morning or in the evening, you do not catch bass in August. So if you do not fish in the evening, but you catch fish in August, you fish early in the morning. *(M, E, A)*

17. $p \supset (q \supset r)$
$(p \supset q) \supset p$
$\therefore p \supset (q \cdot r)$

18. $(p \supset q) \cdot ((p \vee q) \equiv r)$
$(r \cdot \sim r) \supset (q \cdot \sim p)$
$\therefore r \supset p$

19. $r \equiv q$
$r \equiv p$
$p \equiv q$
$\therefore p \supset (q \cdot r)$

20. $\sim (p \vee r)$
$\sim r$
$(p \vee p) \supset q$
q
$\therefore (r \cdot q) \vee \sim q$

TRUTH TABLE SHORT-CUT

An argument such as

(A) If Professor Zool is really learned, then he has elbow patches on his jacket. He really is learned. Therefore he has elbow patches on his jacket.

can be tested in this way:

1. Rewrite the argument in symbols as a statement.
2. Assign *F* to the conclusion.
3. Make corresponding assignments to statements in the premisses.
4. Assign values to the remaining statements in the premisses in such a way (if possible) as to make them all *T*.

If it is possible to make all the premisses *T*, the argument is invalid (*S*), but if it is not possible to make them all *T*, the argument is valid. (A) would be written as follows:

$$((P \supset E) \cdot P) \supset E$$

Now, when the conclusion is marked *F*, the consequent of '*P* $\supset$ *E*' must also be marked *F*.

$$((P \supset E) \cdot P) \supset E$$
$$\quad\quad F \quad\quad\quad\quad\quad F$$

We now try to make each premiss *T*. In order for the first premiss to be *T*, '*P*' *must* be *F*. But if '*P*' is *F*, then the second premiss would be *F*; hence we cannot make the premisses all true, and, consequently, the argument is *valid*.

Consider this argument form:

(B) 1. $p \supset q$
2. p
3. $\sim q \vee r$
4. $r \supset s$
$\overline{}$
$\therefore \quad s$

A truth table would have 2^4 or 16 lines. Using our short-cut method, we have: [1]

[1] The reader can verify that any grouping of the conjunction of premisses is equivalent to any other grouping.

(1)		(2)		(3)		(4)
$((p \supset q)$	•	p	•	$(\sim q \lor r)$	•	$(r \supset s)) \supset s$
$F \quad F$		F		$T \quad F$		$F \quad F \quad F$
T		F		T		T

If premiss (4) is to be T, then 'r' *must* be F. If 'r' is F, and if premiss (3) is to be T, then '$\sim q$' must be T, and so forth. As we see, it turns out that the second premiss is F; thus the argument form is valid and any argument of this form is valid.

If the conclusion of (B) were, say, '$s \cdot q$', then there would be three possible combinations which would make it F:

$$
\begin{array}{ccc}
s & \cdot & q \\
T & & F \quad (1) \\
F & & T \quad (2) \\
F & & F \quad (3)
\end{array}
$$

When there is more than one possible combination for the falsity of the conclusion, then work *each* of these rows. If for *any* of these rows the premisses can be made true, one can stop with that row—the argument form is invalid (S). If, however, this cannot be done for any row, then the argument form is valid.

In this argument form:

$$
\begin{array}{cc}
(((p \cdot q) \supset r) \cdot r) \supset (p & \cdot & q) \\
T & & F \\
F & & T \\
F & & F
\end{array}
$$

the premisses can be made true on each row; thus after working any one, a proof is provided that the corresponding argument is invalid (S).

EXERCISES IV

Use the short-cut method to determine which of the following are valid.

1. $p \cdot q, \therefore p$
2. $p \cdot q, \therefore q \cdot p$
3. $\sim \sim p, \therefore \sim \sim \sim \sim \sim p$
4. $(\sim p \lor \sim q), \therefore p \cdot q$
5. $(p \lor q) \cdot \sim p, \therefore q$
6. $p \supset q, \therefore \sim (p \cdot \sim q)$
7. $(p \supset q) \cdot \sim q, \therefore \sim p$
8. $(p \supset q) \cdot \sim p, \therefore \sim q$
9. $p \lor (q \cdot r), \therefore (p \lor q) \cdot (p \lor r)$
10. $p \lor (q \equiv r), \therefore p \lor q$

11. $(p \cdot q) \cdot r, \therefore \sim ((\sim p \lor \sim q) \lor \sim r)$
12. $p \cdot (q \cdot r), \therefore p \lor q$
13. $((p \supset q) \cdot (q \supset r)), \therefore r \supset p$
14. $(p \lor q) \cdot \sim (p \lor q), \therefore s$
15. $((p \supset q) \cdot p) \cdot r, \therefore q \cdot r$
16. $(p \equiv q) \cdot (p \cdot \sim q), \therefore p$
17. $((p \supset q) \cdot (r \supset s)) \cdot (q \lor s), \therefore p \lor r$
18. $((p \equiv q) \cdot p) \cdot \sim q, \therefore p \cdot \sim q$
19. $((p \supset q) \cdot (r \supset s)) \cdot (q \cdot s), \therefore p \cdot s$
20. $(p \lor q), \therefore \sim (\sim p \cdot \sim q)$

Chapter Ten

ELEMENTARY
INFERENCES

Truth tables enable one to decide in a finite number of mechanical steps whether or not a formula is a tautology. There is a close connection between this procedure and what will be done in this chapter. In this chapter, arguments will be examined, not to see if the statements expressing them are logical truths, but to see whether certain rules allow the conclusion of each argument to be deduced from the premises. In what follows '*P*', '*Q*', '*R*', and so forth, will represent any expression in the symbolism of Chapter Nine.[1] '*P* ⊃ *Q*' will represent an expression whose main connective is '⊃'; '*P* v *Q*' will represent an expression whose main connective is 'v', and so on. To emphasize the form of these expressions we will use mainly capitols in the discussions.

A RULE OF INFERENCE—
MODUS PONENDO PONENS

The rule

(R 1) '*P*' and '*P* ⊃ *Q*' imply '*Q*'.[2]

[1] We will understand that these expressions "make sense," that is, that they are either single letters representing statements or of the form '∼ *P*', '*P* v *Q*', '*P* · *Q*', '*P* ⊃ *Q*', '*P* ≡ *Q*', but not, for example, of the form '∼) *PQ* ((∼ v'. In short they must be such that it is possible to construct a truth table for them.

[2] (R 1) and other rules of inference which state that two or more premisses imply a conclusion are, of course, to be understood as '*P*' and '*P* ⊃ *Q*' *together* imply '*Q*'.

230

applied to the premises:

(P 1)   Mrs. O-P is going to the play.

(P 2)   If Mrs. O-P is going to the play, then she will not visit Mr. O-P.

allows the conclusion:

(C)   Mrs. O-P will not visit Mr. O-P.

where (P 1) is 'P' in (R 1), (P 2) is '$P \supset Q$' and C is 'Q'. (R 1) and any of the rules discussed in this chapter and the following ones which allow a statement to be accepted because certain other statements are already accepted (that is, premisses) are called *rules of inference*. (R 1) is commonly called *modus ponens*.

If (R 1) is applied to the premises:

(P 1) $(A \cdot B) \supset (D \vee A)$

(P 2) $(A \cdot B)$

it allows us to conclude:

(C) $(D \vee A)$

For, as we said above, 'P' and 'Q' in an inference rule represent any truth functional expressions, no matter how complex they may be. Similarly, we can conclude:

(P 1) $(A \vee C) \supset (B \cdot (D \vee E))$

(P 2) $(A \vee C)$

(C) $B \cdot (D \vee E)$

by use of (R 1).

RELATION BETWEEN
"implies" AND '$\supset$'

Before other rules are introduced, it would be well if the connection between '$\supset$' and "implies" were elaborated upon. What, we can ask, is the relation between (R 1) and the tautologous form:

1. $(P \cdot (P \supset Q)) \supset Q$?

First, it should be remembered that when it is said that 'P' implies 'Q', one is talking *about* two formulae—saying that one implies the other. In (1), on the other hand, nothing is talked about—(1) is not a statement but a formula.

Now the relation between '$\supset$' and "implies" can be stated in this way:

(A)   If '$P \supset Q$' is a tautology, then 'P' implies 'Q'.

This is a rather special use of "implies", since it allows the assertion that '*P*' implies '*Q*' even though '*P*' is a contradiction. This does not correspond exactly to our normal uses of the word, since we ordinarily do not take seriously an argument whose premises are known to be contradictory, that is, whose premises contain a statement '*R*' and a statement '~ *R*'. We might think that someone was beginning an odd kind of joke if he said "Let's suppose the Republicans win in November and that they won't win."

But the truth table of '*P* · ~ *P*' shows that the value of this expression is *F* in every case. Thus '(*P* · ~ *P*) ⊃ *Q*' must be true for every assignment of truth values to '*Q*'. Consequently, if the premises of a deductive argument are contradictory, any conclusion 'follows' from these premises. This feature of contradictory premises, it turns out, can be utilized in a certain useful method of proof (the *Reductio ad Absurdum* proof), which will be discussed later. The role of '⊃' as a statement connective in the symbolism is parallel, however, to a great extent, to the role of "implies" in speaking of statements.

OTHER RULES OF INFERENCE

The only requirement of our rules of inference is that they not allow a false conclusion when the premises are true. (A), of course, guarantees that this will not happen. We cannot hope to have rules of inference that allow a true conclusion from every set of true premises—the premisses may be unrelated and there are too many different forms of valid arguments to record in these chapters—but we can write down a relatively few rules that will enable us to validate a great many inferences.

At one stroke (A) provides us with an indefinite number of rules of inference; first, all the tautologies in which the main connective is '⊃' yield rules of inference. Thus (R 1) comes from the tautology

$(P \cdot (P \supset Q)) \supset Q$

Another common form of inference is:

(R 2)   '~ *Q*' and '(*P* ⊃ *Q*)' imply '~ *P*.'

This comes from the tautology

$(\sim Q \cdot (P \supset Q)) \supset \sim P.$

It is commonly called *modus tollens*.

Here, with their traditional names, are some other rules which are often used:

(R 3)   '$\sim P$' and '$(P \lor Q)$' imply 'Q'   (disjunctive syllogism)
(R 4)   '$(P \cdot Q)$' imply 'P'   (simplification)
(R 5)   'P' and 'Q' imply   '$(P \cdot Q)$'   (conjunction)
(R 6)   '$(P \supset Q)$' and '$(Q \supset R)$' imply '$(P \supset R)$'   (hypothetical syllogism)
(R 7)   'P' implies '$(P \lor Q)$'   (addition)
(R 8)   '$(P \supset Q) \cdot (R \supset S)$' and '$(P \lor R)$' imply '$(Q \lor S)$'   (constructive dilemma)

In addition, there are useful equivalences which are double rules of inference:

$$P \equiv \,\sim\,\sim P$$

becomes

'P' implies '$\sim\,\sim P$'

and

'$\sim\,\sim P$' implies 'P'

or, simply

(R 9)   'P' is equivalent to '$\sim\,\sim P$'.

(R 9) is called double negation. Here is an application of the rule:

(P) $\sim\,\sim (p \lor q)$
(C) $p \lor q$ from (P) by use of (R 9).

Another rule is

(R 10)   '$\sim (P \cdot Q)$' is equivalent to '$(\sim P \lor \sim Q)$'.
 '$\sim (P \lor Q)$' is equivalent to '$(\sim P \cdot \sim Q)$'.

These are called *De Morgan's Theorems* after the English mathematician and logician, August de Morgan. Here are two applications of the rule. Notice that the rule, in the second example, is applied to a *part* of a line.

(P) $\sim (\sim p \cdot q)$
(C) $(\sim\,\sim p \lor \sim q)$ (R 10)

(P) $\sim (p \lor q) \cdot r$
(C) $(\sim p \cdot \sim q) \cdot r$ (R 10)

Each of the equivalence rules may be applied to a part of a line or the whole line, but the rules (R 1) through (R 8) can only be applied to a whole line.[3] The other useful equivalences are:

---

[3] This procedure is justified by the fact that since formulae which are logically equivalent have the same truth value, the truth value of the formula in which the substitution is made will not be changed (See Chapter Fourteen, pages 308–310).

(R 11)   '$(P \supset Q)$' is equivalent to '$P \supset (P \cdot Q)$'   (absorption)

(R 12)   '$(P \vee Q)$' is equivalent to '$(Q \vee P)$'

       '$(P \cdot Q)$' is equivalent to '$(Q \cdot P)$'   (commutation)

(R 13)   '$P \vee (Q \vee R)$' is equivalent to '$(P \vee Q) \vee R$'

       '$P \cdot (Q \cdot R)$' is equivalent to '$(P \cdot Q) \cdot R$'   (association)

(R 14)   '$P \cdot (Q \vee R)$' is equivalent to '$(P \cdot Q) \vee (P \cdot R)$'   (distribution)

(R 15)   '$(P \supset Q)$' is equivalent to '$(\sim Q \supset \sim P)$'   (transposition)

(R 16)   '$(P \supset Q)$' is equivalent to '$(\sim P \vee Q)$'   (implication)

(R 17)   '$(P \cdot Q) \supset R$' is equivalent to '$P \supset (Q \supset R)$'   (exportation)

(R 18)   'P' is equivalent to '$(P \cdot P)$'   (tautology)

(R 19)   '$(P \equiv Q)$' is equivalent to '$(P \supset Q) \cdot (Q \supset P)$'

       '$(P \equiv Q)$' is equivalent to '$(P \cdot Q) \vee (\sim P \cdot \sim Q)$'   (equivalence)

The list is redundant. For example, (R 3), disjunctive syllogism, could be dropped from the list. One could get 'Q' from '$P \vee Q$' and '$\sim P$' in this way:

1.	$P \vee Q$	P
2.	$\sim P$	P
3.	$\sim \sim P \vee Q$	from (P 1) by use of (R 9) (double negative)
4.	$\sim P \supset Q$	from (3) by use of (R 16) (implication)
5.	Q	from (P 2) and (4) by use of (R 1) (modus ponens)

But since each rule is commonly used, and since employing extra rules will make the formal validations easier, nineteen rules are given. Although (A) furnishes an indefinitely large number of rules of inference, only these nineteen will be used.

THE VALIDATION OF INFERENCES

Consider now this argument:

(I)   Either the wheat will make 40 bushels or Utah won't get a new car. If the fertilizer is not as it is advertized, the wheat won't make 40 bushels. Therefore, if Utah gets a new car, the fertilizer is as it is advertized.

What is of interest, now, is whether the rules of inference will allow the deduction of the conclusion of the argument from the premisses. If so, then the argument is valid.

Usually, showing that the conclusion does follow—or is derivable— from the premisses involves intermediate steps. Thus, in symbols, (I) is:

$$W \vee \sim C$$
$$\sim F \supset \sim W$$
$$\overline{\therefore C \supset F}$$

Formal validation of (*I*) is written as follows:

1. $W \text{ v} \sim C$ P
2. $\sim F \supset \sim W$ P
3. $\sim C \text{ v } W$ 1 (R 12) commutation
4. $C \supset W$ 3 (R 16) implication
5. $W \supset F$ 2 (R 15) transposition
6. $C \supset F$ 4, 5 (R 6) hypothetical syllogism

Explanation: Each premiss is written on a separate line. The statements which follow from the premisses are written under the premisses and each is numbered. To the right of each of these statements is given its justification or the reason why it can be asserted. For example, the justification of line 3 is to be read: "from line 1 by using (R 12)." The validation is completed when the conclusion of the argument is reached, as in our example on line 6.

No rules can be provided for constructing a formal validation for an argument. Practice is the best method for acquiring the ability to construct validations. Often it is helpful to derive any formulae and try to see from these how to get to the conclusion. Sometimes in difficult cases it is helpful to work backwards from the conclusion.

It should be remembered that, for example, (R 1)—'*P*' and '*P* $\supset$ *Q*' imply '*Q*'—applies where '$\supset$' is the main connective in '*P* $\supset$ *Q*'. Thus this inference would be *erroneous:*

1. $(p \supset q) \cdot r$
2. p
3. $q \cdot r$ 1, 2 (R 1) modus ponens

Similarly, this inference is *erroneous:*

1. $(p \cdot q) \supset r$
2. $q \supset r$ 1 (R 4) simplification

However, as we have seen, the equivalence rules (Rules 9 through 19) can be applied not only to whole statements, but to parts of statements. For example:

1. $\sim \sim (p \cdot q) \supset r$
2. $\sim (\sim p \text{ v} \sim q) \supset r$ 1 (R 10) De Morgan's Theorems
3. $\sim (p \supset \sim q) \supset r$ 2 (R 16) implication
4. $\sim (\sim \sim q \supset \sim p) \supset r$ 3 (R 15) transposition
5. $\sim (q \supset \sim p) \supset r$ 4 (R 9) double negation

CONDITIONAL VALIDATION

A rule can be provided which will enable the convenient deduction of conclusions of the form '$A \supset B$'.

Let 'Pr' represent the conjunction of the premisses of an argument which has the form:

1. 'Pr' implies '$A \supset B$'.

(1) is true if and only if

2. $Pr \supset (A \supset B)$

is a tautology. Now (2) is by (R 17) (exportation) equivalent to:

3. $(Pr \cdot A) \supset B$.

Thus it follows from (A) (see page 231) that (1) is equivalent to:

4. 'Pr' and 'A' imply 'B'.

The rule of conditional proof, as it is called, is:

(RCP) If 'P' and 'A' imply 'B', then 'P' implies '$A \supset B$'.

That is, when we have a validation of the form:

(P 1)
(P 2)
.
.   Premisses
.
(P n)

A   Added Premiss
(S 1)
(S 2)
.   Statements derived in the course of showing that
.   the premisses with the addition of 'A' as a premiss,
.   imply 'B'.
(S n)
_____

B

we have a proof of (1).

Given any argument whose conclusion is of the form '$A \supset B$', a conditional proof of its validity is constructed by assuming the antecedent of its conclusion as an additional premiss and then deducing the consequent. For example, for:

$$W \vee \sim C$$
$$\sim F \supset \sim W$$
$$\overline{\therefore C \supset F}$$

the conditional proof can be written (we will drop the practice of giving rule numbers and employ abbreviations for their names):

1. $W \text{ v} \sim C$ P
2. $\sim F \supset \sim W$ P
3. C Hypothesis for RCP
4. $\sim C \text{ v } W$ (1) Comm.
5. $C \supset W$ (4) Imp.
6. W (3, 5) MP
7. $W \supset F$ (2) Trans.
8. F (6, 7) MP
9. $C \supset F$ (3, 8) RCP (conditional proof)

The addition of conditional proofs will permit the construction of shorter and easier proofs for a number of arguments. In addition (RCP) will permit the derivation of what is called the *reductio ad absurdum* argument. This has already been mentioned in the chapter on paradoxes.

THE *REDUCTIO AD ABSURDUM* RULE

Here is an example of a complete *reductio* argument:

If we parked in this area, we left the car on this street. $(R \supset P)$
If we didn't park on this street, we didn't pass this store. $(\sim P \supset \sim Q)$
But either we passed this store or we parked in this area. $(Q \text{ v } R)$
Now suppose we didn't park on this street.
That means we didn't park in this area and that we didn't pass this store.
But it also means we *did* pass this store.
Thus our supposition was wrong and we must have parked on this street.

This is rather complicated to follow, although in symbols it is less hard to follow. As premisses, we have:

1. $R \supset P$ P
2. $\sim P \supset \sim Q$ P
3. $Q \text{ v } R$ P

and the supposition

4. $\sim P$
5. $\sim R$ (4, 1) MT
6. $R \text{ v } Q$ (3) Comm.
7. Q (5, 3) DS
8. $\sim Q$ (2, 4) MP
9. $Q \cdot \sim Q$ (contradiction)   (7, 8) Conj.
10. P *Reductio ad absurdum* (RAA)

Thus, from the premisses and the negation of the desired conclusion, a contradiction is derived. This means that the adoption of the negated conclusion was unjustified—that the conclusion is derivable.

RAA. If a contradiction is derivable from the premisses and the negation of 'Q', then 'Q' is derivable from the premisses alone.

The proof of RAA is as follows:

By assumption we derive a contradiction, say '$A \cdot \sim A$', from a set of premisses 'Pr' and the negation of a statement 'Q'. Thus, by RCP, '$\sim Q \supset (A \cdot \sim A)$' is deducible from the premisses 'Pr' alone. But since '$\sim Q \supset (A \cdot \sim A)$' is equivalent to '$Q$'— that is, '$\sim Q \supset (A \cdot \sim A) \equiv Q$' is a tautology—by (A), 'Q' is deducible from the premisses 'Pr'.

Of course, the ease with which a contradiction is derivable will determine whether or not the RAA should be used. Suppose we wanted to construct a formal validation for

$$D \vee (I \cdot S)$$
$$D \supset L$$
$$\underline{L \supset S}$$
$$\therefore S$$

A regular validation would probably involve such rules as Taut., Dist., and CD. But we can easily construct a proof using RAA.

1.	$D \vee (I \cdot S)$	P
2.	$D \supset L$	P
3.	$L \supset S$	P
4.	$\sim S$	Supposition
5.	$\sim L$	(4, 3) MT
6.	$\sim D$	(2, 5) MT
7.	$I \cdot S$	(1, 6) DS
8.	S	(7) Simp.
9.	$S \cdot \sim S$	(8, 4) Conj.
10.	S	(9) RAA

CONSISTENCY (S)[4] OF PREMISSES

Among valid formal arguments we can distinguish two kinds—those with premisses which are contradictory and those with premisses which are not contradictory. The RAA method of proof, as we have seen, involves deriving a contradiction from a set of premisses—one of which is the contradictory of the conclusion—in order to see whether the conclusion is derivable. This procedure is unobjectionable even though the premisses augmented by the negation of the conclusion are inconsistent, since we are, as it were, deliberately making use of a feature of incon-

---

4 Here again, the test of consistency is not universal so we indicate how the test is made by '(S)'.

sistent premisses to show that they are inconsistent. Ordinarily, however, we are not interested in what can be inferred from inconsistent or contradictory premisses. As was mentioned near the beginning of this chapter, we do not normally take them seriously.

However, the argument

$$P$$
$$\sim P$$
$$\therefore Q$$

is formally valid. In fact

'P' and '$\sim P$' imply 'Q'

is, by (A), a rule of inference since

$(P \cdot \sim P) \supset Q$

is a tautology.

Let us call arguments which are formally valid and whose premisses are consistent "demonstrative" arguments. These are arguments whose premisses may *all* be true so that validations of these arguments show that *if* the premisses are true, the conclusion is (necessarily) true. In order to distinguish demonstrative arguments from nondemonstrative arguments we must find a way to check the consistency (S) of the premisses. To check the consistency of the premisses, one needs to see if the truth of one premiss (or more) guarantees the falsity of another; that is, one needs to see if the premisses can all be true. If the premisses can all be made true, they are consistent (S). If they cannot, then they are inconsistent.

One procedure to test the consistency (S) of the premisses is to assign **T** to the simplest premiss and then proceed to see if the remaining premisses can be made true. (This procedure is similar to the short-cut truth tables in Chapter Nine, pages 227–228. There, after assigning **F** to the conclusion, we proceeded to try to make the premisses **T**.) Suppose, for example, that the premisses of an argument are:

1. $P \supset Q$
2. $\sim P \vee R$
3. $\sim R$
4. $\sim R \supset Q$

We will write it on one line, assign **T** to '$\sim R$', and see if we can make all the premisses **T**.

$P \supset Q$	$\sim P \vee R$	$\sim R$	$\sim R \supset Q$
F T T	**T T F**	**T**	**T T T**
	(P must be **F**)		(Q must be **T**)

Thus all the premisses are made **T**. This means the premisses are consistent (**S**). Suppose, though, we also had this premiss added to (1) through (4):

5. $\sim R \supset \sim Q$

Since '$\sim R$' is **T** and 'Q' is **T**, '$\sim R \supset \sim Q$' would be **F**. Thus with this addition the five premisses could not all be made true. This means the five premisses are inconsistent. An argument which has these five premisses is not, then, a demonstrative argument.

The usefulness of the above procedure is not confined, of course, to distinguishing demonstrative arguments from those which are not. It is useful whenever it is necessary to decide on the consistency (**S**) of any set of statements.

EXERCISES I

A. These exercises employ only the first nine rules. Provide the justification for each step. Omit commutation.

1. 1. $P \supset Q$ P
    2. $Q \supset R$ P
    3. $P \supset R$
2. 1. $P \supset Q$ P
    2. $R \supset S$ P
    3. $P \vee R$ P
    4. $(P \supset Q) \cdot (R \supset S)$
    5. $Q \vee S$
3. 1. $\sim \sim (P \cdot R) \vee S$ P
    2. $(\sim \sim (P \cdot R) \vee S) \vee R$
4. 1. $(P \cdot (S \vee R)) \supset (\sim S \vee \sim R)$ P
    2. $(\sim S \vee \sim R) \supset (S \cdot R)$ P
    3. $(P \cdot (S \vee R)) \supset (S \cdot R)$
5. 1. $\sim P$ P
    2. $P \vee Q$ P
    3. Q
6. 1. $(P \vee Q) \supset R$ P
    2. $\sim (\sim P \cdot \sim Q)$ P
    3. $(\sim \sim P \vee \sim \sim Q)$
    4. $P \vee \sim \sim Q$
    5. $P \vee Q$
    6. R
7. 1. $P \supset Q$ P
    2. $(T \supset (R \vee S)) \supset (U \cdot V)$ P
    3. $P \vee (T \supset (R \vee S))$ P

	4.	~ (U · V)	**P**
	5.	(P ⊃ Q) · ((T ⊃ (R v S)) ⊃ (U · V))	
	6.	Q v (U · V)	
	7.	Q	
	8.	Q v (~ R · ~ S)	

8. 1. P **P**
2. P v Q
3. (P v Q) v (R · ~ S)
4. ((P v Q) v (R · ~ S)) v Q
5. (((P v Q) v (R · ~ S)) v Q) v (R ⊃ ~ Q)

9. 1. P ⊃ (P · (R · ~ S)) **P**
2. P **P**
3. P · (R · ~ S)
4. R · ~ S
5. R
6. R v P

10. 1. ((P v Q) v (~ R v ~ S)) · T **P**
2. (P v Q) v (~ R v ~ S)
3. ~ (P v Q) **P**
4. ~ R v ~ S
5. ~ ~ R **P**
6. ~ S

B. Devise a validation for each of the following. Any of the rules may be needed.

1. 1. G ⊃ (S ⊃ U)
2. G
3. ~ U
∴ ~ S

2. 1. N ⊃ M
2. M ⊃ D
3. M ⊃ P
4. ~ P
5. M v N
∴ D

3. 1. B ⊃ J
2. H ⊃ D
3. ~ (~ J v ~ D) ⊃ U
4. ~ U
∴ ~ B v ~ H

4. 1. P
2. (P v R) ⊃ D
∴ P · D

5. 1. ~ ((A v A) v D) ⊃ Z
2. ~ Z
3. ~ Z ⊃ ~ D

∴   *A*

6.   1.   *E* ⊃ *F*
     2.   (*F* ⊃ *D*) · (*F* ⊃ *C*)
     3.   ~ *D* v ~ *C*
   ∴   ~ *E*

7.   1.   *T* ⊃ (*C* · *O*)
     2.   *T* · *B*
     3.   (*F* · *F*) v ~ (~ *W* · *B*)
     4.   *W* ⊃ ~ (*C* v *D*)
   ∴   *F*

EXERCISES II

These exercises employ all the rules.

A.   Provide justification for each step.

1.   1.   *P* v *Q*   P
     2.   ~ ~ (*P* v *Q*)
     3.   ~ (~ *P* · ~ *Q*)
     4.   ~ ~ *P* v ~ ~ *Q*

2.   1.   (*P* v *Q*) v (*R* · ~ *S*)   P
     2.   *P* v (*Q* v (*R* · ~ *S*))
     3.   (*Q* v (*R* · ~ *S*)) v *P*
     4.   *Q* v ((*R* · ~ *S*) v *P*)

3.   1.   *Q* ⊃ ~ *R*   P
     2.   *P* ⊃ (*Q* · *R*)   P
     3.   ~ (*Q* · *R*) ⊃ ~ *P*
     4.   (~ *Q* v ~ *R*) ⊃ ~ *P*
     5.   (*Q* ⊃ ~ *R*) ⊃ ~ *P*
     6.   ~ *P*

4.   1.   ~ *T*   P
     2.   *P* ⊃ ((*Q* · *S*) ⊃ (*T* v *R*))   P
     3.   (*S* · *Q*) · *P*   P
     4.   (*P* · (*Q* · *S*)) ⊃ (*T* v *R*)
     5.   *P* · (*S* · *Q*)
     6.   *P* · (*Q* · *S*)
     7.   *T* v *R*
     8.   ~ ~ *T* v *R*
     9.   ~ *T* ⊃ *R*
    10.   *R*

5.   1.   *P* · *Q*   P
     2.   (*P* · *Q*) v ~ (*P* v *Q*)
     3.   (*P* · *Q*) v (~ *P* · ~ *Q*)
     4.   *P* ≡ *Q*

6.   1.   *P* · *Q*   P
     2.   ~ *R* ⊃ *S*   P

    3. $(P \cdot Q) \cdot (\sim R \supset S)$

    4. $(P \cdot Q) \cdot (\sim \sim R \vee S)$

    5. $(P \cdot Q) \cdot (R \vee S)$

    6. $((P \cdot Q) \cdot R) \vee ((P \cdot Q) \cdot S)$

7. 1. $P \equiv (Q \cdot R)$ P

    2. $(P \supset (Q \cdot R)) \cdot ((Q \cdot R) \supset P)$

    3. $(\sim (Q \cdot R) \supset \sim P) \cdot (\sim P \supset \sim (Q \cdot R))$

    4. $\sim \sim ((\sim (Q \cdot R) \supset \sim P) \cdot (\sim P \supset \sim (Q \cdot R)))$

    5. $\sim (\sim (\sim (Q \cdot R) \supset \sim P) \vee \sim (\sim P \supset \sim (Q \cdot R)))$

    6. $\sim ((\sim (Q \cdot R) \supset \sim P) \supset \sim (\sim P \supset \sim (Q \cdot R)))$

    7. $\sim ((\sim (Q \cdot R)) \supset \sim P) \supset \sim ((Q \cdot R) \supset P)$

    8. $\sim ((\sim Q \vee \sim R) \supset \sim P) \supset \sim ((Q \cdot R) \supset P)$

8. 1. $(P \vee Q) \equiv (R \cdot S)$ P

    2. $((P \vee Q) \cdot (R \cdot S)) \vee (\sim (P \vee Q) \cdot \sim (R \cdot S))$

    3. $((P \vee Q) \cdot (R \cdot S)) \vee \sim ((P \vee Q) \vee (R \cdot S))$

    4. $\sim ((P \vee Q) \vee (R \cdot S)) \vee ((P \vee Q) \cdot (R \cdot S))$

    5. $((P \vee Q) \vee (R \cdot S)) \supset ((P \vee Q) \cdot (R \cdot S))$

    6. $((P \vee Q) \vee (R \cdot S)) \supset ((R \cdot S) \cdot (P \vee Q))$

    7. $((P \vee Q) \vee (R \cdot S)) \supset (((R \cdot S) \cdot P) \vee ((R \cdot S) \cdot Q))$

B. Devise validations for the following arguments. Use the suggested letters to represent the appropriate statements.

1. If Alberta Peach goes to the movie tonight, she will be unhappy if the movie is not a romance. She will go, she says, and the movie is a travelogue not a romance. So she will be unhappy. (M, R, U)

2. Although the flock would not be disturbed unless the wolf howled, it is false that either the wolf or the dog howled last night. So neither was the flock disturbed nor did the dog howl. (F, W, D)

3. Dr. Friendly, the ethics teacher, told Dr. Freund, the psychologist: "If you would keep the crabgrass out of your lawn, then if our kids got along, we could get along. Since our kids get along and we don't, I must conclude that you don't keep the crabgrass out of your lawn." (C, K, W)

4. If Prof. Goodshot owned a gun, he would have used it if he saw the thief. He owned a gun, but didn't use it. So he didn't see the thief. (G, U, T)

5. Either Gumdrop was elected or our leaders failed and the township will suffer a depression. If Gumdrop was elected, there won't be a depression for the township. However, there will be a depression for the township, so our leaders failed. (G, L, T)

6. Certainly Mrs. Freund and Mrs. Friendly would get along if their husbands would, and if one was an ethicist and the other a psychologist they would get along. But Freund is a psychologist and Friendly is an ethicist. So their wives will get along. (F, M, E)

7. The poultry is either sick along with the swine or, unlike the swine, they are depressed by the cloudy weather but in good health. The cattle never get sick unless the swine do, so the cattle are sick. (P, S, C)

8. The president will not lose his job unless the dean, who swings a lot of weight, objects to something the president does. The dean, who is a fair man, will object to an action of the president only if it is unjust. The president will not do anything unjust unless he is ignorant of the situation. So if the president does lose his job he will have acted in ignorance of the situation. (D, P, U, I)

9. Suppose no one claims the book you found now that you have advertised it as lost. You can not sell the book if you flunk Ethics even though you advertised it as lost and no one claims it. If Dr. Freund finds out you sold the book, you will flunk Ethics; and he will. So you can't sell it. (A, N, F, S, Fr)

10. If Dr. Freund reads a paper, Dr. Friendly will criticize it. And if Dr. Friendly criticizes it, the criticism will not be both fair and amiable. The criticism will be fair, however. So if Freund reads the paper, the criticism will not be amiable. (P, C, F, A)

11. If Byron Eval is a crook he is either harmful or dangerous. But Byron is not harmful, so if he is a crook he is dangerous. (C, H, D)

12. Either Russia and the United States will trust one another and disarm or there will be a thermonuclear war, but not both. There will be a war. Therefore Russia and the United States will not trust one another. (R, D, W)

13. If Brigette buys dinner, Ben pays the tip, and if Brigette does not buy dinner, they walk home. Also, if they walk home, Brigette is furious with Ben. So if Ben does not pay the tip, Brigette is furious with Ben. (D, A, B, C)

14. If we go to the ball game and it does not happen that the team loses or that we miss the bus on the way back, then we will enjoy the afternoon. It never happens that if we do not enjoy the afternoon the team loses. Now we will go to the ball game and either we will enjoy the afternoon or we will not miss the bus. So I predict we will miss the bus. (W, T, M, E)

15. Either Dierdre will become a movie star and either make a lot of money or have a big family, or she will become a movie star and either spend a lot of time playing golf or become a good actress. The only sure conclusion is, though, that she will become a movie star. (D, M, F, G, A)

EXERCISES III

Construct a validation using RCP for the following.

1. $A \supset B$
$\therefore A \supset (A \cdot B)$

2. If Myrtle likes her new dress, she will buy five more just like it. If she buys five more just like the new one she will be broke—unless she does not like the new one. If she is broke, she will starve—unless she does not buy five dresses just like the new one. So if Myrtle likes her new dress, she will starve. (L, F, B, S)

3. If you are all ready, we will leave immediately, unless there is a flat tire. Either there is a flat tire or there is a hole in the street. I see you are all ready. So if there is not a flat tire, we will leave immediately. (L, R, F, H)

4. $A \supset ((B \cdot C) \vee E)$
$(B \cdot C) \supset \sim A$
$D \supset \sim E$
$\therefore A \supset \sim D$

5. $(P \vee Q) \supset R$
$(S \vee T) \supset ((A \vee B) \supset P)$
$\therefore S \supset (A \supset R)$

6. If Otto Ott went shopping, then he took his wife; and he took his father if he had something expensive to buy. So if Otto went shopping and had something important to buy, he took his father and his wife. (S, W, F, E)

EXERCISES IV

Construct a validation using RAA for the following.

1. $B \vee \sim C$
C
$\therefore B$

2. $B \supset A$
$\sim (A \cdot \sim C) \supset B$
$\therefore A$

3. $\sim B \supset E$
$D \supset \sim E$
$\sim (\sim D \cdot \sim B)$
$\therefore B$

4. If we borrow our neighbor's boat, we will water ski. But if we water ski, we won't feel like playing ball. Now either we won't borrow the boat or we will feel like playing ball. So if we borrow the boat, we won't water ski. (B, W, P)

5. Either Dr. Freund and Dr. Friendly are crotchety or their wives are. If the Drs. are crotchety, their dogs are. If their wives are crotchety then their kids are. Therefore either their dogs or their kids are crotchety. (F, W, D, K)

EXERCISES V

Which of the following sets of premisses are consistent?

1. $P \equiv Q$
$Q \cdot \sim P$

2. $\sim Q \vee R$
$\sim R \cdot P$
$\sim (\sim Q \cdot R)$

3. $A \vee B$
$\sim B \supset A$
$B \equiv A$
B
$\sim A$

4. If Ed caught any fish they were either bluegills or crappies. If he used worms he caught bluegills and if he used minnows he caught crappies. He did not have worms, though, and did not catch crappies. He did not catch anything. (*F, B, C, W, M*)

5. Albertine can check out another book if and only if she either pays her fine or pays for the late book. If she does not pay the fine she will flunk Ethics. She will pay for the book if and only if she does not pay the fine. (*A, F, B, E*)

6. If Allwet is a logician then either he is lazy or a fraud. If he is a fraud he will be exposed—unless he is lazy. He will not be exposed and he is not a logician. (*A, L, F, E*)

7. $P \lor (Q \cdot R)$
$R \equiv (P \supset Q)$
$Q \supset \sim P$
$S \lor Q$
$(Q \cdot \sim R)$

8. $A \supset B$
$\sim A \cdot \sim C$
$B \supset (D \supset C)$
$A \supset (E \lor B)$
$E \supset (F \cdot D)$

EXERCISES VI

Devise a validation (if possible) if the premises of the argument are consistent. Some arguments cannot be formulated validly in terms of statements.

1. $\sim (P \lor Q) \lor R$
$P \cdot S$
$\therefore P \cdot R$

2. $(S \supset Q) \supset R$
$(P \cdot S) \supset Q$
$\therefore P \supset R$

3. If she wrote a good story, she will surely get it published. If she gets it published she will not both begin her vacation and begin her novel. If she does not begin her vacation she will not be published. She won't be published and has begun her novel. So she will get her story published. (*S, P, V, N*)

4. Either it is not the case that either Perry or Melvin went to the party or it is true that both Sarah and Rachel did. I know Sarah did not go, so Melvin didn't. (*P, M, S, R*)

5. $((S \cdot C) \supset Q) \cdot (\sim Q \cdot C)$
$B \equiv C$
$S \cdot (Q \lor B)$
$\therefore B \supset S$

6. $(A \lor B) \supset (C \cdot D)$
$(D \lor E) \supset F$
A
$\therefore F$

7. If she either swims or water skis, she'll get sunburned and thirsty. If she gets either thirsty or hungry she'll want to borrow some money. She is swimming now, so she'll want to borrow some money.   (*S, W, B, T, H, B*)

8. $P \supset R$
$(\sim P \text{ v } R) \supset (S \supset Q)$
$\therefore P \supset (S \supset Q)$

9. $(B \supset L) \cdot (L \supset \sim R)$
$(T \supset M) \cdot (M \supset \sim R)$
$(R \text{ v } C) \cdot (B \text{ v } T)$
$\therefore \sim C$

10. If I take geology and either political science or government then I will not work part time. But I will work part time and I will take political science. So I will not take geology.   (*P, Q, R, S*)

11. $\sim A \supset \sim B$
$A \supset C$
$B \text{ v } D$
$D \supset E$
$\therefore E \text{ v } C$

12. $\sim A \text{ v } \sim B$
$(A \supset C) \cdot ((A \cdot C) \supset B)$
$\therefore (A \cdot C) \supset \sim A$

13. $P \supset (Q \text{ v } (R \cdot S))$
$\sim R \text{ v } \sim S$
$\sim Q$
$\therefore \sim P$

14. $(S \cdot L) \supset V$
$(L \cdot V) \supset C$
S
$\therefore L$

15. If Addle gets a poodle and an orangutang, her rooster will die laughing. If she gets a poodle but not the orangutang, the rooster will not die laughing. So if she does not get a poodle the rooster will die laughing if and only if she gets an orangutang.   (*P, O, R*)

16. $(P \supset Q) \cdot (R \supset S)$
$\sim (Q \equiv R)$
$(\sim P \supset R) \text{ v } (Q \equiv R)$
$\therefore Q \text{ v } S$

17. $P \supset Q$
$R \supset S$
$S \text{ v } Q$
$\therefore R \text{ v } P$

18. You will take all those courses if and only if you do not take a fourteen hour job. You will not take a fourteen hour job. So if you take all those courses, either I will eat my hat or you don't know what you are doing.   (*C, J, E, K*)

19. $H \supset N$
$H \supset (N \supset M)$

$H \supset (M \supset B)$

$\therefore B \supset H$

20. $X \supset (Y \cdot \sim Z)$

$\sim X \equiv P$

$(Y \cdot Z) \cdot \sim P$

$X \lor Z$

$\therefore Y \supset P$

21. If you fish an Abdul, you will catch bass and not get caught in the weeds. But it is not the case that either you fish an Abdul and not catch bass or you get caught in the weeds. So you will fish an Abdul and you will not get caught in the weeds. (A, B, C)

22. A house will sell only if it is correctly colored, and that house is correctly colored only if it has red or orange or yellow trim. I own the house. It has a red trim. So it probably will sell. (S, C, R, O, Y, W)

23. It is not true that either Adele bleaches her hair or tints it. If she has an important date she bleaches it and if she does not have an important date she tints it. But she has not tinted it or bleached it. Therefore she does not have an important date. (B, T, I)

24. $(J \lor R) \supset (D \cdot V)$

$\therefore \sim J \lor D$

25. $U \supset (V \lor W)$

$(W \cdot X) \supset Y$

$\sim Z \supset (X \cdot \sim Y)$

$\therefore U \supset (V \supset Z)$

26. If working hours drop, then leisure and recreation will increase. If either leisure or wages increase, then people will be happy. Either wages will increase or working hours will drop. Therefore people will be happy. (H, L, R, W, P)

27. $W \supset (S \lor B)$

$N \supset (B \lor A)$

$\sim B$

$\therefore (S \lor A) \supset W$

28. $(A \lor S) \supset (T \cdot V)$

$T \supset C$

C

$\therefore A \lor S$

29. Executives will be discharged if they think or are different. Therefore, if an executive thinks, he ought to be discharged. (E, T, D)

30. $(R \cdot F) \lor D$

$\sim D \lor F$

$\therefore F$

Chapter Eleven

QUANTIFICATION

There are many arguments which are clearly valid but whose validity cannot be established by the methods introduced in the previous chapters. Here is an example:

(A)   All unemployed are lazy.
Some philosophers are unemployed.
Therefore some philosophers are lazy.

Contrast this argument with

(B)   Either Bridey Murphy was a hoax or there is reincarnation.
There is no reincarnation.
Therefore Bridey Murphy was a hoax.

Using the symbolism introduced in the preceding chapters, (B) would be symbolized:

$$p \lor q$$
$$\underline{\sim q}$$
$$\therefore p$$

The validity of this form can easily be shown by employing truth tables or by constructing a formal validation, for its validity depends on the way constituent statements are related by statement connectives.

However, (A) resists such treatment. Using the existing symbolism, we would write (A):

$$p$$
$$\underline{q}$$
$$\therefore r$$

249

This form is clearly invalid (*S*). The validity of (A) depends on the internal *structure* of each statement. That is, the validity of (A) depends on the use of the words "all" and "some" and on the way in which "unemployed," "lazy," and "philosopher" are related by these words as well as on the way the statements are related. Thus to provide methods for testing arguments like (A), we first need to introduce techniques for symbolizing the internal structure of statements.

THE EXISTENTIAL QUANTIFIER

Let us begin by considering the second premiss of (A):

1. Some philosophers are unemployed.

In order to symbolize (1) in a convenient way, the idea of a (individual) *variable* is needed. We will use the letters '*x*', '*y*', '*z*' (variables) in such a way that they are replaceable by a name of an object or individual or by a description of one. The variables, in this role, are analogous to the variables in algebra, for example, in

$$(x + y)^2 = x^2 + 2xy + y^2$$

where they are (ordinarily) replaceable by numerals. Analogously the '*x*' in

x is longer than two feet

is replaceable by "F. D. Roosevelt," "the second largest planet," "the pen I am using," and so on.

Capital letters will not be variables but representations, or translations, of *predicates*. ("Predicates," like "individuals," will be understood in its broadest sense.) Thus "unemployed" might be represented by '*U*' and "longer than two feet" might be represented by '*L*'. In addition, we will adopt the convention that a variable written to the right of a predicate letter, for example, '*Ax*', will be read "*x* is *A*."

According to these conventions,

2. *Ux*

would represent the incomplete sentence

3. *x* is unemployed.

(3) is said to be *unquantified*. By this is meant: there is no indication as to how many individuals are to be understood as being unemployed. There is nothing in English which corresponds exactly to (3). (3) has a resemblance, however, to formulae in algebra, so expressions such as (2)

and (3) will also be referred to as formulae or, occasionally, as statement forms.

Obviously (3) differs from (1); (3) is not, for example, true or false— nor is any formula. Thus in order for (1) to be rendered in symbols, the so-called *existential quantifier* '($\exists x$)' is introduced. This symbol will correspond to the phrase "There is at least one object '*x*' such that. . . ." It is called the existential quantifier because in using it one is asserting the existence of an object or entity '*x*' and because it indicates something about the number of '*x*'s the predicate is asserted of.

To say that

1. Some philosophers are unemployed.

is to assert the existence of philosophers and to say they are unemployed. "Some," as it is normally used, for example, in (1), is used to indicate that more than one philosopher is unemployed. But we will construe (1) as:

There is at least one individual such that that individual is a philosopher and is unemployed.

so that, employing the new symbols, (1) becomes

($\exists x$) (*x* is a philosopher and *x* is unemployed)

and, letting '*P*' represent "philosopher":

4. ($\exists x$) ($Px \cdot Ux$)

(4) is the standard symbolic rendering of (1). The occurrences of '*x*' in '($Px \cdot Ux$)' refer back to the quantifier '($\exists x$)'. They serve to indicate places where the *same* name or description is to occur.

It may appear that the introduction of this elaborate symbolic apparatus to express a statement like "some philosophers are unemployed" is excessively complex. This, as will be seen in this and the following chapters, is not the case. The complexity of the symbolism increases only because the logical complexity of the notions symbolized increases.

Commonly, the following statements can be rendered as '($\exists x$) ($\cdots x$ $\cdots$)'—where '($\cdots x \cdots$)' indicates that '*x*' is the only variable in the formula—without losing those properties on which rests the validity of the argument in which they appear.

A majority—A majority of students (*S*) are underpaid (*U*):
      ($\exists x$) ($Sx \cdot Ux$)

A few—A few mathematicians (*M*) are not well paid (*W*):
      ($\exists x$) ($Mx \cdot \sim Wx$)

A number—A number of children (C) should be muzzled (M):

$(\exists x) (Cx \cdot Mx)$

A minority—A minority of newspapers (N) are Democratic (D):

$(\exists x) (Nx \cdot Dx)$

Some—Some Indians (I) are not pacifists (P):

$(\exists x) (Ix \cdot \sim Px)$

Many—Many Irishmen (I) are neither politicians (P) nor policemen (O):

$(\exists x) (Ix \cdot \sim (Px \text{ v } Ox))$

At least one—At least one Indian (I) dislikes Nehru (D):

$(\exists x) (Ix \cdot Dx)$

Quite a few—Quite a few logic books (L) are obscure (O):

$(\exists x) (Lx \cdot Ox)$

Other expressions, such as "most," "scarcely any," and so on, can often be symbolized in terms of '$(\exists x)$'. This is not to say, of course, that

Most students voted for Smith.

and

Scarcely any students voted for Smith.

mean the same thing, but that the role each may play in a certain context may be the same. One could use either to answer the question, for example, as to whether anyone voted for Smith. (In the next sections the reasons for symbolizing a statement in a particular way are discussed in more detail.)

THE UNIVERSAL QUANTIFIER

We have seen that the second premiss of (A) is to be symbolized:

$(\exists x) (Px \cdot Ux)$.

We will now consider how the first premiss of (A)

All unemployed are lazy

is to be symbolized. Consider, first, a simple predicate 'R' which will be "is at least two feet long." The formula

1. All x are at least two feet long.

will be understood as

2. It is not the case that there is at least one x such that it is not at least two feet long.

or, more perspicuously,

3. $\sim (\exists x) \sim Rx.$

It will be convenient to introduce another symbol '(x)', called the *universal quantifier*, and write (3)—and thus (1) and (2)—as

4. $(x)\ Rx$

(4) may also be read

Everything is at least two feet long.

Now, to digress a moment, it must be mentioned that it is convenient, in logic, to interpret an assertion such as

All flying saucers are atomic powered.

as *not* suggesting by itself, that there are such things as flying saucers. Often, of course, statements of the form:

5. All _____ are _____.

are made in contexts in which the existence of the objects or individuals named or described is evident, as when, for example, the following is uttered by a philosopher:

All philosophers are impecunious.

But even these statements in these contexts will not be understood, by themselves, to suggest, or indicate that there exists such objects as are named or described in the subject term. The statements of form (5) will be understood, in other words, as saying

If something *is* a _____, then it is a _____.

Thus, the two examples are to be understood as:

If something is a flying saucer, then it is atomic powered,

and

If something is a philosopher, then it is impecunious.

In logic, then,

All unemployed are lazy.

means the same as the following:

If anyone is unemployed then he is lazy
Given any x, if x is unemployed, then x is lazy
(x) (if x is unemployed, then x is lazy)
$(x)\ (Ux \supset Lx)$,

where '*U*' is "unemployed" and '*L*' is "lazy." Now

(A)   All unemployed are lazy.
Some philosophers are unemployed.
Therefore some philosophers are lazy.

can be symbolized as follows—taking '*P*' to be "philosopher":

$(x) (Ux \supset Lx)$
$(\exists x) (Px \cdot Ux)$
$\therefore (\exists x) (Px \cdot Lx)$

New methods must be developed in order to check the validity of arguments such as these. The next chapters are devoted to this task.

The following statements can all be translated as '$(x) (Bx \supset Ex)$':

Every baseball game is exciting.
Each baseball game is exciting.
Any baseball game is exciting.
All baseball games are exciting.

(This is not to say that "every," "any," "each," and "all" mean the same thing, but that they may have similar roles in an argument.)

In addition, the following can also be translated by use of the universal quantifier:

If something is a radish, then it is edible.
A radish is edible.
The radish is edible (that is, "radishes are edible").
Radishes are edible.

And, using negation,

No one went to the fire.
None went to the fire.
Nobody went to the fire.

can all be expressed

$(x) (x$ is a person $\supset \sim (x$ went to the fire)).

CONTEXT

It is an important fact that the logical structure of a statement is not always apparent. For example, one can not always tell that a statement should be understood as being a general statement from the fact that this or that word occurs in the statement. One might expect, for instance, that

All members are not going.

would always be translatable by '(x)'—as '$(x) (Mx \supset \sim Gx)$'. But it commonly means

Some members are not going.

and so, should become—in those contexts,

$(\exists x) (x$ is a member $\cdot \sim (x$ is going$))$

Notice also that the two statements (listed above)

A radish is edible.
The radish is edible.

are exactly the same, except that the first begins with the indefinite article "a" and the other with the definite article "the." But it is clearly not the case that every statement beginning with "a" or "the" is a general statement translatable into the symbolism by the universal quantifier. The statement

1. A salesman sold Ed a dictionary.

does not mean

2. All salesmen sold Ed a dictionary.

Nor does

3. The argument of Ed's against legalized gambling is fallacious.

mean

4. All arguments of Ed's against legalized gambling are fallacious.

And, it should be noted,

The radish is edible.

would be counted as a general statement only when one is referring to "the radish" as a species, and not when one is referring to an individual radish.[1]

When these articles are used as part of a reference to individual objects, as in (1) and (3), the universal quantifier can not be used since the statements are not general statements. Sometimes the existential quantifier can be used:

$(\exists x) (x$ is a salesman $\cdot x$ sold Ed a dictionary$)$

(3) customarily must receive a more elaborate treatment since the arguments in which such statements are used are generally more complex

---

[1] In this connection think of the joke with "A woman has a baby every thirty seconds."

than the types considered in this book. In some cases such statements as (3) can be treated as statements containing names, however. (See the next section.)

Now let us consider different ways in which a statement should be translated and note how the nature of the translation changes depending on the argument in which the statement occurs. A translation must fulfill two requirements:

> The translation must be faithful to the meaning of the original statement.
> The translation must be such as to preserve the validity of an argument in which the statement occurs.

One does not always know, of course, whether the argument to be symbolized is valid, so it may be necessary to try all available translations to be sure that the second rule is observed. If the statement in question is superfluous to the argument, the translation is arbitrary.

Suppose this statement occurs in an argument:

(C)   Three linguists want to drop the "b" in "lamb."

Depending on what properties of (C) need to be preserved, there are the following possibilities for translation into the symbolism:

If (C) occurs in an argument which is valid only because of the role of the statement connectives in the argument [as in (B), page 249], (C) could be replaced by 'P', a statement variable or constant.

If the argument depends on the structure of the sentence [as in (A), page 249], and if the force of "three" is just that of "some," then (C) would be symbolized:

1. $(\exists x)\ (x$ is a linguist $(L) \cdot x$ wants to get rid of "b" in "lamb" $(W))$

or

2. $(\exists x)\ (Lx \cdot Wx)$

Suppose three is a majority of linguists voting on whether to get rid of the "b" in "lamb." And suppose a way is needed to state that exactly three voted against the "b" or that a majority did. One way to do this is by the use of the idea of identity ('$=$'). Consider this version of (C):

3. $(\exists x)\ (\exists y)\ (\exists z)\ (Lx \cdot Ly \cdot Lz \cdot Wx \cdot Wy \cdot Wz \cdot (x \neq y) \cdot (y \neq z) \cdot (x \neq z))$

This is to be read: There is x and y and z such that x is an L, y is an L, and z is an L and x is a W, y is a W, and z is a W and x is not y, y is not z, and x is not z. Since x, y, and z are variables, it must be indicated that they will be replaced by names or descriptions of *distinct* individuals, hence it must be stipulated that $x \neq y$, and so forth. Since version (3) exhibits finer logical properties of (C) than do (1) and (2), versions (1) and (2) could be replaced by (3) in any symbolism in which the symbols used in (3) occur.

If the names of the linguists were known, the fact that they are linguists and oppose the "b" in "lamb" can be simply stated in symbols. (See the next section.) Let 'a', 'b', and 'c' represent the names of the linguists. (C) can then be written:

$La \cdot Lb \cdot Lc \cdot Wa \cdot Wb \cdot Wc$.

If the three linguists were the only linguists of the group that figure in the argument, then (4) would become

(x) (x is a linguist $\supset$ x wants to drop the "b" in "lamb"),

or

(x) ($Lx \supset Wx$),

or, finally, just

(x) (Lx),

where the predicate 'L' is now "is a linguist who wants to drop the 'b' in 'lamb'."

INDIVIDUAL CONSTANTS

We will use such letters as 'a', 'b', 'c' to *replace* names of particular individuals or things and descriptions of individuals or things.[2]

Letters used in this way are called (individual) *constants*. They are, like the predicate constants, simply representations or replacements of the English words. Thus the following are to be symbolized as indicated.

Brutus was not a baseball player: $\sim Ba$
Tokyo is the largest city in the world: La
The earth is pear-shaped: Pa
The present Prime Minister of England is wise and athletic: ($Wa \cdot Aa$)
If the largest city in the world is not England, then babies are illogical:
$\sim Ea \supset (x) (Bx \supset Ix)$

Constants ('a', 'b', 'c', and so on) are distinguished from variables ('x', 'y', 'z', and so on) in the following ways: 'Fx' is a formula, or statement

---

2 The only (nontrivial) way of distinguishing names and descriptions is by reference to the use of the words. For example, the words "the Methodist student's center" are often used as the name of a building, but can be used as a description of the place about four inches (depending on the student) behind the belly button of a Methodist student. This name, however, is also descriptive in an obvious way, compared, for instance, to "John"—it describes whose center this is.

form.[3] It is not a statement—not something which is true or false. In this way it is like '$x^2 = 15$'—it would not make sense to say of '$x^2 = 15$' that it is true or false. Neither '$x^2 = 15$' nor 'Fx' state anything. But 'Fa' is a statement—it is either true or false. If we take 'F' as "is disappearing from the scene," then 'Fx' and 'Fa' differ as

___ is disappearing from the scene.

and

The bat winged robin is disappearing from the scene.

differ.

Quantified statements such as

There are some bat wingers left on the scene.

which would be rendered in symbols as

$(\exists x)\ Gx$

are also statements which are true or false even though a variable occurs in 'Gx'. The reason is as follows: Suppose we had a complete list—by name or description—of all the objects in the universe (assume there is a finite number). Then, if 'P' is a predicate of some sort, to say

$(\exists x)\ Px$

is to say that one or another (at least one) of the objects—'a', 'b', 'c', and so on—is 'P'. That is

$Pa \lor Pb \lor Pc \lor \cdots$

will be true if and only if '$(\exists x)\ Px$' is true.

Similarly, to say that

$(x)\ Px$

is to say that *each* of the objects is 'P', that is,

$Pa \cdot Pb \cdot Pc \cdots$

is true if and only if '$(x)\ Px$' is true.

Thus

Robins exist.

is true if and only if

Either a is a robin or b is a robin or c is a robin or $\cdots$

[3] It is often convenient to use capitals as predicates without specifying what they replace.

And to say

Everything is rotten.

is to say

a is rotten and b is rotten and c is rotten and $\cdots$

So if we think of the universe as consisting of a finite number (n) of objects, then for any unquantified formula '$(\cdots x \cdots)$' (in which 'x' is the only unquantified variable):

1. $(\exists x) (\cdots x \cdots) \equiv (\cdots a \cdots) \text{ v } (\cdots b \cdots) \text{ v } (\cdots c \cdots)$
    $\text{v} \cdots \text{v} (\cdots n \cdots),$

when 'n' is the name of nth object, and

2. $(x) (\cdots x \cdots) \equiv (\cdots a \cdots) \cdot (\cdots b \cdots) \cdot (\cdots c \cdots)$
    $\cdots \cdots (\cdots n \cdots).$

Thus if '$(Ax \supset Dx)$' is the formula '$(\cdots x \cdots)$', then, replacing 'x' in each disjunct of (1) by 'a', 'b', and so on:

$(\exists x) (Ax \supset Bx) \equiv (Aa \supset Ba) \text{ v } (Ab \supset Bb) \text{ v } (Ac \supset Bc) \text{ v} \cdots \text{v} (An \supset Bn),$

and, similarly:

$(x) (Ax \supset Bx) \equiv (Aa \supset Ba) \cdot (Ab \supset Bb) \cdot (Ab \supset Bb) \cdots \cdots (An \supset Bn).$

MULTIPLE QUANTIFIERS AND MANY-PLACED PREDICATES

In this section we will enlarge our notation so that we can symbolize statements in which the predicates are more complex, and more than one variable is necessary.

Often a statement is made in which something is said about two different individuals or things, for example:

Grant defeated Lee.
Mrs. Blue is the wife of Henry Blue.
Joan was sitting on her bike.

In order to reproduce the more subtle form of these statements, the notation must be augmented, for two variables will be needed to express these subtler forms. Thus,

x defeated y.
z is the wife of y.
x was sitting on z.

are formulae corresponding to the above statements. Each of the form-ulae will be true or false when the variables are replaced by names or descriptions.

In order to symbolize the formulae completely, the words "defeated," "is the wife of," and "was sitting on" must be replaced by letters, (say) '*D*', '*W*', and '*S*'. These letters represent complex predicates, or *relations* between two individuals. We obtain

> *x D y*
> *z W y*
> *x S z*

as the symbolizations of the formulae above. In order to make the nota-tion more uniform, however, we will write

> *Dxy*
> *Wzy*
> *Sxz*

taking care that the variables are in proper order.

Now to symbolize a statement in which two or more variables are to be used, it is best to proceed in stages, taking one variable at a time. For example, consider

1. All the boys in the class of '66 married pretty girls.

The initial quantifier is

> (*x*) (*Bx* ⊃ *x* married a pretty girl),

where '*B*' is "is a boy in the class of '66." Then

> *x* married a pretty girl.

becomes ('*P*' is "is a pretty girl" and '*Mxy*' is "*x* married *y*")

> (∃*y*) (*Py* · *Mxy*).

Finally (1), altogether, is

2. (*x*) (*Bx* ⊃ (∃*y*) (*Py* · *Mxy*)).

This says, in our somewhat stilted language; for any object '*x*', if that object is a boy in the class of '66, then there exists another object '*y*' such that it is a pretty girl and *x* married *y*. Notice that although only one variable may be used in translating (1)

> (*x*) (*Bx* ⊃ *Gx*),

where '*Gx*' is "*x* married a pretty girl," one can not simply put one variable into (2): for

2'. (*x*) (*Bx* ⊃ (∃*x*) (*Px* · *Mxx*))

says, among other things, that 'x' married 'x', which is impossible. Whether one or more variables are needed in the symbolization depends (again) on the argument in which the statement occurs.

Next, consider

3. Whoever took the watch will be apprehended by someone.

This should be written out first in terms of one of the variables to be used:

4. (x) (x took the watch $\supset$ x will be apprehended by someone)

Next, since the consequent of (4) will be symbolized, it is treated separately;

$(\exists y)$ (x will be apprehended by y).

Thus (3) becomes

(x) (x took the watch $\supset$ $(\exists y)$ (x will be apprehended by y)),

or, using obvious abbreviations,

5. $(x) (Wx \supset (\exists y) (Axy))$.

We assumed that the fact that 'x' and 'y' are persons need not be explicitly stated. If the sense of an argument requires the explicit statement, then (3) would be

$(x) ((Px \cdot Wx) \supset (\exists y) (Py \cdot Axy))$.

A statement such as

6. All boys (B) and some girls (G) in the class of '66 (C) are married (M).

would become (construing "is married" as a simple predicate)

7. $(x) ((Bx \cdot Cx) \supset Mx) \cdot (\exists y) ((Gy \cdot Cy) \cdot My)$,

that is, (6) says that all the boys in the class of '66 are married, *and* some girls in the class of '66 are married. Note that the following says the same

8. $(x) ((Bx \cdot Cx) \supset Mx) \cdot (\exists x) ((Gx \cdot Cx) \cdot Mx)$

as does

$(y) ((By \cdot Cy) \supset My) \cdot (\exists y) ((Gy \cdot Cy) \cdot My)$.

In this example, the meaning of the symbolic statement does not change when one variable is used, as in (8), since (6) can be treated as two conjoined statements and the initial quantifier does not affect the second formula of the conjunction. We say, in this case, that the *scope* of the initial quantifier does not extend to the second part of the conjunction.

In general we will use parentheses in such a way that the *scope* of a quantifier extends—except for intervening quantifiers—from the left parenthesis immediately following the quantifier to its mate—the right parenthesis. The scope of '(x)' in (2), then, is '$(Bx \supset (\exists y)(Py \cdot Mxy))$', and the scope of '$(x)$' in (7) and (8) is '$((Bx \cdot Cx) \supset Mx)$'. The scope of '$(\exists y)$' in (2) is just '$(Py \cdot Mxy)$'. A formula can be within the scope of two or more quantifiers.

Now an occurrence of a variable which lies within the scope of a quantifier using this variable is said to be *bound* by that quantifier, and an occurrence of a variable which is not bound is said to be *free*. Our incomplete statement form

x is a two-foot radish.

contained a free occurrence of a variable, and the quantified formula

$(\exists x)$ (x is a two-foot radish).

contained a bound occurrence of the variable.

In

$(\exists x)(y)(Fx \cdot Gy \cdot Yz) \cdot (z)(Mxz)$

(a) the first occurrence of 'x' is bound by '$(\exists x)$';
(b) the occurrence of 'y' is bound by '(y)';
(c) the first occurrence of 'z' is free;
(d) the second occurrence of 'x' is free;
(e) the second occurrence of 'z' is bound by '(z)'.

We will say, further, that 'z' is free in 'Mxz' and bound in '$(z)(Mxz)$'. The reason that (2′) did not say the same as (2) is that the variable in 'P___' and 'Mx___' was bound in (2) by the quantifier '$(\exists y)$', but in (2′) the variable was bound by the initial quantifier. In (8), however, the variable in '$(Bx \cdot Cx) \supset Mx$' and '$(Gx \cdot Cx) \cdot Mx$' was governed by just the quantifiers that governed the variables in (7). Clearly, one must be careful in changing variables. The sense of a statement is often changed when scope is disregarded in changing variables.

Predicates such as "_____ is married" we will call single-placed predicates, and predicates such as "_____ married _____," "_____ is the brother of _____," "_____ is less than _____," "_____ is between _____ and _____," and so on, will be called two-place, three-place (and so on) predicates, depending on how many individuals "participate in," or are related by the predicates.

Finally, consider two further examples involving translations with multiple quantifiers:

9. Nobody succeeds without someone getting ulcers.
10. No one succeeds without someone failing.

In (9) the person who gets ulcers may or may not be the person who succeeds, so our translation should preserve these possibilities:

(x) $(x$ succeeds $\supset$ $(x$ gets ulcers $\lor$ $(\exists y)$ $(y$ gets ulcers$)))$,

where x and y are understood to be people; or, more simply:

(x) $(x$ succeeds $\supset$ $(\exists y)$ $(y$ gets ulcers$))$

where 'x' and 'y' are understood to be people and where the 'y' that gets ulcers may be the 'x' that succeeds. But in (10), the person who fails cannot be the person who succeeds, that is:

(x) $(x$ succeeds $\supset$ $(\exists y)$ $(y$ fails $\cdot$ $(y \neq x)))$.

Often inferences such as

He has no brothers, but his father has two children. Therefore he has a sister.

depend for their validity not only on statement connectives and quantifiers but on the logical characteristics of the predicates themselves. The study of these inferences is a branch of logic called "relation theory." We will not consider these inferences in the following chapters but will consider only those whose validity depends on the properties of quantifiers and statement connectives.

EXERCISES I

Express the following statements in the form: $(\exists x)$ (_____). Suggested predicate letters follow each.

1. Political arguments are often just noise. (Px: x is a political argument; Nx: x is just noise.)
2. Not every birthday party is a success. (Bx, Sx)
3. Just any old theme won't do for Dr. Freund. (Tx, Fx)
4. Many books in his library are magnificently bound. (Bx, Mx)
5. Abner told his secret to very few. (Px, Sx)
6. Almost no one can beat the Yankees this year. (Bx, Yx)
7. Most of Pasteur's friends had great faith in him. (Px, Fx)
8. Only a few students flunk logic. (Sx, Fx)
9. When the starter shot, he hit a number of players. (Px, Hx)
10. That bouquet has weeds in it. (Bx, Wx)
11. There were only a few votes against the Aiken-Bottum bill. (Vx, Ax)
12. She'll find few admirers among locomotive greasers. (Lx, Ax)
13. The flowers are mostly lovely. (Fx, Lx)
14. There is an escape from school. (Ex, Sx)
15. The majority of exercises in texts are fascinating. (Ex, Fx)
16. Some birds can fly backwards. (Bx, Fx)
17. Hardly any horse would start at thirty below zero. (Hx, Sx)

18. Not all fires are hot. *(Fx, Hx)*
19. After many a summer, some swans die. *(Sx, Dx)*
20. People are not all out of step with Abner. *(Px, Ax)*

EXERCISES II

Express the following statements in terms of (x) or (∃x). Use one variable.

1. Political arguments are just noise.
2. All political arguments are just noise.
3. It is not true that all political arguments are not just noise.
4. The only arguments that are just noise are political.
5. It is not true that every political argument is just noise.
6. Political arguments are not just noise.
7. Not all offensive fullbacks are offensive.
8. Only old shoes are comfortable.
9. If anyone brings his dog, it will be fed.
10. No one brings his dog to class.
11. Women do virtually no work.
12. Not every historical event is treated in its proper perspective.
13. Not any historical event is treated in its proper perspective.
14. Engina has lost several bicycles in the lake.
15. No one likes alarm clocks before ten.
16. Scarcely any poets showed up for the rally.
17. If someone goofs, nothing can save him.
18. If anyone goofs, nothing can save him.
19. Only the gods are lazy.
20. All the gods are lazy.

EXERCISES III

Express the following statements in terms of the quantifiers and two variables.

The reader will find it profitable, at first, to symbolize the following in stages. Thus consider

1. Any good instructor is able to answer some of the questions of all of his students.

Assuming, in this case, that three variables are used, the first stage would be

(a) (x) (x is a good instructor ⊃ x is able to answer some of the questions of all of his students)

Next, the consequent becomes

(b) (∃y) (y is a question · x is able to answer the y's of all his students)

And, finally, the second statement of (b) becomes

(c) (z) (z is a student ⊃ x is able to answer the y's of z)

The result is

1'. (x) $(x$ is a good instructor $\supset$ $(\exists y)$ $(y$ is a question $\cdot$ (z) $(z$ is a student $\supset$ x is able to answer the y's of $z)))$

or

1". (x) $(Ix \supset (\exists y) (Qy \cdot (z) (Sz \supset Axyz)))$.

Here, then, are the statements to be translated.

1. Everyone enjoys an occasional cup of coffee.
2. There are some drivers who love to frighten pedestrians.
3. Some amateurs play better than many pros.
4. Many students actually enjoy reading texts.
5. Everyone hates a coward.
6. All the world loves a lover.
7. Laugh and the world laughs with you.
8. Cry and you cry alone.
9. There is no candidate that everyone would vote for.
10. There is a (positive) number which is less than all other numbers greater than 0.
11. Some will not vote for anyone.
12. For every number x and y, if x is less than y then x is not equal to y.
13. All Jane's relatives like all her friends.
14. Every canvasback watches some hunter.
15. No one likes to have any of his toes stepped on.
16. For every man there is a woman.
17. Not everyone will join in every song.
18. Not every book has some interesting pages.
19. Some students work every exercise.
20. There is no number which is greater than every other number.

EXERCISES IV

List the free variables and the bound variables in each of the following formulae.

1. $(x) (Fx \cdot Gy)$
2. $(x) (\exists y) (Fx \cdot Gy) \supset Hxy$
3. $(x) (z) (\sim Fxyz) \supset (y) (Gx \cdot Hy)$
4. $(x) (\sim Fx) \supset (\exists y) (z) (Gx \cdot Hxyz)$
5. $(x) (Fx) \supset (\exists y) (Gxy)$
6. $(x) (\exists y) (Gxy \cdot Fx) \supset (z) (Hxz)$

EXERCISES V

Devise statements which can be translated into 1–6 after the free variables are bound by quantifiers.

Chapter Twelve

ARISTOTELIAN
LOGIC

Aristotle (382–322 B.C.), the great philosopher, was the first man to study arguments systematically and was the originator of the notion of logical form. One subject of his studies—contained in what is called the *Organon*—is a particular type of argument, called the *syllogism*. Although the syllogism is a very common form of inference it is only one of many types of inferences that will be of interest in the next chapters. So our interest in the logic of Aristotle is primarily historical, although the theory of the syllogism does provide an excellent introduction to the study of inferences involving quantifiers and the logic of classes.

(Actually, Aristotle's original work has been modified to some extent and this account should properly be called a modern account of Aristotelian logic.)

SYLLOGISMS

Aristotelian logic studies what is called the *syllogism*. A syllogism, in Aristotelian logic, is an argument in which a categorical statement is presented as derived from two premises, each of which is a categorical statement. The three categorical statements contain altogether just three terms, each of the terms appearing in two statemens. A *term*, here, will mean a name or a descriptive word or phrase.

To understand this definition one must first see what statements in classical logic are called *categorical statements*. The four kinds of statements called categorical statements are illustrated by the following: [1]

1. All of Shakespeare's plays are immortal.
2. No play of Shakespeare's is immortal.
3. Some of Shakespeare's plays are immortal.
4. Some of Shakespeare's plays are not immortal.

In classical logic these statements are distinguished by a terminology and by code letters as follows (where '*S*' and '*P*' are replaceable by terms):

Universal affirmative   *A*:   All *S* is *P*[2]
Universal negative   *E*:   No *S* is *P*
Particular affirmative   *I*:   Some *S* is *P*
Particular negative   *O*:   Some *S* is not *P*

The term which appears before "is"—the *copula*—or a form of "to be," is called the *subject term,* while the term after the copula is called the *predicate term.* Only statements with an *A, E, I,* or *O* form are categorical statements.

An example of a syllogism would be this (the first argument in Chapter Eleven):

1. All unemployed are lazy.
   Some philosophers are unemployed.
   Therefore some philosophers are lazy.

(1) is an argument composed of these three categorical propositions:

All *U* is *L* (an *A* proposition)
Some *P* is *U* (an *I* proposition)
Some *P* is *L* (an *I* proposition).

There are only three terms ('*U*', '*L*', and '*P*'), and each of the terms appears in two statements.

THE SIX CONDITIONS OF VALIDITY

In classical logic the validity of a syllogism was ascertained by means of five rules (with one added later). To understand these rules one must know the meaning of "middle term," "minor term," and "distribution."

The predicate term in the conclusion is called the *major term* of the syllogism. The subject term of the conclusion is called the *minor term.*

---

[1] For the relationships between these statements see the discussion of the square of opposition in the Appendix.

[2] This phrasing has become standard. The correct translation of Aristotle's "Omni *S* est *P*" is "Every *S* is *P*."

The remaining term which appears in the premisses is called the *middle term*. Thus in (1) "philosopher" is the minor term, "lazy" is the major term, and "unemployed" is the middle term.

The final technical expression needed for the statement of the rules is that of a term's being either *distributed* or *undistributed*. Here is a table showing which terms in each of the categorical statements are distributed and which are undistributed:

	Subject term	Predicate term
A	distributed	undistributed
E	distributed	distributed
I	undistributed	undistributed
O	undistributed	distributed

The six rules as traditionally stated are:

Rule 1:   The middle term must be distributed at least once.

Rule 2:   No term undistributed in the premisses may be distributed in the conclusion.

Rule 3:   If both premisses are negative (**EE, EO, OE,** or **OO**), no conclusion is possible.

Rule 4:   If one premiss is negative, the conclusion must be negative.

Rule 5:   If neither premiss is negative, the conclusion must be affirmative (**A** or **I**).

Rule 6:   If both premisses are universal (**AA, EA,** or **AE**), the conclusion cannot be particular (**I** or **O**).

If a syllogism satisfies all six rules it is regarded as valid. If it fails to satisfy one or more rules it is invalid. If a rule does not apply, the rule is satisfied.

Consider how the rules apply to example (1).

1.   All U is L.
Some P is U.
_____
Some P is L.

The middle term 'U' is distributed in the first premiss so Rule 1 is satisfied. No terms are distributed in the conclusion so Rule 2 does not apply. Rules 3 and 4 do not apply. Rule 5 is satisfied since the conclusion is affirmative. Rule 6 does not apply. So the syllogism is valid.

EXERCISES I

Indicate whether any rule or rules are violated in the following syllogisms:

1.   All bathtubs are hard.
All dishpans are things which hold jello.
Therefore all bathtubs are things which hold jello.

2. All things which happen by chance are departures from law.
   All departures from law are punishable offences.
   Therefore all things which happen by chance are punishable offences.
3. All Athenians are people who have fears.
   Some Athenians are philosophers.
   Therefore some philosophers have fears.
4. All conservative Republicans are those who favor a reduction of the power of the federal government.
   All anarchists favor a reduction of the power of the federal government.
   Therefore all conservative Republicans are anarchists.
5. All of Shakespeare's plays are immortal.
   Timon of Athens is a play of Shakespeare's.
   Therefore *Timon of Athens* is immortal.

NOTE: Singular propositions were treated as universal statements.

6. All philosophers are useless.
   No English teachers are philosophers.
   Therefore no English teachers are useless.
7. All wealthy men are dishonest.
   No wealthy men are philosophers.
   Therefore no dishonest people are philosophers.
8. No Methodist is a believer in predestination.
   No Baptist is a believer in predestination.
   Therefore all Baptists are Methodists.
9. No working men are people who like sales taxes.
   All working men are underpaid.
   Therefore some who are underpaid are people who like sales taxes.
10. All city bosses are Democrats.
    All Democrats are pragmatists.
    Therefore some pragmatists are not city bosses.
11. All folk music is simple.
    All folk music is honest.
    Therefore some honest things are simple.

Do you see any problems in connection with the application of Rule 6? Is 11, above, invalid? (See Appendix.)

SORITES AND ENTHYMEMES

Since the time of Aristotle, the syllogism has been extensively studied and a number of forms of arguments which are not of syllogistic form have been compared with it. Some of these, after suitable interpretation and modification, can be written as syllogisms and assessed by the rules of the syllogism. The two most important of these are the sorite and the enthymeme.

A *sorite* is an argument with three or more premises, each of which is an *A, E, I,* or *O* statement. Thus, one form of a sorite is the following:

1. Some *A* is *B*.
2. All *B* is *C*.
3. All *C* is *D*.
4. No *D* is *E*.

∴ Some *A* is not *E*.

This happens to be a valid sorite and one can show that it is by the rules of the syllogism in the following way. The first two premisses, regarded as two premisses of a syllogism, yield the conclusion (C 1) (below)

2. All *B* is *C*.
1. Some *A* is *B*.

∴ Some *A* is *C*. (C 1)

Then, regarding the third premiss and (C 1) as two premisses of a second syllogism we get (C 2):

3. All *C* is *D*.
(C 1) Some *A* is *C*.

∴ Some *A* is *D*. (C 2)

Now, with (C 2) and the fourth premiss we get

4. No *D* is *E*.
(C 2) Some *A* is *D*.

∴ Some *A* is not *E*. (C 3)

(C 3) is, of course, the conclusion of the sorite. Since each of the syllogisms is valid, and since each of the premisses of the syllogisms is either a premiss of the sorite or a statement deduced from the premisses of the sorite, it is clear that the sorite is a valid argument.

In general the procedure is always the same: two premisses are chosen from the premisses of the sorite which yield a conclusion (C 1) which, together with another premiss of the sorite, will yield a second conclusion (C 2). This procedure is followed until the conclusion of the sorite is obtained. Some ingenuity, or trial and error, is needed if the, premisses are not given in order.

Another form of argument to which the rules of the syllogism can be applied is the *enthymeme*. This kind of argument is just a syllogism with a premiss or the conclusion left out of the explicit statement of the argument. It is very common for such omissions to be made. A premiss may not be uttered or written out explicitly because it is trivially or obviously true, because it occupies the attention of the audience at the moment, or for any other reason which makes it unnecessary to state it in order that the argument be understood.

Here is an example involving an unstated minor premiss. One can imagine an unhappy instructor, after some students have filed in late, telling the class, ". . . some of you are not conscientious students. For no really conscientious student is late for class two days in a row." Here the minor premiss of the following syllogism is omitted:

No student who is late for classes two days in a row is a conscientious student.
Some students in this class have been late two days in a row.

∴ Some students in this class are not conscientious.

The missing premiss states what is occupying the mind of the instructor and he knows that the students are aware of this, so he does not bother to state it.

The conclusion of a syllogistic inference may also be left unstated— because it is obvious, or because the one who states the argument may feel that the force of the argument will be enhanced if he lets the audience draw the conclusion. An orator, for example, may, at the height of his oration, say,

Everyone who is easily influenced and unaware of the threat to our ideals needs to be protected from this insidious propaganda. Some of the citizens of this country are easily influenced and ignorant of this threat, and so are, unfortunately, our children. The conclusion is clear. (Pause) Thank you for listening.

The reader may verify that this is a valid syllogism—when the conclusion is added.

The syllogism is not very complex and, partly for this reason, is often not fully stated. The term "enthymeme" applies only to those arguments which are of syllogistic form when fully stated. But there are many other forms of arguments other than the syllogism which are also relatively simple and which are often abbreviated in speech. It is seldom, in fact, that an argument is presented in formal dress—phrases are rephrased, premisses omitted, and various garnishments of emphasis and style are added. The logician's main task, however, lies in deciding on the validity of arguments which are explicitly and fully stated.

EXERCISES II

The following examples of sorites are taken from Lewis Carroll's *Symbolic Logic*. Rearrange each into a series of valid syllogisms. The employment of synonyms might be necessary at times to get them into syllogistic form.

1. All babies are illogical.
   No one is despised who can manage a crocodile.

Illogical persons are despised.

Therefore no babies can manage crocodiles.

2. No terriers wander among the signs of the zodiac.

Nothing that does not wander among the signs of the zodiac is a comet.

Nothing but a terrier has a curly tail.

Therefore all creatures with curly tails are non-comets.

3. Which conclusion can be derived from the following premisses:

All writers who understand human nature are clever.

No one is a true poet unless he can stir the hearts of men.

Shakespeare wrote *Hamlet.*

No writer who does not understand human nature can stir the hearts of men.

None but a true poet could have written *Hamlet.*

4. Find the conclusion here also:

No one takes in the *Times,* unless he is well-educated.

No Hedgehogs can read.

Those who cannot read are not well-educated.

5. When I work a logic example without grumbling, you may be sure that it is one that I can understand.

These Sorites are not arranged in regular order, like the examples I am used to.

No easy example ever makes my head ache.

I can't understand examples that are not arranged in regular order, like those I am used to.

I never grumble at an example, unless it gives me a headache.

What is the conclusion?

EXERCISES III

Supply the missing premiss or conclusion of each of the following enthymemes:

1. All Athenians are corrupt because all men are corrupt.

2. Our poets should be honored because a real poet is rare.

3. J.F.K. was a human being so J.F.K. made mistakes.

4. Since all English think the Commonwealth is something of world importance when it isn't, you also think this.

5. This Broadway play is the best of the season since all the New York critics say it is.

6. Europe should have its own nuclear deterrent since major nations have always developed the best weapons possible.

7. We need to increase the size and power of our military forces because Russia is increasing the size of hers.

8. The story is often repeated of Robespierre's reply when he was accused by some of having identified the "enemies of the state" with his personal enemies. "I deny the accusation," he is reported to have said, "and the proof is that you still live."

Chapter Thirteen

INFERENCE
INVOLVING
QUANTIFIERS

It has already been pointed out that the ordinary Aristotelian syllogism is not valid merely because of the role of the statement connectives in the syllogism. The role of the quantifiers is also essential to its validity. In this chapter we will introduce elementary rules of inference which will make possible the validation of many inferences, including those of the traditional syllogism. For centuries the syllogism occupied logicians almost exclusively. But the advances in logic, beginning with the work of Boole, Frege, Whitehead, and Russell,[1] in the latter part of the nineteenth century and the early part of the twentieth century, have shown that syllogisms are a small part of the indefinitely large number of inferences capable of being analyzed by formal methods.

It should be evident by now that in logic, the study of inference, the most elementary inferences are used in analyzing and describing more complex ones. In this chapter, complex inferences involving quantifiers will be analyzed in terms of rules of inference which allow the simplest kinds of inference.

UNIVERSAL GENERALIZATION

It is common in geometry to begin a demonstration with

1. Let A be a right triangle. Then . . .

[1] George Boole and Gottlob Frege were early contributors to logic. Bertrand Russell and Alfred North Whitehead were the authors of the comprehensive treatment of logic and the foundations of mathematics—the *Principia Mathematica*.

or, in logic:

2. Suppose T is a tautology. Then . . .

The demonstration then proceeds to show that something is true of the (arbitrary) right triangle, and the discussion of the (arbitrary) tautology yields some information about the tautology. No *particular* right triangle or tautology is being discussed, but one is justified in supposing that what is shown or asserted is true of *any* right triangle or tautology.

In everyday discussion, we find statements such as

3. A single man making more than $500 a year must pay income tax.

which can be stated in the same form:

4. Let x be a single man making more than $500 a year. x must pay income tax.

Again, one is justified in concluding from (3) or (4) that *all* single men making more than $500 a year must pay income tax. In general, given the statement:

For an arbitrary individual of a certain class, such and such is true.

one may conclude that

For all individuals of that class, such and such is true.

This is the form of the first rule of inference—called *universal generalization* (UG). In symbols:

(UG) 'Pa' implies '$(x)\ Px$',

where 'a' is a new symbol corresponding to the 'A' in (1), the 'T' in (2), and 'x' in (4). (See below)

NOTATION AND TERMINOLOGY

The symbol 'a', in (UG), is not a variable, nor is it a constant. It is not, like a constant, just a convenient way to write a name or description, nor is it, like a variable, replaceable by a name or description. It is called an *ambiguous name* to distinguish it from ordinary names (or constants). Its role in the symbolism is similar to that of the "John Doe" used, for example, in showing how an income tax form is to be filled out—as well as the symbols in the previous examples: (1), (2), and (4). "John Doe" is not to be construed as the name of any *particular* individual, but could be construed as the name of some (arbitrary) tax payer.

Since an ambiguous name (we will use 'a', 'b', 'c' as ambiguous names) is not a variable, it is not bound by a quantifier nor can it be part of one. Note that, on the other hand, the ambiguous name cannot be treated as an ordinary name, for (UG) would not be a valid inference if '*a*' were just a name (a constant). For suppose someone was speaking of the bigamist Feditch and the statement was made that, as a matter of fact,

Feditch had six wives.

One could not, obviously, infer from this that

Every individual had six wives.

We will reserve '*a*', '*b*', '*c*' for ambiguous names; '*x*', '*y*', '*z*' for variables; we will use capital letters for predicates; and we will use, when possible, the initial letters (small letters) of names or descriptions (constants) to represent them. Thus '*h*' will be used for "Harding." Since there will be occasions on which both ambiguous names and constants (proper names and descriptions) will be referred to, we will call them *terms,* and regard '*t*' as being either an ambiguous name or a constant.

'(x) Px' in (UG) and in the other rules which we will introduce is to be understood as representing formulae such as the following:

5. (x) Ax
6. (y) $(Ay \supset (By \cdot Cy))$
7. (y) $((Fy \cdot Gy) \supset (Hy \text{ v } Jy))$
8. (x) (y) $(Ax \supset By)$

That is, '(x) Px' represents any formula in which the initial quantifier (whatever it is) has as its scope the whole of the remainder of the formula. '(x) Px', therefore does *not* represent the following formulae:

(x) $Fx \supset Gx$
$(\exists y)$ (x) $(Ay \cdot Bx)$
(y) $Fy \supset (x)$ Gx

Thus if (UG) is applied to

7'. $(Fa \cdot Ga) \supset (Ha \text{ v } Ja)$
8'. (y) $(Ab \supset By)$,

where '*a*' and '*b*' are ambiguous names, it yields (7) and (8). But (UG) could not be applied to (7') to get

7''. $(Fa \cdot Ga) \supset (x)$ $(Hx \text{ v } Jx)$

since (7'') does not have the form '(x) Px' but

$Qa \supset (x)$ Px.

That is, the scope of '(x)' is not the entire formula.

If there are two or more occurrences of an ambiguous name '*a*' in a formula, the application of (UG) will require replacing *all* the occurrences of '*a*' and only the occurrences of '*a*' by a variable. Thus the application of (UG) to

$(Fa \cdot Gab) \supset \sim Fa$

yields

$(x) ((Fx \cdot Gxb) \supset \sim Fx)$

or

$(x) ((Fa \cdot Gax) \supset \sim Fa)$.

Since the other rules need to be qualified in this way, it will simplify the discussion and presentation of them if we adopt the conventions that in the statement of the rules:

(A) '*Px*' indicates that the only free variable in '*Px*' is '*x*'.
(B) '*Pa*' (or '*Pt*') indicates that in every place in which a free variable occurs in '*Px*', '*a*' (or '*t*') occurs.

Thus, if '*Px*' is a representation of

$Qx, Qx \supset Rx, Qax \lor Rb, (y) (Qxy \supset Ry)$, and so on,

the corresponding formulae '*Pa*' are

$Qa, Qa \supset Ra, Qaa \lor Rb, (y) (Qay \supset Ry)$, and so on.

If no variable occurs free in a formula, '*Px*', '*Pa*', and '*Pt*' are the same—that is, just the original formula. We call '*Pa*' or '*Pt*' a *substitution instance* of '*Px*'. Thus in (UG), '*Pa*' is a substitution instance of '*Px*'.

Later we will need to add further restrictions to the application of (UG). It should be noted that the rule (UG) and the formulation of the other rules are only intended to apply to inferences in which one variable is involved. In the last section of this chapter the conditions under which the rules can be applied to validate inferences involving more than one variable will be discussed.

UNIVERSAL INSTANTIATION

The second rule of inference is called *Universal Instantiation* (UI). This rule allows the derivation of (2) and (3) from (1), and (5) and (6) from (4).

1. Everything is a two-foot radish $((x) Rx)$.
2. Any particular thing is a two-foot radish (Ra).

3. Popeye is a two-foot radish   (*Rp*).
4. Every President finally succumbed to the will of the people ((x) ($Px \supset Sx$)).
5. Such and such President finally succumbed to the will of the people (*Pa* ⊃ *Sa*).
6. Harding, if he was a President, finally succumbed to the will of the people (*Ph* ⊃ *Sh*).

That is, (UI) allows us to conclude that something—which may be named or ambiguously named—is such and such if we are given the fact that everything is such and such. In symbols:

(*UI*) '(x) *Px*' implies '*Pt*'.

Even if the Harding referred to in (6) is not Warren G. Harding, the twenty-ninth President, but Edgar Harding the flagpole sitter, (6) still follows from (4) and is true if (4) is true. Thus (UI) does not permit a false conclusion to be drawn from true premises.

We will now consider an argument and apply, or consider the application of (UI) and (UG) in the validation of arguments. For example, consider this argument:

All men are selfish.
Feditch is a man.
Therefore Feditch is selfish.

In our symbolism this becomes (replacing "Feditch" by '*f*'):

(x) (*Mx* ⊃ *Sx*)
Mf
∴ *Sf*

The premises, in the routines of the validations of Chapter Ten, are:

A. 1. (x) (*Mx* ⊃ *Fx*)   P
   2. *Mf*   P

We apply (UI) to line 1:

   3. *Mf* ⊃ *Sf*   (1) UI

and then apply (R1) to lines 2 and 3:

   4. *Sf*   (2, 3) MP

Notice that this is a syllogism and that its validation is simple and requires no rules which sound as contrived as those used in Chapter Twelve. Now consider the inference (a syllogism):

All men are mortal.
All bachelors are men.
Therefore all bachelors are mortal.

Here is the validation:

B. 1. $(x) (Mx \supset Dx)$ P
    2. $(x) (Bx \supset Mx)$ P
    3. $Ma \supset Da$ (1) UI
    4. $Ba \supset Ma$ (2) UI
    5. $Ba \supset Da$ (3, 4) HS

And, finally, applying (UG) to line 5, we have

    6. $(x) (Bx \supset Dx)$ (5) UG

It was said that (UG) could not be applied to a formula in which the term to be universalized was a proper name. Notice this was not done in (B)—'*a*' in (B) was an *ambiguous* name. Also notice that (UG) could not be applied to line 4 of (A) since '*f*' is a proper name.

Here is an example of an argument with three premisses:

All surgeon's are M.D.'s.
No M.D. is perfect.
Ben Casey is a surgeon.
Therefore Ben Casey is not perfect.

C. 1. $(x) (Sx \supset Mx)$ P
    2. $(x) (Mx \supset \sim Px)$ P
    3. Sb P
    4. $Sb \supset Mb$ (1) UI
    5. $Mb \supset \sim Pb$ (2) UI
    6. $Sb \supset \sim Pb$ (4, 5) HS
    7. $\sim Pb$ (3, 6) MP

EXISTENTIAL INSTANTIATION

We now introduce the final rules needed to construct validations of arguments involving quantified statements in which the rules are applied to only one variable.

The first is called *Existential Instantiation* (EI). It allows the inference from

1. There are some Utahans who have never swum in the Great Salt Lake.
2. Some folks actually like hominy.

to the statements (respectively):

3. So-and-so (resident of Utah) has never swum in the Great Salt Lake.
4. So-and-so actually likes hominy.

where 'so-and-so' is to be regarded as an ambiguous name. Existential instantiation can be stated as follows:

(EI) '$(\exists x)\ Px$' implies 'Pa'.

Although the role of the symbols 'a', 'b', and so on, in (EI) is not identical with their role in (UI), we will continue to call them ambiguous names. Later a condition will be placed on this rule. One cannot infer from (1), of course, that a particular Utahan has never swum in the lake, so the ambiguous name in (EI) could not be a proper name.

EXISTENTIAL GENERALIZATION

The second rule involving existential quantification is analogous to (UG); it is called *Existential Generalization*. (EG) allows the inferences from the following:

1. Horace has had enough candy.
2. So-and-so backed into my fender last night.
3. John Q. Public ate his cake and had it too.

to:

1. There is someone who has had enough candy.
2. There is someone who backed into my fender last night.
3. There is someone who ate his cake and had it too.

That is, if a true statement is made about an individual, *either* by use of a name or an ambiguous name, one can surely conclude (or understand) there *is* an individual of whom the statement is true. In (2) and (3), 'so-and-so' and 'John Q. Public' were taken as rough equivalents to the symbolism's ambiguous names. So, if 't' is a term,

(EG) 'Pt' implies '$(\exists x)\ Px$'.

RESTRICTIONS

It was said earlier that a condition must be placed on the application of (EI). To see why this condition is necessary, consider the two statements:

There are some Utahans who have swum in the Great Salt Lake.
There are some Utahans who have never swum in the Great Salt Lake.

Suppose these statements were used in the following erroneous argument:

D. 1. $(\exists x)\ (Ux \cdot Sx)$ P
    2. $(\exists x)\ (Ux \cdot \sim Sx)$ P

3.	$Ua \cdot Sa$	(1) EI
4.	$Ua \cdot \sim Sa$	(2) EI
5.	$Sa \cdot Ua$	(3) Comm.
6.	Sa	(5) Simp.
7.	$Ua \cdot \sim Sa \cdot Sa$	(4, 6) Conj.
8.	$(\exists x)(Ux \cdot \sim Sx \cdot Sx)$	(7) EG

This argument is obviously erroneous, for from the two true premisses the contradiction "Some Utahans have not swum in the Great Salt Lake and have swum in the Great Salt Lake" has been derived. The trouble arose when those Utahans who have never swum in the Great Salt Lake were named (ambiguously) by the same symbol 'a' that was used to name (ambiguously) those Utahans who have swum in the Great Salt Lake. To avoid such erroneous inferences a different ambiguous name must be used in successive applications of (EI). Thus, (EI) becomes:

(EI) '$(\exists x) Px$' implies 'Pa'—provided 'a' does not occur previously in the validation.

Since no such restriction applies to (UI) it is necessary to use (EI) before (UI) in validations. The importance of this will be evident in the next example. If (UI) is used to obtain line 3 before (EI) is used, according to the new restriction on (EI) a second ambiguous name must be introduced into the validation. This, as the reader will note, would introduce undesirable complications.

Some students do not go to college picnics.
All students who want to get ahead go to college picnics.

E.	1.	$(\exists x)(Sx \cdot \sim Cx)$	P
	2.	$(x)((Sx \cdot Ax) \supset Cx)$	P
	3.	$Sa \cdot \sim Ca$	(1) EI
	4.	$(Sa \cdot Aa) \supset Ca$	(2) UI
	5.	$\sim Ca \cdot Sa$	(3) Comm.
	6.	$\sim Ca$	(5) Simp.
	7.	$\sim Ca \supset \sim (Sa \cdot Aa)$	(4) Trans.
	8.	$\sim (Sa \cdot Aa)$	(6, 7) MP
	9.	$(x) \sim (Sx \cdot Ax)$	(8) UG ?

Notice that we have again arrived at a conclusion which does not follow from the premisses. The conclusion in the 'validation' says that it is false that there is a student who wants to get ahead, and this does not follow from the premisses. A further restriction is needed on the rules of inference.

The difficulty can be put in the following way; suppose that everything is at least two feet long, that is, that '$(x) Tx$'. When (UI) is applied to '$(x) Tx$', we get 'Ta'. 'a' here is the ambiguous name of some (arbitrary) thing. Thus (UG) could be applied, correctly, to 'Ta' to obtain '(x) Tx' again. However, if just some things are at least two feet long, 'Ta' could still be obtained by applying (EI) to '($\exists$ x) Tx'. But now the application of (UG) to 'Ta' would be incorrect, for the inference from '($\exists$ x) Tx' to '(x) Tx' is incorrect. Thus the application of (UG) must be restricted to those formulae containing ambiguous names which have been introduced into the validation by (UI). (UG), then, cannot be applied to formulae containing ambiguous names introduced by (EI). Notice that in the proof above, (UG) was applied to the ambiguous name 'a' which was introduced in line 3 by (EI).

For convenient reference in studying the following examples, all the rules with their restrictions are listed below.

(UG) 'Pa' implies '(x) Px'—where 'a' is an ambiguous name introduced by an application of (UI).
(UI) '(x) Px' implies 'Pt'.
(EI) '($\exists$x) Px' implies 'Pa'—provided 'a' does not previously occur in the validation.
(EG) 'Pt' implies '($\exists$x) Px'.

EXAMPLES

Here now are a number of examples in which the applications of the rules can be studied.

Many fish are night feeders, and every night feeder has good ears. But nothing that has good ears has good eyes, so many fish do not have good eyes.

In symbols:

F. ($\exists x$) ($Fx \cdot Nx$)
   (x) ($Nx \supset Ex$)
   (x) ($Ex \supset \sim Yx$)
   $\therefore$ ($\exists x$) ($Fx \cdot \sim Yx$)

The validation is as follows:

1. ($\exists x$) ($Fx \cdot Nx$)   P
2. (x) ($Nx \supset Ex$)   P
3. (x) ($Ex \supset \sim Yx$)   P
4. $Fa \cdot Na$ (1) EI
5. $Na \supset Ea$ (2) UI
6. $Ea \supset \sim Ya$ (3) UI
7. Fa (4) Simp.
8. $Na \cdot Fa$ (4) Comm.
9. Na (8) Simp.

10.	Ea	(5, 9) MP
11.	$\sim Ya$	(6, 10) MP
12.	$Fa \cdot \sim Ya$	(7, 11) Conj.
13.	$(\exists x)(Fx \cdot \sim Yx)$	(12) EG

Note that (EI) is used *before* (UI). This is done since it is necessary that the *same* ambiguous name occur in 'Fa' and 'Ya' so that (EG) can be applied to their conjunction to obtain the conclusion. If (UI) were applied before (EI), the same ambiguous name could not be used.

Quakers and members of Peace Movements are either deluded or they are right in their views. A man is a true Christian if and only if he is a Quaker. No true Christian is deluded. Hence Quakers are right in their views.

In symbols:

$(x)((Qx \; v \; Mx) \supset (Dx \; v \; Rx))$
$(x)(Tx \equiv Qx)$
$(x)(Tx \supset \sim Dx)$
$\therefore (x)(Qx \supset Rx)$

The validation, using RCP, is as follows. Note that (UG) is applied after the conditional proof is finished (on line 15). If (UG) were applied to line 10, we would have "Everything is a Quaker," which does not follow from the premisses. (UG) will *not* be applied to lines which are a part of a conditional proof. That is, (UG) may *not* be applied to the premiss of a conditional proof, or to any line derived from that premiss.

G.	1.	$(x)((Qx \; v \; Mx) \supset (Dx \; v \; Rx))$	P
	2.	$(x)(Tx \equiv Qx)$	P
	3.	$(x)(Tx \supset \sim Dx)$	P
	4.	$(Qa \; v \; Ma) \supset (Da \; v \; Ra)$	(1) UI
	5.	$Ta \equiv Qa$	(2) UI
	6.	$Ta \supset \sim Da$	(3) UI
	7.	$(Ta \supset Qa) \cdot (Qa \supset Ta)$	(5) Equiv.
	8.	$Qa \supset Ta$	(7) Simp.
	9.	$Qa \supset \sim Da$	(6, 8) HS
	10.	Qa	Hypothesis for RCP
	11.	$\sim Da$	(9, 10) MP
	12.	$Qa \; v \; Ma$	(10) Add.
	13.	$Da \; v \; Ra$	(4, 12) MP
	14.	Ra	(11, 13) DS
	15.	$Qa \supset Ra$	(10, 14) RCP
	16.	$(x)(Qx \supset Rx)$	(15) UG

Notice that the proof could be shortened by symbolizing the first premiss: $(x)(Qx \supset (Dx \; v \; Rx)) \cdot (x)(Mx \supset (Dx \; v \; Rx))$, and by symbolizing the second premiss as simply: $(x) (Qx \supset Tx)$, since '$(x) (Tx \supset Qx)$ and '$(x) (Mx \supset (Dx \lor Rx))$' do not play a role in the deduction.

No one with good sense who is buying a sailboat buys a used sailboat unless he consults an expert. Charles, who is buying a sailboat, doesn't believe in experts and will not have a boat checked by one. But he is almost broke and, of course, if someone is almost broke he buys a used sailboat. We can conclude that there are some people who don't have good sense who are buying sailboats.

H. 1. $(x) ((Sx \cdot \sim Ex) \supset \sim Gx)$ P
    2. $\sim Ec$ P
    3. Bc P
    4. $(x) (Bx \supset Sx)$ P
    5. $(Sc \cdot \sim Ec) \supset \sim Gc$ (1) UI
    6. $Bc \supset Sc$ (4) UI
    7. Sc (3, 6) MP
    8. $Sc \cdot \sim Ec$ (2, 7) Conj.
    9. $\sim Gc$ (5, 8) MP
   10. $(\exists x) \sim Gx$ (9) EG

Notice that there are also phrases in this argument which are, so to speak, extraneous to its validity. The phrases "Charles doesn't believe in experts" and "who is buying a sailboat" do not figure essentially in the argument. This is a common feature of arguments, of course, and will be a feature of some of the arguments in the exercises. Symbolizing the extraneous phrases is unnecessary, and merely complicates the validation.

Arguments in which more than one variable needs to be symbolized present further difficulties in the general case. These difficulties will be discussed in the next section. There are, however, classes of arguments involving more than one variable for which no additional conditions on the rules are necessary. Here, for example, is one in which a multiple-place predicate occurs:

Most folks hate phoneys, so most people will hate Edgar if he is a phoney.

I. 1. $(\exists x) (Fx \cdot (y) (Py \supset Hxy))$ P
    2. $Fa \cdot (y) (Py \supset Hay)$ (1) EI
    3. $(y) (Py \supset Hay) \cdot Fa$ (2) Comm.
    4. $(y) (Py \supset Hay)$ (3) Simp.
    5. $Pe \supset Hae$ (4) UI
    6. Fa (2) Simp.
    7. $Fa \cdot (Pe \supset Hae)$ (5, 6) Conj.
    8. $(\exists x) (Fx \cdot (Pe \supset Hxe))$ (7) EG

GENERAL RULES

We now consider what further restrictions on the rules (UG), (UI), (EI), and (EG) are necessary in order to validate a number of other valid arguments.

Consider first of all the true statement of arithmetic (regard the variables as taking numbers as values and '=' as a two-placed predicate): $(x) (\exists y) (x^2 = y)$, that is, for every number 'x' there is a number 'y' which is the square of 'x'. As the rules stand, the following bogus inference can be validated:

1.	$(x) (\exists y) (x^2 = y)$	P
2.	$(\exists y) (a^2 = y)$	(1) UI
3.	$a^2 = b$	(2) EI
4.	$(x) (x^2 = b)$	(3) UG
5.	$(\exists y) (x) (x^2 = y)$	(4) EG

The conclusion is false—it says that there is a number 'y' which is the square of every number. Clearly a restriction must be introduced to block such procedures. The restriction, on (UG), is this: (UG) may not be applied to 'Pa' if 'a' occurs in a step obtained by (EI). Since 4 was obtained by applying (UG) to '$a^2 = b$' where this step was obtained by applying (EI) to '$(\exists y) (a^2 = y)$', this application of (UG) is no longer allowed.[2]

Also, there is a restriction which must be applied to both (EG) and (UG). It is necessary because of the following: suppose the nth line of a validation were

$n.$ $(y) (y^2 = a)$　　　　　　　　　——————

Applying (EG), we get:

$n + 1.$ $(\exists y) (y) (y^2 = y)$　　　　　　　　　EG

and since, by reason of the interpretation of the quantifiers, the outside quantifier is redundant, we have the false conclusion:

$n + 2.$ $(y) (y^2 = y).$

If (UG) were applied to line (n) so that line $(n + 1)$ was '$(y) (y) (y^2 = y)$' the conclusion would be the same. Thus these steps must not be allowed. The restriction is that (UG) and (EG) may not be applied when the variable introduced becomes bound by a quantifier of the original formula.

---

[2] This restriction is more severe than necessary, but it is made so for the sake of simplicity. It was needed in the previous section.

Finally, no free variables are allowed in the premisses. This holds also for premisses introduced as hypotheses in conditional proofs. This restriction does not hamper the validation of arguments considered in this chapter but it simplifies the statement of the rules. Here, then, are the rules in their final form:

(UI) '$(x) Px$' implies 'Pt'.

(EG) 'Pt' implies '$(\exists x) Px$'.

(EI) '$(\exists x) Px$' implies 'Pa', where 'a' does not previously appear in the validation.

(UG) 'Pa' implies '$(x) Px$', where 'a' is neither introduced by (EI) nor appears in a step obtained by (EI).

Also:

1. No free variables occur in the premisses.
2. Neither (UG) or (EG) can be applied when 'x' becomes bound by a quantifier in Pa or Pt.
3. (UG) cannot be applied to the premiss of a conditional proof or to any line depending on that premiss.

Now consider some examples in which the new restrictions need to be observed.

J. 1. $(x) (Fx \supset (y) (Gy \supset Cxy))$ P
   2. $(\exists x) Fx$ P
   3. Fa (2) EI
   4. $(\exists y) Gy$ Hypothesis for RCP
   5. Gb (4) EI
   6. $Fa \supset (y) (Gy \supset Cay)$ (1) UI
   7. $(y) (Gy \supset Cay)$ (3, 6) MP
   8. $Gb \supset Cab$ (7) UI
   9. Cab (5, 8) MP
  10. $(\exists x) Cxb$ (9) EG
  11. $(\exists y) (\exists x) Cxy$ (10) EG
  12. $(\exists y) Gy \supset (\exists y) (\exists x) Cxy$ (4, 11) RCP

Note that the hypothesis introduced on line 4 is quantified as is 'Gy' in the conclusion. No free variable is thus introduced into the validation. Notice also that (UI) cannot be applied to line 6 since the formula does not have the form '$(y) Py$' but '$Fa \supset (y) Py$'. The next example illustrates situations in which the restrictions on (UG) must be observed.

K. 1. $(x) (Fx \supset (y) (\exists z) Gxyz)$ P
   2. $(\exists x) Fx$ P
   3. Fa (2) EI
   4. $Fa \supset (y) (\exists z) Gayz$ (1) UI
   5. $(y) (\exists z) Gayz$ (3, 4) MP

6.	$(\exists z)\ Gabz$	(5) UI
7.	$Gabc$	(6) EI
8.	$(\exists z)\ Gabz$ [3]	(7) EG
9.	$(\exists y)\ (\exists z)\ Gayz$	(8) EG
10.	$(\exists x)\ (\exists y)\ (\exists z)\ Gxyz$	(9) EG

In line 8, (UG) cannot be used, since 'b' appears in a line (7) which was obtained by (EI). (UG) cannot be applied to either 7 or 9, of course, since the ambiguous names with reference to which the generalization is made were introduced by (EI). Note also that three different variables occur in line 10—they are necessary by restriction 2. Here is another example involving RCP.

L.	1.	$(x)\ (y)\ ((Ax \cdot By) \supset (\exists z)\ Cz)$	P
	2.	$(y)\ (z)\ (Gyz \supset By)$	P
	3.	$(\exists y)\ (\exists z)\ Gyz$	P
	4.	$(\exists z)\ Gaz$	(3) EI
	5.	Gab	(4) EI
	6.	$(z)\ (Gaz \supset Ba)$	(2) UI
	7.	$Gab \supset Ba$	(6) UI
	8.	Ba	(5, 7) MP
	9.	$(y)\ ((Ac \cdot By) \supset (\exists z)\ Cz)$	(1) UI
	10.	$(Ac \cdot Ba) \supset (\exists z)\ Cz$	(9) UI
	11.	Ac	Hyp RCP
	12.	$Ac \cdot Ba$	(8, 11) Conj.
	13.	$(\exists z)\ Cz$	(10, 12) MP
	14.	Cd	(13) EI
	15.	$Ac \supset Cd$	(11, 14) RCP
	16.	$(\exists z)\ (Ac \supset Cz)$	(15) EG
	17.	$(\exists x)\ (\exists z)\ (Ax \supset Cz)$	(16) EG

INVALID[4] ARGUMENTS

To show the invalidity of the arguments involving single-place predicates, it is not enough to fail to show them valid. If one fails to show that an argument is valid, this is not a guarantee that it cannot be shown to be valid. It might merely mean that one lacks the ingenuity. We will adopt the ideas discussed in Chapter Eleven, pages 258–259, to show the invalidity of arguments involving quantification. To use that method, however, we will have to express quantified statements as non-quantified statements—which can easily be done. We have already seen

---

[3] Lines (7) and (8) are not necessary to the validation, of course; they are introduced only for illustrative purposes.

[4] Once again: the test of invalidity is not comprehensive, nor (see the last paragraph) decisive.

how to do this (under the assumption that the individuals in the universe do not exceed a finite number n—see Chapter Eleven, pages 258–259). If there is only one individual 'a' in the universe,

'(x) Fx' and '$(\exists x)$ Fx' are both equivalent to 'Fa'.
'(x) $(\exists y)$ $(Fx \cdot Gy)$' is equivalent to '$Fa \cdot Ga$'.
'$(\exists x)$ (y) $(\exists z)$ $(Fx \supset (Gy \cdot Hz))$' is equivalent to '$Fa \supset (Ga \cdot Ha)$'.

and so on.

If there are three individuals in the universe 'a', 'b', and 'c',

'(x) Fx' is equivalent to '$Fa \cdot Fb \cdot Fc$'.
'$(\exists x)$ Fx' is equivalent to 'Fa v Fb v Fc'.

Multiple quantifiers present no problem. We simply apply the general definitions:

'(x) Fx' is equivalent to '$F(1) \cdot F(2) \cdot \cdots \cdot F(n)$'.
'$(\exists x)$ Fx' is equivalent to '$F(1)$ v $F(2)$ v $\cdots$ v $F(n)$'.

(where there are n individuals in the universe and (1), (2), etc., are the names of these individuals). For example, '(x) $(\exists y)$ $(Fx \cdot Gy)$' says that for every 'x', a 'y' can be found such that '$Fx \cdot Gy$'. Thus (supposing there are two individuals 'a' and 'b') '(x) $(\exists y)$ $(Fx \cdot Gy)$' becomes

$$(\exists y)\ (Fa \cdot Gy) \cdot (\exists y)\ (Fb \cdot Gy),$$

and then

$$((Fa \cdot Ga)\ \text{v}\ (Fa \cdot Gb)) \cdot ((Fb \cdot Ga)\ \text{v}\ (Fb \cdot Gb)).$$

And since '$(\exists y)$ (x) $(Fx \cdot Gy)$' says that there is a 'y' such that for all 'x's, '$(Fx \cdot Gy)$' holds, we have

$$(\exists y)\ (x)\ (Fx \cdot Gy) \equiv (x)\ (Fx \cdot Ga)\ \text{v}\ (x)\ (Fx \cdot Gb)$$
$$\equiv ((Fa \cdot Ga) \cdot (Fb \cdot Ga))\ \text{v}\ ((Fa \cdot Gb) \cdot (Fb \cdot Gb)).$$

Similar considerations apply to other combinations of quantifiers.

It turns out that an argument involving quantifiers is *invalid* if in some universe with at least one individual, the premisses can be assigned the value "true" and the conclusion turns out false.[5]

Now let us see how this works. Consider the syllogism

All lollipops are dangerous weapons.
Some dangerous weapons are not good to eat.

∴ Some lollipops are not good to eat.

---

[5] In these chapters we have been assuming that at least one thing exists. If we did not assume this, we could not infer '$(\exists x)$ Fx' from '(x) Fx', and it is convenient to be able to do this.

In symbols:

$(x) (Mx \supset Nx)$
$(\exists x) (Nx \cdot \sim Px)$

$\therefore (\exists x) (Mx \cdot \sim Px)$

In a universe of one individual (a):

$Ma \supset Na$
$Na \cdot \sim Pa$

$\therefore Ma \cdot \sim Pa$

If we call 'Ma' false and 'Na' and '$\sim Pa$' true, the premisses are true and the conclusion is false. Thus the argument is invalid. Here is another invalid syllogism:

Some monkeys are clever.
Some Sophomores are clever.

$\therefore$ Some Sophomores are monkeys.

If there is just one individual in the universe:

$Ma \cdot Ca$
$Da \cdot Ca$

$\therefore Da \cdot Ma$

This is valid *in this* universe, but if the universe has two members, the argument is:

$(Ma \cdot Ca) \text{ v } (Mb \cdot Cb)$
$(Da \cdot Ca) \text{ v } (Db \cdot Cb)$

$\therefore (Da \cdot Ma) \text{ v } (Db \cdot Mb)$

which (as the reader can show) is invalid with a particular assignment of truth values.

It should be clear that this procedure to check invalidity is indecisive. Suppose, for example, we had an argument in which one of the premisses was

$(x) (\exists y) Fxy \cdot (x) \sim Fxx \cdot (x) (y) (z) ((Fxy \cdot Fyz) \supset Fxz).$

In order to find a universe in which this formula could be true, we would have to check all finite universes (supposing we started with a one-member universe, and then checked a two-member universe, and so on), which is impossible. The statement will come out true only if the universe contains an infinite number of individuals—that, for example, of the positive integers—with 'Fxy' as "x is less than y." We do not, in other words, have a mechanical way of checking whether an argument (in the general theory of quantification in which many-placed predicates are allowed) is valid or invalid, although we do have a mechanical way of checking truth functional arguments, that is, the truth tables.

EXERCISES I

A. Symbolize the following arguments and validate them if possible.

1. Curious cats die young.
   Most bold cats are curious.
   _____
   Most bold cats die young.

2. No coffee cups are unbreakable.
   Some things made of aluminum are coffee cups.
   _____
   Some things made of aluminum are not unbreakable.

3. All Athenians were bigoted.
   No real philosopher is bigoted.
   _____
   No real philosophers were Athenians.

4. Some poets are bums.
   All poets are hungry.
   _____
   Some of the hungry are bums.

5. All those who want to get reelected are politicians.
   Some of those who want to get reelected don't deserve to be.
   _____
   Some politicians don't deserve to be reelected.

6. All professional wrestlers are athletes.
   No athletes are good actors.
   _____
   No good actors are professional wrestlers.

7. All professional wrestlers are athletes.
   No athletes are good actors.
   There are some good actors.
   _____
   Some good actors are not professional wrestlers.

8. Some people never get lost.
   Everyone wants to find a pot of gold.
   _____
   Some who want to find a pot of gold never get lost.

B. Construct validations where possible for those arguments found in the exercises for Chapter Twelve.

   Do the same with the following:

1. No news is good news and some news is bad. So some news is not only not good but bad news.

2. Georgia dates only boys that have tuxedos and since Edgar doesn't have one, he can't get a date with Georgia.

3. One will make the Dean's list if he doesn't go to movies and doesn't carouse. Since Edgar has never caroused and doesn't like movies he will make the Dean's list.

4. Some students are very intelligent but not very conscientious. Every student is only human, however. Students, of course, are not all very intelligent, but every girl is. And so some humans are not girls.

5. Members of Xi Xi are either screwballs or athletes. Since at least one Xi Xi is not an athlete, this means that at least one Xi Xi is a screwball.

6. A man will catch bass in August if and only if he fishes at night or is phenomenally lucky. Ham Hanks catches bass in August, so Ham is either a night owl or very lucky.

7. No one who is a defendant will be convicted if he is innocent. Anyone who is tried is a defendant. Anyone who is not convicted is acquitted. Therefore if anyone is tried, he is acquitted if he is innocent.

8. None of Audrey's suitors like any of her relatives but all of her suitors like all of her girl friends. Audrey does have a number of suitors. So there is someone who likes Audrey's girl friends but does not like her relatives.

9. All of Mrs. Gee's boarders are fastidious students. If one of her boarders complains he is justified in doing so. If a fastidious person doesn't have a room with a bed he complains. There are boarders with no bed in their room. Therefore some boarders who are fastidious complain.

10. Lewis Carroll, the author of *Alice in Wonderland,* devised this argument.

   1. The only animals in this house are cats;
   2. Every animal is suitable for a pet that loves to gaze at the moon;
   3. When I detest an animal I avoid it;
   4. No animals are carnivorous, unless they prowl at night;
   5. No cat fails to kill mice;
   6. No animals ever take to me, except what are in this house;
   7. Kangaroos are not suitable for pets;
   8. None but carnivora kill mice;
   9. I detest animals that do not take to me;
  10. Animals that prowl at night always love to gaze at the moon.

The conclusion: I always avoid a kangaroo.

HINT: Divide the argument into nine syllogisms. The first one is

   1. All (animals in this house) are (cats).
   5. <u>All (cats) are</u> (mice killers).
  11. All (animals in this house) are (mice killers).

The second begins:

   8. All (mice killers) are (carnivora).
  11. All (animals in this house) are (mice killers).

EXERCISES II

Find validations for the following arguments.

1. If one player loses to another, he pays some penalty to the other. When Stan played Al, he lost to Al, so he paid Al some penalty.

2. (x) (y) $((Fx \supset Gx) \supset (Ay \supset By))$
$(\exists x) \sim Fx$
$(\exists y) Ay$
$\therefore (\exists x) Bx$

3. All freshmen will eat anything that is between two slices of bread. No freshman will eat anything that is not fried. There are such things as freshmen and there are things between two slices of bread. Consequently there are some things that are fried.

4. (x) (y) $(Bx \supset (Gy \supset \sim Fxy))$
$(\exists x)$ $(\exists y)$ $(\sim (Bx \cdot Gy) \supset Hxy)$
(x) (y) $(Hxy \supset Ix)$
(x) (y) Fxy
$\therefore (\exists x) Ix$

5. All gamebirds will fly when flushed by a dog. Every dog will flush a game bird if he gets very close to it. Each fall many dogs get very close to many game birds. So each fall many game birds are flying.

6. There are, of course, many Republican senators. Each of them will vote for at least one bill sponsored by a Democrat, but none will vote for a bill sponsored by a left-wing Democrat. So some of the bills sponsored by Democrats are not sponsored by the left-wing Democrats.

7. All cracker barrel politicians are shouters. There are some of the cracker barrel politicians who are such that no voter and they trust one another. $((\exists x) (Px \cdot Cx \cdot (y) (Vy \supset \sim Tyx)))$. There are, of course, voters. If any politician is such that he doesn't trust any voter he won't win. Also if A and B don't trust one another, then B and A don't trust one another. Therefore, some cracker barrel politicans won't win.

8. $(\exists x)$ (y) $(\sim Dx \supset (\sim Gy \cdot Dxy))$
$\therefore (\exists x)$ (y) $(Gy \supset Dx)$

EXERCISES III

Check the following to see if they are invalid.

1. Some towns are south of San Diego and some towns are north of San Diego. Thus, some towns which are south of San Diego are not towns which are north of San Diego.

2. All men are inclined to be greedy and selfish. Therefore all those who are inclined to be greedy are inclined to be selfish.

3. All A is B.
All C is A.
Therefore some C is B.

4. Every citizen is either a patriot or a traitor. Patriots alone are honorable. Some citizens are honorable, and therefore, some citizens are traitors.

5. Some B is not C.

Some C is D.

Therefore some B is not D.

EXERCISES IV

Find a validation of the following, if possible. For some, only (R 1) through (R 20) are needed; others require the quantification rules. If a validation is not forthcoming, check to see if the argument is invalid.

1. Edgar hates anyone who believes there will be a tax cut. Henry believes there will be one, so Edgar hates Henry.

2. Either Henry is not in favor of a tax cut or there is something wrong with his thinking. If the GNP is down, then Henry is in favor of a tax cut. Thus, if there is not anything wrong with his thinking, the GNP is not down.

3. Anyone who feels there will be a tax cut has something wrong with his thinking. Only a few narrow-minded businessmen feel there will be a tax cut. Therefore some narrow-minded businessmen have something wrong with their thinking.

4. If there will be a tax cut, no one will be happy if the national debt is increased. And if the debt is not increased expenditures will be decreased. Expenditures have increased and so there will not be a tax cut.

5. If anyone feels there will be a tax cut, there is either something wrong with his thinking or he knows no political philosophy. Henry feels there will be a tax cut, so if there is nothing wrong with his thinking, he knows no political philosophy.

6. Every businessman feels there will be a tax cut, although some feel it will not come right now. Thus, if businessmen feel there will be a tax cut, they feel it will not come right now.

7. If prices are high, there will not be a tax cut. Either Henry wants a tax cut or prices are high. If Henry wants a tax cut, no one else does. However, some others do want a tax cut. So there will not be a tax cut.

8. Anyone who is in favor of a tax cut is not worried about the federal debt. Each businessman is either in favor of a tax cut or is not worried about the federal debt. Some, of course, are in favor of a tax cut. So some are not worried about the debt.

9. If someone is not in favor of a tax cut, he is not wealthy and not a businessman. If he is not in favor of reducing the federal debt, he is not in favor of a tax cut. Thus, everyone who is either a businessman or is wealthy is in favor of reducing the federal debt.

10. Everyone in favor of a tax cut will vote for that staunch **advocate of** the bill, Senator Clog. Some who are in favor of reducing the federal **debt will** not lend money to anyone who will vote for Senator Clog, so they, of course, will lend money to no one in favor of a tax cut.

Chapter Fourteen

AXIOM SYSTEMS

We turn now to ideas which are not drawn primarily from the general features of language and inference but which are of interest in theories. These ideas involve a way of organizing the knowledge embodied in a theory and, more abstractly, a way of investigating the formal relationships of certain of the concepts of logic, mathematics and science. Therefore, there will be no prolonged discussions in this chapter of the connections between our development of the axiom system and language or theories. In Part III, Chapter Nineteen, there is a discussion of this method of organizing scientific theories.

In order to present the ideas of this chapter clearly, we will concentrate on the system and the various methods of assessing it, such as the methods for testing the consistency of axioms. And in order to do this within a reasonable number of pages, we will choose a simple system, but one which will have some interest—the statement calculus.

THE ANATOMY OF AN
AXIOM SYSTEM

An axiom system, whether it be in logic, mathematics, or the sciences, has four main divisions:

1. the vocabulary (including definitions, notational conventions, and so forth);
2. the axioms or postulates;

3. the rules of inference (or rules of derivation);
4. the theorems.

Let us consider each of these in turn.

The Vocabulary

In this division belong the symbols, entities, concepts, and so forth, that are defined or described in the system. Some symbols may be presented undefined—that is, without an explicit definition. These are often called *primitive* expressions. Their meaning is sometimes said to be given *implicitly* through their use in the axioms and theorems of the system. Thus if we used the symbols '*a*', '*b*', '*c*' for numerals we might introduce a symbol '*o*' into an axiom system and stipulate that it is a constant, a relation between two numerals, and is defined by the axioms

1. *a o a*
2. If '*a o b*' then '*b o a*'
3. If '*a o b*' and '*b o c*' then '*a o c*'.

The symbol '*o*' is used in (1), (2) and (3) as '=' is used in arithmetic, so '*o*' could be construed (though not necessarily) as '='. Often the primitive expressions are meant to be construed (along with the rest of the system) in a particular way. For example, in the preceding chapters, we were interested in only one way of construing '·', 'v', and so forth, although there are other interesting ways to construe these terms. (Although it is not possible to indicate here the importance and wide use of implicit definitions, it is of interest to note that some of the most fundamental concepts of the physical sciences are formally introduced into these sciences by implicit definition. For example, the 'electron' is implicitly defined in physics by the wave equations of quantum theory. The equations do not simply describe the behavior of an electron as, for example, the equations of the orbits of planets describe the orbits. For an electron is not described, or describable, independently of the equations, although a planet—as an observable thing—is describable independently of the equations of its orbit.)

Other expressions can be explicitly defined in terms of the primitive ones; for example, if '~', 'v', and parentheses are primitive expressions, '*p* · *q*' can be defined as '~ (~ *p* v ~ *q*)', or if '(*x*)' and '*Fx*' were primitive expressions along with '~', '(∃ *x*) *Fx*' could be defined as '~ (*x*) ~ *Fx*', [where '*p*' and '*q*' and '*x*' are understood to be variables and '*F*' a (predicate) constant].

In any abstract system which is meant to receive some interpretation, certain combinations of symbols are without interest, for example, '*pp* ⊃ ~ ⊃ ~ v'. Therefore, certain ones are singled out—usually by specifying how they are built up from the symbols. These are often called well-formed formulae, and the rules specifying what the well-formed formulae are, are called *formation* rules.

Axioms

The axioms or postulates are ordinarily a relatively small number of statements which are deemed for some reason or for some purpose, acceptable without proof. Commonly, the reason for accepting them without proof is the evident truth of the statements as interpreted in a certain way; that is, when the symbols are given a certain meaning. Prior to being given a meaning, the symbols have no meaning and the axioms are said to be uninterpreted. And the reason for taking certain ones of these interpreted statements as axioms, rather than others whose truth is just as evident, is that derivation of theorems is more convenient (or is possible).

In our simple system the axioms will all be tautologies—in fact they can be shown to be tautologies by use of the truth tables. The axioms in our simple system will be much like some of Peano's [1] postulates for elementary number theory, for example,

1. There are no two numbers with the same successor (that is, if $n \neq m$, then $n + 1 \neq m + 1$).
2. Zero is not the successor of a (positive) number.

Given the usual meaning of the terms, these two postulates are very much like our logical truths—their truth is quite evident.

The reasons for accepting certain statements as axioms in mathematics, however, differ markedly from the reasons for accepting statements as axioms in the advanced sciences. In the sciences, the truth of axioms or postulates generally rests on factual grounds. They may be the expression or embodiment of common knowledge about the way things are and thus seem intuitively true, or, their evident truth may be due to more complicated factors (Chapter Nineteen, pages 439–441). For example, the First Law of Thermodynamics (the principle of the conservation of energy) was considered to be intuitively true and was accepted without question, but the Second Law

(Postulate of Clausius): A transformation whose only final result is to transfer heat from a body at a given temperature to a body at a higher temperature is impossible.

was not considered to be intuitively true. In fact, many attempts were made to disprove it. These "laws" and others, such as Newton's laws in mechanics, are such that their position in the organization of their sci-

---

[1] G. Peano, an Italian mathematician, contributed much to the axiomatization of arithmetic. He showed that arithmetic could be derived from just five axioms.

ences is much like that of the axioms of a mathematical theory or the axioms of a logical system such as the one in this chapter. Formal deductions made from these laws and postulates yield other laws of the sciences. ("Formal deduction" in this connection includes not only logical transformation but also mathematical transformation.)

Uninterpreted axioms, of course, cannot be said to possess any kind of truth since they are not logical truths or empirically true. There is, for example, a standard way of writing the axioms of the mathematical theory called *group theory*.

$(x)\ (y)\ (z)\ (x\ o\ (y\ o\ z) = (x\ o\ y)\ o\ z)$
$(x)\ (x\ o\ e = x)$
$(x)\ (x\ o\ x^{-1} = e)$

The symbol 'e' is a constant, and 'o' and '$^{-1}$' are operation symbols. These symbols have no "hereditary" meaning, and the lines of symbols cannot be said to state anything. Their interest lies partially in the fact that there are many mathematical interpretations of them. After an interpretation is given to them, of course, they do state something. (In the exercises, some of these interpretations are given.)

Rules of Inference and Theorems

The rules of inference (also called rules of derivation and rules of transformation) allow the acceptance of formulae or statements other than axioms. The series of formulae or statements arrived at by application of the rules of inference to the axioms or previously established formulae or statements is called a *proof*, or a *derivation*. The formula or statement which terminates the proof is generally called a *theorem*. In the preceding chapters the notion of a rule of inference has become familiar in connection with the validations of arguments. In an axiom system there is an interest in keeping the number of rules of inference to a minimum—just as the rules of inference in the study of arguments in quantification theory were kept to a minimum—as well as the number of axioms. The point of doing this is twofold: In complex systems, the possibility of inadvertently introducing axioms or rules which allow the derivation of a contradiction is kept to a minimum; and, generally, proofs which are intended to demonstrate such things as whether contradictory formulae can be derived are easier to devise. This will be evident later in this chapter.

In mathematics and the sciences, rules of inference are seldom explicitly stated, but the inferences made commonly are made in accordance with those rules of the preceding chapters. There are, to be sure, inferences embodied in English and the techniques of mathematics which cannot be analysed in terms of—or reduced to—the elementary ones already studied. Part of the job of the logician is to *make* explicit all rules of inference and to see whether they can be analysed in terms of more elementary inferences.

In general, the theorems of an axiom system are logical truths or tautologies if and only if:

1. the axioms are logical truths or tautologies, and
2. the rules of inference allow only the establishment of further logical truths or tautologies.

The theorems obtained in the system which will be described in this chapter will be tautologies in the sense associated with truth tables. (It must be shown, of course, that the rules of inference allow only the derivation of tautologies. This will be done at the end of the chapter.) The theorems of science are not generally said to be logical truths since the axioms or fundamental principles of the sciences are not generally said to be logical truths.

THE VOCABULARY, AXIOMS, AND RULES OF INFERENCE

The system will be presented without suggesting which interpretations can be made of it or which is primarily intended.[2]

Symbols

1. '*p*', '*q*', '*r*', . . . are variables.
2. '∼' is a constant.
3. 'v' is a constant.
4. Parentheses are used to mark the scope of '∼' and 'v'. The scope of '∼' is shown by the pair of corresponding left and right parentheses immediately following '∼', and the scope of 'v' is shown by the innermost corresponding left and right parentheses containing 'v'.

Definitions

(D 1) '$(p \supset q)$' is defined as '$(\sim (p) \text{ v } q)$'.
(D 2) '$(p \cdot q)$' is defined as '$\sim (\sim (p) \text{ v } \sim (q))$'.
(D 3) '$(p \equiv q)$' is defined as '$((p \supset q) \cdot (q \supset p))$'.

---

2 Of the many ways to present this system, the one in the *Principia Mathematica* (Cambridge, 1910–1913), has been chosen. This book, written by Bertrand Russell and Alfred North Whitehead, is one of the early classic treatises of symbolic logic.

Well-Formed Formulae

It is obviously impossible to list all the formulae which will be of interest, and it is difficult to give a list of properties that these formulae
must possess. Instead a *recursive* definition of a well-formed formula, or
wff, will be given. A recursive definition of an expression '*A*' enables one
to decide in a finite number of approved steps whether something is an
'*A*'. The definition is as follows:

1. A variable is a wff.
2. If '*p*' is a wff, then '$\sim (p)$' is a wff.
3. If '*p*' and '*q*' are wffs, then '$(p \text{ v } q)$' is a wff.

For example, '$(r \supset (p \text{ v} \sim (p)))$' is, by definition, '$(\sim (r) \text{ v } (p \text{ v} \sim (p)))$'.
Now for '$(\sim (r) \text{ v } (p \text{ v} \sim (p)))$' to be a wff, '$\sim (r)$' and '$(p \text{ v} \sim (p))$' must,
by 3, be wffs. For '$\sim (r)$' to be a wff, by 2, '*r*' must be a wff—which it
is, by 1. And, by 3, '$(p \text{ v} \sim (p))$' is a wff if '*p*' and '$\sim (p)$' are. But '$\sim (p)$'
is a wff, by 2, if '*p*' is, and '*p*' is, by 1.

On the other hand, '$\text{v v } (p)$' fails to be a wff. It fails 3 since 'v' is not
a wff, by 1. And '$\sim ((()$' is not a wff since, by 2, '(' must be a wff, which
it is not, by 1.

A *part* of a wff will be any wff which is a part of the given wff. Thus,
'*p*', '$\sim (p)$', '$(\sim (p) \text{ v } (q))$', and so on, are all parts of the wff '$((\sim(p) \text{ v }$
$q) \supset \sim (q))$'. But '$\sim (q$', '$((\sim$', '$q) \supset \sim (q)$' are not parts of the wff
since they are not wffs.

It will be convenient to eliminate most of the parentheses since they
are not an essential part of the vocabulary. One easy way to do this is
to stipulate conventions regarding the scope of the constants: each constant (below) will override all those to the left of it.

$\sim, \cdot, \text{v}, \supset, \equiv.$

Thus

$$(((\sim (p) \cdot q) \text{ v } q) \supset p)$$

becomes just

$$\sim p \cdot q \text{ v } q \supset p$$

since '$\supset$' overrides the other constants, 'v' overrides the remaining ones,
and so on. Similarly,

$$p \equiv ((q \cdot \sim (r)) \text{ v } p)$$

becomes

$$p \equiv q \cdot \sim r \text{ v } p$$

and

$$(p \supset r) \cdot (q \text{ v} \sim (p))$$

becomes

$$(p \supset r) \cdot (q \text{ v} \sim p).$$

Finally the discussion will be simplified if there is some way to refer to arbitrary wffs. Let P, Q, R, . . . refer to arbitrary wffs and $\sim P$, $P \text{ v } Q$, $P \cdot Q$, and so on, refer to wffs of the forms '$\sim$ _____', '_____ v _____', '_____ $\cdot$ _____', and so on, respectively (where the blanks are to be filled by 'p', '$p \text{ v } q$', '$p \supset r \text{ v } q$', and so on). We will consider 'P', 'Q', and so forth, as being symbols of English, and we will not use quotes for them.

Rules of Derivation

(R 1) If $P \supset Q$ and P are either axioms or derived formulae, then Q is a derived formula.

(R 2) Any wff may be substituted for any variable if the substitution is made for every occurrence of that variable.

(R 3) Any wff P which is a part of an axiom or derived formula may be replaced by Q if and only if P and Q are definitionally equivalent.

(R 1), *modus ponens,* is already familiar. (R 2) allows the following substitution. From

$$p \supset q \cdot (\sim r \text{ v } p)$$

we get, by substituting '$q \cdot r$' for 'p':

$$q \cdot r \supset q \cdot (\sim r \text{ v } q \cdot r).$$

(R 3) allows, for example, the substitution of '$r \supset \sim q$' for '$\sim r \text{ v} \sim q$' as follows:

$$p \equiv p \cdot (\sim r \text{ v} \sim q)$$

becomes

$$p \equiv p \cdot (r \supset \sim q).$$

Proofs

A proof is a sequence of wffs

P_1
P_2
P_3

.

.

.

.

P_n

such that P_i (an arbitrary wff) is either an axiom or a theorem or a wff obtained by the rules from one or more of P_1, P_2, P_3, . . . , P_{i-1}. P_n will be called a *theorem*. Except for the axioms, each P_i is a derivable formula.

Axioms

The axioms are

(A 1) $p \vee p \supset p$
(A 2) $q \supset p \vee q$
(A 3) $p \vee q \supset q \vee p$
(A 4) $(q \supset r) \supset (p \vee q \supset p \vee r)$

These are the first four axioms of the *Principia Mathematica*. The fifth axiom was subsequently shown to be derivable from the first four by the logician Paul Bernays. This is to say that the fifth axiom was not *independent*. In general, given a set of formulae P_1, P_2, . . . , P_n, the set is said to be an independent set if and only if P_i is not derivable from the other formulae. The same definition applies whether the formulae in the set are axioms of a deductive system or premisses of an inference. The method we will present to show the independence of the axioms can thus be applied to the premisses of the arguments in Chapter Ten.

These remarks hold also for our subsequent proof of the *consistency* of the axioms; that is, the same methods will apply to the premisses of Chapter Ten. A set of formulae is said to be consistent if, for every wff P, P and $\sim P$ are not both derivable. The importance of this notion comes from the fact that if P and $\sim P$ are both derivable, then *any* formula is derivable. That is, $P \cdot \sim P \supset Q$ is a logical truth whatever Q is. Now if P and $\sim P$ were both derivable, $P \cdot \sim P$ would be derivable. Then, by *modus ponens* (R 1), Q is derivable. A theory in which *any* statement logically follows from the axioms or laws of the theory is commonly regarded as useless, so consistency is an important notion. Independence of axioms is not as important as consistency. The independence of axioms can simplify, however, the study of the system, since if the axioms are not independent, there are superfluous formulae to deal with in investigations of, for example, the consistency of the set.

The completeness of an axiom system is also important. To say that a set of axioms is complete is to say, roughly, that from the axioms one can deduce all that is meant to be deduced. For example, we wish our axioms to be such that all logical truths which can be shown to be such by the truth tables are derivable. This is one of the ways in which the axioms are complete. They are also complete in a slightly stronger sense which will be explained on page 309.

THEOREMS

We will now prove some theorems to illustrate what proofs are and how they are devised. At the right side of each line the justification for that line will be given. For example, '(5, 6) (R 1)' will mean that the line is obtained by application of (R 1) to lines 5 and 6. '(8) (R 2) (p/q)' will mean that the line is obtained from line 8 by an application of (R 2) in which 'p' is replaced by 'q'. [Instead of Theorem 1 we write (T 1).] (R 3) (D 3) means (D 3) is used in applying (R 3).

(T 1) $(p \supset \sim p) \supset \sim p$

Proof   1. $p \vee p \supset p$ (A 1)
        2. $\sim p \vee \sim p \supset \sim p$ (1) (R 2) $(p/ \sim p)$
        3. $(p \supset \sim p) \supset \sim p$ (2) (R 3) (D 1)

The proof is a sequence of wffs which terminates with the theorem to be proved. Line 1 is simply axiom one (A 1), line 2 is obtained from line 1 by substituting '$\sim p$' for 'p' in (A 1). This is justified by (R 2). Line 3 is obtained from line 2 by replacing '$\sim p \vee \sim p$' with '$p \supset \sim p$'. This is justified by (R 3) and (D 1).

(T 2) $(q \supset r) \supset ((p \supset q) \supset (p \supset r))$

Proof   1. $(q \supset r) \supset (p \vee q \supset p \vee r)$ (A 4)
        2. $(q \supset r) \supset (\sim p \vee q \supset \sim p \vee r)$ (1) (R 2) $(p/ \sim p)$
        3. $(q \supset r) \supset ((p \supset q) \supset (p \supset r))$ (2) (R 3) twice (D 1)

Often, when it is not confusing, it is convenient to shorten a proof by carrying out two or more substitutions on the same line. The notation is obvious.

(T 3) $(p \vee q) \vee r \supset (p \vee q) \vee (q \vee r)$

Proof   1. $q \supset p \vee q$ (A 2)
        2. $r \supset q \vee r$ (1) (R 2) twice (q/r) (p/q)
        3. $(q \supset r) \supset (p \vee q \supset p \vee r)$ (A 4)
        4. $(r \supset q \vee r) \supset (p \vee q) \vee r$ (3) (R 2) thrice (q/r)
             $\supset (p \vee q) \vee (q \vee r)$ $(p/p \vee q)$ $(r/q \vee r)$
        5. $(p \vee q) \vee r \supset (p \vee q) \vee (q \vee r)$ (2) (3) (R 1)

Line 3 results from two applications of (R 2). Line 4 results from three applications of (R 2) to line 3. These applications, that is, the substitutions, will be thought of as being made simultaneously. This is not necessary but it is expedient. It makes it unnecessary, in this case, to change the variables in line 3 to avoid confusion in making substitutions one after the other.

(T 4) $\qquad\qquad\qquad\qquad\qquad p \vee \sim p$

Proof   (Exercise)

(T 5) $\qquad\qquad\qquad\quad \sim p \vee \sim q \supset \sim (p \cdot q)$

Proof   1. $\sim p \vee \sim \sim p$ $\qquad\qquad\qquad$ (T 4) (R 2) $(p/ \sim p)$
$\qquad$ 2. $p \supset \sim \sim p$ $\qquad\qquad\qquad\quad$ (1) (R 3) (D 1)
$\qquad$ 3. $\sim p \vee \sim q \supset \sim \sim \sim (\sim p \vee \sim q)$ $\qquad$ (2) (R 2) $(p/ \sim p \vee \sim q)$
$\qquad$ 4. $\sim p \vee \sim q \supset \sim (p \cdot q)$ $\qquad\qquad$ (3) (R 3) (D 2)

Notice that in the proof of (T 5), instead of citing (T 4) as line 1 and then applying (R 2) to obtain '$\sim p \vee \sim \sim p$', line 1 is the result of applying (R 2). These departures from the definition of proof are inessential and do make the proof easier to write and read, so we will continue calling the sequences proofs.

The following are theorems—some proofs are easy and some require ingenuity.

(T 6) $(p \vee q) \supset ((r \vee q) \vee p)$
(T 7) $(r \vee (p \vee q)) \supset (r \vee (p \vee (q \vee s)))$
(T 8) $((p \vee q) \vee (q \vee r)) \supset (p \vee (q \vee r))$
(T 9) $((p \vee q) \vee r) \supset (p \vee (q \vee r))$
(T 10) $(p \vee (q \vee r)) \supset ((p \vee q) \vee r)$
(T 11) $\sim p \vee p$
(T 12) $p \supset (q \supset (p \cdot q))$
(T 13) $((p \vee q) \vee r) \equiv (p \vee (q \vee r))$
(T 14) $(p \vee q) \equiv (q \vee p)$
(T 15) $p \supset \sim \sim p$
(T 16) $\sim \sim p \supset p$
(T 17) $\sim \sim p \equiv p$
(T 18) $(p \supset q) \supset (\sim q \supset \sim p)$
(T 19) $(\sim q \supset \sim p) \supset (p \supset q)$
(T 20) $(\sim q \supset \sim p) \equiv (p \supset q)$
(T 21) $(p \cdot q) \supset (q \cdot p)$
(T 22) $(p \cdot q) \equiv (q \cdot p)$
(T 23) $p \equiv p$
(T 24) $p \cdot q \equiv \sim (\sim p \vee \sim q)$
(T 25) $p \supset q \equiv (\sim p \vee q)$
(T 26) $(p \vee q) \equiv \sim (\sim p \cdot \sim q)$
(T 27) $p \cdot (q \cdot r) \equiv (p \cdot q) \cdot r$
(T 28) $p \cdot q \supset p$

DERIVED RULES

A derived rule is a rule used to eliminate the repetitions of steps (of a proof) which often are involved in a proof. It is derived, in this system, from the theorems already proved. Thus, from (T 1)

(T 1) $(p \supset \sim p) \supset \sim p$

we get the derived rule

(DT 1) If $P \supset \sim P$ (is derived) then $\sim P$ (is derivable)

or, more succinctly,

(DT 1) If $P \supset \sim P$, then $\sim P$.

The use of (DT 1) and the other (DT's) is justified because of the following: Suppose there is a line of proof

n. $(p \cdot r) \supset \sim (p \cdot r)$

and it is necessary to derive

$n + m$. $\sim (p \cdot r)$.

Clearly, we could proceed from line n as follows:

$n + 1$. $p \vee p \supset p$ (A 1)
$n + 2$. $\sim p \vee \sim p \supset \sim p$ (R 2) $(p/ \sim p)$
$n + 3$. $(p \supset \sim p) \supset \sim p$ (R 3) (D 1)

and then, by (R 2) obtain

$n + 4$. $(p \cdot r \supset \sim (p \cdot r)) \supset \sim (p \cdot r)$ (R 2) $(p/p \cdot r)$

and, by (R 1) from (n) and $(n + 4)$

$n + 5$. $\sim (p \cdot r)$

but since lines $n + 1$, $n + 2$, and $n + 3$ are a repetition of the proof of (T 1), it would be convenient to have some way to eliminate them. This is what the derived rule (DT 1) does. From n, $n + 5$ can be derived by citing (DT 1). Clearly, the use of derived rules can always be foregone, so that they are not an essential part of the system—as are (R 1) through (R 3).

Similarly, the other theorems justify shortcuts. For example, (T 2) justifies going from the lines

n. $p \supset q$

and

   m. $q \supset r$

to

   $m + 1.$ $p \supset r.$

That is, (T 2) yields the rule

   (DT 2)   If $P \supset Q$ and $Q \supset R$ then $P \supset R$

and, of course, the less useful rule

   (DT 2)   If $Q \supset R$ then $(P \supset Q) \supset (P \supset R)$.

In the proofs of the theorems (T 6) through (T 28), the derived rules (DT 2) and (DT 12) will prove useful.

INTERPRETATION

Our axiom system has been presented without an indication of how it is to be understood. We have, however, used the symbols that were used in replacing the statement connectives "and," "or," "not," "if-then," and "if and only if," and the variables can clearly be construed as statement variables, so it is quite evident that the axioms and theorems can be construed as statement forms of the sort studied in Chapter Eight. We have mentioned also that the axioms and the theorems are tautologies and can be shown to be such by the truth tables. This way of construing the axioms and theorems will be called the *primary interpretation of the system.*

There are other ways of interpreting the system. One is the class interpretation in which the variables are construed as class variables and the symbols '$\sim$', 'v', '$\cdot$', '$\supset$', '$\equiv$' are taken to be relations between classes. (See Chapter Fifteen.) Another is the arithmetic interpretation which will be used in studying the independence and consistency of the axioms. This interpretation, which is described in detail in the next section, consists in construing the undefined symbols as arithmetic operations and allowing the variables to take on numbers as values.

CONSISTENCY

The proof of the consistency of the axioms cannot proceed by attempting to derive the negation of some formula already derived to show that the axioms lead to an inconsistency, or contradiction. For we may not find one within a finite period of time, and if we didn't, we could not be sure that there is none which is derivable along with its negation. Thus, though we *might* show the axioms to be inconsistent, we could not show, by this method, that the axioms are consistent. Working *within* the system, so to speak, will not ever yield assurance that the axioms are consistent, so another method is adopted.

The proof of consistency is a proof *about* the axioms and is on that account sometimes called a "metalogical" result. The proof will not and cannot be formulated within the system since the result is not a theorem derivable from the axioms. It will simply be stated in English (which is sometimes called the *metalanguage* when results of investigations of axiom systems are stated in it). Similar remarks apply to proofs of independence and completeness. In each case these results are *about* the axiom system—not theorems derivable from the axioms.

We will specify a particular interpretation (or *model*) for the system. Each variable may take on one of two values—in order to keep track of these we arbitrarily call them 1 and 2. The negation of a variable or formula will have that value which is not the value of the variable or formula. That is,

P	$\sim P$
1	2
2	1

The value of formulae of the form $P \vee Q$, will be the "product" of the values of P and Q; that is,

P	Q	$P \vee Q$
1	1	1
2	1	2
1	2	2
2	2	2

The axioms, expressed in terms of '$\sim$' and 'v' for convenience, are

(A 1) $\sim (p \vee p) \vee p$
(A 2) $\sim q \vee (p \vee q)$
(A 3) $\sim (p \vee q) \vee (q \vee p)$
(A 4) $\sim (\sim q \vee r) \vee (\sim (p \vee q) \vee (p \vee r))$

We will now calculate the value (1 or 2) of each axiom just as we proceeded with truth tables:

p	$\sim$	$(p \vee p)$	v	p
1	2	1	2	1
2	1	2	2	2

p	q	$\sim q$	v	$(p \vee q)$
1	1	2	2	1
2	1	2	2	2
1	2	1	2	2
2	2	1	2	2

p	q	$\sim$	$(p \vee q)$	v	$(q \vee p)$
1	1	2	1	2	1
2	1	1	2	2	2
1	2	1	2	2	2
2	2	1	2	2	2

r	p	q	$\sim$	$(\sim q$	$\vee r)$	v	$(\sim$	$(p \vee q)$	$\vee$	$(p \vee r))$
1	1	1	1	2	2	2	2	1	2	1
1	2	1	1	2	2	2	1	2	2	2
1	1	2	2	1	1	2	1	2	1	1
1	2	2	2	1	1	2	1	2	2	2
2	1	1	1	2	2	2	2	1	2	2
2	2	1	1	2	2	2	1	2	2	2
2	1	2	1	1	2	2	1	2	2	2
2	2	2	1	1	2	2	1	2	2	2

We have the result: if the variables and connectives of the axioms receive a particular interpretation, each axiom takes the same value—2. Now it must be shown that every *theorem* takes the same value under the interpretation, that is, that *no* theorem will take the value 1. To do this, rather than test every theorem—which is impossible since there is an infinite number of them—we show that the rules of inference do not allow the *derivation* of a formula which has the value 1. It will follow that every theorem has the value 2. This will, of course, mean that it is not possible to derive a formula P when $\sim P$ has the value 2 according to the interpretation. And if it is not possible to derive a formula P *and* a formula $\sim P$, then it follows that the axiom system is consistent. For, it is to be remembered, by definition, a system is consistent if P and $\sim P$ are not both derivable.

First, then, let us consider (R 1). We must show that Q must assume the value 2 if P and $P \supset Q$ have the value 2. $P \supset Q$ is the same as $\sim P \vee Q$. Consider:

P	$\sim P$	v	Q
2	1	2	

In the above table, the problem is posed: If P is 2—that is, if P is derivable—and $\sim$ P is 1 and $\sim P \vee Q$ is 2, what value must Q have? Not 1, since that would mean $\sim P \vee Q$ must be 1, which it is not; so Q is 2. Thus any formula Q has value 2, *if* the formulae P and $\sim P \vee Q$ both have the value 2. (R 1) enables only formulae with the value 2 to be derived.

(R 2) is no less obvious. Consider: any arbitrary axiom or theorem that involves two variables (for example) can be changed by (R 2) into a formula involving one variable, two, three, or more. If an individual variable is replaced by another individual variable, either different from or the same as the other variable, clearly no *new* calculation would be required to evaluate the resulting formula. But suppose an additional variable *is* introduced by substitution: for example, we apply (R 2) to

(A) $\sim q$ v $(q$ v $p)$

to get

(B) $\sim (r \cdot s)$ v $((r \cdot s)$ v $p)$.

What would be the difference in calculating the values of A and B? Suppose we begin with B by calculating the values of '$(r \cdot s)$'. The only possible values of '$(r \cdot s)$', if 'p' is either 1 or 2, are 1 and 2. But this also holds for 'q', that is, the only possible values of 'q' when 'p' is 1 are 1 and 2, and 1 and 2 when 'p' is 2. Thus there is no difference—after '$(r \cdot s)$' receives a value—in the calculations.

The general situation—where an axiom or theorem involves n variables—is not essentially different from this example, as a moment's reflection on the method of calculating values will show. The substituted expression can only assume values 1 and 2—the same values which, in all combinations, have figured in the calculation before substitution.

The situation with (R 3) is simpler; substitution of '$p \supset q$' for '$\sim p$ v q', for example, could not change the value of any formula containing them because it will have the same value for each particular assignment of values to 'p' and 'q', by definition.

Exercise: The reader should verify each assertion in the above discussion by examples.

INDEPENDENCE OF THE AXIOMS

The reasoning of the proof for the independence of the axioms is as follows: We will devise an interpretation such that three axioms take on a particular value for each possible combination of values for the variables and the other axiom does not. This shows that the three axioms taking on the same value do not imply the fourth, and thus that the fourth axiom is independent of the other three. This follows because of what we have already shown in the proof of consistency, namely: If a set of axioms takes a particular value under an interpretation, then all the formulae *derivable* from the axioms themselves take on the same value. Thus if it is possible to interpret the four axioms in such a way that one has a different value, this one is not derivable from the other three. If we can find such an interpretation for *each* axiom, we will have shown that the axiom set is independent.

We will indicate how to show the independence of (A 1) here and will indicate how to show the others' independence in the exercises.

The interpretation is again arithmetic.

P	~P
0	1
1	0
2	2

P	Q	P v Q
0	0	0
1	0	0
2	0	0
0	1	0
1	1	1
2	1	2
0	2	0
1	2	2
2	2	0

Computing the value of the first axiom, we obtain:

~	(p	v	p)	v	p
1	0	0	0	0	0
0	1	1	1	0	1
1	2	0	2	2	2

Note that a 2 occurs in the last row. The rest of the axioms, however, have all 0's as values, for example (A 2):

~	q	v	(p	v	q)
1	0	0	0	0	0
0	1	0	0	0	1
2	2	0	0	0	2
1	0	0	1	0	0
0	1	0	1	1	1
2	2	0	1	2	2
1	0	0	2	0	0
0	1	0	2	2	1
2	2	0	2	0	2

The reader can verify that the other axioms will also have all 0's in the column under the main connective.

COMPLETENESS

It has been shown in the last section that all derivable formulae are tautologies. That is, the consistency proof shows that all the formulae derivable from the axioms take on a particular value under an interpretation which gives the same value to each axiom. Since, by the truth tables, each axiom is a tautology, every formula derivable from them will also be a tautology. Thus, if it can be shown that all tautologies are derivable from the axioms, we will have the result that

(A) The class of derivable formulae is the same as the class of tautologies.

Thus the system will be shown to be complete in the sense that formulae derivable from the axioms are just what they were intended to be—all the tautologies—and no formulae which are not tautologies are derivable.

Instead of proving (A) directly, however, we will show how (A) can be proven by an indirect route. We will show how to prove the axioms to be complete in this sense:

(B) The addition of an independent axiom makes the augmented axiom set inconsistent.

If (B) is provable, then (A) is provable, for (A) is deducible from (B) in the following way.

Suppose there is a tautology which is not derivable from the axioms. It is added as an axiom. And suppose it can be shown—as we will see presently—that the augmented axiom set is inconsistent—that a contradiction is derivable from the augmented set. This would mean (by the *reductio ad absurdum* proof) that the original supposition was wrong. Thus there is no tautology not derivable from the axioms. This result—that all tautologies are derivable—and the result previously obtained—that all derivable formulae are tautologies—yield (A).

In order to prove (B) we will need three assumptions which involve what is called the *conjunctive normal form* of a formula. So it will be convenient to describe, first, what the conjunctive normal form, or CNF, of a formula is. Suppose a formula P is expressed in terms of '$\sim$', 'v', and '$\cdot$' only. Then, using the following equivalences: [3]

(a) $\sim (p \cdot q) \equiv \sim p \text{ v} \sim q$
(b) $\sim (p \text{ v } q) \equiv \sim p \cdot \sim q$
(c) $\sim \sim p \equiv p$
(d) $p \text{ v } (q \cdot r) \equiv (p \text{ v } q) \cdot (p \text{ v } r)$
(e) $p \cdot (q \text{ v } r) \equiv (p \cdot q) \text{ v } (p \cdot r)$

a formula is obtained which is a conjunction of disjunctions in which negation signs have only variables as scopes. For example, let P be

1. $\sim ((p \text{ v } q) \cdot \sim q \text{ v } r \cdot q)$.

[3] Our use of these equivalences will be seen to be justifiable by the proof of II (below). The reader should note that, unless the equivalences are definitions—so that (R 3) could be used in obtaining the CNF—we are not at liberty to substitute as we do to obtain a CNF.

Then using (b) we get

   2. $\sim ((p \text{ v } q) \cdot \sim q) \cdot \sim (r \cdot q).$

Using (a) twice

   3. $(\sim (p \text{ v } q) \text{ v } \sim (\sim q)) \cdot (\sim r \text{ v } \sim q)$

and then using (b) and (c)

   4. $((\sim p \cdot \sim q) \text{ v } q) \cdot (\sim r \text{ v } \sim q).$

Now all negation signs have variables as scopes. Finally, using (d) we get the CNF of *P:*

   5. $(q \text{ v } \sim p) \cdot (q \text{ v } \sim q) \cdot (\sim r \text{ v } \sim q)$

The three assumptions which will be needed in the proof of (B) are:

   I.   Every wff can be put into CNF.
   II. The procedures just described yield a CNF of *P* which is derivable from the axioms if and only if *P* is derivable.
   III. If a CNF is not derivable, at least one of its conjuncts will not contain a variable *and* its negation.

(Each of these assumptions requires proof, of course. In the exercises some hints will be given about how to prove them.)

Now we can proceed with the proof of (B), that is, we can now proceed to show that if the axiom system is augmented by a tautology not derivable from the original set, a contradiction can be derived.

Suppose *P* is a wff which is not derivable from the axioms, and let *Q* be the CNF of *P*. *Q* will be of the form

   6. $R_1 \cdot R_2 \cdot R_3 \ldots \cdot R_i \cdot \ldots R_n,$

where R_i (an arbitrary conjunct) is a disjunction of variables. For example, '$(q \text{ v } \sim q)$' in (5) above is R_2 in the CNF of the above example. Since *P* is not derivable, by II *Q* is not derivable either. So, by III, at least one of the *R*'s (say R_c) must not contain a variable *and* its negation.

Now, using (R 2), two different substitutions may be used on R_c. First, for every variable which is not negated, '*p*' is substituted; and for every variable which is negated, '$\sim p$' is substituted. If, for example, R_c is

   7. $\sim p \text{ v } q \text{ v } \sim r \text{ v } s,$

this first substitution will yield

   8. $\sim \sim p \text{ v } p \text{ v } \sim \sim p \text{ v } p.$

Clearly, this is equivalent to '*p*'.

The second substitution is: for every variable which is not negated, '$\sim p$' is substituted, and for every variable which is negated, 'p' is substituted. Thus, according to this method, R_c becomes

9. $\sim p \vee \sim p \vee \sim p \vee \sim p$

which is, clearly, equivalent to '$\sim p$'.

Thus, from P we can derive Q and from Q we can derive *both*

10. $R_1 \cdot R_2 \ldots \cdot p \cdot \ldots R_n$.
11. $R_1 \cdot R_2 \ldots \cdot \sim p \cdot \ldots R_n$.

And, finally, from (10) and (11) we can derive 'p' and '$\sim p$', respectively. Now suppose P were added as an axiom. It would *then* be derivable from the augmented set, but then, as we have shown, two inconsistent formulae could be deduced. This means that if *any* nonderivable formula were added to the four axioms of our system, two inconsistent formulae could be deduced. This completes our proof of consistency in sense (B).

SUMMARY

The essential features of an axiom system, whether it be in logic, mathematics, or science, are

1. the vocabulary and rules for determining well-formed formulae
2. the axioms
3. the rules of inference and the notion of a proof
4. the theorems.

In this chapter a simple axiom system is described—that system whose axioms and theorems are tautologies. It is then demonstrated that

1. the axioms are independent in the sense that no one axiom can be derived from the other three by the rules of the system.
2. the axioms are consistent in that no formula $\sim P$ can be derived by the rules if the formula P is derivable by the rules.
3. the axiom system is complete in the sense that if a formula not derivable by the rules from the axioms is added to the axioms, the axioms are then inconsistent.

EXERCISES I

In connection with the proof of consistency, show that the value of wff '$p \supset (q \vee \sim p)$' is not changed (in the arithmetic interpretation used in the proof) by the use of (R 2) in replacing

1. 'p' by '~ p'
2. 'p' by 'p · q · r'
3. 'p' by 'q · ~ q'
4. 'p' by '~ q'.

Show that the value of the wff is not changed by replacing 'q' by the wff's in 1 through 4.

EXERCISES II

1. Show the axiom 2 is independent using the model:

p	~ p		p	v	q	or		v	0	1	2
0	2		0	0	0			0	0	0	0
1	1		1	0	0			1	0	1	2
2	0		2	0	0			2	0	2	2
			0	0	1						
			1	1	1						
			2	2	1						
			0	0	2						
			1	2	2						
			2	2	2						

2. Show axiom 3 is independent using the model:

p	~ p		v	0	1	2	3
0	1		0	0	0	0	0
1	0		1	0	1	2	3
2	0		2	0	2	2	0
3	2		3	0	3	3	3

3. Show axiom 4 is independent if:

p	~ p
0	1
1	0
2	3
3	0

EXERCISES III

Find the conjunctive normal form of the following:

1. $p \supset (p \supset q)$
2. $p \equiv ~ p$

3. $(p \supset q) \cdot \sim q \supset \sim p$
4. $(p \supset q) \cdot (q \supset r) \supset (p \supset r)$
5. $p \cdot q \equiv \sim (\sim p \vee \sim q)$

Which of the above are tautologies?

EXERCISES IV

Why is it true that the CNF of a wff P is derivable if and only if P is derivable?

EXERCISES V

Show that if a CNF is not derivable, at least one of its conjuncts will not contain an individual variable and its negation. What must be true of each conjunct of a derivable CNF?

EXERCISES VI

1. Show that the axioms for group theory:
    (a) $(x) (y) (z) (x \; o \; (y \; o \; z) = (x \; o \; y) \; o \; z)$
    (b) $(x) (x \; o \; e = x)$
    (c) $(x) (x \; o \; x^{-1} = e)$

can be interpreted with the individual variables as integers, and 'e' and 'o' as arithmetic constants, and 'x^{-1}' as an operation on 'x'.

2. What interpretation can be given 'e' and 'x^{-1}' if we take the individual variables to be positive fractions with 'o' as multiplication?

3. What interpretation can be given the axioms if 'o' is construed as subtraction?

4. Suppose the variables are fractions—can 'o' be division?

EXERCISES VII

Prove the theorems (T 6) through (T 28).

Chapter Fifteen

CLASSES

In this chapter we symbolize and discuss a *part* of the logic carried in such expressions of English as:

Every student *is a member of* the TGIF club.
Our group *is included in* the group that goes to the World's Fair.

as well as many others.

We will be speaking, that is, of classes of things, collections of objects, aggregates or sets of individuals, and the notions of being a member of a class or set or collection or aggregate and of being included in a class or set or collection or aggregate.

MEMBERSHIP AND INCLUSION

It is necessary to distinguish between *class-membership* and *class-inclusion*. To say that

1. Dogs are domesticated.

is to say that every dog—or every member of the class of dogs—has a certain property—that of being domesticated. But there is a larger class of things which has this property of being domesticated and hence we will interpret statements like (1) as

2. The class of dogs is included in the class of domesticated things.

that is, as an expression of *class inclusion*.

On the other hand, to say

3. Woofer is a dog.

is to say of Woofer that he is a *member of* the class of dogs.

Notice that in (1) a class is said to be part of another class, and in (3) an individual is said to be a member of a class. Here are other examples of statements of class membership:

4. The sun is in our galaxy.
5. Noodles Romanoff was in the Black Eight Mob.
6. The Yankees are contenders for the pennant.

In (6) it is asserted that a team—which is itself a class of baseball players —is a member of another class—the class of contenders (teams) for the pennant. So, as in (6), a class is sometimes said to be a member of another class—when the class is referred to *as* a unit or individual.[1]

7. Our group is one of the groups going to the fair.

Note that in each case [(6) and (7)] the class which is said to be a member of another class is referred to as a unit, or an individual—that is, "the Yankee team" and "our group." However, it is always a class which is said to be included in another class. If it was asserted that

8. Our group is part of the group going to the fair.

one would have asserted that one class (our group) is included in (a part of) another class (the group going to the fair). Other examples of statements of class inclusion are

9. The stars are heavenly bodies.
10. His children are very bright children.

Often we identify two things as being the same, or identical or similar, by pointing out that they have certain properties or characteristics in common. But rather than using this method of deciding whether two classes are the same, we define as *identical classes* those which have the same members. Thus the class of things which are the two immediate predecessors of J. F. Kennedy as President and the class of things which are the two immediate successors of Franklin Roosevelt as President are identical because the same individuals comprise both classes. Thus the English statement

11. The two immediate predecessors of J. F. Kennedy are the two immediate successors of F. D. Roosevelt.

---

[1] The word "individual" is used in its broadest sense throughout this chapter. Thus, a team or league or player may in different contexts be referred to *as* an individual.

asserts the identity of the two classes mentioned. And,

12. The planets are the satellites of the sun.

is a statement that the members of the class of planets are identical with the members of the class of satellites of the sun.

The word "is"—or a form of the verb "to be"—has different uses. Three of these uses are embodied in the notions of class identity:

13. The neighbor's dogs are the ones that keep me awake.

class inclusion:

14. Crappies are game fish.

and class membership:

15. Tweeter is a dog.

Thus the logic of classes is, in part, a formalization of different uses of "to be." We will introduce a symbol for each of these three meanings of "to be." If A and B are arbitrary classes,[2]

$$A = B$$

means that the members of the class A are identical with the members of the class B. And

$$A \subseteq B$$

means that the class A is included in the class B—that is, that the members of A are also members of B. If some member of A were not also a member of B then it would not be true that A is included in B. And, if 'b' is an individual and A is a class,

$$b \in A$$

means that 'b' is a member of A.

The notions of class identity and class inclusion can be characterized in terms of class membership. Thus

(A) $A = B$ if and only if (x) $(x \in A \equiv x \in B)$.

In the case of class inclusion, a distinction must be made between inclusion and proper inclusion. First, the general case of inclusion may be characterized:

(B) $A \subseteq B$ if and only if (x) $(x \in A \supset x \in B)$.

Note that (B) does not rule out the case where $A = B$. That is, if $A \subseteq B$, then either $A = B$ or A is included in B but not identical with B. In

---

2 We will omit quotes around expressions for classes.

the latter case, we say that A is *properly* included in B. In this case, each member of A is also a member of B, but there is at least one member of B which is not a member of A. In symbols, with '$\subset$' signifying proper inclusion;

(C) $A \subset B$ if and only if $A \subseteq B$ and $\sim (A = B)$.

If $A \subseteq B$, A is said to be a *subclass* of B. Clearly every class is a subclass of itself; that is, for an arbitrary class C, $C \subseteq C$ since $C = C$. If $A \subset B$, A is said to be a *proper subclass* of B. No class is a proper subclass of itself, since there is no member of a class C which is not a member of C.

CLASS COMPLEMENT,
THE NULL CLASS,
AND THE UNIVERSE OF DISCOURSE

If A is an arbitrary class, then the *complement* of A, in symbols $\overline{A}$, is the class composed of all individuals which are not members of A.

Often we have occasion to speak about individuals of a class and certain groups or classes within the larger class. For example, we may speak of the class of '39 of our alma mater, and of certain individuals (boys, football players, nuts, and so forth) within that class. And once it is understood that we are speaking with reference to this class, we can speak of "the football players and the rest" without explaining that "the rest" means the rest of the class.

We will say that in this context the class of '39 is a *"universe of discourse."* The universe of discourse is those individuals or that class of individuals of which we are speaking. Now if a universe of discourse is not specified in speaking of the class A and its complement $\overline{A}$, we will understand that the individuals in A plus the individuals in $\overline{A}$ constitute all individuals (or objects, items, and the like) in the largest universe of discourse—every individual. But if the universe is limited—to the class of '39 or the fish in Lake Hubert—and we speak of A as the class of football players or bass, then $\overline{A}$ will be, respectively, the class of nonfootball players of the class of '39 and the nonbass (northerns, crappies, bluegills, and others) in Lake Hubert.

Sometimes we will want to speak of the complement of a class A *with respect to* a class B. We express this as

$B - A$

that is, the members of B less the members of A comprise the class which is the complement of A with respect to B. If A is properly included in

B, the class $B - A$ will have some members. If A is the same class as B, then $B - A$ is empty. The empty class has a special name—the *null* class —and some noteworthy properties. For every set B, by definition, the null class, which is designated by 'Λ', is included in B;

$$\Lambda \subseteq B$$

and, if B has at least one member

$$\Lambda \subset B.$$

Further, and this can be taken as the definition of Λ,

$$(x) \sim (x \in \Lambda).$$

If any set B is identical with or included in $\overline{\Lambda}$, then B is empty. We ignore such phrases as "this set is empty" or "there is no one in the kitchen" and "that set is empty" or "there is no one in the basement", in so far as they may suggest that there are different null classes. The null class may be referred to in different ways, but there is only one; that is,

$$(x) \sim (x \in A) \supset A = \Lambda.$$

The complement of the null class $\overline{\Lambda}$ or V relative to a universe of discourse is called the universal class. Thus if the universe of discourse is the fish in the St. John's River, V is comprised by all these fish. Every class in the universe of discourse is a subclass of V

$$A \subseteq V$$

and every individual in the universe of discourse is a member of V

$$(x) (x \in V).$$

OPERATIONS ON CLASSES

We introduce now the ideas of the *intersection* and *union* of classes.

The intersection of two classes A and B is a class comprised of members of A which are also members of B. The symbol for this class is

$$A \cap B.$$

Thus if A is the class of senators and B is the class of Republicans, $A \cap B$ is the class of Republican senators. So

$$(x) (x \in A \cap B \equiv (x \in A) \cdot (x \in B)).$$

If classes are represented by circles, letting all members of the class lie within the circle, then $A \cap B$ would be the members in the intersection of the circles (the shaded part):

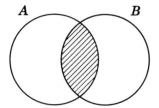

The union of two classes A and B is a class comprised of all members of A and all members of B. The symbol for this class is

$A \cup B$.

Thus $A \cup B$ is the class comprised of all Republicans together with all senators. And so,

$(x) (x \in A \cup B \equiv (x \in A) \text{ v } (x \in B))$.

The shaded parts of the circles below represent $A \cup B$:

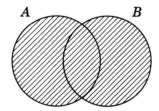

If a class of objects is cited individually or "spelled out," the best notation to use in discussions of class union and intersection is that mathematicians use for sets. Braces always form a class and individuals (or classes regarded as individuals) are cited individually within the braces, separated by commas. Let the class A of senators be

Mundt, Hickenlooper, Dirkson, Humphrey, . . .

and the class B of Republicans be

Smith, Jones, Miller, Mundt, ...

The order in which we write the names is of no importance. If

$x \in \{$Mundt, Hickenlooper, . . .$\}$

that is, if '$x \in A$', then 'x' is either Mundt or Hickenlooper or . . . , and so forth. Then the union of A and B is

$A \cup B =$ Smith, Mundt, Jones, Nixon, Humphrey, . . .

that is, *all* the members of both classes, and their intersection is

$A \cap B =$ Mundt, Dirkson, . . .

that is, the members the two classes have in common. Thus suppose C is $\{1, 2, 3\}$, D is $\{2, 5, 6\}$, and E is a class whose members are '1' and $\{2, 5\}$, that is, $E = \{1, \{2, 5\}\}$. Then,

$$C \cap E = \{1\} \quad \text{(a class with just one member)}$$
$$D \cap E = \Lambda \quad \text{(since } D \text{ has as members neither '1' nor } \{2, 5\})$$
$$C \cup E = \{1, 2, 3, \{2, 5\}\} \quad \text{(or } \{\{2, 5\}, 3, 1, 2\} \text{ and so on)}$$
$$D \cup E = \{2, 5, \{2, 5\}, 6, 1\}.$$

It is convenient to distinguish between an individual and the class comprised by it. Thus '1' is an individual, $\{1\}$ is a class, and $\{\{1\}\}$ is a class which has the class $\{1\}$ as its only member. $\{\{2, 5\}\}$ is not the same class as $\{2, 5\}$, since the former has only one member, namely $\{2, 5\}$, and the latter, $\{2, 5\}$, has two members. As a final example, suppose

$$X = \{\{1, 5\}, \{2, 3\}\}$$
$$Y = \{1, 5\}$$
$$Z = \{1, 5, 2, 3\}.$$

That is, X has as members $\{1, 5\}$ and $\{2, 3\}$; the members of Y are '1' and '5' and the members of Z are '1', '5', '2' and '3'. Then

$$Y \in X$$

since $\{1, 5\}$ is a member of X, but Y is not included in X: that is, $\sim (Y \subset X)$, since the members of Y are not members of X. However

$$Y \subset Z$$

since the members of Y are members of Z and there is at least one member of Z, for example, '2', which is not a member of Y. But $\sim (Y \in Z)$, since $\{1, 5\}$ is not one of the members of Z.

CATEGORICAL STATEMENTS

In translating statements in the language to our new class symbolism, we must observe the following rules:

(a) Do not change the meaning
(b) Do not confuse membership and inclusion and identity.

As examples, let us begin with the A, E, I, and O statements.[3] Consider

1. All men are mortal.
2. Our team is one of those that played in the tournament.
3. The Packers are the champion players.

[3] The reader may regard the symbolization of the A, E, I, O statements in terms of classes as interpretations of these statements.

(1) expresses class inclusion (and proper inclusion since animals are also mortal). (2) expresses class membership, and (3) says of two classes that they are identical. Only (1) is to be understood as an *A* statement. In general, an *A* statement is symbolized as

$$M \subseteq T$$

so as to leave open the possibility that the two classes are identical.

An *E* statement expresses the fact that one class is included in the complement of another:

4. No Miss Americas are freshmen.

or "All Miss Americas are nonfreshmen." In symbols,

$$M \subseteq \overline{F}.$$

An *I* statement such as

5. Some fish in Lake Hubert are smallmouths.

says that the class which is the intersection of the classes "fish in Lake Hubert" and "smallmouths" is not empty. To express this in symbols (where "$\neq$" will mean "is not identical with"),

$$F \cap S \neq \Lambda.$$

The *O* statement

6. Some mailmen are not afraid of dogs.

says that there are individuals in the class of mailmen who are not in the class of those afraid of dogs, that is,

$$M \cap \overline{A} \neq \Lambda.$$

VENN DIAGRAMS AND THE
VALIDITY OF ARGUMENTS

Many of the relations and operations on classes can be visualized. One of the first systematic attempts to do this and to show that the validity of certain arguments including the syllogism can also be visually demonstrated is due to the mathematician Euler. The logician Venn later introduced a modified version of Euler's diagrams which we use here.

We will use a rectangle to indicate that all individuals in the universe of discourse lie within it. Different classes will be represented by circles—all members of a class will lie within the circle. Thus, if *A* and *B* are arbitrary classes the diagram will be

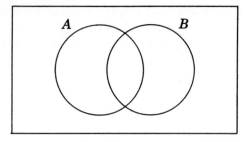

Now assertions about *A* and *B* will be represented in the following ways.

   1. "All *A* are *B*" or $A \subseteq B$

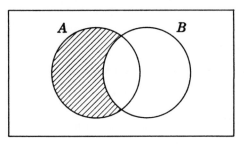

That is, all members of *A* not in *B* are deleted—the result being that all *remaining* members of *A*, if any, are in *B*.

   2. "No *A* are *B*" or $A \subseteq \overline{B}$

The complement of *B* is the class comprised of all individuals outside the circle *B* and within the rectangle, so (2) becomes

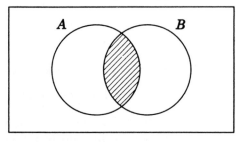

The nondeleted individuals in *A*, if any, are now *all* in the complement of *B*.

   The **I** statement calls for additional notation. To diagram

   3. "Some *A* are *B*" or "$A \cap B \neq \Lambda$"

we put a cross (an individual) in the intersection of *A* and *B* to indicate that there is an individual there.

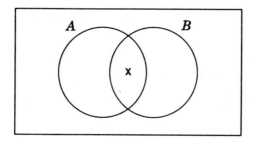

In

4. "Some A are not B" or $A \cap \bar{B} \neq \Lambda$

the same device is used to show an individual is in A but not in B.

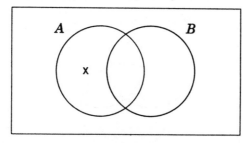

Since a syllogism involves three terms which can be interpreted as classes, we need to show three classes in the rectangle to represent the syllogism. The only requirements in drawing three circles to represent three classes are that each must intersect with the other, and they must mutually intersect. Here is how the validity of a syllogism is demonstrated.

(P 1) All taxi drivers (T) are death-dodgers (D).
(P 2) Some mailmen (M) are taxi drivers (T).

Some mailmen (M) are death-dodgers (D).

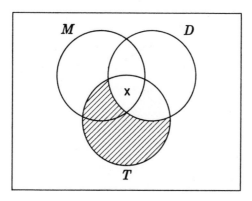

Step 1: Delete all *T*'s which are not *D*'s (P 1).
Step 2: Put a cross in the intersection of *M* and *T* (what is left of *T*) (P 2).

The diagram now *shows* the truth of the conclusion, that is, there is an individual which is in *M* (is a mailman) *and* which is in *D* (is a death-dodger). *Only* the premisses are marked in the diagram. For the sake of uniformity the lower circle will always represent the middle term, the left circle the minor term, and the right circle the major term.

Here is another example:

All *A* are *C*.
Some *B* are not *A*.
_____

Some *B* are not *C*.

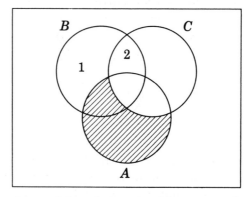

For the first premiss we delete the *A*'s outside *C*. Now the second premiss presents a problem. We want to show that there is an individual in *B* but not in *A*. But there are two areas (marked 1 and 2 in the diagram) in which we could put the cross. Instead of choosing one, we put linked crosses in the two areas to indicate that that individual which is in *B* but not *A* *may* be in either area, that is,

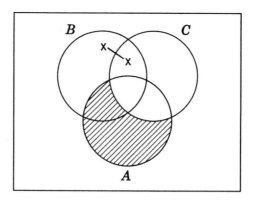

The conclusion says that some B's are not C's. Clearly we are not justi-fied in concluding this since the cross may be in area 2. It is not *neces-sarily* in area 1 as it would have to be if the conclusion were valid.

And finally,

> Some C are A.
> All A are B.
> _____
> Some B are C.

First, crosses are put in 1 and 2 and linked together.

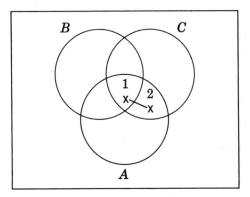

Second, all A's outside B are deleted.

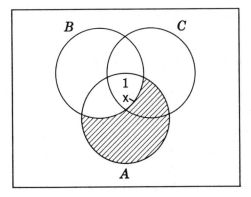

Now one cross is deleted and one is not. In such cases it is to be under-stood that the C which is in A is in 1, not 2, since there are no A's in 2. The syllogism is, therefore, valid, since it shows that there is a B in C.[4]

---

[4] The uses of Venn diagrams are not limited to checking the validity of syllogisms. The interested reader may consult P. Suppes' *Introduction to Logic* (Princeton: Van Nostrand, 1957).

IDENTITIES

Some of the relations between classes will be informally demonstrated in this section. It is possible to construct formal proofs of these relations in the formal logic of quantification theory, but this requires lengthy discussion and some additions to the axiom system of the previous chapter. Instead we will simply describe how to show that these relations hold.

Consider, for example,

   1. $A \cap B = B \cap A$.

This is a rather obvious truth, as a glance, a diagram, or a second's reflection will show. By definition

   (a) $x \in A \cap B \equiv (x \in A) \cdot (x \in B)$,

and it is a logical truth that

   (b) $(x \in A) \cdot (x \in B) \equiv (x \in B) \cdot (x \in A)$

so that, substituting on the right side of (a)

   (c) $x \in A \cap B \equiv (x \in B) \cdot (x \in A)$.

Also by definition

   (d) $x \in B \cap A \equiv (x \in B) \cdot (x \in A)$.

So that, substituting the left side of (a) for the right side of (c) we get

   (e) $x \in A \cap B \equiv x \in B \cap A$

which is (1) by definition. We will use substitution of equivalent expressions freely.

Leaving out the obvious steps, the demonstration may be written in an abbreviated form:

   1. $x \in A \cap B \equiv x \in A \cdot x \in B$ Def. (Definition)
              $\equiv x \in B \cdot x \in A$ L.T. (Logical Truth)
              $\equiv x \in B \cap A$ Def.

where each expression on the right side of the equivalence is equivalent to each of the others.

Thus the demonstration of

   2. $A \cap (B \cup C) \equiv (A \cap B) \cup (A \cap C)$

would appear thus:

   2. $x \in A \cap (B \cup C) \equiv x \in A \cdot x \in (B \cup C)$ Def.
              $\equiv x \in A \cdot (x \in B \vee x \in C)$ Def.

$$\equiv (x \in A \cdot x \in B) \text{ v } (x \in A \cdot x \in C) \qquad \text{L.T.}$$
$$\equiv x \in (A \cap B) \text{ v } x \in (A \cap C) \qquad \text{Def.}$$
$$\equiv x \in (A \cap B) \cup (A \cap C) \qquad \text{Def.}$$

The demonstration of a conditional statement, such as:

3. $A = B \supset A \cap C = B \cap C$

is a little more complex; so we add a word of explanation:

(a) $x \in (B \cap C) \equiv x \in (C \cap B)$ This is identity (1) above.

(b) $\overset{\text{Hyp. } (A = B)}{x \in (A \cap C)} \equiv x \in (C \cap B)$ Substitute A for B on the

(c) $A = B \supset (x \in (A \cap C) \equiv x \in (B \cap C))$.   left side—this is justified by the hypothesis that $A = B$.

In a line such as (b) which holds only under a hypothesis it is well to indicate this by writing the hypothesis above it. Lines (a) and (c) hold as they stand. Note the resemblance of this proof to conditional proofs.

Here, then, are a number of useful identities and other relations.

1. $A \cup \Lambda = A$
2. $A \cap V = A$
3. $A \cup B = B \cup A$
4. $A \cap B = B \cap A$
5. $A \cup (B \cap C) = (A \cup B) \cap (A \cup C)$
6. $A \cap (B \cup C) = (A \cap B) \cup (A \cap C)$
7. $A \cup \overline{A} = V$
8. $A \cap \overline{A} = \Lambda$
9. $A \cup A = A$
10. $A \cap A = A$
11. $A \cup V = V$
12. $A \cap \Lambda = \Lambda$
13. $\Lambda \neq V$
14. $\overline{\overline{A}} = A$
15. $A = \overline{B} \supset B = \overline{A}$
16. $A \cup B \neq \Lambda \supset A \neq \Lambda \text{ v } B \neq \Lambda$
17. $A \cap B \neq \Lambda \supset A \neq \Lambda$
18. $A \cup (B \cup C) = (A \cup B) \cup C$
19. $A \cap (B \cap C) = (A \cap B) \cap C$
20. $A \cup (A \cap B) = A$
21. $A \cap (A \cup B) = A$
22. $\overline{A} \neq A$
23. $\overline{(A \cup B)} = \overline{A} \cap \overline{B}$
24. $\overline{(A \cap B)} = \overline{A} \cup \overline{B}$
25. $A - A = \Lambda$
26. $A - (A \cap B) = A - B$
27. $A \cap (A - B) = A - B$

28. $(A - B) - B = A - B$
29. $(A - B) - A = \Lambda$
30. $(A - B) \cup B = A \cup B$
31. $(A \cup B) - B = A - B$

BOOLEAN ALGEBRA AS
AN AXIOM SYSTEM

A Boolean algebra is, strictly, any interpretation—such as that of a class calculus—of the identities (1) through (8), plus an axiom asserting the existence of two distinct entities

(A) $(\exists A)\ (\exists B)\ (A \neq B)$

and appropriate definitions and rules of inference. We will assume that '=', 'v' and '~' (and the other connectives) are defined in the standard way. An expression is defined as follows:

1. Any of $A, B, C, \ldots$ is an expression.
2. If A is an expression, $\overline{A}$ is an expression.
3. If A and B are expressions, $A \cap B$ is an expression.

If '—' and '$\cap$' are taken as primitive symbols, and A, B, C as variables, the definitions will be as follows:

(D 1) $A \cup B \equiv \overline{\overline{A} \cap \overline{B}}$
(D 2) $\Lambda \equiv A \cap \overline{A}$
(D 3) $V \equiv \overline{\Lambda}$
(D 4) $A \subset B \equiv A \cap B = A$
(D 5) $A - B \equiv A \cap \overline{B}$

If A and B are expressions, '$A = B$' is a statement; and if 'P', 'Q' are statements, '$P \supset Q$' is a statement.

The rules of inference are as follows:

(R 1)   'P' is implied by 'Q' and '$Q \supset P$'.
(R 2)   If 'P' is implied by the hypotheses '$Q_1, Q_2, Q_3, \ldots, Q_n$,' then '$Q_1, Q_2, \ldots, Q_n \supset P$' is deducible.
(R 3)   The result of substituting any expression for a variable through 'P' is deducible from 'P'.
(R 4)   The result of substituting an expression identical to an expression in 'P' is deducible from 'P'.

Here are three sample proofs demonstrating the use of each rule of inference. The proofs are condensed and informal. The numbers (n) refer to the identities listed in the previous section, except when (R 1) or (R 2) is used. In this case the numbers (n) refer to the lines of proof used in (R 1) or (R 2). We omit mention of obvious substitutions.

Assuming (9) is proved:

10. $A \cap A = A$

    1. $A \cap (\bar{A} \cup A) = (A \cap \bar{A}) \cup (A \cap A)$ (R 3) (6) Sub $\bar{A}$ for B and A for C

    2. $A \cap V = \Lambda \cup (A \cap A)$ (R 4) (7), (8)

    3. $A = \Lambda \cup (A \cap A)$ (R 4) (2

    4. $A = A \cap A$ (R 4) (1)

32. $A \cap (B \cap A) = A \cap B$

    1. $(A \cap A) \cap B = A \cap (A \cap B)$ (R 3) (19) Sub A for B and B for C

    2. $(A \cap A) \cap B = A \cap (B \cap A)$ (R 4) (4)

    3. $A \cap B = A \cap (B \cap A)$ (R 4) (10)

33. $\bar{A} \cap A = \bar{A} \supset A = V$

    1. $\bar{A} \cap A = \bar{A}$ Hypothesis

    2. $\Lambda = \bar{A}$ (R 4) (8)

    3. $\Lambda = \bar{A} \supset A = V$ (R 4) (15) Sub A for B and Λ for A

    4. $A = V$ (R 1) (2), (3)

    5. $\bar{A} \cap A = \bar{A} \supset A = V$ (R 2) (1), (4)

CONCLUSION

At the end of this part it may be well to describe what has been done and what could have been done (which has elsewhere been done).

First we investigated some of the logical properties of language and devised rules of inference which would allow inferences which are valid because of the role played by statement connectives. Then we considered some of the logical properties of the quantifiers "all," "every," "some," and so on, and added rules of inference to the ones involving statement connectives so that we were able to validate many familiar forms of arguments whose validity depended not only on the roles of the statement connectives but on the roles of the quantifiers.

The next step in this direction would have been to introduce—as was mentioned—rules which would make possible the validation of *all* inferences involving many-placed predicates. And the next—to introduce variables as predicates so that even more complex inferences could be validated. This system, in axiomatic form, is sometimes called the predicate calculus of second order. The versatility of this system is needed, for example, to express Peano's fifth postulate (see page 295) or the principle of mathematical induction:

If a predicate holds for the number 1, and if when it holds for any particular number, it holds also for its successor, then the predicate holds for every number.

In symbols, where 'P' is a predicate variable and 'x' and 'y' numbers,

$(P)\ (P(1) \cdot (x)\ (y)\ ((P(x) \cdot (\text{Successor } (x\ y)) \supset P(y))) \supset (x)P(x))$.

Thus it is necessary to introduce predicate variables to express inferences used in elementary high-school algebra. There is no reason, moreover, why a predicate should not have a predicate, for we say "thriftiness is a desirable quality" or "truth is a universal solvent." So *orders* of predicates are introduced—predicates of predicates have predicates, and so on, until there is an infinite number of orders of predicates. This was done in Whitehead and Russell's *Principia Mathematica* in order to develop the theory of real numbers.

Thus much elaboration of our axiom system—in which only the axioms for the statement calculus were given—is needed in order to develop parts of mathematics.

The logic of classes, of which we developed a part in this chapter, is closely connected to set theory, to Boolean algebra, and to modern algebra.[5] As was shown, our identities (1) through (8) plus the existence axiom are a set of axioms for Boolean algebra.

The philosophical implications and importance of these extensions of our systems of inference and axioms are much debated. But there is no doubt at all that the study of formal logic is of great help not only in the study of theories—to which we turn next—but in revealing and unravelling some of the rich, and often hidden, logic of our language.

EXERCISES I

Disregarding tenses, put the following statements into one of the following forms (a) through (c):

(a) $A \subset B$
(b) $A \in B$
(c) $A = B$,

where A and B may be individuals or classes.

[5] See Garrett Birkhoff and Saunders Maclane, *A Survey of Modern Algebra*, rev. ed. (New York: Macmillan, 1953); and Fronz E. Hohn, *Applied Boolean Algebra*, 2nd ed. (New York: Macmillan, 1964).

1. Borneo is one of the world's largest islands.
2. The Polish logicians did as much as any other group working in symbolic logic.
3. Virtuous men are great men.
4. The greatest ball player was Harvey Handspit.
5. Galileo's real opinions were suppressed.
6. Sophomores are the biggest nuisances.
7. Diesels are internal combustion engines.
8. The appropriations for the national parks of Alaska are now included with those of the national parks of the other states.
9. Auxins are hormones.
10. Nobody knows the trouble he's seen.

EXERCISES II

Here is a set of assertions.
(a) Which are true for all classes A, B and C?
(b) Think of classes, if possible, which make those assertions true which are not true for all classes.

1. If $A \subset B$ and $B \subset C$ and $B = C$ then $\sim (C \subset A)$.
2. If $A \in B$ and $\sim (B \subset C)$ then $A \in C$.
3. If $A \subseteq B$ and $B \in C$ then $A \in C$.
4. If $A \subset B$ and $B \subseteq C$ then $\sim (C \subset A)$.
5. If $A \in B$ and $B \in C$ then $A \in C$.
6. If $A \subset B$ and $B \subset C$ then $A \in C$.

EXERCISES III

Given $A = \{1, 7, \{2, 6\}, \{3, 8, \{5\}\}, 2\}$

1. How many members does A have?
2. Is $\{1, 7\}$ included in A?
3. Is $\{1\}$ included in A? A member of A?
4. Is $\{7, \{2, 6\}\}$ a member of A? Included in A?
5. Is $\{5\}$ included in A?
6. Is 2 a member of A?

EXERCISES IV

Given
$A = \{1, 2, 3\}$
$B = \{3, 4, 5\}$

$C = \{6, 7, \{1, 2, 3\}\}$

$D = \{1, \{3, 4, 5\}\}.$

(a) Find the class E which is:

1. $A \cap B$
2. $C - \{A\}$
3. $(C \cap D) \cup A$
4. $D \cap A \cap B$
5. $(B \cup D) - (A \cup C)$
6. $(A - C) \cup (B - C)$
7. $(C - D) \cup (A - B)$
8. $\{A\} \cap B \cap C \cap \{D\}$
9. $A \cup B \cup \{C\}$
10. $(A \cap B) - (A \cup B)$

(b) Which of the following assertions are true?

1. $A \cap B = \Lambda$
2. $C \cap D = \Lambda$
3. $B \subset D$
4. $B - A \in C$
5. $D - C = A \cup B$
6. $B \in D \cup C$
7. $D \cap A \in C$
8. $A \cap C \subset D$

EXERCISES V

Diagram these syllogisms to see if they are valid.

1. All artists have creative imagination and all artists are good carpenters; so no good carpenters have creative imagination.

2. All P are M.
    All M are S.
    Therefore some S are P.

3. Some P are M.
    All M are S.
    Therefore some S are P.

4. No P are M.
    All S are M.
    Therefore no S are P.

5. No M are P.
    Some S are M.
    Therefore some S are not P.

6. All P are M.
    No S are M.
    Therefore some S are not P.

7. What additional premiss is needed in 2 and 6 to make the arguments valid?

EXERCISES VI

A. Prove the identities using an informal proof.

B. Prove the identities (9) and (11) through (31) as theorems of the Boolean Algebra.

EXERCISES VII

Reduction Problems. Show informally, using identities (1) through (31) that the following identities hold.

(Example)

(a) $(A \cap B \cap \bar{C}) \cup (B \cap C) \cup \bar{A} \cup (C \cap D) \cup \bar{B} \cup C \cup (D \cap E) = V$

We proceed to group unions and intersections of a class and its complement. Using (18) repeatedly we get

(b) $(A \cap B \cap \bar{C}) \cup (\bar{A} \cup \bar{B} \cup C) \cup (B \cap C) \cup (C \cap D) \cup (D \cap E) = V$

Now, with (24) and substitution

(c) $(A \cap B \cap \bar{C}) \cup (\overline{A \cap B \cap \bar{C}}) \cup (B \cap C) \cup (C \cap D) \cup (D \cap E) = V$

Using (7) and substitution

(d) $V \cup (B \cap C) \cup (C \cap D) \cup (D \cap E) = V$

And, finally, by several applications of (11)

(e) $V = V$

1. $\bar{A} \cup (B \cap C \cap D) = (\bar{A} \cup B) \cap (\bar{A} \cup C) \cap (\bar{A} \cup D)$
2. $(\overline{A \cap B}) \cap (\overline{A \cap C}) \cup \bar{C} \cup (D \cap E) \cup (A \cap (B \cup C)) = V$
3. $(A \cap \bar{B}) \cap ((B \cap C) \cup D) = A \cap C$
4. $((A \cap \bar{B}) \cap (\bar{A} \cup D)) \cup ((A \cap \bar{B}) \cap (A \cup D)) = A \cap \bar{B}$
5. $A \cup (B \cap C) \cup (D \cap E) \cup \bar{C} \cup (\bar{A} \cup B) \cap (A \cup C) = V$

Part 3

THE LOGICAL STRUCTURE OF SCIENCE

Chapter Sixteen

SCIENCE AND HYPOTHESES

It is not uncommon to distinguish the practical aim of science from the theoretical aim. The *practical aim* of science is the application of scientific knowledge. (It is generally assumed that such an application is in the interest of man.) All of us, of course, see the results of this application and feel the impact of this application on our lives. It is easy to make a list of applications of scientific knowledge which affect our lives. For example, all these things are made possible through the application of scientific knowledge: X-ray machines, nuclear power plants, automobiles, television, computers, insecticides, the new drugs and medicines, rockets, and plastics.

This knowledge is attained by men seeking and finding empirically testable explanations for certain observed phenomena. The body of statements which makes up established explanations is what is called *scientific knowledge*. The *theoretical aim* of science is to achieve such explanations. People sometimes speak of the "ideal of science." This generally is used to mean the attainment of systematic explanations of the whole field of experience by displaying what is observed as exemplifying the operation of a single, interrelated system of laws or principles. The theoretical aim of any particular science is the explanation of distinguishable classes of phenomena. The theoretical aim of the sciences collectively is to attain, as far as possible, the ideal of science.

Certain logical aspects of the theoretical aim of the sciences—the explanation of observed phenomena—are considered in this part of the book. By "sciences," as the word is used here, is meant the natural

337

sciences, physical and biological, and also the social sciences (psychology and anthropology, sociology, economics, and the like).

In this chapter we will examine four famous episodes from the history of science in order to describe clearly what a scientific explanation, or hypothesis, is, how scientists come upon scientific hypotheses, how hypotheses differ (logically) from one another, and how they are tested and justified. In addition we will examine the roles of induction and deduction in each of the four episodes and the relation between induction and deduction generally.

FOUR EPISODES FROM
THE HISTORY OF SCIENCE

Torricelli's Hypothesis

For ages people have known (P_1) that to drain a liquid from a barrel there needs to be an opening near the bottom and one at the top of the barrel, and (P_2) that if one sucks up liquid in a tube and closes the top with his finger, the liquid will not run out.[1] In the Middle Ages these phenomena, P_1 and P_2, were explained in terms of the notion of a "full universe." This hypothesis involved the principle that "nature abhors a vacuum." The first phenomenon (P_1) is explained by the hypothesis in this way: if water flows out of the bottom without there being a hole for air to get in, a vacuum will result. But by the principle ("nature abhors a vacuum") this is impossible. Thus one needs an opening to let in the air. We can easily see how the "full universe" hypothesis also explains the second phenomenon.

In Galileo's *Dialogues Concerning Two New Sciences,* published in 1638, he notes that (P_3) a suction pump (like those in roadside parks) will not raise water more than a certain height. Galileo's student, Torricelli, was struck by this and asked "Why?" Torricelli hypothesized that the earth is surrounded by a "sea of air." He argued that if the earth were surrounded by a "sea of air" and if air had weight, then there would be an air pressure on all objects submerged in this sea of air, exactly as there is water pressure below the surface of the ocean. If this hypothesis is true, then P_3 is explained—the pump creates a vacuum in the tube so that there is no atmospheric pressure in the top of the tube to oppose that pressing down on the water outside the tube.

---

[1] It will be convenient for us to refer to statements describing phenomena such as the two cited above by the letter *"P."*

The water rises to a certain height because the pressure forces it to do so. We can also see how Torricelli's hypothesis explains P_1 and P_2.

Torricelli found that the limit to which water can be made to rise is 34 feet. If his hypothesis is correct, then it can be deduced (P_4) that mercury, which is fourteen times heavier than water, can be made to rise in a tube (or be held up in a tube) only about thirty inches (see outline of deduction at end of this chapter). Around 1643 Torricelli performed an experiment which verified this prediction. He took a glass tube over thirty inches long which was closed at one end, filled it with mercury, placed his finger over the opening, inverted the tube, submerged the bottom (open) end in a dish of mercury, and removed his finger. The mercury dropped until the column was about thirty inches high. A vacuum was created thereby in the top of the tube. This verification of a deduction from his hypothesis also went against the "full universe" hypothesis, since the empty space in the tube was a vacuum "created by nature."

Other statements were also deduced from the hypothesis. For example: if we live in a sea of air which exerts a pressure, then (P_5) the pressure should diminish as we rise to the "surface." If the pressure so diminishes, then the height of a mercury column should decrease as the column is carried up a mountain. Blaise Pascal in 1648 had his brother-in-law carry an inverted tube of mercury up the Puy-de-Dome in southern France. The experiment was repeated five different times, with the same result —the column went down as the brother-in-law climbed. Also an observer at the bottom of the mountain watched a tube during the experiment and found that the level remained unchanged. Pascal had thus verified P_5.

Notice these features about the above episode. For years people had known P_1 and P_2. The explanation for P_1 and P_2 which was thought to be satisfactory was the "full universe" hypothesis. Generally, a *hypothesis* in science is an explanation or *proposed* explanation for phenomena. Torricelli was *struck* by P_3 because the "full universe" hypothesis did not adequately explain P_3. This is often what leads to the formulation of a hypothesis—some phenomenon is noted because it does not fit in with the commonly held explanations of things; the new hypothesis is formulated to explain this and the old relevant phenomena. Torricelli asked what would explain P_1, P_2, and P_3. His "sea of air" hypothesis was his answer to this question. He then proceeded to test his hypothesis. The way he and others went about this was to deduce other P's from the hypothesis and see if they were true. For example, as was noted, P_4 and P_5 were deduced and tested. In the course of this testing it was noticed that the old "full universe" hypothesis did not provide an adequate explanation for these P's.

Also this feature should be noticed: If one were to ask, "What justification is there for Torricelli's hypothesis?" or "Why is Torricelli's hypothesis true?" the justification would take (at least up to Pascal's time) more or less this form:

Torricelli's hypothesis explains the known P's connected with the matter to be explained.
If Torricelli's hypothesis is true, then certain other P's are true.
By experiment it is found that these P's are true.
The competing hypotheses cannot adequately explain these P's.
Torricelli's hypothesis does not conflict with what is known to be true.
Therefore Torricelli's hypothesis is true.[2]

This argument is called an *inductive* argument. The nature of such arguments and how they differ from deductive arguments will be considered in the last section of this chapter.

William Harvey's Hypothesis

In 1628 William Harvey announced his hypothesis that the blood in the human body circulates from the heart, which is a pump, through the arteries to the veins and back to the heart through the veins.

What led Harvey to this hypothesis? To answer this, we must first understand the theory about the blood system which Harvey's hypothesis replaced. For it was, as we will now see, the inability of the existing theory to explain certain discovered facts (P's) about the blood system which led to Harvey's hypothesis.

Aristotle taught that blood was composed in the liver from the digested foods. From there it was carried to the heart by the great vein, the vena cava, then pumped back through the vena cava and its branches to the members of the body. The Alexandrian physicians Erasistratus and Herophilus added to this theory the assumption that, while the veins carried blood, the arteries carried a subtle kind of air, or vital spirit. The Greek physician Galen discovered, however, that the arteries were not mere airpipes, but that they contained blood. The accepted theory in the sixteenth century, often called the Galenic view, was as follows (see figure).

[2] The use of "true" here should not be taken as an indication that we have taken sides in the controversy over the complex issue in the philosophy of science: Do the theoretical terms employed in science refer to entities in the way in which terms like "sticks" and "stones" do? Theories *are* commonly said to be true, so we use the word "true" here without intending that this should be taken as entailing the view that the answer to the question is affirmative. For a good general description of these views and issues, see Nagel's *The Structure of Science*, Chap. 6, and for detailed treatments see the works cited in the footnotes of this chapter.

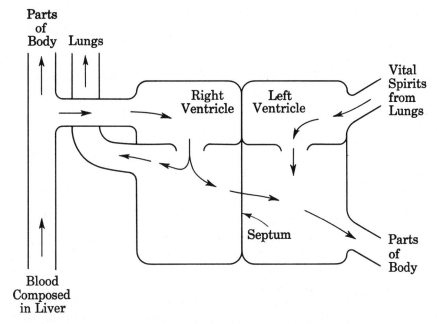

Parts
of
Body   Lungs

Blood
Composed
in Liver

First, the blood is composed from the digested food in the liver; some of this blood goes through the veins to nourish parts of the body. Most of it passes up the great vein of the body, the vena cava, to the right ventricle of the heart. Some of this blood is squeezed up what is now recognized as the pulmonary artery (though it was thought at that time to be a vein) into the lungs for its nourishment and then it goes to other parts of the body. The rest of the blood passes through the septum (the thick wall dividing the heart into two chambers or ventricles). There the blood is mixed with "vital spirits" from the air which comes down from the pulmonary vein (which was thought to be an artery). This blood then goes through the aorta artery to the parts of the body. Second, there is no connection between the veins and the arteries. Blood gets to the arteries from the veins by passing through the septum. Third, the blood neither lies stagnant nor does it circulate through either the veins or the arteries. The blood is like a stream with thousands of places where it empties. Those holding the Galenic view even spoke of the "ebb and flow" of the blood.

In the sixteenth century three discoveries were made which Harvey saw were incompatible with the Galenic theory. First, in 1543, Vesalius, a professor of surgery in Padua, probed the septum but was unable to find a passage. But having faith in the Galenic theory his reaction to this was: ". . . none of these pits penetrate (at least according to sense) from the right ventricle to the left; therefore indeed I was compelled to marvel at the activity of the Creator of things, in that the blood should sweat from the right ventricle to the left through passages escaping the sight." [3]

Second, in 1553 Servetus found that blood passes from the pulmonary artery to the pulmonary vein *through* the lungs. And third, Harvey's teacher, Fabricius, noticed the system of *valves* in the veins which give free passage of blood *toward* the heart, but obstruct it from flowing *away* from the heart.

Harvey saw that the hypothesis which would explain all these phenomena would be: the blood passes through the veins to the right ventricle of the heart, is pumped into the lungs through an artery, passes from the lungs into a vein, flows back into the heart, out through an artery to the parts of the body, and back again through the veins—in short, the blood circulates through the veins and arteries.

This hypothesis explains all the known facts (P's), whereas the Galenic theory and others considered do not. Furthermore, this hypothesis explains in a more satisfactory way the known fact that the heart pumps into the arteries, in the space of half an hour, more than the whole of the blood in the body. According to the Galenic hypothesis, all this blood was constantly being composed in the liver from the juices of the food. How could this be? According to Harvey's hypothesis, the blood being pumped out is the same blood which comes in; this explains where the great quantities of blood come from. Thus the fact that Harvey's hypothesis explained the known P's, whereas the Galenic theory and other considered hypotheses did not, provided good grounds for Harvey's hypothesis.

Harvey's explanation can be directly tested; that is, we can observe the blood, veins, and so forth to see whether his hypothesis is true. But he could not directly test it. For one thing, Harvey did not have microscopes with which to see the blood passing from the arteries, through the capillaries, to the veins. So he indirectly tested his hypothesis. For example, he studied the blood systems of living animals and found they all corresponded to his hypothesis about the blood systems of human beings; he found support for his hypothesis in the facts observed in diseases—for example, organisms can quickly spread throughout the entire body once they enter the blood stream; and examining the veins of the arm, he showed that the limb is swollen with blood when the veins are compressed, and emptied of blood when the arteries are compressed. These are P's which we would expect if Harvey's hypothesis were true. The discovery of these P's provided strong additional grounds in support of Harvey's hypothesis—strong enough to make Harvey's the accepted theory.

[3] A. R. Hall, *The Scientific Revolution* (Boston: Beacon, 1957), p. 139.

The same features noted in connection with the Torricelli episode are found here. There is, however, one difference which for our considerations is most important. Both Harvey's and Torricelli's hypotheses were indirectly tested, while Harvey's hypothesis could have been and was eventually directly tested. Torricelli's hypothesis, on the other hand, cannot be directly tested. What is meant here by *"indirectly testing* a hypothesis" is "deducing *P*'s from the hypothesis and then checking to see if the *P*'s are true." To *test* a hypothesis *directly* is to observe the things referred to by the terms in the hypothesis and see if in fact they are related as they are related in the hypothesis.[4] As was indicated, if Harvey had had the equipment, he could have directly tested his hypothesis. He could have, in a word, seen the blood circulating in the way he thought it did. But one cannot see the sea of air or feel the pressure of a normal atmosphere. The testing of such a hypothesis must be indirect. The difference between direct and indirect testing and the difference between the two kinds of hypotheses will become clearer as we examine the last two episodes.

Newton's Corpuscular Theory of Light

Since 300 B.C. it has been known that light travels in a straight line and that light refracts. If a beam of light is passed through an opening toward a dark background, this phenomenon will occur:

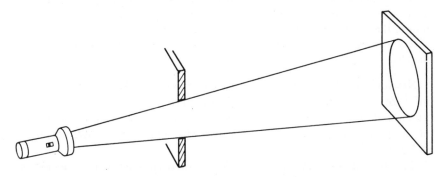

---

[4] Some philosophers take the view that knowledge about things such as hearts, stones, and tables is to be analyzed in terms of knowledge about sensations, or sense data. In this view hearts, tables, and measuring instruments are inferred, nonobservable entities in the same way that elementary particles and other theoretical entities are inferred, nonobservable entities. Now, though this choice may be unfortunate, we have chosen not to concern ourselves with these questions in this elementary treatment of the nature of scientific statements and how they are related to observed facts. So "observable facts" is here understood to refer to all those things which we ordinarily take to be observable. (Statements designated by the letter "*P*" are assumed to contain nonlogical terms which refer only to observable things—objects, events, and so on).

If the light did not travel in a straight line, the white area on the dark background would either be larger or smaller. Light, when it passes through a glass plate or when it passes from the air through water, refracts, as illustrated here:

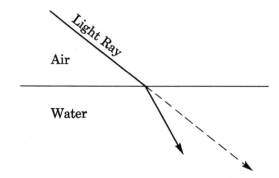

The dotted line shows the path the light would take if it were not refracted.

In 1666 Newton reproduced another familiar phenomenon connected with light. Here is Newton's own description of what he did:

> In the year 1666 (at which time I applied myself to the grinding of optick glasses of other figures than spherical) I procured me a triangular glass prism, to try therewith the celebrated phenomena of colours. And in order thereto, having darkened my chamber, and made a small hole in my window-shuts, to let in a convenient quantity of the sun's light, I placed my prism at its entrance, that it might thereby be refracted to the opposite wall. It was at first a very pleasing divertisement, to view the vivid and intense colours produced thereby.

Newton's explanation of this phenomenon was that white light is a mixture of corpuscles of different kinds. The prism separates these corpuscles. The separate corpuscles belong to different colors. The glass of the prism exerts a force which causes the separation of the corpuscles of light.

The hypothesis that light is made up of corpuscles which behave according to the laws of motion governing all bodies is called the corpuscular theory of light. As we have seen, it explains the prism phenomenon. In addition, it explains why light travels in a straight line and why it refracts. The light source emits particles of light which travel along straight lines as a bullet would do. Light refracts when it hits a substance like water because the water exerts a force which changes the direction of the particles. This hypothesis also explains why light reflects off, say, a mirror. The corpuscles bounce as an elastic ball thrown against a wall bounces.

Additional P's follow from the corpuscular theory. (Just *how* they follow will not be explained in detail.) For example, if all the beams of the separate colors resulting from the light's passage through the prism were passed through a second prism, it follows from the theory that white light would again appear. Also if a beam of the separated, homogeneous light, were passed through a prism, the theory says that the same color would result since the corpuscles cannot be split any further. Last, from the theory it follows that light, when it reaches water after traveling in the air, will increase its speed, since the water exerts a force which changes its direction.

The first and second P's were shown to be true by Newton. This direct testing of these P's provided strong support for his hypothesis. The testing of the third P had to wait until a way was devised to measure the speed of light. But since the corpuscular theory explained the existing P's, and since the P's which followed from the theory and could be tested were found to be true, this provided strong grounds for affirming that the theory was true. But as we will see in the next chapter, there arose another hypothesis which also explained these P's and which, for reasons we will examine, took the place of the corpuscular theory.

Rumford's Hypothesis that Heat is Motion

When two bodies are brought into contact, one of a higher temperature than the other, eventually they will reach the same temperature. The picture of heat "flowing" from one body to another as water flows from a high level to a lower level is suggested here. But one finds, for example, that a piece of iron weighs no more when it is red hot than when it is ice cold. If heat is conceived of as a substance which "flows," then it is weightless. For a time it was thought that heat was such a substance.

This weightless heat-substance was called *caloric*. The caloric theory of heat was the theory which assumed the existence of such a substance. This hypothesis explains a wide range of P's. For example, it explains why two bodies of different temperatures reach the same temperature when brought into contact with each other. It explains why substances expand when heated, and a number of other phenomena.

But there are some commonly known phenomena which it is difficult for the caloric theory to explain. Heat can be created by friction, say, by rubbing two sticks together. But we think that a substance is something which can be neither created nor destroyed (conservation of matter). Can the caloric theory explain how heat can be created by friction? Defenders of the theory thought it could without denying the principle of the conservation of matter. The sticks rubbing against each other changes some property of the wood. This change in the wood produces a change in specific heat or heat capacity of the wood—it goes *down*.[5] Thus the unchanged quantity of heat produces a higher temperature.

It happens that there are simple methods for determining the specific heat of a substance. It is easy to take two identical pieces of wood and induce heat in the one by friction and in the other by contact with a radiator. If the two pieces of wood then have the same specific heat, it looks as if either the assumption that heat is a substance or the assumption that substance cannot be created would have to be given up.

Such an experiment was performed more than one hundred and fifty years ago by Count Rumford. Here is his own account:

It frequently happens, that in the ordinary affairs and occupations of life, opportunities present themselves of contemplating some of the most curious operations of Nature; and very interesting philosophical experiments might often be made, almost without trouble or expense, by means of machinery contrived for the mere mechanical purposes of the arts and manufactures.

I have frequently had occasion to make this observation; and am persuaded, that a habit of keeping the eyes open to every thing that is going on in the ordinary course of the business of life has oftener led, as it were by accident, or in the playful excursions of the imagination, put into action by contemplating the most common appearances, to useful doubts, and sensible schemes for investigation and improvement, than all the more intense meditations of philosophers, in the hours expressly set apart for study. . . .

Being engaged, lately, in superintending the boring of cannon, in the workshops of the military arsenal at Munich, I was struck with the still more intense Heat (much greater than that of boiling water, as I found in my experiment) of the metallic chips separated from it by the borer. . . .

From whence comes the Heat actually produced in the mechanical operation above mentioned?

Is it furnished by the metallic chips which are separated by the borer from the solid mass of metal?

If this were the case, then, according to the modern doctrines of latent Heat, and of caloric, the capacity ought not only to be changed, but the change undergone by them should be sufficiently great to account for all the Heat produced.

But no such change had taken place; for I found, upon taking equal quantities, by weight, of these chips, and of thin slips of the same block of metal separated by means of a fine saw and putting them, at the same temperature (that of boiling water), into equal quantities of cold water (that is to say,

---

[5] A pound of water, for example, has a greater heat capacity or specific heat than a pound of mercury, since less heat is needed to raise the temperature of mercury one degree than to raise the temperature of the water one degree.

at the temperature of 59½° F.) the portion of water into which the chips were put was not, to all appearance, heated either less or more than the other portion, in which the slips of metal were put.

And, in reasoning on this subject, we must not forget to consider that most remarkable circumstance, that the source of the Heat generated by friction, in these Experiments, appeared evidently to be *inexhaustible.*

It is hardly necessary to add, that anything which any *insulated* body, or system of bodies, can continue to furnish *without limitation* cannot possibly be a *material substance;* and it appears to me to be extremely difficult, if not quite impossible, to form any distinct idea of anything, capable of being excited and communicated, in the manner the Heat was excited and communicated in these Experiments, except it be MOTION.

Rumford was, as he says, "struck" by the amount of heat produced in the boring of the cannon. Here was a phenomenon which he noticed because of its apparent conflict with the caloric theory.[6] Rumford then noticed the explanation the caloric theory gives for this phenomenon. That is, he noticed that according to the caloric theory it must be the case that the heat capacity changes. He then performed the simple experiment with the chips which, as we see, falsified the statement which follows from the caloric theory.

In the final paragraphs of Rumford's account we find his hypothesis. What would explain the known phenomena connected with heat? Some of these are, for example: two bodies of different temperatures acquire the same temperature when in contact, most substances expand when heated, heat is produced by friction, and the amount of heat generated by friction is, as Rumford says, apparently "inexhaustible." (This fourth phenomenon, by the way, would be difficult to explain by the caloric

---

[6] Often important basic observations take place because of the observer's knowledge of some theory. Charles Darwin wrote: "How odd it is that anyone should not see that all observation must be for or against some view, if it is to be of any service." Karl Popper writes: ". . . the belief that we can start with pure observations alone, without anything in the nature of a theory, is absurd; as may be illustrated by the story of the man who dedicated his life to natural science, wrote down everything he could observe, and bequeathed his priceless collection of observations to the Royal Society to be used as inductive evidence. This story should show us that though beetles may profitably be collected, observations may not.

"Twenty-five years ago I tried to bring home the same point to a group of physics students in Vienna by beginning a lecture with the following instructions: 'Take pencil and paper; carefully observe, and write down what you have observed!' They asked, of course, *what* I wanted them to observe. Clearly the instruction, 'Observe!' is absurd. (It is not even idiomatic, unless the object of the transitive verb can be taken as understood.) Observation is always selective. It needs a chosen object, a definite task, an interest, a point of view, a problem." [Karl R. Popper, *Conjectures and Refutations* (London: Routledge and Kegan Paul, 1963), p. 46. © Karl R. Popper 1963. Used by permission of Routledge and Kegan Paul Ltd. and Basic Books, Inc.]

theory.) Rumford's answer was that one should conceive of heat as motion (kinetic theory of heat) [7] rather than as a substance.

Using this and the other episodes as examples we will now elaborate the distinction between the two kinds of hypotheses encountered (those which can only be indirectly tested and those which can be directly and indirectly tested) and the nature of the justification for affirming a hypothesis (inductive arguments).

EMPIRICAL AND THEORETICAL HYPOTHESES, THEORIES, AND LAWS

Both Newton's and Rumford's hypotheses are like Torricelli's in that they can only be indirectly tested. Hypotheses like these are often called *theoretical hypotheses,* while hypotheses like Harvey's that can be tested directly are called *empirical hypotheses* (or experimental hypotheses). These terms are intended to emphasize three related differences:

First, empirical hypotheses state that certain relationships exist between observable things or features of things.[8] Theoretical hypotheses state that certain relationships exist between unobservable things or features of things. For example, Harvey's hypothesis involves observable things and processes: the blood in the veins, the flow of the blood towards the heart, and so forth. Newton's hypothesis involves light corpuscles, while Rumford's involves molecules. Both light corpulscles and molecules are unobservable. They are commonly called *theoretical entities. Second,* empirical hypotheses can be directly tested, whereas theoretical hypotheses can only be indirectly tested. *Third,* empirical hypotheses can be affirmed (as inductive generalizations) on the basis of statements which refer to the observable things or features of things to which the terms in the generalization refer, whereas theoretical hypothe-

[7] The kinetic theory of heat assumes that objects are made up of an enormous number of particles or *molecules* moving in different directions, colliding with each other, and so forth. There is an average speed of the molecules of any given substance. Heat is the motion of the molecules. The heat of an object thus increases as the average speed of the molecules increases.

[8] To make this clearer, we would say that observable criteria can be given for each of the nonlogical terms—for example, "flood," "pendulum," "tornado" —of an empirical hypothesis, while this cannot be done for the nonlogical terms—for example, "sea of air," "atom," "magnetic field," "gene"—of theoretical hypotheses. (Characteristics which when present in something constitute a justification for calling that thing X, are criteria for the word 'X'. See Chapter Three, pages 72–78.) It should be noted that, in general, the relations between theoretical and empirical hypotheses are very complex, and our simplified presentation of the relations between them is not wholly accurate on that account. See P. K. Feyerabend's "Explanation, Reduction, and Empiricism," *Minnesota Studies in the Philosophy of Science,* Volume III.

ses are only affirmed on the basis of different and varied statements.

This third difference is explained and illustrated by comparing the justification one might give for Harvey's empirical hypothesis with the justification one might give for Torricelli's, Newton's and Rumford's hypotheses. If one were to set out to determine whether Harvey's hypothesis was true he would examine several human beings. The form of the justification would thus be (ignoring present day knowledge):

Individual one has blood which circulates.
Individual two has blood which circulates.

.

.

.

Individual n has blood which circulates.
Therefore, in humans, blood circulates.

(In this case, perhaps only one premiss would be necessary—see the next section.) In contrast, the justification of Torricelli's and Rumford's hypotheses, at one time in the history of science, took more or less the following form [for Newton's justification, premiss (4) was missing]:

1. The hypothesis explains the relevant phenomena.
2. If the hypothesis is true, then certain phenomena (will) occur.
3. By experiment it is found that these phenomena do occur.
4. The competing hypotheses cannot adequately explain these phenomena.
5. The hypothesis is compatible with existing knowledge.
    Therefore the hypothesis is true.

Depending on the time (in the history of science), and the hypothesis, and the phenomena to be explained, there will be found certain variations among the premisses which constitute good grounds for affirming a theoretical hypothesis. For example, sometimes the hypothesis itself can be deduced from (or explained by) an established theoretical hypothesis. If so, this fact would provide an additional premiss in the justification of the hypothesis. (The form of justification for hypotheses introduced to explain established hypotheses also takes a somewhat different form.) When (1) through (5) are true of a hypothesis, the hypothesis is sometimes said to be, using Karl Popper's term, *corroborated*. Ordinarily, when a hypothesis is corroborated it is spoken of as "established." Corroborating a hypothesis differs from indirectly testing a hypothesis since indirect testing is only what is involved in premisses (2) and (3). Also, if a hypothesis cannot be directly tested, it is desirable, if not necessary, that it be corroborated. However, if it can be directly tested, then corroboration is superfluous.

Though the words "hypothesis," "theory," and "law" are used in a number of different ways in science, very often the distinctions can be understood in this way: A general statement or collection of statements when first introduced to explain relevant phenomena is called a *hypothesis*. When the statement or collection is made up of empirical statements which are verified by testing, they are called laws (*empirical laws*). When the statement or collection is made up of theoretical statements which have been corroborated, the collection is called a *theory*. And when the statement or collection achieves wide corroboration, these statements are called laws (*theoretical laws*).[9]

Examples of empirical laws are:

Lead melts at 327°C.
Orbiting objects follow elliptical paths.
The angle of reflection of a light ray is equal to the angle of incidence.
Reduced taxes lead to increased business investments.
When water in an open container is heated it evaporates.
The velocity of sound is greater in less dense gases than in more dense ones.
Children of blue-eyed parents are blue-eyed.

These laws are clear instances of empirical laws, and even though it is not possible to state (nonarbitrarily) what is observable and what is not, one can give obvious instances of theories which involve references to nonobservable objects, properties, and phenomena. Thus the law explaining the sun's radiation as the result of nuclear fission and laws about the behavior of electrons and other elementary particles—in fact the whole set of laws pertaining to atomic phenomena—are theoretical laws. Also laws pertaining to the role of the DNA molecule in heredity and the growth of an organism, laws (if the statements are acceptable as laws) pertaining to the ego-id conflict, and laws about the shape and action of fields of force are strictly theoretical laws.

To some extent all theories are tentative, and to stress this in the following chapters, we will sometimes refer to the statements of a theory as *assumptions*. Some theories, such as those of the atom and of the gene, are continually undergoing revision, while other theories, such as those of Torricelli and Rumford, are relatively secure from such modification (except as revision of atomic theory, for example, make it necessary to modify Rumford's original idea). Psychoanalytic theory is an example of a theory which postulates theoretical entities—the id, ego, superego—and which is extremely controversial, especially in the details of the theory; it thus will in all probability be revised and modified to a great extent as time goes on.

---

[9] Laws which are often called *ideal laws*—for example, pressure of an ideal gas whose temperature is constant varies inversely with its volume—are discussed in Chapter Nineteen, pages 439–440. The relationship between the concepts *empirical law*, *theoretical law*, and *ideal law* is also discussed.

INDUCTION AND DEDUCTION

In logic the word *induction* is now customarily used to refer to an argument in which the premisses do not entail the conclusion but rather are (or are presented as being) evidence or grounds for the truth of the conclusion. Inductive arguments, for the purposes of this discussion, can be usefully divided into two classes:

(A)   Those arguments in which a general statement is affirmed on the basis of the truth of particular statements which contain the same terms as those found in the general statement. The following argument form (often called *induction by enumeration*) is an example: [10]

A_1 is B
A_2 is B
    .
    .
    .
A_n is B
Therefore all A's are B.

(B)   Those inductive arguments that do not involve induction of kind (A), in which a statement is affirmed on the basis of the truth of statements which are evidence for it or good grounds for it.

Inferences of the first kind, (A), are illustrated in the four episodes. Pascal, for example, had his brother-in-law carry the barometer up the mountain several times before concluding that the height of the mercury decreases as the altitude increases. Part of Pascal's justification for the general statement—barometers fall when their altitude increases—thus was:

1.   The first time the barometer was taken up the mountain (that is, its altitude increased) it fell.
     The fifth time the barometer was taken up the mountain (that is, its altitude increased) it fell.
     Therefore barometers fall when their altitude increases.

Often one test is sufficient to warrant such a conclusion. For example, the testing of the P that homeogeneous light stays the same when passed through a prism did *not* involve this kind of argument:

2.   The first homeogeneous light passed through the first prism remained the same.

[10] Other examples are those arguments with premisses satisfying what are called *Mill's Methods*. These are discussed in detail in the next chapter.

The second homeogeneous light passed through the second prism remained the same.

The nth homeogeneous light passed through the nth prism remained the same.

Therefore homeogeneous light when passed through a prism remains the same.

The testing of this generalization took just one carefully conducted experiment. Newton took great care to be sure that he was experimenting with an accurate, pure prism and he realized that the conditions under which he experimented were such that no accidental factors could influence the results. Thus he was justified in making the generalization from just one experiment.

Empirical hypotheses, as we pointed out, can be affirmed (as inductive generalizations) on the basis of statements which refer to the observable things or features of things to which the terms in the generalization refer. That is, they can be justified by induction by enumeration [or other forms of induction of kind (A)].

Induction inferences of the second kind are also found in the episodes. As we have seen, in each we find arguments of this form:

3. The hypothesis explains the relevant phenomena.
   If the hypothesis is true, then certain P's are true.
   By experiment it is found that these P's are true.
   The competing hypotheses cannot adequately explain these P's.
   The hypothesis is compatible with existing knowledge.
   Therefore the hypothesis is true.

In each episode, arguments with this form contained premises which constituted good grounds for affirming the hypothesis being considered.

Some have thought that hypotheses in science are arrived at solely through inductive inferences of the first kind (A). This view is sometimes called *inductivism* (Karl Popper's term). Inductivism can be understood as either the view that scientific hypotheses are *discovered* by, for example, inductive enumeration [or other forms of induction of kind (A)] or the view that this is true and, in addition, scientific hypotheses are *justified* by, for example, inductive enumeration [or other forms of kind (A)]. Supposing the four episodes examined are representative of the context of discovery and justification of scientific hypotheses, it can be concluded that inductivism is, on the whole, mistaken. For, considering the context of discovery, the hypotheses were not discovered by inductive enumeration or any other induction of kind (A). That is, it was not the case, for example, that A's were observed followed by B's and this occasioned the formulation of a hypothesis (A's are B). For, first, three of the hypotheses contain terms which refer to unobservables. And, second, and more importantly, the hypotheses were arrived at by answering the question: Why do such-and-such phenomena occur? As it is sometimes put, hypotheses are "the free creation of the mind" (Einstein's favorite characterization). However, there are certain controls on this creation—not just *any* hypothesis reasonably explains a given set of related phenomena. What controls such "creations" is such things as one's general knowledge and knowledge of the particular subject matter. Turning to the context of justification, it has been argued that though empirical hypotheses are or can be justified by, for example, induction by enumeration, theoretical hypotheses cannot. Justification of theoretical hypotheses involve the complex inductive argument which we here are calling corroboration.

Another mistaken belief that some have held is that inductive inferences are the only kinds employed in science. As we have seen, inductive inferences are employed in testing certain P's and in setting down the grounds for affirming either an empirical or theoretical hypothesis. But deduction is also employed in all four episodes. In each case certain P's were deduced from the hypotheses and then tested.

For example, in relating Torricelli's adventure we spoke of a deduction that he made. In outline, it may have been something like this:

Hypothesis: (a) The sea of air exerts a constant pressure in all directions at a given altitude.

Data: (b) The pressure exerted downward by air pressure will sustain 34 feet of water in a tube which is open at one end and closed at the other, filled with water, inverted, and set in a container of water. This is equivalent to the statement that a suction pump will only draw water 34 feet. [(b) means that the pressure exerted downward by the water in the tube, that is the weight, is matched by the air pressure, preventing the rise of the water level of the container into which the tube empties.]

(c) Since mercury is fourteen times as heavy as water, a calculation will show that the same air pressure will sustain a thirty-inch column of mercury in a tube.

Conclusion: (d) Therefore only a thirty-inch column of mercury will be sustained.

This outline bears little resemblance to the formal deductions of Part II. Nevertheless, the similarities exist and the form of Torricelli's inference is a deduction. The hypothesis and the data form premises and, given numerous definitions and conventions, the deduction could be formalized in such a way that the rules of inference of Part II (plus others not discussed) and the transformations of mathematics would yield the conclusion.

We may briefly describe here four main areas in which deduction plays a role in science.

First, deductive arguments are often given in response to requests to explain some phenomenon or law. These can only be given with established laws as premises, or as some of the premises. An example is the explanation of why, in terms of Torricelli's law, about thirty inches of mercury is sustained in the present day barometer.

Second, deductive arguments are utilized in checking the consistency of theories and their compatibility with other theories. A theory is forthwith rejected if it is self-contradictory, and it is ordinarily regarded with suspicion if there is a logical incompatibility between it and another established theory. Later we will discuss examples illustrating this.

Third, deductions, as we have already seen, are utilized in deriving testable consequences (P's) from theories or hypotheses. The techniques of psychoanalysis, for example, are based on consequences of Freud's theories and provide some verification of them. The supposition that light travels faster in water than it does in air is a consequence of Newton's theory of light. The consequences of a theory can be regarded as predictions. Thus, by deduction, Newton was able to predict that light would travel faster in water than it does in air, and Torricelli was able to predict that air pressure will sustain only thirty inches of mercury.

Fourth, deductions also figure—in complex ways—in the *applications* of science; in plotting the trajectory of an orbital flight; in the development of new vaccines, new varieties of wheat, new advertising techniques; in the invention of labor-saving devices and countless other things. These, however, are in the province of the applied sciences: engineering, agronomy, preventive medicine, horticulture, and so on.

How exactly does induction differ from deduction? As was discussed in Chapter Seven, a deductive argument is one in which the conclusion is presented as being entailed by the premises. If the conclusion is entailed, then it would be a formal contradiction to affirm the premises and deny the conclusion. Arguments (1) and (2) in this section are inductive arguments. As we can see, the premises of each of the arguments do not entail the conclusion. For example, there is no formal contradiction in asserting that the barometer fell five times when it was taken up the mountain and denying that barometers *always* fall when altitudes are increased. Similarly there is no formal contradiction in affirming the premises and denying the conclusion of (3), no matter what statements replace the hypotheses and P's. The conclusion is not presented as being entailed by the premises which are stated, but, rather, the premises are presented as evidence or good grounds for affirming the conclusion.

Traditionally, the logician, besides being interested in deductive logic, has dealt with *inductive logic*. That is, he has been interested in the analysis of inductive inferences with the aim of formulating rules by which good inductive inferences can be distinguished from poor ones.[11] In the next chapter we will examine some of these traditional rules. As we will see, these traditional rules do not provide a way of telling a correct inductive inference from an incorrect one. General rules of this sort cannot be provided, though in particular circumstances rules for a correct induction can be given.

SUMMARY

Each of the episodes examined involves the following steps:

First: The formulation of a hypothesis which explains relevant phenomena.

Second: Deductions from the hypothesis of statements (*P*'s) describing other phenomena.

Third: Testing these *P*'s.

Fourth: Evaluation of the hypothesis and competing hypotheses on the basis of testing of these *P*'s.

In science, the method involving these four steps is sometimes called the *hypothetico-deductive* method. The hypothetico-deductive method contains the steps which generally lead to the formulation, testing, and, in part, the establishing of a hypothesis.

Scientific hypotheses, theories, and laws can be classed into two groups: theoretical hypotheses, theories, and laws; and empirical hypotheses, theories, and laws. The members of the first group differ from those of the second in that they involve theoretical entities such as light corpuscles, molecules, and the "sea of air." They can only be indirectly tested, and they can only be corroborated. A statement in science is corroborated when its justification has the form, or a variation of the form, indicated in (3) on page 352 of this chapter.

EXERCISES

Consider each of the following passages in terms of these questions: What phenomena (*P*'s) are to be explained? What hypotheses are employed to ex-

---

[11] This tradition is traceable to Mill, who wrote: "The business of Inductive Logic is to provide rules and models (such as the syllogism and its rules are for ratiocination) to which, if inductive arguments conform, those arguments are conclusive and not otherwise." (*A System of Logic*, Bk. III, Chap. IX, section 6.)

plain them? Are the hypotheses empirical or theoretical? Are there any competing hypotheses? What verification or corroboration is to be found or could be found for the hypotheses?

1. In a series of postmortem examinations of tubercular rats, Johannes Fibiger, a pathologist of the University of Copenhagen, found three that suffered from stomach cancers. This was strange, since rats rarely suffer from tumors of the stomach. Fibiger made a visit to the dealer who had been supplying him with these rats, and on questioning found that those sent to his laboratory had all come from a sugar refinery. Was there anything peculiar about this refinery which could account for the unusually large percentage of stomach-cancerous mice from this spot? He investigated the place and found nothing unusual except a high infestation with cockroaches, which formed a fairly large part of the diet of its rats. Could he find some connection between roaches, rats, and cancer? Cancer as a disease of filth had been spoken about for years, and vermin were said to be responsible for the so-called "cancer houses," private homes from which emerged many a human cancer victim of the same family.

Fibiger planned a controlled experiment. He collected thousands of the refinery roaches and fed them to rats from another breeding establishment. The rats enjoyed this strange treatment, and for three years—that was the normal life span of his rodents—Fibiger remained sceptical. Then they died, and one by one he opened them up. To his astonishment, he found many stomach cancers. Fibiger made a careful microscopic study of the growths. He discovered in every case they had formed around a parasitic worm, the same worm to which the roach had been host before it was fed to the rat. The larva of the worm coiled up in the muscles of the rat, later developing into an adult worm in the animal's stomach. Around this the tumerous growth had appeared. Fibiger had actually for the first time produced artificial cancer in a laboratory animal.

(BERNARD JAFFE, *Outposts of Science*) [12]

2. On the 7th of January 1610, at one o'clock in the morning, when he directed his telescope to Jupiter, he observed three stars near the body of the planet, two being to the east and one to the west of him. They were all in a straight line, and parallel to the ecliptic, and they appeared brighter than other stars of the same magnitude. Believing them to be fixed stars, he paid no great attention to their distances from Jupiter and from one another. On the 8th of January, however, when, from some cause or other, he had been led to observe all the stars again, he found a very different arrangement of them: all the three were on the west side of Jupiter, *nearer one another than before,* and almost at equal distances. Though he had not turned his attention to the extraordinary fact of the mutual approach of the stars, yet he began to consider how Jupiter could be found to the east of the three stars, when but the day before he had been to the west of two of them. The only explanation which

[12] Bernard Jaffe, *Outposts of Science* (New York: Simon and Schuster, 1935).

he could give of this fact was, that the motion of Jupiter was *direct*, contrary to astronomical calculations, and that he had got before these two stars by his own motion.

In this dilemma between the testimony of his senses and the results of calculation, he waited for the following night with the utmost anxiety; but his hopes were disappointed, for the heavens were wholly veiled in clouds. On the 10th, two only of the stars appeared, and both on the east of the planet. As it was obviously impossible that Jupiter could have advanced from west to east on the 8th of January, and from east to west on the 10th, Galileo was forced to conclude that the phenomenon which he had observed arose from the motion of the stars, and he set himself to observe diligently their change of place. On the 11th, there were still only two stars, and both to the east of Jupiter; but the more eastern star was now *twice as large as the other one*, though on the preceding night they had been perfectly equal. This fact threw a new light upon Galileo's difficulties, and he immediately drew the conclusion, which he considered to be indubitable, '*that there were in the heaven three stars which revolved round Jupiter, in the same manner as Venus and Mercury revolved round the sun.*' On the 12th of January, he again observed them in new positions, and of different magnitudes; and, on the 13th, he discovered a fourth star, which completed the *four* secondary planets with which Jupiter is surrounded.

(SIR DAVID BREWSTER, The Martyrs of Science)

3. It was thought at the time of Francesco Redi that there was "spontaneous generation." Supposed evidence for this was the appearance of worms on meat after a few days. Redi observed that not only worms appear but also small objects (he called them "eggs" though they are pupae) and many flies appear. Redi wrote: "Having considered these things, I began to believe that all worms found in meat were derived from the dropping of flies and not from the putrefaction of the meat." He then tested his hypothesis by eliminating the flies. First he sealed meat in a glass, and then he covered the glass with "fine Naples veil" which would not allow flies to enter. Even after many days no worms were seen, though in an open glass the meat had become wormy.

(Adapted from JAMES B. CONANT, Science and Common Sense) [13]

4. Pasteur, during his work on lactic acid fermentation, wrote:

"One knew that ferments originated from the contact of albuminous substances with oxygen gas. One of two things must be true, I said to myself; either ferments are organized entities and they are produced by oxygen alone, considered merely as oxygen, in contact with albuminous materials, in which case they are spontaneously generated; or if they are not of spontaneous origin, it is not oxygen alone as such that intervenes in their production, but the gas acts as a stimulant to a germ carried with it or existing in the nitrogenous or fermentable materials."

Pasteur then passed air through a red-hot tube and into a sterilized flask

---

[13] James B. Conant, *Science and Common Sense* (New Haven: Yale University Press, 1961).

containing fermentable material. The material did not ferment. On the other hand, when ordinary air was put into the flask the material fermented.

But one who held that fermentation is produced by oxygen alone and not from germs in the air could also have accounted for the results of these experiments.

Pasteur then placed his solution in flasks, sealed the flasks, and heated them. When he broke the tips of the flasks in the country, eight out of seventy-three showed signs of fermentation. When he broke twenty of them on a glacier (the Mer de Glace), only one showed such signs, while when he broke others in his room in the inn at Chamonix, ten out of thirteen showed signs of fermentation. Air could thus enter many flasks and not cause fermentation.

5. From the lecture notes of Professor Samuel Williams, the Hollis Professor of Mathematics and Natural Philosophy at Harvard from 1780–1788:

Take some combustible substance and let it be inflamed or set fire: In this state inclose it in a vessel containing a small quantity of atmospherical air. Effect: The combustion will continue but a short time and then cease. Part of the combustible substance is reduced to ashes and the other part remains entire. And the air appears to be changed and altered. . . . Here then we have a representation of what the chemists call phlogiston and of the air's being loaded with it. In the confined air the combustible matter continues burning until the air becomes loaded with something that prevents any further combustion. And being confined by the closeness of the vessel, whatever the matter be with which the air is loaded, it is confined within the vessel and cannot escape. . . .

It seems, therefore, from this experiment that phlogiston must be a real substance, and that the air is loaded or saturated with it. For what can the inclosing the combustible matter in the phial do but to prevent the escape or dispersion of some real substance? And is it not evident that so long as the air can receive this substance from the combustible matter so long the body will continue burning; and that as soon as the air is saturated and can receive no more of the phlogiston, the combustion must cease for no more phlogiston can escape or be thrown out from the burning body. And therefore when fresh air is admitted to receive phlogiston, the combustion will again take place. . . . And hence are derived the phrases of phlogisticated and dephlogisticated air. By phlogisticated air is intended air which is charged or loaded with phlogiston, and by dephlogisticated air is meant air which is free from phlogiston; or which does not contain this principal element of inflammability.

6. In 1772 Antoine Lavoisier wrote this note and sent it to the French Academy: "About eight days ago I discovered that sulfur in burning, far from losing weight, on the contrary gains it; . . . it is the same with phosphorus; this increase of weight arises from a prodigious quantity of air that is fixed during the combustion and combines with the vapours.

"This discovery, which I have established by experiments that I regard as decisive, has led me to think that what is observed in the combustion of sulfur and phosphorus may well take place in the case of all substances that gain in weight by combustion and calcination; . . ." [14]

14 Taken from James B. Conant, *op. cit.,* pp. 176–177.

Lavoisier's explanation is that something from the air, or the air itself, is absorbed in combustion.

His classic experiment to support his theory is:

"Mercury heated in common air produces a red material (an oxide, we would say, a 'calx' to the chemists of the eighteenth century). In a closed space about one-fifth of the air disappears in this process. The red material weighs more than the metal from which it was formed. Therefore something has disappeared from the air and combined with the metal. The red material, the oxide or calx, is next strongly heated in an enclosed space with the sun's rays brought to a focus by a large lens or 'burning glass,' a gas is evolved, and the metal regenerated. The new gas is the 'something' which disappeared from the original air, for the amount is the same, and the calx has lost weight in the right amount. The new gas (oxygen) mixed with the residue from the first experiment yields a mixture which is identical with common air." [15]

7. Avogadro (and some of his contemporaries) were impressed by the quantitative relationship that had been found to hold when *gaseous* elements combine. Here we are considering not weight but volumes of gases, let it be carefully noted. One illustration will suffice. If a mixture of hydrogen gas and oxygen gas is exploded by a spark, the following relationship is found to hold: 1 volume of oxygen + 2 volumes of hydrogen = 2 volumes of water vapor. (Any units of volume, for example cubic feet, may be used to express this relation.) The relation between volumes is very simple: 1 to 2 to 2. Other gaseous elements were likewise found to combine in a volume relationship expressed by *small whole numbers*.

Avogadro made two assumptions to account for the whole-number relationship between the *volumes* of gaseous elements which combine to form compounds. The first was that *equal volumes of gases under the same conditions of temperature and pressure contain the same number of particles*. The second was that the particles of hydrogen and oxygen are each composed of *two* atoms united together.

With the aid of these assumptions Avogadro accounted for all the known facts about chemical reactions between gases and was led to the conclusion that the water molecule was composed of two atoms of hydrogen and one of oxygen, that is, it is to be represented by H_2O.

(JAMES B. CONANT, *Science and Common Sense*) [16]

8. Botanists have been trying for nearly a century to discover the process by which plants shed their leaves. One of the first clues that attracted their attention was the fact that some plants develop a distinct layer of cells at the base of the leaf stalk and leaves then break off at that point. But the so-called "separation layer" proved to be a false clue. Many plants have no such layer, and many others have one but their leaves do not separate at that place.

. . . .

The two major parts of a leaf are the flat blade and the stalk by which the blade is attached to the plant stem. . . . When the blade of a leaf is cut off,

[15] *Ibid.*, pp. 189–190. Used by permission of Yale University Press.
[16] *Ibid.*, pp. 200–201.

the remaining leaf stalk soon separates and drops from the stem. . . . The first substantial hint as to the internal mechanism controlling fall came when it was found that even if only a tiny piece of the leaf blade was left on the stalk, the leaf would stay on the stem just as long as if it had a complete blade. This indicated that the substance in the blade that prevented the fall of the leaf must be active in very minute amounts. . . .

The hormone was soon identified. It is the plant growth substance, auxin. The substance, as a later investigator found, not only kept debladed coleus leaves growing but delayed their fall. . . . The general conclusion was that auxin produced in the leaf blade moves down into the leaf stalk, and there inhibits leaf fall in direct relation to how much auxin there is. This conclusion was confirmed in a qualitative way for the leaves of other plants and for a number of kinds of fruits. . . .

The control of leaf fall by auxin seemed to be completely clear. It was, in fact, *too* clear. . . .

While thinking over this theory of leaf fall, I was struck by the odd circumstance that each leaf seemed to be acting as an independent entity. The theory implied that the fall of a leaf depended only on how much auxin was coming into its stalk from its own blade. Now in most cases we know of, the behavior or development of one part of a plant is subject to inhibitions and stimulations from other parts of the plant. One therefore had to suspect the completeness of the hypothesis that leaf fall was totally independent of influence from the rest of the plant. Furthermore, while the hypothesis seemed to explain what prevented leaves from falling, it left unclear what causes them to fall when they do.

With these thoughts in mind, we planned some experiments to try to detect influences from the rest of the plant. These involved trials of various patterns in deblading the leaves of a plant. Coleus leaves grow in pairs, the two members of each pair coming from opposite sides of the stem. The usual practice had been to deblade one of each pair, leaving the "sister" leaf intact as a control. Now, if the fall of each leaf was controlled independently within itself, it should be immaterial in what pattern the leaves up the stem were debladed, or how many of them were. But experiments showed that the pattern of deblading did make a consistent, though small, difference in the time of leaf fall, and that when *all* the leaves (except those in the bud at the apex of the stem) were debladed, the fall was strikingly slowed down!

The most obvious conclusion was that the presence of intact leaves in some way speeded the fall of debladed leaves. Indeed their presence accelerated the fall even of old leaves that were not debladed, for when the blades were removed from all the younger leaves, the old ones remained on longer than they would have otherwise.

It seemed, then, that leaf blades produce not only a substance (auxin) which inhibits falling but also a substance which speeds falling. What might this substance be? The most likely candidate was ethylene. This ingredient of illuminating gas has long been known to cause trees' leaves to fall, and recently it has been learned that some ethylene is naturally present in plant tissues; it is emitted by ripening fruit and by leaves. However we were unable in an extensive series of experiments to find any evidence that ethylene from leaves speeded leaf fall.

Although we scoured the research literature, we could find no other leads that proved fruitful. We therefore decided to look more closely at the experimental plants. It was then we noticed something we should have seen before. In every experiment we had left untouched the tiny leaves in the apical bud at the top of the stem. And every treatment that speeded the fall of leaves lower on the stem had at the same time accelerated the growth of the apical leaves. We now noticed a clear correlation between this growth and the time of the debladed leaves' fall. They fell just when the bottom leaves of the apical bud above them reached a length of 70 or 80 millimeters. Fast leaf fall seemed to be closely tied up with the presence just above of leaves 70 to 80 millimeters long.

When a leaf reaches this size it attains its maximum production of auxin. It was beginning to look as if the primary cause of speeded leaf fall was auxin production by the apical bud leaves above the debladed leaves. Further analysis indicated that the presence of intact leaves lower on the stem speeds leaf fall indirectly by speeding the growth of these apical leaves.

This view was confirmed by the following experiment. Many plants were prepared in which the young leaves were debladed and the older leaf pairs left intact. As in earlier experiments, the presence of the older leaves low on the stem speeded the fall of the debladed leaves above them, so long as the apical bud was left intact. But when the apical bud was cut off, the debladed leaves in that set of plants fell much more slowly. If, however, synthetic auxin was applied in place of the cut-off bud, the debladed leaves fell as fast as if the bud were on. Thus the experiments confirmed our surmise that auxin from the apical bud speeds the fall of debladed leaves.

These experiments, along with others which there is not space to describe, show that the fall of leaves is controlled by an "auxin-auxin balance." Auxin both slows and speeds leaf fall. So long as a leaf's own blade produces enough auxin to overcome the effect of auxin coming from younger leaves above, the leaf will stay on the plant. But as soon as its production of auxin drops to less than the critical rate—because of old age, too much shade, insect attack or deblading—the auxin from the younger, more rigorous leaves above causes the leaf to fall. Such a system has obvious adaptive value. The old and infirm are shed by the action of a hormone from the young and vigorous.

(WILLIAM P. JACOBS, "What Makes Leaves Fall?") [17]

9. If one puts a small dish of sugar water near a beehive, the dish may not be discovered for several days. But as soon as one bee has found the dish and returned to the hive, more foragers come from the same hive. In an hour hundreds may be there.

Why is this? It seems that the first bee must pass on a message to the other bees.

[17] William P. Jacobs, "What Makes Leaves Fall?" in *Plant Life: A Scientific American Book* (New York: Simon and Schuster, 1957). Reprinted with permission. Copyright © 1957 by Scientific American, Inc. All rights reserved.

To discover how the message is passed on we conducted a large number of experiments, marking individual bees with colored dots so that we could recognize them in the milling crowds of their fellows and building a hive with glass walls through which we could watch what was happening inside. Briefly, this is what we learned. A bee that has discovered a rich source of food near the hive performs on her return a "round dance." (Like all the other work of the colony, food-foraging is carried out by females.) She turns in circles, alternately to the left and to the right. This dance excites the neighboring bees; they start to troop behind the dancer and soon fly off to look for the food. They seek the kind of flower whose scent they detected on the original forager.

The richer the source of food, the more vigorous and the longer the dance. And the livelier the dance, the more strongly it arouses the other bees. If several kinds of plants are in bloom at the same time, those with the most and the sweetest nectar cause the liveliest dances. Therefore the largest number of bees fly to the blossoms where collecting is currently most rewarding. When the newly recruited helpers get home, they dance too, and so the number of foragers increases until they have drained most of the nectar from the blossoms. Then the dances slow down or stop altogether. The stream of workers now turns to other blossoms for which the dancing is livelier. The scheme provides a simple and purposeful regulation of supply and demand.

(KARL VON FRISCH, "Dialects in the Language of the Bees") [18]

[18] Karl von Frisch, "Dialects in the Language of the Bees," in *Scientific American*, Vol. 207, No. 2, August 1962. Reprinted with permission. Copyright © 1962 by Scientific American, Inc. All rights reserved.

Chapter Seventeen

CRUCIAL
EXPERIMENTS
AND INDUCTIVE
TECHNIQUES

In the last chapter we noticed, among other things, how a theoretical hypothesis is justified. In this chapter we will be interested in:

1. what leads to the abandonment of an empirical hypothesis,
2. what leads to the abandonment of a theoretical hypothesis,
3. how certain empirical statements are established by inductive techniques.

CRUCIAL EXPERIMENTS AND
EMPIRICAL HYPOTHESES

Empirical hypotheses are from time to time falsified. The Galenic theory about the behavior of the blood is an example of an empirical hypothesis which was falsified. Eventually by observation it was seen that all the statements which make up the theory were false, for example, the statements that the blood is produced in the liver and that there is no connection between the veins and arteries.

Another example of a falsified empirical hypothesis is the belief, held around 1890, that air consists only of nitrogen and oxygen. Rayleigh found that nitrogen removed from air was slightly heavier than nitrogen removed from other sources. The difference was one part in a thousand. The explanation seemed simple: nitrogen prepared from air is not pure nitrogen. Rayleigh and others then employed various methods for removing hydrogen, and isolated a residue gas which was about 1% of the weight of the nitrogen. This gas was called argon. The hypothesis that air consists only of nitrogen and oxygen was falsified by Rayleigh's experiment.

Experiments which falsify empirical hypotheses are often called *crucial experiments*. As we will see shortly, there is another group of experiments connected with theoretical hypotheses also called "crucial experiments." These experiments are related to theoretical hypotheses in a way different from the way in which Rayleigh's experiment was related to the nitrogen-oxygen hypothesis.

In preparation for the discussion which follows it should be noted that in these two episodes singular observation statements (for example, this liver does not produce blood, and this sample of air contains argon) logically entailed the falsity of the empirical hypothesis. That is, to take the second example, this is a valid argument:

This representative sample of air contains nitrogen, oxygen, and argon.

Therefore it is false that air consists only of nitrogen and oxygen.

CRUCIAL EXPERIMENTS AND THEORETICAL HYPOTHESES[1]

Can theoretical hypotheses be falsified in the way in which empirical hypotheses can? At first sight it would seem that they too can be fasified in a relatively direct fashion. Statements (*P*'s) which can be directly tested are deducible from a theoretical hypothesis (*H*). Suppose on experimentation it is found that such a *P* is false. Does it not necessarily follow that the theoretical hypothesis is false? For, it seems, what we have here is a simple instance of the valid argument form called *modus tollens:*

1. *H* implies *P*.
   Not-*P*.
   Therefore not-*H*.

But (1) simplifies certain important logical and semantic features found in most scientific contexts. When these are made clear it can be seen that a falsified *P* which is deduced from the theory does not necessarily entail the falsity of the theory.

[1] The account of crucial experiments found here conforms (more or less) to P. Duhem's view found in *The Aim and Structure of Physical Theory*. An important and serious criticism of this view is found in some of the essays by Adolf Grunbaum, for example, "The Duhemian Argument," in *Philosophy of Science,* Vol. 27, 1960.

Logical Features

From the caloric theory—the theory that heat is a weightless substance—as we have seen in the last chapter, this P was deduced: If a body changes its temperature through friction, then its specific heat must change. The experiment which Count Rumford performed showed there is no change in specific heat when a body changes its temperature through friction. Did this experiment falsify the caloric theory? There are two things to note here. First, the deduction of this P from the theory involved the assumption (among other assumptions) that matter can neither be created nor destroyed. And, second, the theory is made up of more than one assumption. Thus the relevant structure of this deduction is this:

$[(A_1, A_2, \ldots, A_n)$ and $D]$ implies P.
P is false.
Therefore $[(A_1, A_2, \ldots, A_n)$ and $D]$ is false,

where the A's stand for the assumptions of the theory H, and D stands for the nontrival assumption or assumptions needed, in addition to the theory, to make the *formal* deduction. Now it should be noted that if a conjunction of statements is said to be false, as the above conclusion has it, then it logically follows only that at least one of the statements in the conjunction is false. One or more of the assumptions which make up D may be false or one or more of the assumptions which make up H may be false. From the fact that P is falsified, in any case, it does not necessarily follow that the theory is false.

Generally, if the assumption or assumptions of D are not well established relative to the body of assumptions which make up the theory, an assumption or assumptions which make up D are given up rather than the theory. Consequently, the effect, in such cases, of a falsified P which is deduced from the theory is that the theory is left intact. On the other hand, when the D is established, then one or more of the assumptions of the H must be modified or abandoned or the theory must be given up. This brings us to an important semantic issue.

Semantic Features

How is the phrase "X theory" (where a name such as caloric, corpuscular, or molecular replaces the 'X') used in science? If what is called "X theory" is a certain set of specific assumptions, and if *each* of these assumptions is necessary in order to call a set of statements "X theory," then if the D is established and if a P which is deduced from the theory is falsified, the result must be the abandonment of X theory. For if a P which is deduced from the theory is falsified, then either an assumption (or assumptions) must be modified or abandoned, and thus the theory abandoned, or an assumption (or assumptions) of D must be modified or abandoned. But generally the name of a theory is not used in this way. How it is used can be illustrated schematically as follows: Certain assumptions are necessary to call a set of statements "X theory," but the remaining assumptions are not. Suppose what is called X theory is made up at one time of these four assumptions: A_1, A_2, A_3, and A_4. Let us suppose A_1 is necessary, in that if that were given up we would not call A_2, A_3, A_4, plus any other assumptions "X theory." But if either A_2, A_3, or A_4 were given up we would call what is left, plus certain other assumptions, "X theory," since it is still essentially like the old set of assumptions. There are, let us imagine, cases where we would be in doubt whether to call a set—say, A_1 and A_2, plus other assumptions, without A_3 and A_4—"X theory." The consequences of this use of "X theory" is that certain assumptions can be modified or abandoned, and we would still speak of the set of assumptions as "X theory." (An illustration of this is found in the next section.)

In summary, the falsification of a P or P's deduced from a theoretical hypothesis with the help of nontrivial subsidiary assumptions D do not entail the falsity of the hypothesis—that is, the falsity of one or more of the essential assumptions of the theory. Rather, the falsification of such P's entails the falsity of the conjunction of assumptions which made up the H and D. Thus no observation statement (or statements) entails that a theory is false, whereas observation statements can entail that an empirical hypothesis is false.

What accounts for this difference between theories and empirical hypotheses can easily be seen. To deduce a singular observation statement from a statement contained in an empirical hypothesis, often all that is needed is a singular statement as in this example:

Air is composed only of oxygen and hydrogen.
This X is a representative sample of air.
Therefore this X is composed only of oxygen and hydrogen.

And if the conclusion here is false, it logically follows that the first premiss, the empirical hypothesis, is false (assuming the particular premiss to be true). But to deduce an observation statement from a theory involves employing all or most of the assumptions of the theory, plus the assumptions in D (plus singular propositions if a singular observation statement is to be deduced). It is this impossibility of deducing observation statements from particular statements of the theory which accounts for the logical impossibility of a falsified P which is deduced from the theory implying the falsity of a theory.

"DEATH BLOWS"

Many times in the history of science falsified P's have, as it is often put, "dealt death blows" to the theoretical hypotheses from which they were derived. Rumford's experiment is often described as having dealt a death blow to the caloric theory. Now if his experiment did not entail the falsity of the theory, what is meant by saying that it dealt it a death blow? A theory is *dealt a death blow* when, first, a P which is deduced from it is falsified; second, all the assumptions involved in the D are well established; and third, certain assumptions of the theory other than the *essential* assumptions are regarded as well established. The result of falsifying such a P will be the abandonment of the theory—that is, the abandonment of the essential assumption(s) of the theory. An experiment which determines whether a P related to an H in this way is true is called a *crucial experiment*. There are thus two kinds of crucial experiments: those which falsify or do not falsify an empirical hypothesis and those which deal or do not deal a death blow to a theoretical hypothesis. Rumford's experiment was a crucial experiment of the second kind.

Let us consider another classical example of a crucial experiment which dealt a death blow to a theory. Recall Newton's corpuscular theory of light, discussed in the last chapter. The theory, it will be remembered, describes light as made up of particles which are emitted from light sources. The theory also supposes that these particles are attracted and repelled according to Newton's laws of motion for bodies. For example, the particles which make up water attract the light particles from the air when the distance between the water particles and light particles is small. These assumptions explain why light travels in a straight line, why it reflects and refracts, the prism phenomenon—in short, they explain all the then known light-phenomena. The theory also implies the following consequence: the index of refraction of light passing from one medium into another is equal to the velocity of the light particle within the medium it penetrates, divided by the velocity of the same particle in the medium it leaves behind. (We will not try to review all the assumptions and steps employed to deduce this P from Newton's hypothesis.) From this proposition a second one follows: light travels faster in water than in air.

The testing of this deduced P had to wait until the speed of light could be measured. When means were devised for such a measurement, the experiment was performed by Foucault and he found that the light was propagated less rapidly in water than in air. Some thought that this experiment condemned once and for all the corpuscular theory of light.

In a sense this is true, and in a sense this is not true. It did deal a "death blow" to the corpuscular theory of light; no scientist since then has regarded light as merely a collection of corpuscles. But the theory, we recall, is made up of *several* assumptions. One or more of these must be given up or changed in the light of Foucault's experiment. However the assumption which might need modification so that the theory is compatible with Foucault's experiment need not *necessarily* be the assumption that light is made up of projected corpuscles. If this were retained in the modified theory, we would speak of it as the same theory. But since the other assumptions which *could* be given up or modified were regarded as more or less established, Foucault's experiment dealt the death blow.

When a theory is to be modified in the face of disconfirmed P's, and when it is to be abandoned, and when one should stop modification and abandon a theory in the face of disconfirmed P's is all a matter of extreme complexity, ordinarily, and involves factors not subject to general rules.

FACT OF THE CROSS

Suppose that there are two rival theoretical hypotheses for the same group of phenomena. And suppose from H_1 (a given hypothesis), P_1 follows and from H_2, not-P_1 follows. In addition, let us imagine that the testing of P_1 is a crucial experiment for both theories. That is, no matter what the outcome of the test, one of the theories will be dealt a death blow. The result of the test, consequently, will be that one theory will be abandoned and the other will be corroborated and thus will be the accepted theory. Newton called such an experiment in his *Novum Organum* a "fact of the cross," borrowing this expression, as he says, from the crosses which at an intersection indicate the various roads.

Actually Foucault's experiment was thought to be an experiment of this kind. For at the time there were two competing theories about the nature of light—Newton's corpuscular theory and Huygens' wave theory. Huygens' wave theory supposed that light consisted of waves propagated within ether. The wave theory, as was the case with Newton's hypothesis, explained all the then known light-phenomena. But a consequence of the wave theory was that light travels more quickly in air than in water. The result of Foucault's experiment was the abandonment of the corpuscular theory and an acceptance of the wave theory.

Some have not only thought that experiment and observation can demonstrate the falsity of a theory but have argued that observations can demonstrate the truth of a theory. In fact Jean Arago, the celebrated French astronomer, wrote as if he believed the Foucault experiment demonstrated that Huygens' theory was true and Newton's false. As we have already seen, the results of experiments cannot entail the falsity of a theory, though they can deliver the theory a death blow. And it is easy to see how some, having *modus tollens* in mind, might have thought that observations do entail the falsity of a theory. But what led some to think that experiments could demonstrate the certainty of a theory? The explanation seems to be this: If, it is argued, we enumerate all the theoretical hypotheses which can explain a set of phenomena, and if by experiment all are shown to be false but one, then this remaining hypothesis must be certain. Now this argument presupposes the following questionable assumptions: First, that there is a single theoretical explanation for a set of phenomena; second, that observation statements do entail the falsity of a theory; and, third, that it is possible to enumerate all the possible hypotheses which explain a set of phenomena. Since Arago seems to have thought that light must either be made up of particles or be a wave, he believed that Newton's theory and Huygens' theory exhausted the possible explanations for light-phenomena. Since he believed that Foucault's experiment demonstrated the falsity of Newton's theory, we can see why he thought that this experiment demonstrated the certainty of Huygens' theory.

SUMMARY

Observation statements do entail the falsity of empirical generalizations but do not entail the falsity of theories.

A theory can conflict with observation—that is, consequences can be deduced from the theory which conflict with observation. But such deductions involve the use of many or most of the assumptions in the theory plus certain subsidiary assumptions. Theories, however, can receive death blows from the results of experiments. A theory is dealt a death blow when (1) an observation statement which is deduced from it is falsified by experimental observation, (2) all the assumptions involved in the D (assumptions needed for the derivation in addition to those which make up the hypothesis) are established, and (3) certain assumptions of the theory other than the essential assumptions are regarded as well established.

EXERCISES I

In each of the following passages:

What hypotheses or competing hypotheses are found?
Are the hypotheses theoretical or empirical?
Are they tested?

Does any test establish a hypothesis or deal a "death blow" to a hypothesis? What is the effect of the test or tests?

1. In the early nineteenth century the German geologist Abraham Werner propounded the geological theory called "Neptunism." The theory was offered as an explanation of rock formations. Werner held that at one time the earth was covered by an ocean. All the rock strata had been deposited by processes of crystallization, chemical precipitation, or mechanical sedimentation.

"First of all came the primitive rocks, such as granite, which had crystallized out of the primeval ocean: these were entirely devoid of fossils. Then came the transitional rocks such as the micas and the slates, containing a few fossils, which had been precipitated from the ocean. Next there were the sedimentary rocks, richer in fossils, such as coal and limestone, formed by the deposition of solids from the waters. Finally there were the derivative rocks, such as sand and clay, which were derived from the others by a process of weathering. Werner thought that volcanoes were due to coal catching fire underground, the heat generated melting the neighbouring rocks, and forcing the eruption of volcanic lava from time to time. Thus, for Werner, heat was not an important geological force: volcanic action due to burning coal was a late and subsidiary rock-forming agency, appearing only after the main strata had been laid down." [2]

One of the obvious shortcomings of this theory was the lack of an explanation for the disappearance of the ocean after the rock strata had been formed. James Hutton, an amateur scientist of Edinburgh, put forward a theory which employed only geological forces which are in operation today." The interior of the earth, Hutton held, was composed of molten lava, the solid surface of the earth serving as a containing vessel, which was closed apart from the volcanoes that served as safety valves. From time to time, he thought, the molten rock escaped through cracks just beneath the earth's surface and tilted up the overlying sedimentary strata. The molten rock then solidified to form the crystalline rocks, such as basalt and granite, thus giving the mountains with their crystalline cores and sedimentary sides.

. . . .

"Werner's followers argued against Hutton, first, that molten rock would not become crystalline on solidification but would be glassy like lava, and secondly, that some rocks, like limestone, would decompose if subject to heat. Hall observed in a glass factory at Leith that if molten glass were allowed to cool very slowly it became crystalline and opaque, whilst if it were cooled more quickly it became glassy and transparent. He presumed that molten rock would behave in a similar way, and accordingly he obtained some lava from Vesuvius and Etna, and melted it in the blast furnace of an iron works. As he had expected, the molten rock became crystalline, like basalt, when allowed to cool slowly, and glassy, like lava, when cooled rapidly. Hall showed further that if lime-

2 Reprinted from *Main Currents of Scientific Thought*, by S. F. Mason, by permission of Abelard-Schuman Ltd. and Routledge and Kegan Paul Ltd. All rights reserved. Copyright 1953.

stone were heated in a closed vessel, it did not decompose as the Neptunists thought, but melted and became marble on cooling as Hutton suggested." [3]

During the period between 1790 and 1830 the study of fossils in rocks was begun. Fossil remains of land animals of different ages were found in different rock layers. This gave new support to Hutton's theory. Some Neptunists responded by claiming that the agents of these formations were a *series* of catastrophic floods.

Around 1819 Sedgwick and Murchison studied the early rocks containing no fossils in coal mines and the like. They concluded that this rock was formed by the solidification of molten rock, not by crystallization from water.

2. Those who believed that microorganisms could arise *de novo* without parents, did in fact accept that life was continually being created anew from inanimate matter. This belief came to be known as the doctrine of spontaneous generation. . . .

Among the many other types of experiments that Pasteur designed to rule out spontaneous generation, one is worth some emphasis by virtue of its very simplicity and decisiveness and because it finally silenced his opponents and settled the issue—at least for the time being. A fermentable fluid was put into a flask, the long neck of which was then heated and drawn into the form of an S tube (hence the name "swan-neck flask"). When the liquid was boiled, the vapor forced the air out through the orifice of the neck. As the fluid became cool again, the air slowly returned to the flask, but was washed in the moisture that condensed in the curves of the neck after heating was interrupted. Under these conditions, any dust or particle carried by the air was trapped in the neck, and the fluid in the flask remained clear, sterile. However, when the neck of the flask was broken, and the unwashed air allowed to come into contact with the fluid, then microscopic life immediately began to develop.

Despite the spectacular success of these experiments, there were still unforeseen difficulties to overcome. They arose from the fact, then unknown but now well understood, that certain species of bacteria form heat-resistant spores. In some of the early experiments these spores persisted in the fluid that was presumed to have been sterilized by heating, and when they germinated, they gave rise to bacterial growth even though access to outside air had been prevented. These difficulties arising from the presence of heat-resistant spores were eventually overcome, and Pasteur was able to prepare his swan-neck flasks in such a manner that the broth remained sterile in them all.

In Pasteur's words, "Never will the doctrine of spontaneous generation recover from the mortal blow of this simple experiment."

(RENE DUBOS, *Pasteur and Modern Science*) [4]

3. When something, say a match, burns, it appears that something is released from the match. According to a theory of combustion formulated by two German chemists, Becher and Stahl, in the 17th and 18th centuries, when a

---

[3] *Ibid.*, pp. 325–336. Used by permission.

[4] Rene Dubos, *Pasteur and Modern Science*, Science Study Series, Anchor Books (Garden City, New York: Doubleday, 1960), pp. 58–59 by permission of Doubleday and Heinemann Educational Books, Ltd., London.

substance was burnt 'phlogiston' was said to escape in the form of fire and flame.

One application of the 'phlogiston' theory was eventually to lead chemists into much confusion and to help to bring about its downfall. It arose in this way. When a metal, such as copper or lead, is sufficiently heated, it turns into a powdery substance and its metallic properties are lost. (The same thing happens in the familiar rusting of iron, but there without the application of heat.) The chemists of that time explained this by saying that a metal, when heated, lost its 'phlogiston', leaving the powdery residue, which they called a calx. They knew that if this calx was heated afresh with charcoal, it was converted back again into metal; and charcoal, since it would burn away almost entirely, was held to be very rich in 'phlogiston'. The heating of the calx with charcoal had therefore restored enough 'phlogiston' to the calx to reconstitute the original metal. Thus a metal was a compound of its calx and 'phlogiston'; and the process of heating a metal to give it calx, called calcination, was a decomposition, a kind of combustion in which 'phlogiston' escaped from the metal.

It was known, on the other hand, that, when a metal was calcined, the weight of the residual calx or powder was greater than the original weight of the metal taken. But how could the weight increase, since something material, namely 'phlogiston', had been lost from the substance of the metal? In answer to this, some of the chemists who accepted the 'phlogiston' theory were driven to suppose that 'phlogiston' did not gravitate as other matter, but levitated—that it naturally rose upwards to the heavens whereas other substances naturally tended to fall to the earth—that it had a negative weight, as we might say."

(DOUGLAS MCKIE, "The Birth of Modern Chemistry") [5]

Antoine Lavoisier, the founder of modern chemistry, believed that air played an important part in combustion. He believed that in combustion things combine with air and that this explains why the calx has a greater weight. Lavoisier in a famous experiment succeeded in separating hydrogen and oxygen from the air. He noted that things would burn in the presence of oxygen but not with hydrogen. He then reasoned that when hydrogen burns it should, according to his theory, combine with oxygen. All attempts by Lavoisier and others failed until Cavendish found that when hydrogen burns, water is produced. After this experiment the phlogiston theory was gradually abandoned. (Also see the experiment described in exercise 6 of last chapter.)

There were attempts to modify the phlogiston theory in the face of these experiments. According to the modified theory, when metal is heated it turns to pure earth and its phlogiston goes into the air. The earth then combines with water from the air to form calx.

4. When the moon is on the horizon it looks much bigger than when it is high in the sky (zenith moon). However in photographs its image is the same size. This is also true of the image in the eye.

[5] Douglas McKie, "The Birth of Modern Chemistry," in *A Short History of Science* (Garden City, New York: Doubleday, 1958), pp. 70–71. Used by permission of Routledge and Kegan Paul, Ltd. and The Free Press of Glencoe, Inc.

Two explanations have been advanced for this: the apparent-distance theory and the angle-of-regard theory. According to the first theory, the moon looks bigger because it seems further away. Any object seen through filled space, such as the horizon moon, is perceived as being more distant than an object just as far away but seen through empty space, such as the zenith moon. It is well known that an observer perceiving two equal images and receiving sensory information that one object is farther away than the other, correctly sees the farther one to be larger. According to the second theory the moon looks smaller because the viewer raises his eyes or head to look at it.

Some years ago Edwin G. Boring subjected the apparent-distance theory to what he considered a critical test. He asked people to judge the relative distance of the zenith and horizon moons. Most said the horizon moon seemed nearer. He then had subjects match moons of the same size on a screen. Those they saw at eye level they said were larger.

In 1957 Lloyd Kaufman and Irvin Rock investigated the phenomenon. They devised an optical apparatus which simulated the moon against the sky. With the use of this instrument they found that the horizon moon looks larger whether or not the eyes are raised. The moon in the same region of the sky was the same whether or not the eyes were elevated. They concluded that Boring's findings on eye elevation were peculiar to the methods he employed.

In Kaufman and Rock's words: "We therefore turned to the apparent-distance theory. Boring had rejected it because his subjects said that the horizon moon appeared to be nearer than the zenith moon. But, we wondered, did they really see the horizon moon as nearer? Or were they judging it to be nearer precisely because it looked bigger, effectively turning the reasoning upside down? In that case the reported distance would be a secondary phenomenon, an artifact of the very illusion it was supposed to test. To check this possibility we showed our subjects pairs of artificial moons of different diameters and instructed them to compare their relative distances. Whenever the zenith moon was larger, the subjects said it was nearer than the horizon moon; when it was smaller, they said it was farther away."

Kaufman and Rock then made additional experiments to confirm that the horizon moon looks larger only because it is seen over terrain. After this they showed the moon looks larger when it is seen over a more distant horizon, and that the illusion increases with the degree of cloudiness. When the horizon was inverted, the moon looked smaller. They also found that the framing-effect one gets in cities enhances the size of the horizon moon. Last, they showed that color has no effect on the illusion.

Kaufman and Rock concluded from all this that they had "tested" the apparent-distance theory and "provided evidence that it is correct."

(Taken from Lloyd Kaufman and Irvin Rock, "The Moon Illusion") [6]

[6] Lloyd Kaufman and Irvin Rock, "The Moon Illusion," in *Scientific American*, Vol. 207, No. 1, July 1962. Reprinted with permission. Copyright © 1962 by Scientific American, Inc. All rights reserved.

EXERCISES 11

Again review exercises at the end of the last chapter and analyze them, in so far as possible, in the way the above were analyzed.

TRADITIONAL INDUCTIVE TECHNIQUES AND CORRECT INDUCTIVE ARGUMENTS

Induction by Enumeration

In the last chapter two forms of inferences commonly called inductive were described and discussed. Here are examples of the first kind of inference (A):

1. An A is B.
   Therefore all A's are B (or A is B).
2. A_1 is B.
   A_2 is B.
   .
   .
   .
   A_n is B.
   Therefore all A's are B (or A is B).

We have already seen an example of an inference like (1). Newton deduced from his theory of light that homogeneous light stays the same when passed through a prism. To test this Newton passed some homogeneous light through a prism, noted that it stayed the same, and concluded that homogeneous light stays the same when passed through a prism. His inference thus was:

3. The homogeneous light which was passed through the prism stayed the same.
   Therefore homogeneous light stays the same when passed through a prism.

As we can see, (3) has the form of (1). What makes this inference correct and prevents it from being an instance of the hasty generalization fallacy is this: First, Newton used a prism which did not have any peculiar properties which would have an effect on the homogeneity of the light. Second, the conditions under which the experiment took place were carefully controlled and exactly reproducible. Third, Newton took great care to make sure that the light *was* homogeneous. If Newton had not taken such care he never would have made the inference found in (3). Thus an inference of the form (1) is correct when such precautions are taken. No general rules, however, can be laid down for when sufficient care has been taken. What constitutes sufficient care depends on the particular situation and the nature of the generalization. In addition, only one who is experienced in the field and an expert in the subject matter is in position to make the judgment that sufficient care has been taken.

Arguments with form (1) are also employed in what is called sampling. When someone makes a judgment about a whole on the basis of what he knows about some part of the whole, this is often called *sampling*. When farmers take their wheat to the elevator the buyer has a problem in determining the quality of the whole truckload of wheat. The buyer may have his tester take a portion of grain from the front of the load, a portion from the back, one half way down, and two on each side from the bottom. The tester then dumps all of this into a sack, shakes it, and takes out a handful. The quality of the wheat is determined on the basis of this handful of wheat. The tester, as we can see, makes this inference:

4. The handful (*A*) is of quality X.
Therefore the whole load is of quality X.

This inference has the form of (1). Here again this inference is correct— if the procedure described above is followed. What prevents this from being an instance of the hasty generalization fallacy? The tester has taken care to make sure that the handful is representative of the whole. If he had not, if he had just reached in the truck and taken a handful and in- ferred the quality of the truck load from the quantity of the handful, then (4) would, possibly, be incorrect, since it is not an uncommon prac- tice to "stack" such loads. The single handful may not be representative of the quality of the load for other reasons. In general, sampling in- ferences which have the form of (1) are correct depending on whether *A* is representative of all *A*'s—in our example, whether the handful is representative of the truck load. However, what determines whether *A* is representative depends on the particular context or circumstance. No general rules can be laid down which allow the correct judgment that an *A* is representative, though, as we all know, handbooks are written which give such rules for particular subject matter, such as wheat sam- pling, population sampling, and so forth. These handbooks are written by men who have studied and have experience in the particular subject matter. In addition, it should be noted that the rules in these books contain explicit directions sufficiently detailed to insure that a good or fair sample is obtained regardless of the particular circumstances.

Arguments which have the second form above (2) are instances of what is generally called induction by enumeration. Though such arguments are frequently found in everyday life, they are not often found in science, especially the physical sciences. Ordinarily the scientist has taken sufficient care as Newton did so that the inference is like (1) rather than (2), or so that premises like those in (2) are used in conjunction with other kinds of premises from which it is concluded that A is B. The nature of these additional premises will be discussed in the next section.

The observation that A_1 is B, A_2 is B, and so on, or that when A_1 happens, B happens, and so on, often leads to the hypothesis that A's are B or A causes B or B causes A. For example, finding that person 1 who has lung cancer is a cigarette smoker, person 2 who has lung cancer is a cigarette smoker, and so forth, naturally suggests that cigarette smoking causes or is the important factor in the cause of lung cancer. The testing of this hypothesis, however, involves much more than finding more persons with lung cancer who smoke cigarettes. Some of the additional techniques employed in testing such a hypothesis will now be discussed.

Mill's Methods

The usual additional inductive techniques employed to establish (and sometimes discover) causal connections have come to be known as *Mill's methods*. They are called this because John Stuart Mill was one of the first to formulate them and give them names. Mill wrote that these inductive inferential methods were "the mode of discovery and proving laws of nature." Mill thought that the business of science was to discover the causes of things. He also thought that his methods were used to discover causal connections and to establish causal connections. The discovery of causes of things, however, is but one part of the activities of science. The primary theoretical aim of science is to explain phenomena. And, as we have argued, induction is not generally employed in the formation of explanations (see discussion of "inductivism" in last chapter). However, Mill's methods are sometimes employed in the discovery of causal connections or functional relations between two or more factors. In addition, and more important, they are generally employed to establish causal and functional connections, especially in the social sciences. Some commentators on Mill's writings believe that he had only the social sciences in mind when he formulated his methods. Here are Mill's five methods.

Method of Agreement

Imagine that there is some phenomenon P which interests us, and we would like to know its cause. Let the antecedent factors be represented by capital letters. And let "$\rightarrow$" express "is followed by." If we find:

$$A \ B \ C \to P$$
$$A \ D \ E \to P$$

this provides grounds, Mill says, for asserting that A is the cause of P.[7] Mill calls an inductive inference of this kind the *method of agreement*. Mill writes in this respect:

If two or more instances of the phenomenon under investigation have only one circumstance in common, the circumstance in which alone all the instances agree is the cause (or effect) of the given phenomenon.

(JOHN STUART MILL, *A System of Logic*)

The example Mill gives of the employment of this method is: [8]

Instances in which bodies assume a crystalline structure are found to have been preceded by instances which have in common only one antecedent, namely, the process of solidification from a fluid state. This antecedent, therefore, is the cause of the crystalline structure.

Method of Difference

If we find this:

$$A \ B \ C \to P$$
$$B \ C \to \text{not-}P$$

this provides grounds for our saying, Mill tells us, that A is the cause of P. Mill called this inference the *Method of Difference*. According to Mill:

If an instance in which the phenomenon under investigation occurs, and an instance in which it does not occur, have every circumstance in common save one, that one occurring only in the former; the circumstance in which alone the two instances differ is the effect, or the cause, or an indispensable part of the cause, of the phenomenon.

(MILL, *A System of Logic*)

Mill's example is: [9]

A man in the fullness of life is shot through the heart; he is wounded and dies. The wound is the only circumstance that is different; hence, his death is caused by the wound.

---

[7] All arguments which have premises which satisfy these "methods" are instances of inductions of the kind A, discussed in the last chapter. The use of the letters 'A', 'B', 'C', and 'D' in this and the following formulations of Mill's methods are not meant to suggest that just this many factors are involved. There may be more—or fewer.

[8] The phrasing of this example is taken from L. S. Stebbing, *A Modern Introduction to Logic*, 2nd ed. (London: Methuen, 1933), p. 334.

[9] The phrasing of this example is taken from Stebbing, *op. cit.*

Joint Method of Agreement and Difference

If we find this:

$A\ B \to P$
$A\ C \to P$
$B\ C \to$ not-P
$\quad B \to$ not-P
$\quad C \to$ not-P

we have grounds for saying A is the cause of P. Mill called this the *Method of Agreement and Difference*. And we can see why: the inductive inference involves both of the first two methods. He wrote:

> If two or more instances in which the phenomenon occurs have only one circumstance in common, while two or more instances in which it does not occur have nothing in common save the absence of that circumstance, the circumstance in which alone the two sets of instances differ is the effect, or the cause, or an indispensable part of the cause, of the phenomenon.

> (MILL, *A System of Logic*)

Method of Residues

Suppose we know that A, B, and C together is the cause of a, b, and c. Suppose by using the above techniques we find that A is the cause of a and B is the cause of b. This provides grounds, according to Mill, for saying that C is the cause of c. Mill calls this inference the *Method of Residues*. He writes:

> Subduct from any phenomenon such part as is known by previous inductions to be the effect of certain antecedents, and the residue of the phenomenon is the effect of the remaining antecedents.

> (MILL, *A System of Logic*)

Many commentators believe that the Method of Residues is in no sense an inductive method, even in the sense in which Mill usually understood this phrase.[10] Often this method is omitted in descriptions of Mill's methods.

Method of Concomitant Variations

Last, if some modification of, say, A without any modifications of B and C always results in a modification of P, this provides grounds for saying A is the cause of P. Mill calls this inference the *Method of Concomitant Variations*. He writes:

---

[10] Cf. Stebbing, *op. cit.*, p. 333.

Whatever phenomenon varies in any manner whenever another phenomenon varies in some particular manner, is either a cause or an effect of that phenomenon, or is connected with it through some fact of causation.

(MILL, *A System of Logic*)

Mill thought that this method was to be used to establish causal connections when the other four could not be used. He thought, for example, that to establish a causal relation between the earth's movement and the movement of a pendulum one must use this last method.

The inductive methods are illustrated in this simple, imagined example: Once upon a time a farmer noticed that where he had put manure earlier in the season, the plants were excellent (enumeration). Furthermore, he noticed that the crops were excellent in all of the various places on his land where he put the manure (method of agreement). He also noticed that in those places where he had not put manure the plants were not doing as well as in the manured places (method of difference). He concluded that manure is responsible for the excellent plants (method of agreement and difference). This judgment was further confirmed when he noticed that where the quality of the crops was high this was directly proportional with the amount of manure he had dropped (method of concomitant variations)—supposing, of course, he didn't drop too much.

Let us now examine two real-life examples in which Mill's inductive techniques are employed. In the first example the techniques are employed to support the claim that two factors are causally related, while in the second example the methods are employed to disprove such a connection.

Mill's techniques are employed from time to time to test deductions from theoretical hypotheses. Pascal's testing of a deduction from the "sea of air" theory, discussed in the last chapter, employed such techniques. From the "sea of air" hypothesis it followed that the pressure of the air diminishes as we rise. The barometer measures the pressure of air. Thus we should find that mercury in a barometer goes down as the barometer is raised in its altitude. To test this, he employed (1) induction by enumeration, (2) the method of difference, and (3) the method of concomitant variation.

First he found:

1. A_1 (climbing up the mountain) $\rightarrow D$ (dropping of mercury in barometer)
   $A_2 \rightarrow D$
   .
   .
   .
   $A_5 \rightarrow D$

Second, Pascal had friends watching a barometer at the side of the mountain while his brother-in-law made the climbs. He found this:

2. $A B C P$ (shared conditions) → D

    $B C P$ → not-D

Finally, the brother-in-law noticed that the mercury changed as he climbed, that is:

3. Changes in A → changes in D

From (1), (2), and (3) Pascal concluded that mercury in a barometer goes down as the barometer is raised.

Here is the second example. An economist, Dr. Luigi Laurenti, conducted studies of the relation of property value to racial integration in housing. The purpose of this study was to find out if this widely held belief is true: property values fall significantly when Negro or other nonwhite families move into a previously all-white neighborhood. The first paragraph below, taken from a magazine article on Dr. Laurenti's work, summarizes a 1961 study; the rest of the passage, also taken from the article, concerns a study in 1955.[11]

> Dr. Laurenti analyzed over a five-year period the sales of 10,000 homes in San Francisco, Oakland, and Philadelphia. As Negroes, Japanese, Chinese, Filipino, or Mexican families began moving into a white neighborhood, Dr. Laurenti went to work. First, he selected another neighborhood as similar as possible to the first one, with the exception that it never did become integrated. Then he amassed facts and figures on the values of the homes in both areas for the period of a year before the first minority family moved in to a point five years later. After comparing the prices in both neighborhoods, Dr. Laurenti found: In 40% of the comparisons, there was *no* difference in property values before and after the neighborhood became integrated; in 45% of the comparisons, property values *rose* anywhere from 5 to 26%; in only 15% of the cases did property values drop, and then only by 5 to 9%.

....

> In 1955 with the help of expert appraisers and brokers in the areas to be studied, he carefully matched all-white areas with racially mixed areas of up to 70% non-white populations. A total of 39 neighborhoods were compared to discover price differences. And, as mentioned earlier, sales data were collected for a period well before the first non-white family moved in, as well as for several years after mixed occupancy. Let's take a closer look at one of the test neighborhoods studied.

> Oceanview, in San Francisco, is typical. Until January, 1948 this was an all-white neighborhood. Oceanview covers 20 blocks in the Ocean Avenue district near San Francisco's southern city limits. Except for some light commercial de-

---

[11] Joanne Gemar, "Property Values and Race" in *The Californian*, June 1962, pp. 14–15. Copyright 1962, *The Californian*. Used by permission.

velopment along one main street, the use of land is entirely residential. The 600 homes are mostly single-family, owner-occupied. They are mostly of frame construction, with exteriors finished in stucco, and have five rooms. It generally is a younger neighborhood, 70 per cent of its homes having been built since 1940. The homes have been well kept by their owners, many of whom are of Irish and Italian backgrounds.

Dr. Laurenti then located another neighborhood closely comparable to Ocean-view in all of the important price-determining respects, except that it has remained all white. In choosing Sunnyside, which is a short way northeast of Oceanview, he found some increase in size—30 blocks with 850 homes—but no significant difference. In the age, type and market value of the homes, in the general topography and pattern of land use, in the relationship to the center of the city, shopping areas and transportation facilities, in the income class and social status class of the occupants, Oceanview and Sunnyside were very much alike.

After the first non-whites, a Negro family, moved into Oceanview in January, 1948, others followed suit. By the end of the year there were 10 Negro families. Several years later Negro occupancy had reached 100 families (about 18% of the population of Oceanview).

Both Oceanview and Sunnyside rose steadily in value during the 24-quarter observation period. At the beginning, houses were selling in Oceanview for $10,112, in Sunnyside for $9,747. Six years later homes in Oceanview were selling for $11,446, an increase of 13.2%. At the same time, Sunnyside homes were selling for $10,865, an increase of 11.5%. So, there was no appreciable difference. Neither the fact of Negro occupancy nor the extent of their moving in seemed to affect real estate values.

One after another, the other 37 neighborhoods studied revealed the same conclusions. And it remained true whether the number of non-whites stayed low, around 3% of the population, or whether it became heavy, up to 70%.

In the 1961 study the hypothesis is tested by employing the methods of difference and agreement. If the hypothesis were true, then Dr. Laurenti should find:

1. San Francisco neighborhood: *I* (integration) → *LPV* (lower property values)
   Oakland neighborhood: *I* → *LPV*
   Etc.

(Since each of the communities differed, (1) would be an application of the method of agreement.)

2. Neighborhood 1: *I A B C* (factors in common) → *LPV*
   Neighborhood 2: not-*I A B C* → not-*LPV*

But, as we see, practically no detrimental effect on property values resulted, and most of the time a rise in values took place. That is, (1) and (2) were not found to be the case.

In the second study the methods of difference and agreement are used in the same way with the same results. For example, if the hypothesis were true, then we would expect:

3. Oceanview: *I A B C* (significant factors in common) → *LPV*
   Sunnyside: Not-*I A B C* → not-*LPV*

As Dr. Laurenti reported, this was not found to be the case. In addition, no relation was found between the increase of minority families and property values. If there were a connection, then it is likely that concomitant variation should have been seen—that is, property values should have decreased as the number of minority families increased.

Mistakes can obviously occur in employing these deductive techniques. Employing one, two, or all the methods does not necessarily insure that the conclusion is established. For example there is the story of the scientific drinker who on:

Monday, drinks scotch and soda → being drunk
Tuesday, drinks bourbon and soda → being drunk
Wednesday, drinks rum and soda → being drunk

.

.

.

.

and concludes that it is the soda he must quit drinking if he is to keep from being drunk. The drinker has here employed the method of agreement and has mistakenly concluded that the soda is the cause of his being drunk. If he had employed the method of difference he would not have made this mistake. Sometimes, however, the employment of several inductive methods can lead to mistakes. For example, the story is told that in the New Hebrides the natives believe that lice keep a person healthy. They observe that almost all healthy natives have lice, whereas sick natives generally do not have lice. As we can see, they employ both simple enumeration and the method of difference and agreement. The arrow here means "concomitant with."

1. Person 1: *L* (lice) → *H* (good health)

   .

   .

   .

   Person *n*: *L* → *H*
2. Person 1: *L A B C* → *H*
   Person 2:   *A B C* → not-*H*
3. Person 1: *L A B C* → *H*
   Person 2: *L D E F* → *H*

(where $A, B, C, \ldots$ would be things such as age, sex, weight, diet, occupation, living conditions, and the like). From (1), (2), and (3) they conclude that lice keep a person healthy. As we can easily see, they have committed the false cause fallacy. The presence of lice is not the cause of health; rather, lice, being leaches, naturally survive best on healthy hosts. The mistake the natives make is thinking in (2) that all the relevant factors to health are the same except L, or that there is no common relevant factor other than L in (3).

Suppose in the Oceanview-Sunnyside example some factor was present in Sunnyside that was not in Oceanview, and this factor caused the Sunnyside values not to rise as they would have if it had not been there. For example, suppose property taxes for some reason were greatly increased in Sunnyside. Under these conditions one would be unjustified in concluding that I had no effect on LPV from the findings that:

Oceanview: $I\ A\ B\ C \rightarrow \text{not-}LPV$
Sunnyside: $\text{not-}I\ A\ B\ C \rightarrow \text{not-}LPV$

where, as we remember, $A\ B\ C$ stand for such things as age, type, and market value of the homes, topography and pattern of land, relationship to the center of city, shopping areas, and so forth. Dr. Laurenti, as we saw, took precautions against such a mistake. First, he took care to see that no such factor was present. In addition, he studied not one pair but a number of pairs of such communities.

This naturally raises these questions: How can one tell that all *possible* relevant factors are the same in using the method of difference; how can one tell, when using the method of agreement, that there is no common relevant factor but the one in question; and so forth? Here again no general rules can be set down. What is relevant will depend on the particular case. And knowledge of what is relevant in the particular case comes as a result of training, study, and experience. Thus the employment of Mill's techniques does not insure that an inductive inference is correct. A correct inference results not only from the employment of the techniques, but also from proper consideration of the relevant factors. Without the relevant factors being properly considered, the employment of the techniques is not grounds for assurance that the inductive inference is correct.

SUMMARY

Induction by enumeration and Mill's four (or five) inductive techniques are often employed to test empirical hypotheses and observable consequences of theoretical hypotheses. These inductive methods result in correct inferences when proper consideration is paid to relevant factors. No general rules can be set down for determining these factors, though experts can and have laid down directions for particular subject matters.

EXERCISES III

What inductive methods are employed in the following passages?
Are inductive methods employed in the discovery of any hypothesis?
Are any of the conclusions not established by the inductive techniques employed?

1. Christian Eijkman, a Dutch doctor, originally thought that beri-beri is caused by a bacillus. He had noticed, however, that the hens in the courtyard of the prison at which he worked acted as did the human prisoners who had beri-beri. That prompted the thought; could the hens' illness and that of the prisoners have the same cause? For the two had one thing in common: their food. The prisoners were fed almost entirely on polished rice and the hens lived on what the prisoners threw out of their barred windows into the yard. Eijkman next inquired how things were in other prisons, and found that some had many cases of beri-beri and others scarcely any. And what about the diet, was that the same? No. In the prisons with much beri-beri it was the same as in that of which Eijkman was in charge: polished rice. In those with few or no cases, the prisoners were given unpolished rice, which was cheaper. Thus, the actual discovery was made.

Eijkman published a report of his observations. This attracted little attention, so he continued experimenting with animals to test his ideas. He took two lots of hens; to one he gave husked rice, to the other unhusked rice. The hens that had the husked rice contracted that same nervous paralysis he had seen before; the others remained healthy.

The next question Eijkman had to ask himself was: what is the difference between polished and unpolished rice? The silvery husk that the merchant removed to make the rice look more attractive and enable him to charge a higher price also contained the germ of the rice-grain; thus in this germ or husk there must be some stuff, the lack of which caused beri-beri in those fed exclusively on such rice. This important conclusion went unheeded until, years later, a young Pole, Kasimir Funk, learned of it, dug out the reports and experimented on pigeons. He succeeded in extracting from the rice husks those substances of whose presence Eijkman had been convinced, and which could prevent beri-beri. Thus he proved that Eijkman was right. Funk called these substances vitamins.

(Adapted from HUGO GLASER, *The Road to Modern Surgery*) [12]

[12] Hugo Glaser, *The Road to Modern Surgery*, Maurice Michael, trans. (New York: Dutton, 1962).

2. In a New York experiment several drab wooden telephone booths in a ferry terminal were replaced by new aluminum and glass booths. Revenue doubled. From this it was concluded that the booths tempt people to stop and telephone on impulse.

3. In the period from the early 1920's to 1960 the consumption of tobacco products in the United States rose about 30 per cent. Significantly, the rise was due to the use of cigarettes. The use of tobacco in other forms actually declined. During this same period death rates from all infectious diseases declined rapidly except for the death rate from lung cancer. Deaths from lung cancer in the United States climbed from 4,000 in 1935 to 36,000 in 1960. Painstaking studies have clearly shown that the increase in lung cancer is real and not attributable to improved diagnosis.

It was known for some time that lung cancer could result from prolonged and heavy occupational exposure to certain industrial dusts and vapors. This led to the hypothesis that the increase in lung cancer was due to increased exposure of the human population to air contamination of some sort. The factor involved had to be widespread and not confined to any particular occupational group. (In all countries with adequate mortality statistics lung cancer was found to have increased.) Three factors that met the requirements were: fumes from the combustion of solid and liquid fuels, dust from asphalt roads and the tires of motor vehicles, and cigarette smoking.

A number of studies were made comparing the smoking habits of lung cancer patients with the smoking habits of individuals free of the disease. The findings in all the investigations were remarkably similar. Lung cancer is an extremely rare cause of death among nonsmokers, except for those who have had prolonged and heavy occupational exposure to certain dusts and fumes. The death rate from lung cancer was very low for men who had never smoked, it increased with the amount of cigarette smoking, and it was very high for men who smoked two or more packs of cigarettes a day. For those who smoked 40 or more cigarettes per day the death rate from lung cancer per 100,000 man-years was 214.3. 143.9 was the figure for those who smoked 20 to 39 cigarettes a day, and 3.4 for those who never smoked. It was also found that the relative death rate from all causes increases with the degree of inhalation from cigarettes.

(Adapted from E. CUYLER HAMMOND, "The Effects of Smoking") [13]

4. In the part of William Wells' investigations which are related, in his words, below, he used little bundles of wool weighing 10 grains each for collecting dew.

"I now proceed to relate the influence which several differences in the situation have upon the production of dew.

"One general fact relative to the situation is, that whatever diminishes the view of the sky, as seen from the exposed body, occasions the quantity of dew, which is formed upon it, to be less than would have occurred if the exposure to the sky had been complete.

[13] E. Cuyler Hammond, "The Effects of Smoking," in *Scientific American,* Vol. 207, No. 1, July 1962.

"Experiment with elevated board—I placed, on several clear and still nights, 10 grains of wool upon the middle of a painted board, . . . elevated 4 feet above the grass-plot, by means of four slender wooden props of equal height; and at the same time I attached, loosely, 10 grains of wool to the middle of its under side. The two parcels were, consequently, only an inch asunder, and were equally exposed to the action of the air. Upon one night, however, I found that the upper parcel had gained 14 grains in weight, but the lower only 4. On a second night, the quantities of moisture, acquired by like parcels of wool, in the same situations as in the first experiment, were 19 and 6 grains; on a third, 11 and 2; on a fourth, 20 and 4, the smaller quantity being always that which was gained by the wool attached to the lower side of the board.

"Experiment with hollow cylinder—I placed, upright, on the grass-plot, a hollow cylinder of baked clay, the height of which was $2\frac{1}{2}$ feet, and diameter 1 foot. On the grass, surrounded by the cylinder, were laid 10 grains of wool, which, in this situation, as there was not the least wind, would have received as much rain as a like quantity of wool fully exposed to the sky. But the quantity of moisture obtained by the wool surrounded by the cylinder was only a little more than 2 grains, while that acquired by 10 grains of fully exposed wool was 16. . . .

"Other varieties of situation—Dew, however, will in consequence of other varieties of situation, form in very different quantities, upon substances of the same kind, although these should be similarly exposed to the sky.

"(1) In the first place, it is requisite, for the most abundant formation of dew, that the substance attracting it *should rest on a stable horizontal body of some extent.* Thus, upon one night, while 10 grains of wool, laid upon the raised board, increased 20 grains in weight, an equal quantity, suspended in the open air, $5\frac{1}{2}$ feet above the ground, increased only 11 grains, notwithstanding that it presented a greater surface to the air than the other parcel. On another night, 10 grains of wool gained on the raised board 19 grains, but the same quantity suspended in the air, on a level with the board, only 13; and a third, 10 grains of wool acquired, on the same board, $2\frac{1}{2}$ grains of weight, during the time in which other 10 grains, hung in the air, at the same height, acquired only half a grain."

In other experiments, Wells varied the substances on which the wool lay and in still others placed the wool in various positions during different weather conditions.

(WILLIAM WELLS)

5. Puzzled by the fact that hens were refractory to anthrax, he (Pasteur) wondered whether this might not be explained by their body temperature, which is higher than that of animals susceptible to this disease. To test his hypothesis, he innoculated hens with anthrax bacilli and placed them in a cold bath to lower their body temperature. Animals so treated died the next day, showing numerous bacilli in their blood and organs. Another hen was similarly infected and maintained in the cold bath until the disease was in full progress, and then taken out of the water, dried, wrapped, and placed under conditions that

allowed rapid return to normal body temperature. *Mirabile dictu,* this hen made a complete recovery. Thus, a mere fall of a few degrees in body temperature was sufficient to render birds almost as receptive to anthrax as were rabbits or guinea pigs.

(RENE DUBOS, *Pasteur and Modern Science*) [14]

6. In the spring of 1881 a veterinarian named Rossignol succeeded in enlisting the support of many farmers of the Brie district, near Paris, to finance a large-scale test of anthrax immunization.

In the experiment twenty-four sheep, one goat, and six cows were innoculated on May 5 with five drops of a living attenuated culture of anthrax bacillus. This is vaccination—a technique for specifically increasing the resistance of the body to an inimical agent. On May 17 all these animals had been re-vaccinated with a second dose of a less-attenuated culture. On May 31 all the immunized animals were infected with a highly virulent anthrax culture, and the same culture was injected as well into twenty-nine normal animals: twenty-four sheep, one goat, and four cows. When Pasteur arrived on the field on the second day of June he was greeted with loud acclamation. All the vaccinated sheep were well. Twenty-one of the control sheep and the single goat were dead of anthrax, two other control sheep died in front of the spectators, and the last unprotected sheep died at the end of the day. The six vaccinated cows were well and showed no symptoms, whereas the four control cows had extensive swelling at the site of inoculation and febrile reactions. The triumph was complete.

(RENE DUBOS, *Pasteur and Modern Science*) [15]

7. I observed that plants not only have a faculty to correct bad air in six or ten days by growing in it, as the experiments of Dr. Priestly indicate, but that they perform this important office in a complete manner in a few hours; that this wonderful operation is by no means owing to the vegetation of the plant, but to the influence of the light of the sun upon the plant. . . . I found that this operation of the plants is more or less brisk in proportion to the clearness of the day and the exposition of the plants; diminishes towards the close of the day, and ceases entirely at sunset; that this office is not performed by the whole plant, but only by the leaves and the green stalks. . . .

(JAN INGEN-HOUSZ, 1779)

8. Infants at a nursery in a home for delinquent girls and infants in a foundling home were studied. The nursery over a period of time produced normal healthy children, while the foundling home produced children whose development was greatly retarded, who were very susceptible to infection and illness of every kind, and whose mental health deteriorated rapidly while at the foundling home. The infant mortality rate at the foundling home was extremely

14 *Op. cit.,* pp. 138–139.
15 *Ibid.,* pp. 118–119.

high compared to that of the nursery. Dr. Spitz noted the similarities and differences in the environments and treatment of the two groups of infants.

Similarities:

1. Housing condition—much the same—large, pleasant quarters.
2. Food—in both institutions excellent.
3. Clothing—practically the same.
4. Medical care—in the home the children were regularly visited by a physician; in the nursery the children received professional care only when they appeared to need it.
5. Background—the background of the delinquent girls was probably worse than that of the mothers of the children in the home. The latter were often normal women who were unable to support their children. On admission, however, roughly the same level of health was enjoyed by each group of babies.

Differences:

1. Toys—the children in the nursery were provided with more than those in the home—the latter often had none.
2. Visual Radius—in the nursery the children can see through the windows, other children, etc. In the home the cribs were enclosed by sheets on three sides—the other faced a featureless corridor.
3. Radius of Locomotion—in both cases this consists of the bed, which is adequate for an infant. But in the home, owing to a lack of stimulation, apparently, the babies lie supine for many months and a hollow is worn into their mattress, inhibiting their movements.
4. Personnel—in the home there is a head nurse and five assistant nurses for forty-five babies. Each is competent, conscientious, and is a "baby-loving" woman, but each baby has the attention of a nurse only about one-eighth of the time it is awake. In the nursery each child is cared for by his own mother. And due to the nature of penal institutions of this kind, the baby provides the sole outlet of the mother's affection and is the only source of prestige, and so on, so that even more care and attention is given to these babies than babies normally receive.

(It seems evident from these observations, that the continuous care that a mother normally provides her baby, and the nature of that care is of essential importance in the mental and physical health of an infant.)

(RENE SPITZ, *The Psychoanalytic Study of the Child*) [16]

[16] An account of observations of Dr. Rene Spitz in *The Psychoanalytic Study of the Child*, Vol. 1, 1945.

Chapter Eighteen

PATTERNS OF SCIENTIFIC EXPLANATIONS

As was indicated earlier, the primary theoretical function of scientific activity is the explanation of phenomena. In the first part of this chapter are found six examples of scientific explanations. Our interest will be to see in what way they are similar and in what way they differ from each other. In the last part of the chapter we will see how these six examples of genuine scientific explanations differ from explanations which appear to be scientific but which on analysis can be seen to be pseudoscientific explanations. The reader should not judge that the six examples exhaust the *kinds* of explanations found in the sciences.

We will find it useful to refer to what is explained as the *explicandum* and refer to the statements which function as the explanation as the *explicans*. Thus, according to this convention, the parts of an explanation are:

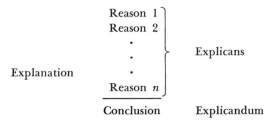

$$
\text{Explanation}
\begin{cases}
\left.
\begin{array}{l}
\text{Reason } 1 \\
\text{Reason } 2 \\
\quad . \\
\quad . \\
\quad . \\
\text{Reason } n
\end{array}
\right\} \text{Explicans} \\
\overline{\text{Conclusion} \qquad \text{Explicandum}}
\end{cases}
$$

DEDUCTIVE EXPLANATIONS

A *deductive explanation* is one in which the explicandum is a logically necessary consequence of the explicans. This type of explanation is commonly regarded as the ideal form of explanation when the explicans contains universal generalizations. Thus it is thought by many that efforts should be made to make all explanations in science conform to this ideal.

In (1) and (2) below are found two explanations[1] which accord with this ideal, though certain trivial assumptions would have to be formulated so that the explicandum in each would be a formal logical consequence of the explicans. In these two examples we find what are called *universal generalizations* in each of the explicans. For example, in (1) the explicans fully formulated would contain this statement: All the planets revolve around the sun. In (2) we find Galileo's empirical law concerning falling bodies—$D = AT^2/2$—and Newton's theoretical law—the change of motion is proportional to the motive force impressed and is made in the direction of the right line in which that force is impressed. As we can see, Galileo's law states something about how *all* falling bodies will always behave, and Newton's law does the same for moving bodies.

1. According to the Ptolemaic view of the solar system (the dominant view in the Middle Ages), the Earth, Venus, and the Sun were thought to be related in this way:

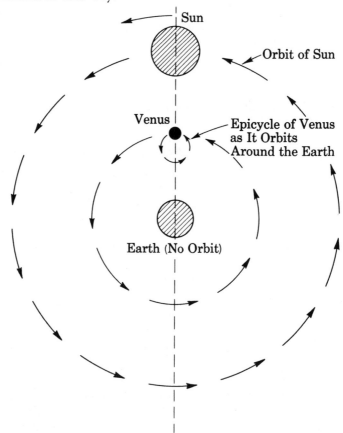

---

[1] For a fuller treatment of these explanations, see I. Bernard Cohen's *The Birth of a New Physics* (New York: Anchor Books, 1960), p. 81 f., p. 117 f.

The center of the epicycle orbit of Venus was thought to be permanently aligned between the center of the Earth and the center of the Sun. Venus thus would move around the Earth with the Sun.

In 1609 Galileo heard a report about an instrument called the telescope and succeeded in constructing "so excellent an instrument that objects seen by means of it appeared nearly one thousand times larger and over thirty times closer than when regarded with our natural vision." He turned the instrument toward the heavens and made a number of discoveries which dealt a death blow to the Ptolemaic system and supported the Copernican system (which maintained among other things that the planets, including Earth, orbited around the Sun).

One such discovery was that Venus exhibits phases. That is, at one time Venus appears as a complete circle, then it is seen as a crescent, then a half circle, and then a crescent, and so forth. The phases can be illustrated as follows:

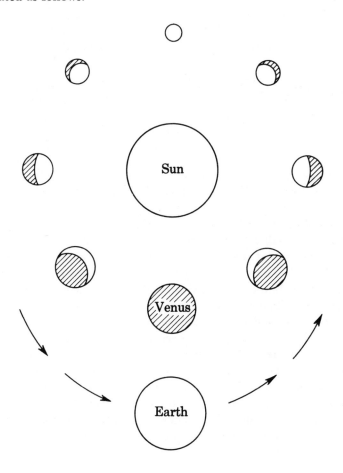

In addition the disc displays different sizes during the phases—largest at phase 5, smallest at 1 and 9.

What would explain these phases of Venus? As one can see, the Ptolemaic picture of the relation between the Earth, Venus, and the Sun does not explain it. In fact Galileo's discovery is in conflict with this system. The phases predicted from the Ptolemaic system are these:

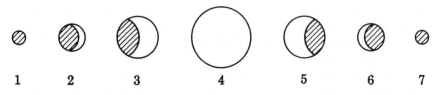

with 4 being the largest and 1 and 7 the smallest. Venus would not display a complete sequence of phases to observers on the Earth. However since the Earth and Venus both orbited around the Sun with Venus (Venus, of course, completing its orbit sooner than the Earth) between the Earth and the Sun, these phases would be predicted:

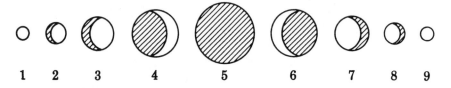

This corresponds to Galileo's observation. Copernicus' hypothesis thus explains the observed phases of Venus, whereas the Ptolemaic hypothesis does not.

2.   If a sailing ship is standing still and a stone is dropped from the top of a mast, it will fall to the foot of the mast. Will the stone fall to the foot of the mast if the stone is dropped while the ship is moving at a constant speed? Many would say it would fall somewhere behind the foot of the mast. If the ship were moving very fast it would fall farther behind the mast than if it were moving slowly. However, this does not happen; the stone will fall to the foot of the mast no matter what the speed of the ship is, so long as its speed is constant. Why is this?

Here briefly is the explanation which Newton gave: According to the law of inertia, every body preserves its state of rest, or uniform motion, unless it is compelled to change that state by an external force. The stone at the moment of release was traveling at the speed the ship was—let us imagine, ten feet a second. If the stone continued on a straight line and did not fall, it would be related to the ship in this way:

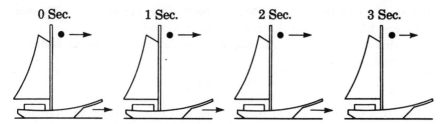

According to Newton's second law of motion, if a force is to slow down the speed of the stone it must act from the direction opposite to the one in which the stone is moving:

In the case of the stone dropped from the mast, resistance from the air is such a force, but its effects are negligible. The stone, however, is a free falling body and the force of gravity will pull it toward the earth's center. But since this force does not act in the direction that the stone is moving, but is, rather, perpendicular to the path of the stone, it will not affect its forward motion. Thus no matter how high the mast is, and no matter how fast the ship is traveling, if the ship is traveling at a constant speed, the stone will land at the same place it would if the ship were standing still.

What in essence has happened here is that from two laws of motion this general statement was seen to follow: "Objects dropped from a body (onto the same body) moving uniformly will hit the same place they would if the body were standing still." If a few trivial assumptions were made explicit, the explanation would be seen to have this form:

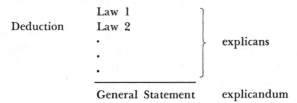

This general statement was thought of in terms of an example—the ship, mast, and stone—for clarity.

Let us suppose that in a particular case a stone dropped from a 114 feet high mast on a ship hits the foot of that mast. The ship, let us suppose, is traveling at a constant speed of ten feet a second. The stone hits the foot of the mast in three seconds. One might ask, "Why does the stone hit the foot of the mast in three seconds?"

Galileo discovered that the distance covered by free falling bodies is computed by this law:

$$D = \tfrac{1}{2}AT^2,$$

where D is distance, A is 32 ft./sec., and T is time. Taking this law plus the law of inertia and the second law of motion together with what are called initial conditions—the mast is 114 feet high, the ship is traveling at a constant speed of ten feet a second, and so on—it could be deduced that the stone would hit the foot of the mast in three seconds. To diagram the application of these laws:

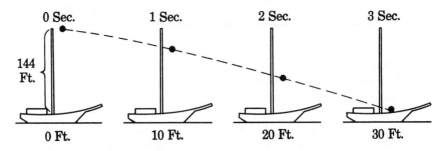

The form of the explanation would be this:

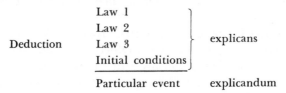

In this example the question "Why?" was asked of a particular event, and the answer took the form of a deduction from laws and a statement of initial conditions, such as, "the ship is traveling at a constant speed of ten feet a second," and "the mast is 114 feet high." If we had started with the laws and initial conditions and deduced this particular event, this would be an example of a *prediction*.

PROBABILISTIC EXPLANATIONS

Many explanations in the sciences are not deductive explanations. These nondeductive explanations are sometimes called *probabilistic explanations*. Generally such explanations take this form:

Probabilistic generalities Statements of initial conditions	explicans
Singular statement	explicandum

A singular statement treats of some particular event, person, and so on. A *probabilistic generality* is a generality which is not stated with strict universality but has forms such as: 'Most X's are Y's' or 'Generally X is Y'. Probabilistic generalities *can* occur in deductive explanations since the distinction between deductive and probabilistic explanations is a distinction based on the way the explicans is related to the explicandum.[2] In a probabilistic explanation the relation is nondeductive. The distinction between probabilistic and deductive explanations has nothing to do with whether the explanation is true or just "probable," as this word is commonly used.

Such a probabilistic explanation will now be considered. It is an explanation of this event: the disappearance of many competing daily newspapers between 1920 and 1962.

In 1920 there were 552 cities with competing daily newspapers. In 1962 there were fewer than 60. Why has this happened? Ben Bagdikian, the chief Washington correspondent of *The Providence Journal,* gave this explanation: [3] The greatest part of the total cost of the daily papers is paid for not by their readers, who barely support the cost of delivery, but by advertisers, who pay 75 to 80 per cent of the total. The prime concern of the advertiser is the cost of getting one line of advertising into the hands of one reader. Thus they will generally advertise with the paper which charges attractive rates. Since the cost of production is about the same, normally, for a large paper as it is for a small paper (the big cost is in the composing room), the larger papers can give lower rates. This results in money flowing to the larger papers without collusion, etc. The result is an almost irresistible trend to monopoly which explains the fact that in 1920 there were 552 cities with competing dailies while today there are fewer than 60.

This explanation can be distilled even further as follows:

Generally between 1920–62 advertisers' money has gone to the larger papers. Generally if a paper cannot get advertisers it cannot survive. The smaller papers have generally not gotten the advertisers' dollar.	explicans
Smaller papers died between 1920–62.	explicandum

[2] For a further discussion of these points, see Chapter Nineteen, pages 441–445. Some laws in science are probabilistic generalities.

[3] Cf. Ben Bagdikian, "Why Dailies Die" in *The New Republic,* Vol. 146, April 1962.

Note that this explicandum is not a deductive consequence of these probabilistic generalizations (or of other appropriate probabilistic or singular statements which we might add to the explicans).

HISTORICAL EXPLANATIONS

In the following example a particular event which happened in the past is explained—the U.S.S.R. built during a particular space of time only a fraction of the nuclear delivery system which they could have built. The explanation, as we will see, takes the form of explaining the *reasons* or motives the leaders of the U.S.S.R. had in doing this.

In 1961 Robert McNamara, the Secretary of Defense of the United States, said the United States nuclear strike force consisted of 17,000 intercontinental bombers, 1,000 medium range bombers, several dozen operational ICBM's, 80 Polaris missiles in submarines, 300 carrier aircraft armed with nuclear war heads, and 1,000 land-based supersonic fighters with nuclear war heads. Semiofficial estimates from Washington gave the U.S.S.R. some 50 ICBM's, 150 intercontinental bombers, and some 400 medium range bombers which cannot cover the United States as the United States nonintercontinental aircraft can cover Russia.

According to a statement of Senator Stuart Symington, the U.S.S.R. in 1961 had only 3.5 per cent of the number of ICBM's predicted in 1956 and only 19 per cent of the bomber strength predicted in 1956. If the U.S.S.R. had the capacity to build such a large nuclear delivery system, why, up to late 1961, had it built such a small system (supposing the semiofficial figures and Senator Symington's sources are correct)?

P. M. S. Blackett, a British physicist and military analyst, provided this *possible* explanation: [4] Blackett says that to understand the possible motives behind Soviet defense policy it is necessary to consider the history of the growth of nuclear weapon power. From 1947 to 1954, during the period of the United States monopoly or overwhelming numerical superiority, the United States defense policy was to destroy Soviet cities in the event of a war. From the U.S.S.R.'s point of view, land forces were the only available counter to this. "The answer to the threat of nuclear attack was the threat of taking over Europe on the ground." The United States strategy of massive retaliation became less and less plausible as the Soviet nuclear stockpile grew. You cannot threaten an enemy with a nuclear attack when you know he can level an attack against you. The

[4] Cf. P. M. S. Blackett, "Steps Toward Disarmament" in *Scientific American*, Vol. 206, No. 34, April 1962.

advent of the ICBM, which is difficult to destroy in flight, increased the stalemate. Two contrasting military theories evolved in response to this situation. The first was minimum deterrence, that is, the possession of a force adequate only for retaliatory attack and highly invulnerable to a first strike attack because of being either underground or hidden. The second was maximum deterrence (or counterforce), that is, the development of a force which could wipe out an enemy without his being able to retaliate substantially, so that if it ever became obvious that an attack was imminent, an attack could be launched before the aggressor's attack. Since, for one thing, the U.S.S.R. could disperse and keep secret its ICBM bases, and since an enormous military bill is a burden for a developing country like the U.S.S.R., they followed the first theory and produced a fraction of the delivery system they could have produced.

Blackett's explanation can be summarized as follows:

> The Soviet leaders believed that a minimum deterrent force, given the vastness of their land and secrecy, would provide an adequate deterrent and be less a burden on the economy than a maximum deterrent force.

> Therefore during 1956–61 the U.S.S.R. built only a fraction of the nuclear delivery system which they could have built.

This explanation is a historical explanation. And since the explicans gives the reasons why a person or persons acted in a certain way, it is often called a *reason-explanation.*

An issue of importance and interest raised concerning historical explanations is: Do historical explanations contain implicit assumptions dealing with probabilistic generalities? No explicitly stated probabilistic generality is to be found in the above historical explanation. However, those who see such generalities implicit in such explanations would argue that a statement like the following is supposed in the explicans: Generally when people believe a plan is possible and the alternatives to it involve burdens not involved in this plan (and some such plan must be followed), people choose this plan. If such generalities are implicit, then reason-explanations in history would have a closer similarity to the earlier examples than they would have without such generalities.

Not all historical explanations or explanations in the other social sciences, for example, sociology and economics, deal with the reasons for a person or persons doing some act. Often, to take one example, the social scientist is interested in the causes which led up to some state of affairs, for example, the Renaissance, or some particular event, for example, the stock market drop on Blue Monday.

FUNCTIONAL EXPLANATIONS

In the human blood stream there are about 7,000 white blood cells (the leucocytes and the lymphocytes). The leucocytes are formed in the red bone marrow in the same regions where red cells arise. They are constantly being formed and disintegrated. Why does the blood contain leucocytes? When they are markedly reduced in number an individual becomes quite susceptible to infections. Great reduction in numbers is fatal. Their primary function is thus to defend the body against infection. They defend against infection by engulfing and destroying the invading organic particles.

In this example the question was asked: Why are there leucocytes in the blood? To ask this question, in this context, is to ask for the *function* of leucocytes in the blood. In turn, to ask for their function in this context is to ask for their role in maintaining life in the human body. Or, to put it another way, given a system S (the human body) and a state B (the state of being a living organism), in asking for the function of X (leucocytes) we want to know how X is related to maintaining S in state B.

There are three interesting aspects of functional explanations. First, to give a functional explanation for some X, one must be able to describe both S and B. Second, since in areas other than biology (even in physics) one is able to describe S's and the corresponding B's, functional explanations for X's can be given in other sciences. Third, functional explanations are, ordinarily, genuine explanations. (The notion of a "genuine explanation" is discussed in the next section.)

EMPATHETIC EXPLANATIONS

Here is what is now generally regarded as the classic example of an empathetic or, as it is sometimes called, a meaningful explanation: Max Weber in his book *The Protestant Ethic and the Spirit of Capitalism*, makes the observation that "business leaders and owners of capital, as well as the higher grades of skilled labour, and even more the higher technically and commercially trained personnel of modern enterprises, are overwhelmingly Protestant." [5] He then employs Mill's Methods and concludes that the explanation for this is to be sought, not only in the

---

[5] Max Weber, *The Protestant Ethic and the Spirit of Capitalism*, tran. Talcott Parsons (London, G. Allen & Unwin, 1930), p. 35.

historico-politico-economic situations, but in the character of Protestant beliefs.

Weber begins his explanation by analyzing the attitude toward life or philosophy of life which those men have who are responsible for modern capitalism. He calls this attitude toward life "the Spirit of Capitalism." According to Weber, the spirit of capitalism is, first, the attitude that it is one's duty or ethical obligation to increase his profits; second, the attitude that profits are an end in themselves (at least in this life), that is, they are no longer sought as a means for satisfaction of material needs or for leisure; and, last, the attitude which seeks profits rationally, systematically, and legally. We can easily see how men with this attitude toward life would direct their activity toward money-making.

He then analyzes the attitude toward life which often emerged from early Protestantism. He calls these psychological consequences "Protestant Asceticism." This attitude can be summarized as the belief that one's work is the task set by God—thus the fulfillment of this task is the highest form of moral activity—and the belief that good works are an indispensable sign of salvation. But by "good works" was meant a *life* of good works. "There was no place for the very human Catholic cycle of sin, repentance, atonement, release, followed by renewed sin." [6] Only by a fundamental change, as Weber says, in the whole meaning of life at every moment and in every action could the effects of salvation be *proved*.

It is not hard for us to see how Weber thinks Protestant asceticism leads to the Spirit of Capitalism, especially if we believe, as Weber does, that many Protestants believed that the attainment of wealth, as a fruit of labor, was a sign of God's blessing. In support of this belief Weber cites (along with other statements) statements made by Protestant clergy. For example, Richard Baxter wrote: "If God shows you a way in which you may lawfully get more than in another way (without wrong to your soul or to any other), if you refuse this, and choose the less gainful way, you cross one of the ends of your calling, and you refuse to be God's steward, and to accept His gifts and use them for Him when He requireth it: you may labour to be rich for God, though not for the flesh and sin." [7] Weber argues that today the spirit of capitalism exists generally without religious basis—"the idea of duty in one's calling prowls about in our lives like the ghost of dead religious beliefs." [8] Most acquire this attitude not primarily through the church but through the existing economic and cultural order. The structure of Weber's explanation is shown in this simplified presentation of his argument:

[6] *Ibid.,* p. 117.
[7] *Ibid.,* p. 162.
[8] *Ibid.,* p. 182.

1. Protestantism (*C*) developed individuals who had the attitude toward life called "Protestant Asceticism" (*Vc*).
2. We all understand *from our own experiences* how *Vc* leads to the attitude toward life called "The Spirit of Capitalism" (*Ve*).
3. Individuals who had *Ve* were primarily responsible for the development of modern capitalism (*E*).

Thus we can understand why *E* developed under conditions *C*.

This explanation connects *C* with *E* by way of psychological states *Vc* and *Ve*. A person is said to understand the connection between *C* and *E* (and thus see the explanation for *C* being connected with *E*) only in so far as he can understand from his own experience how *Vc* is connected with *Ve*. It is this feature which led some to call such explanations *empathetic* or *meaningful explanations*. Such explanations employ what has been called "the operation called 'Verstehen'." This "operation" needs to be performed in order to understand premiss (2) and see that it is true (supposing that it is true).

A much simpler example of an empathetic explanation is this: An investigator of the low marriage rates in a farm area finds that in this area the farmers have had a series of crop failures. He performs "verstehen" and comes up with this explanation:

1. Crop failures (*C*) produce feelings of insecurity (*Vc*).
2. From our own experiences we know that *Vc* leads to a fear of new commitments (*Ve*).
3. *Ve* would lead to low marriage rates (*E*).

Thus we see why *E* occurs under conditions *C*.

Sometimes "verstehen" can be employed to suggest some *C*. Someone might ask, "Why *E*?" The answer would take this form: If *Ve*, then *E*. If *Vc*, then *Ve*. If *C*, then *Vc*. So it would seem that *C* is what explains the occurrence of *E*.

Four points need to be noticed about empathetic explanations: First, premisses like (1), (2), and (3) cannot occur in explanations in the physical sciences for the obvious reason that inanimate and certain organic objects do not have such psychological states. In this sense empathetic explanations are unique to the social sciences. However, in each of the sciences certain subject matter is treated which is not found in any other science. Second, whether or not *C* is the cause or the primary variable related to *E* can be tested. In our second example the investigator might find that in the farm area there have been few if any eligible men. This would falsify the supposition that crop failures account for low marriage rates. Third, a social scientist does not have to have experienced himself the connection between *Vc* and *Ve*, *C*—*Vc*, and *Ve*—*E* to know that there are such connections. Fourth, many philosophers of science see the value of "verstehen" as simply suggesting to the investigator a C and E relation.

SUMMARY

The typical form taken by explanations in the sciences is either:

| Deductive | Universal Law (s) Statement of initial conditions ——————— Particular event | Universal Law 1 Universal Law 2 . . . Universal Law n ——————— Universal generality | Deductive |

or:

| Nondeductive | Probabilistic generalities Statements of initial conditions ——————— Singular statement |

Examples one, two, and three fit into one of these patterns. The question whether historical and functional explanations fit this pattern is a controversial issue. Empathetic explanations, whether or not they fit the pattern, suggest possible relationships between certain C's and E's. All of the explicans in the six examples could be tested, though the test procedures would show certain variations.

It should again be pointed out that the six examples do not exhaust the various kinds of explanations found in the sciences. Nor should it be concluded that the different sciences *necessarily* provide a certain *type* of explanation—that is, that explanations in the biological sciences are necessarily functional. The sort of explanation—of a given phenomenon or historical event or of a group of such things—that is *possible* in the context of a science depends primarily on the stage of the development of that science into a formally organized body of knowledge and, indirectly, of course, on the knowledge available in that science.

EXERCISES I

Classify each of the following as: deductive explanation; probabilistic explanation; teleological explanation; historical explanation; empathetic explanation; none of these. Justify your classification.

1. Why are tornadoes so destructive? A tornado destroys property and causes loss of life because the low pressures lead to the explosion of closed buildings and vehicles and the strong winds blow away whatever lies in their path.

"The reasons for the explosions are well known. The pressure in a tornado may cause a drop of atmospheric pressure by 8 per cent or more in a matter of seconds. Suppose the pressure inside a house is normal atmospheric, about 15 pounds per square inch. If a tornado moves over the house, the pressure outside may suddenly drop by 8 per cent to 13.8 pounds per square inch. Since the pressure inside the house will drop fairly slowly, especially if all the doors and windows are closed, the force on each square inch of wall and ceiling may amount to 1.2 pounds or about 170 pounds per square foot. If the house had a ceiling space 20 by 40 feet in area, the force exerted on the roof would be about 68 tons. This suddenly applied force can blow the roof off the house as if an explosion had occurred. This is especially true for dwellings, because in most houses the roof is held on mainly by its own weight. And it is evident, too, that few walls will survive 170 pounds of force per square foot."

The strong winds associated with the tornado are capable of picking up and moving the entire house. Cars, trucks, trailers, and other heavy objects are frequently carried away. The velocity of these winds has been estimated at 500–700 miles per hour.

(Adapted from LOUIS J. BATTAN, *The Nature of Violent Storms*) [9]

2. How is light energy converted into chemical energy? Nature set herself the task to catch in flight the light streaming towards the earth, and to store this, the most evasive of all forces, by converting it into an immobile form. To achieve this, she has covered the earth's crust with organisms, which while living take up the sunlight and use its force to add continuously to a sum of chemical difference.

These organisms are the plants: the plant world forms a reservoir in which the volatile sun rays are fixed and ingeniously laid down for later use; a providential economic measure, to which the very physical existence of the human race is inexorably bound.

(JULIUS ROBERT VON MAYER, 1845)

3. Why does great display of wealth no longer occur in the United States? John Galbraith in his book *The Affluent Society* gives this explanation:

Such display is now passé. There was an adventitious contributing cause. The American well-to-do have long been curiously sensitive to fear of expropriation—a fear which may be related to the tendency for even the mildest reformist measures to be viewed, in the conservative conventional wisdom, as the portents of revolutions. The depression and especially the New Deal gave the American rich a serious fright. One consequence was to usher in a period of marked discretion in personal expenditure. Purely ostentatious outlays, especially on

---

[9] Louis J. Battan, *The Nature of Violent Storms*, Anchor Books, Science Study Series (New York: Doubleday, 1961).

dwellings, yachts, and females, were believed likely to incite the masses to violence. They were rebuked as unwise and improper by the more discreet. It was much wiser to take on the protective coloration of the useful citizen, the industrial statesman, or even the average guy.

However, deeper causes were at work. Increasingly in the last quarter century the display of expensive goods, as a device for suggesting wealth, has been condemned as vulgar. The term is precise. Vulgar means: "Of or pertaining to the common people, or to the common herd or crowd." And this explains what happened. Lush expenditure could be afforded by so many that it ceased to be useful as a mark of distinction. A magnificent, richly upholstered, and extremely high-powered automobile conveys no impression of wealth in a day when such automobiles are mass-produced by the thousands. A house in Palm Beach is not a source of distinction when the rates for a thousand hotel rooms in Miami Beach rival its daily upkeep. Once a sufficiently impressive display of diamonds could create attention even for the most obese and repellent body, for they signified membership in a highly privileged caste. Now the same diamonds are afforded by a television star or a talented harlot. Modern mass communications, especially the movies and television, insure that the populace at large will see the most lavish caparisoning on the bodies not of the daughters of the rich but on the daughters of coal miners and commercial travelers, who struck it rich by their own talents or some facsimile thereof. In South America, in the Middle East, to a degree in socialist India, and at Nice, Cannes, and Deauville, ostentatious display by the rich is still much practiced. This accords with expectations. In these countries most people are still, in the main, poor and unable to afford the goods which advertise wealth. Therefore ostentation continues to have a purpose. In not being accessible to too many people it has not yet become vulgar.

(JOHN KENNETH GALBRAITH, *The Affluent Society*) [10]

4. In the early 1930's, while the world struggled to escape from the great depression that was shaking capitalism to its foundations, the classically trained economists wrestled to fit facts to orthodox theory. Public policy was in disarray. Classical theory had taught that when demand fell, prices and wages should fall and resources would once again be employed. But the actual effects of the drastic fall in prices on farmers was a disastrous fall in income! . . .

Gardiner Means and other economists were struck by the fact that some prices were more classical than others, that while farm prices had fallen sharply, many industrial prices—those in the great corporate industries—had fallen very little. Working for the Department of Agriculture, Means studied the behavior of 747 prices. This led him to his second major advance, the notion of administered prices.

There are, he found, two principal kinds of prices. One price is set in com-

[10] John Kenneth Galbraith, *The Affluent Society* (Boston: Houghton Mifflin Co., 1958), pp. 91–93. Copyright © 1958 by John Kenneth Galbraith. Used by permission.

petitive markets and changes frequently in response to changes in demand. The other is set by administrative action and held constant for varying periods of time, despite changes in demand. Farm prices are typical market prices. Cement prices are typically administered.

In an administered market, an increase in demand leads to an increase in output. When demand falls, as it did during the great depressions, the price is largely held and output is slashed. This characteristic of rigid prices, Means concluded, was the basic cause of the depression's depth. As demand fell, output instead of price was cut; men were thrown out of work, and their loss of income further reduced total demand.

(BERNARD NOSSITER, "The World of Gardiner Means") [11]

5. Consider the pre-Civil War clash of convictions on slavery in the United States. By and large, the prevailing opinion in the North was that slavery was morally wrong, and in the South that it was morally right. In the debate that raged in those days, both sides appealed to the highest moral authority in support of their respective views. Such a clear-cut division of moral sentiments on geographical lines is most remarkable. It could not have happened by chance and must be explained.

Today most of us would accept the explanation that the different convictions derived from the existence of different institutions. Slavery was a fact in the South. It was woven into the very fabric of southern life. Therefore, a disturbance of slavery meant for southerners a profound change in their way of life. Under the supposition that man usually resists profound changes of established ways (except when the established ways become unbearable), we see that the southern support of slavery was understandable.

But the Marxists wish to delve deeper. . . .

Underlying the clash of conceptions of what is morally right, according to the Marxists, were the clashing economic interests of the ruling classes of the North and the South, respectively. In the South, the ruling class, that is, the owners of the large plantations, derived their incomes and therefore their power, by exploiting agricultural labor. In those days, agricultural labor required no skill and could best be controlled if the laborers were kept in complete ignorance. Slavery, therefore, filled the bill. In the North, however, a new ruling class was emerging—the industrialists, who controlled the means of production in manufacture. Now the increasing importance of machinery made slave labor unfit in factories. The industrial worker had to be at least somewhat literate. More than that, he had to be motivated in a way that a slave could not be. Finally, it was in the interest of the manufacturer to have a fluid labor force, a labor market, a reservoir, from which labor could be recruited and on which it could be dumped when not needed. . . . the industrialist did not buy the whole worker: he bought only the worker's labor. . . .

An ambition to extend the industrial system to the South would therefore be coupled with a conviction that slavery must be replaced by a free labor force. Since high sounding ideals are easier to defend (to oneself as well as to others)

[11] Bernard Nossiter, "The World of Gardiner Means," *The New Republic,* May 7, 1962. © 1962 by *The New Republic.* Used by permission.

than economic self-interest, it is easy to see how the real aim, freedom of contract, became translated quite sincerely into "freedom of person."

(ANATOLE RAPOPORT, *Fights, Games and Debates*) [12]

6. Freud in his *A General Introduction to Psychoanalysis,* recounts how he was called upon to explain why a fifty-three year old happily married woman had *delusions of jealousy.* A young girl, clearly out of jealousy, sent a letter to the woman telling that another young girl was having an affair with her husband. Though the woman clearly saw the accusation was false, she was prostrated by the letter. She suffered as much as she would have if the charges were well-founded. What caused this suffering?

Freud first found out that the letter was provoked by the patient herself. She had said to the young lady, who was then her housemaid, that nothing could be more awful than to hear that her husband was having an affair. During the interview with the patient, Freud found that she had an infatuation for her son-in-law which she was not fully aware of, and she disguised it as harmless tenderness.

From these two observations, Freud provided this explanation for the woman's illness: such a monstrous infatuation was an impossible thing and could not come to her conscious mind. Some sort of relief had to be found since it "persisted" and "unconsciously exerted a heavy pressure." ". . . the simplest alleviation lay in that mechanism of displacement which so regularly plays its part in the formation of delusional jealousy. If not merely she, old woman that she was, were in love with a young man, but if only her old husband too were in love with a young mistress, then her torturing conscience would be absolved from infidelity." Relief came to her by her "projecting" her own state of mind onto her husband.

7. When the group norms are no longer binding or valid in an area or for a population subgroup—. . . deviant behavior becomes more frequent. . . . In a stable community a child is born and raised in a context of established norms which are supported by a social consensus. He tends to interiorize these norms, and they contribute to the establishment of his psychological field of needs, goals and motivations. Generally, the child acts to satisfy his needs in a manner which has the approval of society. If he acts in a deviant fashion, formal and informal controls—including his own ego with its interiorized norms—act to deter the child from further deviant conduct. Unstable community conditions and the consequent weakening of social controls that are congruent with the dominant culture provide fertile ground for the emergence of variant norms and group standards.

(BERNARD LANDER, *Towards an Understanding of Juvenile Delinquency*) [13]

[12] Reprinted from *Fights, Games and Debates* by Anatole Rapoport by permission of the University of Michigan Press. Copyright © by the University of Michigan 1960. All rights reserved. Published in the United States of America by the University of Michigan Press and simultaneously in Toronto, Canada by Ambassador Books Limited.

[13] Bernard Lander, *Towards an Understanding of Juvenile Delinquency* (New York: Columbia University Press, 1954).

8. Why does it appear that man will not always dominate the planet? In the words of Edward Drinker Cope, the great American naturalist: "The highly developed, or specialized types of one geological period have not been the parents of the types of succeeding periods but . . . the descent has been derived from the less specialized of preceding ages." The highly and narrowly adapted flourish, but they move in a path which becomes ever more difficult to retrace or break away from as their adaptation becomes perfected. Their proficiency may increase, their numbers may grow. But their perfect adaptation, so necessary for survival, can become a euphemism for death. Man's specialization has introduced a new kind of life into the universe—one capable within limits of ordering its own environment and transmitting that order through social rather than biological heredity. Nevertheless his physical modifications appear to be at an end, or close to an end, and sooner or later, Cope's law of the unspecialized will have its chance once more.

(Adapted from LOREN C. EISELEY, "Is Man Here to Stay?") [14]

9. To understand how chelation works we must examine the nature of a chemical bond. According to the modern theory of valence, the atoms in a molecule are bound together by electrons, the charged particles that surround every atom. The bond may be established in one of two ways. An atom may transfer one of its electrons to its neighbor. In that case the atom that loses the electron also loses its electrical neutrality and becomes positively charged, while the atom that receives the electron becomes negatively charged. These two "ions" then are held together by the electrical attraction of their opposite charges. The other way in which two atoms may be bound together is by sharing a pair of electrons—as if two persons were held together by a pair of ropes that belonged not exclusively to either individual but to both together. This is called a covalent bond: the chemist represents it by a single line joining the two atoms. Usually each of the two joined atoms supplies one of the two binding electrons. But sometimes one atom supplies both, and that kind of link is called a co-ordinate bond. The chemist's symbol for such a bond is an arrow pointing toward the atom which has received the electrons. Now a chelate ring is simply a group of atoms linked into a ring with one or more co-ordinate bonds. The atoms that donate the electrons are usually oxygen, nitrogen or sulfur; the acceptor atom, grasped in the claw of arrows, is nearly always a metal. In such a ring the metal atom is gripped more firmly than if it were merely attached to atoms in independent molecules. Another way of saying this is that a metal atom is much more prone to unite with two donor atoms in a ring-forming molecule than with the same atoms in two separate molecules. The mechanics of the situation make clear why this is so. To become attached to two separate molecules, the metal atom must capture a donor atom in each molecule separately, and this depends on chance contacts. But when the metal atom becomes attached to one end of a molecule that can form a ring around it, it

14 Loren C. Eiseley, "Is Man Here to Stay?" in *Scientific American Reader* (New York: Simon and Schuster, 1953), pp. 483–489.

easily links up with the other end, for the latter is tethered and cannot range far ahead.

(HAROLD F. WALTON, "Chelation") [15]

10. We know that the substances extracted from plants ferment when they are abandoned to themselves, and disappear little by little in contact with the air. We know that the cadavers of animals undergo putrefaction and that soon only their skeletons remain. This destruction of dead organic matter is one of the necessities of the perpetuation of life.

If the remnants of dead plants and animals were not destroyed, the surface of the earth would soon be encumbered with organic matter, and life would become impossible because the cycle of transformation . . . could no longer be closed.

It is necessary that the fibrin of our muscles, the albumin of our blood, the gelatine of our bones, the urea of our urine, the ligneus matter of plants, the sugar of their fruits, the starch of their seeds . . . be progressively converted into water, ammonia and carbon dioxide so that the elementary principles of these complex organic substances be taken up again by plants, elaborated anew, to serve as food for new living beings similar to those that gave birth to them, and so on *ad infinitum* to the end of the centuries.

(RENE DUBOS, *Pasteur and Modern Science*) [16]

11. The theory [Clark L. Hull's Learning Theory] is introduced by an anecdotal experiment. The subject is a six-year-old child who likes candy and is hungry for it. While she is out of the room a piece of her favorite candy is hidden under the edge of the center book in the lower shelf of a bookcase of several shelves. She is brought into the room, told there is candy hidden under one of the books, and asked if she wants to try to find it. She does, so she proceeds to look for the candy, after she is told that she must replace each book after looking under it, and that she may eat the candy when she finds it. She finds the candy after spending 210 seconds and examining 37 books. The next time she goes right to the lower shelf, and it takes her only 87 seconds and she looks under only 12 books. The next time she finds the candy under the second book examined, and it has taken her only 11 seconds. The next time she doesn't do so well. She starts at the other end of the shelf and works back. The authors speculate that she either was just lucky the time before, or introduced some other notion as a result of her previous experience with hiding games, such as, "He'll probably change the place now that I know it." Thereafter she continues to do better until on the ninth and tenth trials she goes right to the correct book and gets the candy.

According to some psychologists, there are four facts in learning: drive, cue, response, and reward. A *drive* is a strong stimulus which impels to action. The

---

[15] Harold F. Walton, "Chelation" in *New Chemistry* (New York: Simon and Schuster, 1957). Reprinted with permission. Copyright © 1957 by Scientific American, Inc. All rights reserved.

[16] Rene Dubos, *op. cit.*, pp. 74–75.

child's drives were a complex of hunger, a cultivated appetite for candy, and secondary drives related to social participation and social approval. Responses are elicited by *cues*. Cues determine "when he will respond, where he will respond, and which response he will make." The child was given a great many cues. She was told that the candy was under a book, and that she would be permitted to eat it when she found it. Drive impels the individual to *respond* to certain cues. Only if the response occurs can it be rewarded and learned, and one of the tasks of training is so to arrange the situation that the desired response will occur. The little girl was impelled to begin picking up books by her appetite for candy and her knowledge that candy was to be found under a book. Responses made to cues in the presence of drives will be learned if they are *rewarded*. If they are not rewarded, the tendency to repeat them will be weakened. Rewards produce reduction in drives; drive-reduction is, in fact, what makes them rewarding. That is why it is rewarding to be relieved from pain, to drink when thirsty, to eat when hungry. In the case of the little girl, eating the candy was rewarding.

(Adapted from ERNEST L. HILGARD, *Theories of Learning*) [17]

12. The reason why religion is necessary is apparently to be found in the fact that human society achieves its unity primarily through the possession by its members of certain ultimate values and ends in common. Although these values and ends are subjective, they influence behavior, and their integration enables the society to operate as a system. Derived neither from inherited nor from external nature, they have evolved as a part of culture by communication and moral pressure. They must, however, appear to the members of the society to have some reality, and it is the role of religious belief and ritual to supply and reinforce this appearance of reality. Through belief and ritual the common ends and values are connected with an imaginary world symbolized by concrete sacred objects, which world in turn is related in a meaningful way to the facts and trials of the individual's life. Through the worship of the sacred objects and the beings they symbolize, and the acceptance of supernatural prescriptions that are at the same time codes of behavior, a powerful control over human conduct is exercised, guiding it along lines sustaining the institutional structure and conforming to the ultimate ends and values.

(KINGSLEY DAVIS and WILBERT E. MOORE, "Some Principles of Stratification") [18]

13. What is the nature of the forces that hold together the protons and neutrons in an atomic nucleus? In 1935 the Japanese physicist Hideki Yukawa suggested that a new kind of field, consisting of quanta of energy which might take the form of particles of a certain mass, might account for these forces. He pointed out that electrical and gravitational forces, the two chief forces pre-

17 Ernest L. Hilgard, *Theories of Learning* (New York: Appleton-Century-Crofts, Inc., 1948), pp. 77–79.

18 Kingsley Davis and Wilbert E. Moore, "Some Principles of Stratification" in *American Sociological Review*, Vol. 10, pp. 244–245. Used by permission of *American Sociological Review* and the authors.

viously known, could be explained in terms of the emission and reabsorption of light quanta and gravitational quanta respectively. Since the nuclear forces were of a completely different type—not only more powerful but acting over much smaller distances than electrical or gravitational forces—it seemed reasonable to Yukawa to introduce a new type of field which would be responsible for the nuclear forces. . . . Yukawa estimated that the mass of the field quanta exchanged between two nucleons would be about 200 to 300 times that of the electron. He called these field quanta mesons. The mesons were thought of as the nuclear glue binding together the neutrons and protons in the nucleus. Since there were three types of equally strong bonds in the nucleus (neutron-proton, proton-proton, and neutron-neutron) it was assumed that there would be three kinds of mesons, namely, positive, negative and neutral.

(ROBERT E. MARSKAK, "The Multiplicity of Particles") [19]

GENUINE AND PSEUDOSCIENTIFIC
EXPLANATIONS

In this section conditions will be suggested which will enable us to distinguish genuine scientific explanations such as those considered in the first section (pages 389–401), from pseudoscientific explanations such as biological entelechy theories, historical determinism, and astrology. The method employed in arriving at these conditions is this: We will first examine some suggested criteria for distinguishing genuine from pseudo-explanations. We will see how they do demarcate many clear-cut genuine explanations from clear-cut pseudoexplanations, but we will find that there is a significant number of clear-cut genuine explanations which are not properly demarcated from pseudoexplanations (and vice versa) by these criteria. We will then *suggest* a set of conditions which, on the whole, seem to set off clear-cut examples of genuine explanations from clear-cut examples of pseudoexplanations. The section will end with suggestions for those additional conditions which will distinguish genuine scientific explanations which are satisfactory, such as the kinetic theory of heat, and the molecular theory of matter, from those genuine scientific explanations which are unsatisfactory such as the Ptolemaic theory, the caloric theory, and the Galenic theory.

It will be profitable to make mention of the distinction between genuine scientific explanations, pseudoscientific explanations, and nonscientific explanations. A nonscientific explanation is an answer to a why-question, as are scientific and pseudoscientific explanations. But in a nonscientific explanation both the question and the explanation fall outside the area of scientific why-questions and answers. Such questions and answers are sometimes found in such areas as the arts and religion. Often one indication of the fact that they do fall outside the area of scientific why-questions and answers is the impossibility of there being a conflict between these answers and statements in the sciences, but we will not elaborate this point. When, however, an explanation is represented as being in the area of science, then the question can be asked whether the explanation is a genuine scientific explanation or a pseudoscientific explanation.

Unsatisfactory Criteria of Demarcation

How does one tell, generally, when an explanation which is represented as scientific is a genuine explanation and when it is a pseudoscientific explanation? We will begin our reply to this question by considering three unsatisfactory criteria for distinguishing genuine from pseudoscientific explanations. The reason these criteria are unsatisfactory, as we will see, is not that they do not distinguish *some* genuine explanations from some pseudoscientific explanations, but that they exclude from the class of genuine explanations a number of generally recognized genuine explanations and include a number of generally recognized pseudoscientific explanations.

1. An explanation is genuine if the general statements in the explicans are arrived at by induction.

Some have supposed that the difference between a genuine scientific and a pseudoscientific explanation consists in whether the general statements in the explicans were arrived at by induction. By "induction" is meant arguments of the first kind (A) discussed in Chapter Sixteen, that is, arguments, for example, of these forms:

An A is B
$\therefore A$ is B

A_1 is B
A_2 is B
$\cdot$
$\cdot$
$\cdot$
A_n is B
$\therefore A$ is B

If the general statements of the explicans were arrived at by induction, then the explanation is a genuine scientific explanation; and if the general statements were not arrived at by induction, then the explanation is a pseudoexplanation.

This criterion clearly will not do. As we have seen, most explanations for phenomena, empirical laws, and theoretical laws, are each originally arrived at as a "free creation of the mind." That is, they are a response to the question: What explains such-and-such phenomena, or law (or laws)? Thus if (1) were the criterion for demarcation, most theoretical explanations and many empirical explanations would fall into the class of pseudoexplanations.

2. An explanation is genuine if the general statements in the explicans are established by induction.

Generally empirical laws are established by induction, but theoretical hypotheses are not established by induction (in the above sense), but rather through what we have called corroboration. Thus (2) is an unsatisfactory criterion of demarcation, since theoretical explanations under this criterion would be classed as pseudoscientific explanations. However, if we understood "induction" to cover any inference from evidence for a generality to the generality itself, then (2), in substance, would mean that empirical hypotheses, to be genuine, must be tested, and theoretical hypotheses must be corroborated to be genuine. Understood in this way, is (2) a satisfactory criterion for demarcation? Hypotheses have been corroborated at one time and later abandoned because new phenomena or laws were uncovered, consequences from the theory were seen to conflict with observation, and so on. If (2) were the demarcation criterion, then it would follow that many hypotheses and theories in science were at one time genuine and later became pseudoexplanations. In addition, since the possibility exists that the present-day established or corroborated theory might undergo substantial change or even be abandoned at some future time, it is possible that all the presently established theories are pseudoscientific explanations, if (2) is the criterion. This criterion is thus clearly inadequate since our paradigm examples of explanations which we call genuine are those which are regarded as established today no matter whether in the future they still are regarded in this way or are abandoned. Similarly, explanations like Newton's corpuscular theory of light and the Galenic theory of blood circulation are clear-cut cases of genuine scientific explanations even though they have been given up or falsified.

3. An explanation is genuine if there is observational verification of the statements in the explicans.

It has been suggested that one can tell the difference between a scientific and a pseudoscientific explanation by noticing whether the statements which make up the explicans can be verified by observation.

This criterion is also unsatisfactory. First, even explicans of some explanations which are regarded as pseudoexplanations can be verified by observation. For example, consider this explanation:

> When external influences tend to reduce or raise the bodily temperature of an organism, various bodily mechanisms come into play to return the temperature to normal.
> Why?
> Explanation: Homeostasis capacity of the organism.

This explanation is regarded as a pseudoexplanation, since "homeostasis" is a word used to refer to the process described in what is to be explained. It is what is called a circular explanation. However, by observation it can be verified that the human body has homeostasis capacity.

Second, (3) is unsatisfactory because, while empirical explanations can be verified by observation, no theoretical explanation can be verified or directly tested by observation. If (3), then, were our criterion for demarcation, theoretical explanations would be ruled out of the class of genuine scientific explanations, since by not being verified by observation they fail to fulfill (3).

4. An explanation is genuine if and only if falsifiability of the statements in the explicans is possible.

One can, it has been suggested, demarcate genuine from pseudoexplanations by seeing whether the statements in the explicans are falsifiable. If they are falsifiable, then the explanation is a genuine scientific explanation. If they are not falsifiable, then it is a pseudoexplanation.

The above is the criterion of demarcation suggested by the distinguished philosopher of science, Karl Popper. Popper writes: [20]

> Thus the problem which I tried to solve by proposing the criterion of falsifiability was neither a problem of meaningfulness or significance, nor a problem of truth or acceptability. It was the problem of drawing a line (as well as this can be done) between the statements, or systems of statements, of the empirical sciences, and all other statements—whether they are of a religious or of a metaphysical character, or simply pseudo-scientific. Years later—it must have been in 1928 or 1929—I called this first problem of mine the *'problem of demarcation.'* The criterion of falsifiability is a solution of this problem of demarcation, for it says that statements or systems of statements, in order to be ranked as scientific, must be capable of conflicting with possible, or conceivable, observations.

Popper is saying that in order to be classed as scientific, the statements in the explicans must be capable of conflicting with *possible* or *con-*

---

[20] Karl R. Popper, *Conjectures and Refutations* (London: Routledge and Kegan Paul, 1963), p. 39. © Karl R. Popper, 1963. Used by permission of Routledge and Kegan Paul Ltd. and Basic Books, Inc.

ceivable observations. It is easy to misunderstand this criterion. Popper is not saying that an explanation must be false or probably false or possibly false to be ranked as scientific. He is saying that it must be *capable* of conflicting with *conceivable* observation. To make this clear, consider the statement "The sky is blue," which happens to be true today. This statement is thus *not* probably false or even possibly false, for it happens to be true that the sky is blue today. However, one could easily conceive of observations one could make today which would falsify the statement "The sky is blue." Thus the statement is true, but it is also falsifiable, as Popper uses this word. Examples of statements which are not falsifiable would be: "The universe is shrinking in such a fashion that all lengths contract in the same ratio." Or, to take another example, suppose someone said, "All humans are mortal." And suppose we find a human who is two hundred years old. Would the defender of the above assertion admit it was falsified? Suppose we actually found a Struldburg like Gulliver describes in his voyage to Laputa. (The Struldburgs never die. Some are centuries old. They grow old like ordinary people, but whereas most people who live to be ninety or one hundred die, the Struldburgs continue to live, though they suffer the deformities of extreme age.) Suppose the defender still maintained that the Struldburgs are bound to die sometime. At this point we would begin to see that *his claim* is such that it is not falsifiable. The reason for this is most likely that the defender is defining "human" partially in terms of mortality. This being the case, it would be logically impossible to falsify his statement. If the statement or statements in an explicans were like these two examples, that is, not falsifiable, then, if we follow Popper's criterion, they are to be regarded as pseudoscientific explanations.

Let us now consider some examples of scientific explanations which, according to Popper, satisfy, and some which fail to satisfy this demarcation criterion. In the following quotation Popper considers three explanations—one of Freud's, one of Adler's, and one of Einstein's. The first two are pseudoexplanations because they fail to satisfy (4), whereas the third is a genuine explanation since it fulfills (4).[21]

. . . every conceivable case could be interpreted in the light of Adler's theory, or equally of Freud's. I may illustrate this by two very different examples of human behavior: that of a man who pushes a child into the water with the intention of drowning it; and that of a man who sacrifices his life in an attempt to save the child. Each of these two cases can be explained with equal ease in Freudian and in Adlerian terms. According to Freud the first man suffered from repression (say, of some component of his Oedipus complex), while the second man had achieved sublimation. According to Adler the first man suffered from feelings of inferiority (producing perhaps the need to prove to himself that he dared to commit some crime), and so did the second man (whose need was to

[21] *Ibid.*, pp. 35–36. Used by permission.

prove to himself that he dared to rescue the child). I could not think of any human behavior which could not be interpreted in terms of either theory. It was precisely this fact—that they always fitted, that they were always confirmed—which in the eyes of their admirers constituted the strongest argument in favour of these theories. It began to dawn on me that this apparent strength was in fact their weakness.

With Einstein's theory the situation was strikingly different. Take one typical instance—Einstein's prediction, just then confirmed by the findings of Eddington's expedition. Einstein's gravitational theory had led to the result that light must be attracted by heavy bodies (such as the sun), precisely as material bodies were attracted. As a consequence it could be calculated that light from a distant fixed star whose apparent position was close to the sun would reach the earth from such a direction that the star would seem to be slightly shifted away from the sun; or, in other words, that stars close to the sun would look as if they had moved a little away from the sun, and from one another. This is a thing which cannot normally be observed since such stars are rendered invisible in daytime by the sun's overwhelming brightness; but during an eclipse it is possible to take photographs of them. If the same constellation is photographed at night one can measure the distances on the two photographs, and check the predicted effect.

According to Popper, Freud's and Adler's explanations for human actions are such that they are not falsifiable. No conceivable action could be imagined which would not be compatible with these explanations. On the other hand, from Einstein's gravitational theory a consequence follows which is such that observation could show either that it is true or that it is false. In a word, conceivable observable data could be incompatible with Einstein's theory.

The falsifiability criterion, like criteria (1), (2), and (3), does set off some recognized pseudoscientific explanations from some clear-cut genuine scientific explanations. But it is thought by some that this criterion of demarcation is both too restrictive (under it some genuine explanations would be excluded) and too broad (some pseudoexplanations would be included). We will now consider these two objections.

First objection. Popper clearly makes the distinction between theoretical explanations and empirical explanations. Thus when he says that theoretical explanations are falsifiable he means that observable consequences can be deduced from the explanations, as in Newton's gravitational theory, which *can* either conflict or accord with observation. He does not maintain that the statements of the theory can directly conflict, and hence be falsified, or not conflict with observation. But does the falsification of such consequences imply the falsity of the theoretical explanation? This issue, it will be recalled, was discussed in Chapter Seventeen, page 364. It was argued there that theories can be dealt death blows through the falsification of such consequences, but this does not entail the falsity of the theory. And the only way open to supposedly falsify a theoretical explanation is to deduce some consequence which conflicts with observation, since the explanation cannot directly conflict with observation. Thus unless in "falsifiability" Popper means to include "capable of being dealt a death blow," his criterion would exclude theoretical explanations from the class of genuine scientific explanations.

Second objection. Even supposing that theoretical explanations are falsifiable, it does not follow that if an explanation is a pseudoexplanation, then it is not made up of falsifiable statements. And if falsifiability is to be a satisfactory criterion of demarcation, it must be true that obvious pseudoexplanations must not contain falsifiable explicans. But there are explanations which no one would call genuine scientific explanations and which have explicans which are made up of falsifiable statements. For example, the homeostasis example is falsifiable. Another example of a falsifiable pseudoexplanation would be this:

Why does opium produce sleep?
Explanation: Because it has dormitive power.

We assume that here "dormitive power" is not regarded as a defining criterion for "opium." Each of these explanations is clearly circular.

Conditions for a Genuine (Nonpseudo) Scientific Explanation

The conditions we will examine in this section result from noting in what way a group of commonly recognized genuine scientific explanations differ from a group of commonly recognized pseudoexplanations. It might well be that we could come across explanations which could not be classed definitely in either group. Thus our suggested demarcation criterion (the following two conditions) should be understood as a criterion which generally distinguishes genuine from pseudoscientific explanations. Here, then, are the two conditions which must generally be met in order for an explanation not to be a pseudoexplanation:

1. The statements of the explicans do not follow from the explicandum.

This is a *logical* condition for adequacy. An explanation which fails to meet this logical condition would be a form of what is called a circular argument. No circular explanation would be ranked as a genuine scientific explanation; and formally, no statement S_1 which is logically equivalent to S_2 can be regarded as a genuine scientific explanation of S_2. This condition would thus rule out the homeostasis and the opium explanations as genuine explanations.

2.   The statements in the explicans must be testable either directly
or indirectly.

An explanation is directly testable when it is possible in principle to
see by observation whether the things related to the terms in the statements of the explanation are in fact related in the way stated. Empirical
explanations can in principle be directly tested. From time to time, due
to technical or physical difficulties, such explanations must be indirectly tested. All empirical hypotheses are clearly falsifiable. If the things
referred to are observed to be related in the way stated, the statement
is true; if not, then the statement is false. The second condition (2) as
it applies to empirical explanations would be the same as Popper's falsifiability criterion.

An explanation is indirectly testable when it is possible to deduce,
with the help of other assumptions, consequences which can in principle
be directly tested. All theoretical hypotheses are open to indirect but
not direct testing. Sometimes such testing results in a death blow to a
theory with the consequence that the theory is given up. As pointed out,
if "falsifiable" is understood to include "capable of being dealt a death
blow," then this second condition would be the same as Popper's falsifiability criterion.

Three examples of statements which cannot be tested were just considered. If the way Popper regards Freud's and Adler's explanations for
actions of the two men is correct, then their explanations for the two
acts would be examples of untestable explanations and thus would fail
to fulfill condition (2). All the explanations so far considered—the
Galenic theory, Torricelli's "sea of air" explanation, Huygens' wave
theory, Galileo's explanations, Blackett's explanation, and so forth—are
clear-cut cases of testable explanations. And since they all fulfill the
first condition (1) they are all examples of genuine scientific explanations.

From time to time an explanation is so formulated that consequences
follow from the theory which are capable of conflicting with observation. But when these consequences are found, through experiment, to
conflict with observation, the theory is sometimes so modified that it can
no longer be tested. For example during the nineteenth century it was
thought by most authorities that light waves travel through what was
called "ether" in the way in which sound travels through air and in
the way in which a wave travels through water. Luminiferous ether was
thought of as a motionless substance filling all space. If light waves (indicated by the dotted lines) were sent out from the center of a sphere
traveling through space in this manner:

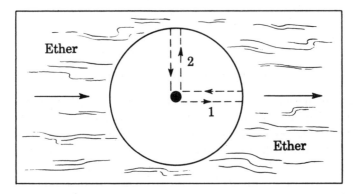

and reflected from the inner surface of the sphere as indicated, then the ether theory, as it was regarded at one time, implies that the waves would not return to the center simultaneously. The ether theory predicted that the first light wave would take longer than the second to make the trip because of the adverse effect of "bucking" the flow of ether. The situation was thought to be analogous to the adverse effect of a river current on the speed of a boat going upstream then back downstream, compared to going across the current and then back. The famous Michelson-Morley experiment in 1887 showed that light waves in such a situation will return simultaneously. There were several modifications that could be made of the ether theory that would make it compatible with the Michelson-Morley experiment. For example it could be argued that the bodies carry their ether with them—that is, drag it along with them— or that bodies contract as they travel through the ether thus shortening the distance the first ray had to travel. Michelson suggested the first modification, and the second possible modification is known as the Lorentz-Fitzgerald Contraction Hypothesis. Michelson's suggestion was upset by Lodge's experiment in 1893 with massive discs. This experiment showed that objects do not drag the ether with them. The Contraction Hypothesis is retained today, but for reasons other than to explain the velocity of light through ether. However, the effects of this modification and others was that ether was regarded as not having any effects on the electrical, optical, or mechanical properties of matter. In a word, no experiment, however ingenious or varied, could show any trace of or detect in any way the ether's effects on anything. Thus, because the theory was reformulated to explain why the ether had no detectable effects, no experiment could possibly conflict with a consequence of the reformulated ether theory.[22]

22 This was Lorentz's idea. One could (and most physicists later did) regard Lorentz's ingenious calculations as showing that there was no such thing as ether—or, at least, that the concept was not needed in physics.

SATISFACTORY AND
UNSATISFACTORY EXPLANATIONS

If an explanation fulfills the two conditions introduced below, then, generally, it is a satisfactory explanation. [Actually (3) overlaps (4).] Generally, if an explanation fails to fulfill one of these conditions, then it is an unsatisfactory explanation—*assuming* it meets conditions (1) and (2) (discussed in the last section). For if it fails to meet (1) and (2), then it is not an unsatisfactory explanation but a pseudoexplanation.

3.   The explicans must be supported by evidence other than the evidence upon which the acceptance of the explicandum is based.

This condition avoids what are generally called *ad hoc* explanations. Michelson's suggestion that the sphere carries its own ether and the Lorentz-Fitzgerald hypothesis were both *ad hoc* hypotheses at the time they were introduced. They were introduced to make the ether theory compatible with the results of the Michelson-Morley experiment. The only "evidence" for them was that they explained how the ether theory was compatible with the experimental data. An explanation which is *merely ad hoc* and is not supported by data other than that which it purports to explain is obviously unsatisfactory. However a hypothesis introduced in this way can either be rejected or established by further investigations. For example, the Lorentz-Fitzgerald hypothesis has been retained within Einstein's relativity theory. Many hypotheses at the time of formulation are *ad hoc* in the sense that all that justifies the assertion of the hypothesis at the time of formulation is merely the fact that it explains the given set of phenomena which prompted it. An explanation ceases to be *ad hoc* when it fulfills (4), below, or when evidence other than that which it is devised to explain is provided for it.

4.   The explicans must be true or corroborated.

In the preceding chapters we came across a number of explanations which failed to meet (4)—for example, the caloric theory of heat, the Galenic theory of the blood-system, the corpuscular theory of light, and the Ptolemaic theory of the solar system. Notice that all of these theories satisfy condition (2). If they had not, then they could not have been shown to be false or not to hold. Thus all of these theories were genuine explanations, but since they were shown to be false or not to hold, they were unsatisfactory genuine explanations.

Examples of Pseudo- and Unsatisfactory Scientific Explanations

The four conditions described in the preceding sections will become clearer as we examine three additional examples of explanations which violate them.

Example one: Why does the existence of strongly knit social bonds between members of a community help to sustain human beings during periods of personal stress? (explicandum) Explicans: Such societies have a great degree of social cohesion.

Assuming that "social cohesion" and "strongly knit social bonds between members of a community" are approximate synonyms, this explanation violates the first condition (1), for the explicans can be seen to follow from the explicandum.

Example two: [23] In the case of normal development of an embryo, a definite part develops into an eye, another part into a foot, and so forth. Hans Driesch, a famous biologist, thought he had shown by experiment that if such parts are removed the mature organism will not necessarily lack an eye or foot, since the formation of these organs will be taken over by other parts of the embryo. If, for example, the upper part of a certain organism (tabularia) is cut off, a new part grows from the surface of the amputation. If, however, the organism is divided in another way, then the very same surface which in the first case produced a head may now sprout a tail. Thus, Driesch concluded, one and the same part of a certain organism contains different "developmental potentialities" out of which may develop different parts according to what is needed for the development of a complete organism. What explains this "developmental potential" of organisms? Driesch says that it is determined by some factor which is nonspatial. He called it *entelechy*. All organic processes are in fact distinguished from inorganic processes by the presence of these entelechies. The entelechy, according to Driesch, is "a teleologically directing factor of nature. . . . There is nothing like it in the inorganic world. . . . Entelechy is not an energy, not a force, not an intensity, not a constant, but—entelechy. . . . Entelechy relates to space, thus belongs to nature; but entelechy is not *in* space—it acts not in space but into space." [24] It is, Driesch says, "indivisible" and "non-localized."

There is some question whether the cutting experiments with the

---

[23] Taken from Moritz Schlick's "Philosophy of Organic Life," *Readings in the Philosophy of Science,* edited by Herbert Feigl and May Brodbeck: Appleton-Century-Crofts, 1953.

[24] Hans Driesch, *History and Theory of Vitalism,* trans. C. K. Ogden. (New York: Macmillan, 1914).

tabularia supported his conclusions about them. But this is not our interest. Rather, we want to know whether his explicans is a genuine explanation. It turns out that it is not, for it fails to fulfill the second condition (2). The notion of entelechy is so formulated as to remove the *possibility* of any kind of testing—direct testing, indirect testing, corroboration, and so on.

Example three: In 1950 Immanuel Velikovsky published a book which became a best-seller, entitled *Worlds in Collision*. The theory found in the book is, in brief, that a giant comet once erupted from the planet Jupiter, passed close to the Earth on two occasions, the first about 1500 B.C., and then became the planet Venus. The comet's first encounter caused the Earth either to stop spinning or to slow down. There was a short retreat and a second passing which caused thunder, earthquakes, and so forth. Several years later a precipitate of carbohydrates formed in the comet's tail fell to the Earth. The second encounter occurred 52 years later and had similar effects on the Earth. The theory is held up as explaining what caused the Red Sea to divide (the slowing of the Earth's spin), the conditions which prevailed for Moses on Mount Sinai, the manna from heaven which kept the Israelites alive for four years (the precipitate from the comet's tail), Joshua's making the sun stand still (the second encounter), and Joshua's toppling the walls with the trumpets (earthquake produced by the Earth's cooling).

Velikovsky's explanation for the Old Testament stories fulfills the first two conditions (1) and (2). It is thus a genuine, as opposed to a pseudoscientific, explanation. However, it is an unsatisfactory explanation because it fails to fulfill conditions (3) and (4). It is essentially an *ad hoc* explanation. The supposed evidence for the theory consists almost entirely of the stories which the theory explains.[25] And the explicans conflicts with facts—for example, no marks which would have resulted from such upheavals have been found on the Earth.

SUMMARY

In these last two sections our interest has been in the following classification:

---

[25] V. Bargmann (Princeton Physics Dept.) and L. Motz (Columbia, Astronomy) in a letter in *Science*, Vol. 38, December 1962, urge reconsideration of Velikovsky's conclusion, on new observation, though they disagree with his theory.

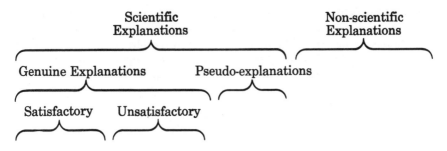

Generally, genuine explanations in science are distinguished from pseudo-explanations if and only if (1) the statements of the explicans do not follow from the explicandum, and (2) the statements of the explicans are testable either directly or indirectly. Generally, satisfactory scientific explanations are distinguished from unsatisfactory ones if and only if (3) the explicans is supported by evidence based on data other than the observational data upon which the acceptance of the explicandum is based, and (4) the explicans is true or corroborated.

EXERCISES II

Using the four characteristics (1, 2, 3, and 4) discussed in this chapter, classify the following as genuine or pseudo-explanations and classify the genuine explanations as satisfactory or unsatisfactory explanations. Justify your choice.

1. "Most of the scientists I know," says Boston University Theologian Edwin Booth, "believe in the immanent principle of life in the organic universe. If they are religious, they call it God. If they are not religious, they have awe and reverence for this principle. But it isn't refined, nor is it personal. It is greater than personal—it is absolutely essential to the principle of life itself."

(*Time,* June 29, 1962)

2. According to Marxism, revolution is inevitable. One reason for this is the operation of "The Law of the Transformation of Quantity into Quality." All things change by imperceptible steps until there arrives a point, which Hegel calls the "node," beyond which a thing cannot vary while remaining the same. That this law exists can be seen when water turns to steam at 100°C. and into ice at 0°C. This change occurs abruptly so that water is at one moment water and at the next moment steam or ice.

3. How do artists come to their material? Freud in his "The Relation of the Poet to Daydreaming" (in *Collected Papers*) writes that some cue in the environment arouses unfulfilled wishes. Rather than just repress these wishes as some of us do, only to have them fulfilled in dreams or in daydreams, the artist also fulfills the wish in artistic work. All people have these wishes:

erotic wishes, wishes for power, honor, riches, and fame. Those who can fulfill them in real life are happy people. Those who cannot, because they lack
the various means to fulfill them, are unhappy people. The artist, who has
more intense wishes than other people to begin with, cannot fulfill these wishes
in real life, but instead fulfills them in dreaming, daydreaming, and in his
work. He is, of course, unhappy, but the explanation for how he comes to his
material is in his being unhappy.

4. Tonight I want to tell you a little bit about astrology, and in particular
to explain its foundations. It has sometimes been claimed by unscientific
astrologers that stars and planets compel our every action. As a scientific astrol-
oger my first task is to correct that impression. The stars do not compel, they
impel. There is a distinction here which I am sure you are all subtle enough
to grasp without my pausing to explain it. I shall therefore go on now to talk
about how we know they impel, and how they impel.

Strangely enough, the main support for the truth of astrology came upon the
scene only recently, several thousands of years after men began to practice our
most ancient of sciences. Modern physics teaches us that the stars are huge
bodies, some of them thousands of times the size and mass of our own sun. Now
these great bodies are constantly giving off vibrations. Ask any astronomer and
he will tell you, for example, that the stars are the source of cosmic rays whose
power in terms of electron-volts is fantastically high. Nor is there reason to
think that cosmic rays are the only kinds of vibrations stars emit, or even the
strongest kind. Well, astrologers have known for centuries how great is the
force of stellar vibrations. The rediscovery of such forces in modern times occasions no surprise on our part.

Now what about these vibrations? Did it ever occur to you how sensitive an
instrument the human body is? You must have realized long ago that nothing
is more intricate and responsive than the mind and nervous system of a creature who is capable of being affected powerfully by a new idea or by the words
of someone long dead. Go to a physiologist or a psychologist and ask him about
the machinery of the brain if you doubt me.

Next, put these two facts together: first, the incalculable forces involved in
the vibrations given off by stars, and second, the exceedingly frail and responsive
machinery of the human mind. How can any man in his right mind deny the
likelihood that so delicate an instrument should respond to so gigantic an influence? Doesn't the seismograph at Fordham register earthquakes in the Sea
of Japan? Of course, yet the seismograph is not nearly so sensitive as the mind,
nor are the greatest quakes comparable in force to the vibrations given off by
a star.

It stands to reason, therefore, that the colossal vibrations of the stars and
planets we are born under must set their stamp somehow on each human being. The truth of astrology is this: over the centuries these character-shaping
influences have gradually been measured, so that today astrology belongs among
the exact sciences. Every newborn child's personality, plastic at birth, is given
its character and permanent cast by the peculiar configuration of heavenly
bodies at the time of the child's birth. This truth has the further merit of ex-

plaining why no two persons are exactly alike. Even with so-called identical twins, the moment of birth is not the same, and with the passing of a few moments the star-picture can change significantly. We know, then, that astrology is an exact science, because if an accurate horoscope is given but fails to agree with the facts of a person's life, it can only mean that the person has made an error in reporting the time or place of his birth!

People who dislike astrology will sometimes say, out of malice, that the stars' distances are sufficient to make the effects of their vibrations negligible. This is easily refuted. First, the space between the earth and stars is nearly a vacuum, empty enough to let vibrations pass almost undiminished in vigor. Second, the Chicago Exposition in 1935 was opened by a ray of light from the star Arcturus hitting a photoelectric cell. If a star as remote as Arcturus can open a fair in Illinois, it is very careless to argue that the stars are too far away to affect our lives.

(JOHN A. OESTERLE, *Logic*) [26]

5. Some psychologists claim that ESP (extra-sensory perception—telepathy, clairvoyance, and the like) has been demonstrated by means of tests with ESP cards. One person turns up cards with five symbols—a square, circle, cross, star and wavy lines. The subject, who cannot see the cards, is asked to tell what card is up. Many subjects have scores which are higher than the laws of chance allow. PK, an abbreviation of "psychokinesis," has also been demonstrated. This is the ability of the mind to control matter, as found in mediumistic levitations, faith healing, haunted house phenomena, etc. By having subjects concentrate on certain faces of dice, it has been found that these faces show up more than the laws of chance allow. ESP and PK are free of space and time restrictions. They both, for example, work just as well when the subject is separated by great distances from the cards or dice. This independence from time and space make these phenomena such that they cannot be explained by any *physical* theory. We must employ *mental* notions as distinct from the physical world. The subjects must be believers in psychic phenomena to have the ESP and PK. This is because a disbeliever will upset the delicate operation of the subject's psi-ability.

(Adapted from MARTIN GARDNER, *Fads and Fallacies in the Name of Science*) [27]

6. Housewives consistently report that one of the most pleasurable tasks of the home is making a cake. Psychologists were put to work exploring this phenomenon for merchandising clues. James Vicary made a study of cake symbolism and came up with the conclusion that "baking a cake traditionally is

[26] Reprinted from John A. Oesterle, *Logic: The Art of Defining and Reasoning*, 2nd ed. © 1963. Prentice-Hall, Inc., Englewood Cliffs, N. J. Used by permission of Prentice-Hall, Inc. and Professor Harry Nielsen, who devised this example.

[27] Martin Gardner, *Fads and Fallacies in the Name of Science* (New York: Dover, 1957), p. 301.

acting out the birth of a child" so that when a woman bakes a cake for her family she is symbolically presenting the family with a new baby, an idea she likes very much. Mr. Vicary cited the many jokes and old wives' tales about cake making as evidence: the quip that brides whose cakes fall obviously can't produce a baby yet; the married jest about "leaving a cake in the oven"; the myth that a cake is likely to fall if the woman baking it is menstruating. A psychological consulting firm in Chicago also made a study of cake symbolism and found that "women experience making a cake as making a gift of themselves to their family," which suggests much the same thing.

The food mixes—particularly the cake mixes—soon found themselves deeply involved in this problem of feminine creativity and encountered much more resistance than the makers, being logical people, ever dreamed possible. The makers found themselves trying to cope with negative and guilt feelings on the part of women who felt that use of ready mixes was a sign of poor housekeeping and threatened to deprive them of a traditional source of praise.

(VANCE PACKARD, *The Hidden Persuaders*) [28]

7. According to Count Alfred Korzybski, the General Semanticist, people are "unsane" when their mental maps of reality are slightly out of correspondence with the real world. If the inner world is too much askew, they become "insane." A principal cause of all this is the Aristotelian mental orientation, which distorts reality. It assumes, for example, that an object is either a chair or not a chair, when clearly there are all kinds of objects which may or may not be called chairs depending on how you define "chair." But a precise definition is impossible. "Chair" is simply a word we apply to a group of things more or less alike, but which fade off in all directions, along continuums, into other objects which are not called chairs. . . .

The non-Aristotelian mental attitude is, in essence, a recognition of the above elementary fact. There is no such thing as pure "chairishness." There are only chair 1, chair 2, chair 3, et cetera! This assigning of numbers is a process Korzybski called "indexing." In similar fashion, the same chair changes constantly in time. Because of weathering, use, and so forth, it is not the same chair from one moment to the next. We recognize this by the process of "dating." We speak of chair 1952, chair 1953, et cetera! The Count was convinced that the unsane, and many insane, could be helped back to sanity by teaching them to think in these and similar non-Aristotelian ways. For example, a neurotic may hate all mothers. The reason may be that a childhood situation caused him to hate his own mother. Not having broken free of Aristotelian habits, he thinks all mothers are alike because they are all called by the same word. But the word, as Korzybski was fond of repeating, is not the thing. When a man learns to index mothers—that is, call them mother 1, mother 2, mother 3, et cetera—he then perceives that other mothers are not identical with his own mother. In addition, even *his* mother is not the same mother she was when he was a child. Instead there are mother 1910, mother 1911, mother 1912, et

28 Vance Packard, *The Hidden Persuaders* (New York: Pocket Books, 1960), pp. 65–66.

cetera. Understanding all this, the neurotic's hatred for mothers is supposed to diminish greatly.

(MARTIN GARDNER, *Fads and Fallacies in the Name of Science*) [29]

8. Dowsing is the art of finding underground water or other substances by means of a divining rod, which is usually a forked stick. The method works with a good dowser. Sometimes a good dowser has difficulty, but this is because of such factors as fatigue, lack of concentration, poor physical condition, worry, too much friction on soles of shoes, all sorts of atmospheric conditions, the presence of electric lines in the area, humidity of soil, tree roots, and so forth. Although an effort can be made to take these factors into account, they are so numerous that in practice to take them all into account would be virtually impossible. This is the major reason that controlled experiment has failed to show that dowsing works. Also it should be kept in mind that the digging often diverts the water which is located by dowsing.

9. Some people think the earth is rotating at a speed of 1,000 miles an hour. But this is clearly impossible. For one thing, if it were moving like this and I threw a rock straight up into the air, then during the seconds that the rock took for its descent, the earth would have moved over a mile, so the rock would hit a mile away. But the rock lands very near the point from which I threw it. Also, if a bird on a tree were to let go, it would be rushed away if the earth is moving anything like 1,000 miles per hour. Just think of those paper cups that we let go when the car is doing a mere sixty! Or suppose the bird sees a worm and lets go of the tree. The earth, in the meantime, goes whirling by at this enormous rate, and obviously, no matter how hard the bird flaps its wings, it can never achieve sufficient speed to reach the worm. But this is ridiculous! Birds catch worms constantly!

10. It is no longer possible to doubt seriously the existence of intelligent life on other planets. True, before the invention of the airplane and radar tracking devices, the thousands of reported sightings of UFO's or "unidentified flying objects" were not enough to constitute convincing evidence. They served only to provoke wonder. But in our own century things have happened which change the picture entirely. In the first place we have on record the sworn testimony of many World War II and Korean pilots, as well as commercial airline pilots, to the effect that their planes were paced for minutes at a time, in bright daylight, by ships of a construction never attempted on earth. Gen. James Doolittle, leader of the first raid on the Japanese mainland, has given testimony of such an occurrence. When human pilots attempted to swing closer for a better look, the strange craft sped away at fantastic speeds, estimated at over 2000 mph.

Beyond such testimony as the above, we know that radar stations have tracked not only giant single ships, such as the one which Captain Mantell, an Air

[29] Martin Gardner, *Fads and Fallacies in the Name of Science* (New York: Dover, 1957), pp. 284–285. Copyright © 1952, 1957 by Martin Gardner. Used by permission.

Force officer stationed near Washington D.C., tried to investigate at the cost of his life, but also, in hundreds of instances, whole squadrons of smaller ships flying in tight formations. Radar experts have testified that the speed, sharp turns, and close formation of these fleets rule out any possibility of finding an explanation in weather phenomena. The blips on the radar screens were unmistakably those of solid objects, some of great size, and these experts, remember, speak from a background of military experience in which there was no room allowed for loose interpretations or confusions of one kind of object with another.

It is plain from the mass of such testimony that the UFO's are not patches of vapor, nor are their radar blips anything like what might be produced by experiments with light reflections in the atmosphere. Their speeds exceed anything achieved on earth, their changes of direction and high rates of acceleration bespeak a degree of engineering knowledge not to be found on earth even at the drawing-board stage.

The core of my argument is this: when we have exhausted all terrestrial possibilities that might explain these objects, our only alternative is the extra-terrestrial hypothesis. And it is fairly easy to exhaust the terrestrial possibilities. The speeds, accelerations, and structural features of these UFO's are simply beyond what our civilization has shown evidence that it is able to produce. Further, the number of such craft indicates an engineering program of dimensions impossible to conceal on earth, even in a territory as vast as the U.S.S.R. Besides, it is obvious that the Russians could not be responsible, for their pioneer work in sputniks is of an order far inferior to the performance of UFO's. If any more is needed to absolve the Russians, we may recall that UFO's have been sighted for many years, whereas the U.S.S.R. has only in the last decade made its great industrial strides.

The simple impossibility, then, of explaining UFO's by reference to what man on earth is capable of, forces us to this hypothesis: there is, quartered somewhere far out in space, a civilization technologically in advance of our own. It is managed by intelligent beings. These beings have shown a sustained interest in what goes on on earth. Their mastery of space and speed keeps them safe from any attempts of ours to study them closely. But that they exist, there cannot be any doubt.[30]

11. . . . there is another experiment one can do at home, this time using an adult as a subject rather than a child. Buy two presents for your wife, again choosing things you are reasonably sure she will find about equally attractive. Find some plausible excuse for having both of them in your possession, show them to your wife and ask her to tell you how attractive each one is to her. After you have obtained a good measure of attractiveness, tell her that she can have one of them, whichever she chooses. The other you will return to the store. After she has made her choice, ask her once more to evaluate the attractiveness of each of them. If you compare the evaluations of attractiveness

---

[30] This example was created by Prof. Harry Nielsen of the University of Notre Dame, and we use it here with his permission.

before and after the choice, you will probably find that the chosen present has increased in attractiveness and the rejected one decreased.

Such behavior can be explained by a new theory concerning "cognitive dissonance." This theory centers around the idea that if a person knows various things that are not psychologically consistent with one another, he will, in a variety of ways, try to make them more consistent. Two items of information that psychologically do not fit together are said to be in a dissonant relation to each other. The items of information may be about behavior, feelings, opinions, things in the environment and so on. The word "cognitive" simply emphasizes that the theory deals with relations among items of information.

(LEON FESTINGER, "Cognitive Dissonance") [31]

[31] Leon Festinger, "Cognitive Dissonance" in *Scientific American,* October 1962, p. 93. Reprinted with permission. Copyright © 1962 by Scientific American, Inc. All rights reserved.

Chapter Nineteen

SOME LOGICAL FEATURES OF SCIENCE

So far, in this section, the scientist's activities have been described in terms of deduction, induction, corroboration, falsification, and explanation. In the foregoing chapters there have been allusions to the logical structure of what might be called the product of these activities. It is now time to examine certain logical features of this product. First we will take a closer look at the logical character of laws. Then we will take a distant look at the general structure of a science—the structure which is commonly considered the ideal structure of a fully developed science. Finally we will discuss the contrast between scientific knowledge and what is sometimes referred to as "common" knowledge.

THE LOGICAL CHARACTER OF SCIENTIFIC LAWS

Two clear-cut examples of the kind of statements called "laws" in science are: Galileo's law concerning free falling bodies—whenever a body falls freely, it has a constant acceleration [1]—and the gas law—all gases, at constant pressure, expand with increasing temperature.[2] On inspection it can be seen that these laws have a universal form, that is, they have the form: Whenever A, then B; All A's are B's; or If anything is A, then

---

[1] The law is: $D = AT^2/2$, where D is distance, A is 32 ft./sec.[2], and T is time.
[2] $V = kt/P$. Although different laws assume different mathematical expression in the formal theories, our remarks in this section are applicable to all. We will not consider, in this section, laws that are not universal.

428

it is also *B*. Statements which have this form, as we have seen, are called universal generalizations. Generally those statements called laws are formulated or can be reformulated so that they display this form.

Though a law is a universal generalization which is true, it does not follow that if a statement is a universal generalization and is true, then it is what we could call a "law." For example, at the moment this universal generalization is true: All the coins in my pocket are pennies. But this is clearly not a law.

Now the problem of interest in this section is how we distinguish those true universal generalizations which are called laws, such as Galileo's law, from true universal statements which are not called laws, such as "All the coins in my pocket are pennies," and other true generalizations.

Constant Conjunction

According to David Hume's classic account of causality, the objective content of a law like Galileo's is nothing more than what is asserted in this statement: There never in the past has been a free falling body that has not had a constant acceleration, there are no such bodies now, and there never will be. According to Hume, a law merely asserts a *constant conjunction* between things, properties of things, or events—in this example, a constant conjunction between being a free falling body and having a constant acceleration. This account does distinguish laws like Galileo's from true universal generalizations like "All the coins in my pocket are pennies." For when the latter is asserted it is not asserted that never in the past has there been a coin in my pocket which was not a penny, there is not now, nor ever will be a coin in my pocket which is not a penny.

However, it seems evident to many that a law, though it does imply a statement of constant conjunction, is not to be understood as merely asserting a constant conjunction or being equivalent to a statement of constant conjunction. For if it were so regarded, then it would be difficult to see how laws would differ from these true universal generalizations which assert a constant conjunction between things:

1. Every sounding of the 12 o'clock whistle at factory *A* in Cincinnati, Ohio, is followed by the workers leaving factory *B* in Columbus, Ohio.[3]

2. All robins' eggs are blue.

It seems evident that (1) and (2) differ from laws, but how do they differ? The common response to this question is as follows: The first uni-

[3] This is a modification of Bertrand Russell's example in *The Analysis of Mind* (London, 1921), p. 97.

versal generalization (1) expresses a coincidental relation between things, and (2) is a generalization arrived at by induction by enumeration. It is quite possible that if robins started to eat different foods or live in different regions their eggs might be purple or red. But a law of nature such as Galileo's does not express a coincidental relationship; and, more importantly, if a body falls freely, then it *must* accelerate at a constant rate—it is impossible that there should be a free falling body which does not fall in this way.

Logical Necessity

This response suggests that laws like Galileo's differ from mere statements of constant conjunction in that laws express a logical necessity—that is, they are logical truths—whereas statements of mere constant conjunction are contingent. There is *some* truth to this view. Earlier, in Part I, the possibility of a sentence being used to make different statements was discussed.[4] It is easy to overlook this possibility in speaking of a law in science, with the result that one fails to note the differences in how such sentences as "Whenever a body falls freely it has a constant acceleration" are used in scientific work. But if proper attention is paid to the use of such a sentence, it may be seen that at one time or in one context it is used to express a logical truth, whereas in another time or in another context it is used to express a contingent statement. That is, in some contexts, what is meant by "free falling body" *is* a body which has a constant acceleration. Thus the statement "Whenever a body falls freely it has a constant acceleration" would be analogous, in such contexts, to, say, "A triangle has three sides" in the context of geometry. In a word, the sentence would be used to express a logical truth. In other contexts, the statement may be regarded as one which could be *false*.

This point is important enough to justify some further explanation. To introduce a new term into the vocabulary of science, a scientist must provide a definition—either explicit or implicit—or explain how the word is to be used. Introducing terms, or providing old ones with new stipulative definitions, ordinarily means introducing new logical truths. But the meaning or definition of a term can and often does evolve gradually. The truth of the statement "Salt is an ionic compound" may once have been a discovery—and the statement may thus have been regarded as a factual statement. But now, in scientific contexts, it is usually regarded as part of the definition of a salt. One can, for these reasons, understand more clearly why someone might be inclined to characterize all laws—or none—(in all ways in which they are regarded and in all uses to which they are put) as logical truths. It is undoubtedly true that

[4] See Chapter Four, pages 112–116.

scientists, philosophers, and those who talk about science are not always careful—and it is not always possible—to distinguish statements which are true because of the way the words are defined—that is, logical truths —from statements whose truth derives from observations. And to complicate matters, what today is a statement of fact may be a logical truth tomorrow—or two centuries later. Therefore a flat and comprehensive statement that no pronouncement of a science is a logical truth (or is not a logical truth) is very probably in error. Consider, for example:

1. All coins are metal.

This happens not to be true, for there are coins made of wood, leather, ivory, and other materials. It is true, however, in the United States, and if one takes the speaker to be referring to United States coins, he would count the statement as true, although not, of course, logically true. But it may come about that for a long period no coins are made which are *not* metal so that the property of being metal comes to be part of the *definition* of a coin. Then one would, with justification, say that (1) is a logical truth, since "being made of metal" is part of the meaning of "coin." To say that some coins are not metal would be to utter a contradiction, just as to say "Some bachelors are married" is (now) to utter a contradiction. (It is possible, however, that at one time it was proper to refer to the husband of a separated couple as a bachelor.)

Now it may well be that a number of what used to be laws in physics, chemistry, and so forth, are now so commonplace that they are regarded as definitions; for example, Newton's first law—$F = ma$—is regarded by some as a definition of force.[5] After all, the point of a definition *is* to indicate how the word is used—either by associating its use with that of a synonym, or by indicating the properties of that which is referred to by the word, or in some other way. And if a statement such as "Force is mass times acceleration" is taken as the rule as to how "force" is to be used, it achieves the status or role of a definition.

In summary, a law sentence can at one time be a logical truth and can at another time be a contingent truth. In addition, at a given time the same law sentence could in one context express a logical truth and in another context express a contingent truth.

But this still leaves the problem of how we are to understand lawlike universal conditionals at those times or in those contexts where they are not used as logical truths. In the remainder of this section we will be concerned with law sentences which are used, or regarded, in this way.

[5] Cf. N. R. Hanson, *Patterns of Discovery* (Cambridge, 1958), pp. 99 ff.

Nomological Universality

At times law statements do not express logically necessary truths, but rather express contingent truths. Many have thought, however, that law statements in such contexts do not express only constant conjunction. Some have supposed that a scientific law expresses a sort of necessity different from logical necessity. A law, it is argued, expresses a "physical necessity," or, as it is often put, a "nomological necessity." Laws, it is thus held, are not only expressions of constant conjunctions but necessary connections which are weaker, however, than logically necessary connections. According to this view universal statements can be divided into logically necessary and contingent statements. And among the class of contingent universal statements, we can distinguish those which express only constant conjunction and those which express nomic necessity.

The controversial issue whether laws express a kind of necessity different from logical necessity will not be directly considered. Rather in the remaining part of this section we will consider characteristics which set off clear-cut examples of what are called "laws" in the sciences from clear-cut examples of universal statements which only express constant conjunction. The result of this review will provide, in part, an explanation of what is meant when we speak of some (universal) statements as "laws" and some as "mere expressions of constant conjunction."

The Meaning of "Law"

What are the frequently cited characteristics which set off universal generalizations which are called laws from expressions of mere constant conjunction? The first is that coincidentally true universal generalizations expressing constant conjunction make reference to a particular individual object (for example, the whistle in factory A) and to particular times (for example, 12 o'clock), whereas law statements generally do not. For example, the two paradigm laws do not make reference to particular things or to any particular time. However, some statements which are called laws, for example, Kepler's law (all planets move on elliptical orbits with the sun at one focus of each ellipse) do make reference to particular individual objects (in the case of Kepler's law—the sun), but they are not restricted to a particular period of time.

Second, law statements support counterfactual conditionals, whereas statements of constant conjunction, like "All robins' eggs are blue," do not. A counterfactual conditional is a statement of this form: For any x, if x were A (even though it is not A at the moment), then it would be B. With respect to Galileo's law we can say: Since his law is true, it is true that if any particular entity were to be a freely falling body (even though it is not at the moment), then it would be falling with constant acceleration. That this relation holds between the law and the counterfactual conditional is what is meant by saying that a law *supports* a counterfactual conditional. Statements of constant conjunction like the above example do not support such conditionals.[6]

Third, law statements which are empirical laws can be supported by induction [kind (A)]—for example, induction by enumeration—but such laws commonly have additional support. They are deducible from established theories. Universal generalizations which merely express constant conjunction are not supported by being deducible from established theories but are supported by induction [kind (A)]. For example, Galileo's law is deducible from more general laws, for example, Newton's laws of motion. There are, however, experimental grounds which involve induction by enumeration for Galileo's law. On the other hand, statements of accidental constant conjunction and statements like "All robins' eggs are blue" are not supported by being deducible from established theories.

Often theoretical laws are deducible from more general theoretical laws, and, as has been indicated, they can be and are corroborated. This third difference can thus be expressed in this way: law statements find support through being deducible from established theories and/or being corroborated [and through induction of kind (A) where it is possible in connection with empirical laws], whereas statements of accidental constant conjunction and statements like "All robins' eggs are blue" do not find support through being deducible from established theories and are not corroborated but are supported by induction of kind (A).

Earlier it was noticed that it is quite natural in distinguishing laws from mere expressions of constant conjunction to say, for example, that if a body falls freely, then it *must* accelerate at a constant rate. The suggestion can now be made that in part (or in full) what is meant or can be meant by saying it "must" accelerate is that if it did not accelerate, this would conflict with an enormous body of established laws. Since mere statements of constant conjunction are not deductively related to any established laws, we do not say what is related in statements of constant conjunctions *must* be related in this way. So those who argue that laws express a nomological necessity are correct—if what is meant in saying that a nomological necessity exists between *A* and *B* is that every *A* must be *B* *in the sense* that if *A* were not *B,* a body of established laws would be false or need to be reconsidered.

Fourth, we can easily imagine evidence which would show that a statement expressing constant conjunction is false, whereas we cannot easily imagine evidence which would show that an empirical law is false or

[6] The reader should test other universal generalizations in this way.

which would lead us to abandon a theoretical law. For example, if someone said that whenever (in the past) anyone has found a robin's egg it
has been blue, and that if any robin's egg is found it will be blue (what
is asserted by "All robins' eggs are blue" understood merely as a constant
conjunction), we could easily imagine those circumstances which would
justify his saying it is *false* that all robins' eggs are blue. He or we could
come across an egg laid by a robin which is not blue. This ease of im-
agining observations which would falsify a constant conjunction statement is characteristic of such statements.

It is difficult, however, to imagine what observations would lead to
an abandonment of theoretical laws. (See Chapter Seventeen.) But it is
also difficult to imagine what observations would falsify empirical laws.

Suppose it were observed that an *A* was not a *B*. What implications
would this have for an established empirical law, All *A* is *B* (assuming
that *B* is not part of the meaning of *A* at the time)? It is likely that the
first reactions would be that the *A* is only apparently not *B*—something,
for example, went wrong with the instruments—or that one of the conditions that are presupposed when it is stated that all *A* is *B* was not fulfilled or that some unknown factor caused *A* not to be *B*. These reactions
show the reluctance to question an empirical law. And this reluctance is
easily explained. Past observations have shown the empirical law to be
(apparently) true and (quite often) the law is deducible from a group of
established theoretical laws which would be cast in suspicion if, indeed,
the empirical law conflicted with observation. However, in principle, if
it is indeed observed that an *A* is not a *B* and if the presupposed conditions are fulfilled, then these observations would falsify the empirical
law.

What would falsify Galileo's law? We are inclined at first to say that
if we observed a free falling body which did not have a constant acceleration, this would falsify it. But under what conditions would we be
justified in saying "This is a free falling body which does not have a
constant acceleration"? If a scientist came across some object which
appeared to be free falling and did not have a constant acceleration, he
would, most likely, search for *disturbing forces*. If that failed, he might
examine the body to see if it differed from bodies whose behavior is
normal. If no relevant factors were discovered, the scientist might save
the law by limiting its scope, that is, by specifying that it is not to be
applied under certain conditions. Long before this point, he would probably suspect the clocks employed. This reluctance to jettison a law such
as Galileo's is partially explained by the fact that it is formally deducible
from Newton's laws, so that dropping Galileo's laws would cast suspicion on the whole structure of mechanics. And there is, of course, a
mass of observational data which supports these statements. Thus it is
a fact that empirical laws can be and are often maintained under the

pressure of apparently disconfirming evidence, and thus it is difficult to say what exactly would constitute disconfirming evidence.

THE LOGICAL STRUCTURE OF A
FULLY DEVELOPED SCIENCE

The natural sciences—physical and biological—and also psychology and the social sciences (anthropology, sociology, economics, and the like), which will continue to be the object of our discussion, can all be described as fulfilling these two conditions:

1. A few central concepts tend to limit the type of knowledge incorporated into the science. For example, the concepts of "wealth," "supply," "consumption," "market," and so on, tend to delineate economics. Political scientists are primarily concerned with the ideas of the "state," "power," "legislation," "justice," and so on; and chemists are primarily interested in "element," "molecules," "reaction," "compound," and so on.
2. The knowledge is organized (or attempts are made to organize it) into a particular form in which the laws or theories are deducible from a few general principles.

We will refer to (1) as the "horizontal" organization of a science and (2) as the "vertical" organization of a science.

The "Horizontal" Organization of the Sciences

The sciences are not just a collection of true statements or laws. They are, first of all, collections of *related* facts, as (1) indicates. The chemist does not talk about strawberries and houses, except as a way of identifying the substances in which he is interested, nor does the astronomer speak of gods or toothpicks. The fact that each science fulfills (1) does not mean, of course, that the sciences are not related. Indeed they are; and often related sciences study the same phenomenon from their different points of view in order to see how the phenomenon can best be explained, or in order to provide a partial explanation which will provide, with the partial explanations of the other sciences, a comprehensive and relatively complete explanation of the phenomenon in question. Thus a cultural anthropologist, a social psychologist, a sociologist and a political scientist may all be interested in Hitler's rise to power, each for different reasons. Each will describe this event in the conceptual system of his science and will be interested in explaining it, if possible, with reference to the laws or general conclusions already established in his field. A biochemist, a chemist, a biologist and a neurologist may all study a particular kind of cell in the living tissue of organisms; and a physicist, an astronomer, and a physical chemist may all be interested in the atmosphere of a planet. As the terms physical chemist, biophysicist, astrophysicist, social psychologist, biochemist indicate, some of these overlapping areas are important enough to deserve names.

The language, the concepts, and the aims of each science, however, are usually readily distinguishable. The political scientist is *primarily* interested in the concept of power structure—that is, the government—and in the associated concepts. The sociologist is primarily interested in the formation and transformation of human groups. The attitudes of these groups, their relationship with each other, and their motivations are all of primary interest to the social psychologist. The cultural anthropologist's study is guided by the concepts of culture, race, diffusion, and so on, as well as various associated sociological concepts. In sciences such as chemistry or sociology there are subsciences—for example, in chemistry there is organic, inorganic, colloidal, biochemistry—each of which concentrates on a particular group of concepts. In physics, there are the (sub)sciences of mechanics, thermodynamics, and many others. And in sociology, there are the narrower sciences of rural sociology, the studies of political and religious groups, and so on, each of which is a division of the science of sociology. This diversification becomes necessary as the scientist finds the study of one particular area becoming more and more complex, so that a subset of the concepts which are of concern to the science now becomes the object of primary concern to a subscience.

The "Vertical" Organization

Deductive Relationships

Each of the experimental sciences and subsciences is, within itself, organized in a particular way. Let us consider the nature of this organization.

Ideally a science is organized as a deductive system. The organization takes this form: general observation statements (empirical laws) are deducible from (explainable by) theoretical laws. Sometimes a group of theoretical laws, a theory, is in turn deducible from more general theoretical laws, which are sometimes called the fundamental principles of a science or subscience, whichever the case may be.[7] The fundamental principles of a subscience are, in turn, deducible from the laws which are most fundamental to the science.

All of this is true, at least, of what is commonly regarded as the ideal form of a science. The logical relations between the phenomena, the empirical laws, the theoretical laws, the most general principles of the subsciences and the most general principles of the science may be the

---

[7] This will be true if the group of theoretical laws is not a separate science.

simple relation of a general statement to particular statements [8] or other deductive relationships such as those discussed in Part II, and mathematical relationships. In fact, the structure of the ideal theory corresponds closely to the formal axiomatic systems discussed in Part II.

It is clear that the axioms of the formal systems of Part II are not like the fundamental principles of a science, for example, the assertions about the path of a particle not subjected to external forces (Newton's first law), or about the relation between supply of and demand for consumer goods. The acceptability of the fundamental laws or principles of a science rests, in the end, on what phenomena are found in the world, but the axioms of the formal systems in logic and mathematics are independent of what sort of world this is.[9]

It is important to note, however, that, despite the different grounds or reasons for accepting each, much similarity exists between the fundamental principles of a theory in science and the logical and mathematical axioms. They play much the same role in their respective systems. The science or theory which reaches a satisfactory state of development is, for many scientists, that science or theory which comes closest to the kind of axiomatic system constructed in logic or mathematics; that is, one in which:

1. there are few fundamental principles;
2. the principles are acceptable and consistent;
3. all the laws of the theory are deducible from the fundamental principles by formal means so that no laws are deducible which are not acceptable.

These conditions are stated in such a way as to draw attention to the corresponding desirable conditions for the axioms of a formal system. Thus (1) relates to independence, (2) to consistency, and (3) relates to completeness. The phrase "by formal means" refers to the rules of inference in formal systems—and the transformations allowed by mathematics.

The theory or science which most closely approximates this ideal is classical mechanics.[10] But many other theories—most of which can be stated in mathematical form—can be formalized to some extent. [To formalize a theory means, roughly, to state it in such a way that it conforms to conditions (1) through (3).]

Thus the general structure of the ideal physical theory might be sketched as follows: [11]

[8] Thus the law of falling bodies—"$D = AT^2/2$"—is a general statement of those laws in which the A—gravitational force—assumes different definite values.

[9] The actual *form* of the laws also depends on the language men have.

[10] Cf. Patrick Suppes, *Introduction to Logic* (Princeton: Van Nostrand, 1957), Chapter 12.

[11] Taken from John Kemeny's *A Philosopher Looks at Science*. Copyright 1959, D. Van Nostrand Company, Inc., Princeton, N. J. Used by permission.

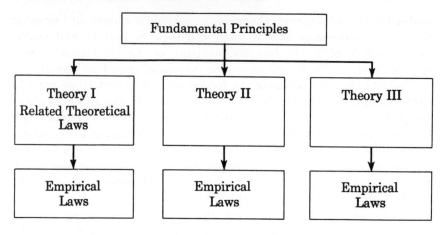

and in particular, in physics:

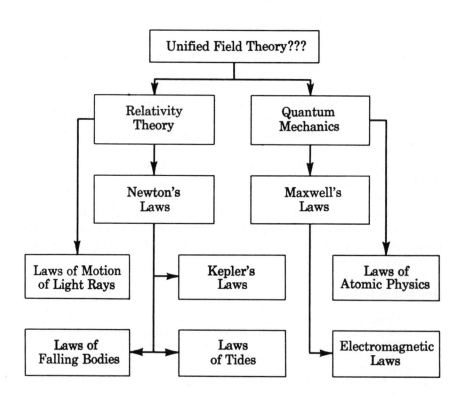

where the fundamental principles conform to the conditions (1) through (3), and where the arrows indicate logical or mathematical entailment. These features are to be found in those sciences which have been formalized—that is, the sciences whose fundamental principles and laws deducible from them have received a symbolic or mathematical formulation. Only such sciences as physics, branches of chemistry, and certain theories in the social sciences, then, are presently close enough to this ideal to be relevant to the discussion of these three aspects of theories.

IDEAL LAWS

Limiting Conditions

How does it happen that so many phenomena are explainable and predictable on the basis of a few relatively simple laws? Newton's or Einstein's laws are able to account for the tides, the behavior of an electron in a transistor, the action of a simple pendulum, the orbit of Mars, and the ease with which one falls off a log. How, in other words, does the scientist achieve the necessary generality in the statement of the fundamental laws—and lesser laws—to be able to deduce such a variety of statements about such diverse phenomena?

The answer is that laws treat, quite generally, of objects, entities, and conditions which are "ideal" or "limiting," in that many properties of the entities or objects and many factors relating to conditions referred to in the laws are simply ignored. The resulting idealized systems—that is, the entities and relations between them, as they are implicitly or explicitly characterized by the laws—have no exact counterparts in nature. In this they are like the geometers' definitions of "ideal" geometric figures. The geometers neglect the discrepancies between *any* circle as it occurs in nature or as it is constructed by someone, and the locus of points equidistant from a fixed point—the geometric circle. Thus the system of points without dimension, lines without width, circles that are (by definition) perfect, and so on, has no counterpart in nature, nor could it have. Similarly, the system of objects, entities, and relations between them characterized in the laws of mechanics has no counterpart in nature since this system is made up of point-masses (that is, dimensionless particles which have mass numbers assigned to them), perfectly homogeneous and rigid levers, fulcrums which do not wear or compress, parts and objects which move without friction or wear, and so on.

Galileo saw that it would be quite impossible to formulate a useful law—or any law at all—which took into account all of the factors which, in nature, influence the fall of a body. So he ignored them and attempted to relate the *essential* factors of gravity, time and acceleration. Just as the geometer ignores the fact that a "real" object must have color, mass, a position in space and time, that edges crumble and are not perfectly formed, so Galileo ignored, first of all, the color and material out of which the body is formed. Also he noticed that different objects fall in air with more nearly equal speeds than they do in water, and he supposed that the less dense the medium in which objects fall, the more nearly equal are their speeds. This meant, he concluded in *Two New Sciences,* that "in a medium totally devoid of resistance all bodies would fall with the same speed." Thus he was led to—and able to—ignore all factors pertaining to air resistance in formulating the relations between speed or velocity, gravitation, time, and acceleration. He knew moreover that it was necessary to do this in order to obtain a useful law: ". . . hence, in order to handle the matter in a scientific way, it is necessary to cut loose from these difficulties (air resistance, friction, and so on) and having discovered and demonstrated the theorems, in the case of no resistance, to use them and apply them with such limitations as experience will teach."

Then, with these complicating factors out of the way, Galileo was able, after formulating and testing a number of hypotheses, to verify the one which is known as the law of falling bodies. If he had tried to incorporate all the variations in the velocity of a falling body due to the volume and shape of the body and the medium through which it falls, he would probably not have succeeded. At any rate, the mathematical expression of such a law would be unwieldly, and the deductive relations between it and the laws of mechanics subsequently formulated would be disastrously complex.

It should be evident that the law of falling bodies is formulated in terms of a limiting condition—that is, the absence of friction—which can only be approximated in an experiment. So verifying this law and others, such as the laws of perfectly rigid levers, is accomplished by approximating the ideal conditions as closely as possible and by extrapolating, that is, correcting for the discrepancies. These are empirical laws even though the procedures involved in verifying them are, in the ways described, indirect. Only allowances for discrepancies need to be observed in applying and verifying these laws.

Ideal Entities

If a law introduces or implicitly defines a concept (as Newton's laws implicitly define a "point-mass") which has no counterpart in nature and could not have because of its lack of properties essential to physical objects, the law is also commonly referred to as an "ideal" law. The distinction between these laws and ideal laws which speak of limiting or ideal conditions is not always clear. Thus Galileo's laws can be regarded as referring to point-masses which, of course, would not encounter friction passing through a medium such as water or air. And the theories involving perfectly elastic walls of a container, or perfectly rigid bodies undergoing a transformation may be regarded as referring either to ideal objects or limiting conditions.

It is of interest to distinguish ideal entities from theoretical entities. One way of putting the difference is: an ideal entity is an entity for which no counterpart in nature could possibly exist; a theoretical entity, on the other hand, is, simply, one which an explanation or theory *requires*—it is an entity which makes an (or *the*) explanation possible. It may be worth noting that some entities are regarded as both ideal and theoretical—they are both necessary to explanations and such that it is impossible that their counterparts occur in nature. One such concept is that of the implicitly defined point-mass.

But the terms "ideal" entity and "theoretical" entity are not commonly used with sufficient precision to enable a nonarbitrary classification of such a theoretical entity as an electron. The properties of the electron are not at one end of a continuum—that is, they are not limiting. An electron cannot be approximated in nature in the way that an ideally elastic wall or a rigid lever can. This would suggest that the electron is not an ideal entity, but is a theoretical entity. On the other hand, the concept of the electron is such that all the properties of individual electrons are exactly the same—and this state of affairs is not duplicated in nature. This would suggest that the electron is an ideal entity.

At any rate, the importance of distinguishing ideal laws lies in their contrast with what we have called probabilistic laws. Probabilistic laws are formulated, ordinarily, when it is impossible to formulate ideal laws and so achieve a simple, elegant deductive system of laws. Galileo could have formulated statistical or probabilistic laws using the data he obtained in experiments if he had not noticed that the less dense the medium is through which bodies fall, the more nearly equal are the accelerations of these bodies so that he could neglect certain factors influencing fall. If he had not seen that he could neglect certain factors, these factors would have necessitated a more complex account of the results of his experiments.

Probabilistic Generalizations

Probalistic generalizations and universal generalizations

As was noted in connection with probabilistic explanations, a law which is a probabilistic generalization is not a universal generalization, but is characterized by the expressions "almost," "usually," and so on.

Various kinds of laws, expressed in different terms, are enough like probabilistic generalizations to allow us to discuss them without having to distinguish between them. The differences are essentially that in some laws the probability that something is the case (or some other statistical measure of regularity) is known precisely enough to allow a mathematical expression to be used. Thus, rather than using the following expressions (we are using "law" now to include probabilistic generalities):

1. It is unlikely that a coin will come up heads twice in a row.
2. Smith has an almost even chance to be elected in 1984.
3. Usually the weakening of a cultural ethos results in a rise in the rate of suicides.

we are sometimes able to assign a definite value (see footnote 15):

1. The probability that a coin will come up heads in two successive throws is $\frac{1}{4}$.

and perhaps eventually we will have highly reliable laws such as:

2'. The probability that a candidate with qualifications A, B, C, and so on, will be elected (in a certain type of community) is .48.
3'. A weakening (a certain magnitude) of a cultural ethos results in a two per cent rise in the rate of suicide.

Now the phrase "the probability that A is B is . . ." is ordinarily [12] taken to be a measure of how often A is B and how often A will be B. To say that an event is highly probable or has a high probability means that the event will occur frequently (relative to the number of possible events). Thus, to say that if two particular coins are tossed the probability is $\frac{1}{4}$ that they will both come up heads means:

(a) In the long run (that is, in a large sample), one time out of every four times the two coins are tossed, two heads will come up.
(b) There are four ways, which are equally probable,[13] in which the coins may fall, and two heads is one way.

(Normally, when the probability of events such as those in (2) and (3) are in question, (b) cannot be determined because of the complexity of these situations.)

Probabilistic generalizations and probabilistic explanations

Earlier the distinction was made between probabilistic explanations (any nondeductive explanations) and deductive explanations. Let us now consider different types of probabilistic explanations; the first being a

[12] There is a great deal of controversy about the meaning of probability in relation to individual events. Cf. Nagel, *The Structure of Science*, p. 561.
[13] That is, "probable" as shown by a large number of trials with these coins.

typical probabilistic explanation; the second and third being deductive, in which probabilistic generalizations are employed. This will amplify the previous remarks about probabilistic explanations. (See Chapter Eighteen.)

Suppose one is interested in finding out how many people in a community will vote for candidate X in a forthcoming election. And suppose that 100 people are picked in such a way that they constitute a representative sample—that is, picked so that from what is learned about these 100 people, the general results of the election can be predicted. The generality established in this way is a probabilistic generalization (or statistical generality) whose worth will depend on how good the sample is. Let us say that for every four voters, three will vote for candidate X. That is,

1. If Y is a member of the community the probability is .75 that he will vote for X.

We recall first how (1) will figure in a probabilistic explanation of

3. Smith will vote for X.

To (1) we add the explanatory premiss (or statement of initial conditions)

2. Smith is a member of the community.

Premisses (1) and (2) give to (3) a probability of .75. This is not a deductive argument, nor would it be a deductive argument if the phrase "the probability is .75" were replaced by the phrase "it is likely" or a similar expression.

Second, let us see how (1) itself might be explained as part of a deductive system of laws along with certain factual conditions. One way this might come about is by the establishment of a general statement of the form:

4. If Y is a member of the community and possesses attribute Z, then, and then only, will he vote for X.

which may be used as a premiss. That is, it may be that one attribute—such as belonging to the same political party—may be found, which is necessary and sufficient to insure that Y votes for X. And if three out of four voters possess this attribute, then (1) follows.

But this is obviously overly optimistic where such complex matters as voting behavior are concerned. It is even unlikely that the behavior of each voter can be explained in terms of a small number of distinct attributes such as the one mentioned, or such as the fact that the voter is a friend of the candidate, or that he votes a certain way because of religious prejudice, and so on. But it is possible. Let us suppose that each member of the sample possesses one or more of the three attributes, and that it was found that:

5. If Y has attribute A, then the probability is r that Y will vote for X.
6. If Y has attribute B, then the probability is m that Y will vote for X.
7. If Y has attribute C, then the probability is n that Y will vote for X.

If the factual statements showing the distribution of these attributes among the members of the sample are added to these laws, then a law like (1) would be *deducible* by the rules of calculating with probabilities and rules of logical inference.

There are a number of remarks to be made about probabilistic laws such as (5), (6), (7), and (1). First it should be noted that it is seldom that the probabilities of such events as voting can be precisely determined in practice, and that there are correlated difficulties of determining which factors bear on the event and whether they have direct bearing or are necessary conditions for the event. Thus the form of probabilistic explanations may vary widely. Second, it should be evident that the range of applicability of such laws—that is, the value of such laws in prediction of election results—is limited to the community, the candidate, and perhaps the voters, referred to in the law. If our concern is with a larger community or a different candidate the same attributes may or may not be relevant. And third, different sets of premisses—that is different explanations—may exist for an individual event. Or to put it in another way, different sets of attributes may yield nearly the same probability for a particular event. This may be due to a lack of exact knowledge as to the relevant factors, or causes, of the event, or this may be due to the fact that, in human affairs, there are different sets of sufficient conditions for the same event.[14]

Probabilistic generalizations and ideal laws

The differences between probabilistic generalizations and ideal laws can now be stated more fully:

1. The most obvious difference (and the one in terms of which the other differences will be explained) is that in an ideal law, "ideal" entities are referred to, or "ideal" conditions are specified or assumed in the law, whereas in a probabilistic generalization the entities referred to are generally familiar ones.[15]

14 Cf. Freudian "overdetermination": Freud maintained that sometimes an action can be accounted for in terms of unconscious notions even though it can be explained by conscious or manifest notions.

15 Theoretical laws, however, are sometimes probabilistic (or statistical)—for example, those which assign a rate of decomposition to a radioactive substance can be construed, or stated, as assigning a probable life to each atom. Thus,

2. The concepts in probabilistic generalizations of the social sciences are incomparably richer and more complex than the concepts which are expressed or introduced in ideal laws. The concept "man" is clearly much more complex than that of a pendulum or silver or atom; and the concept of intelligence is much more complex than that of mass or a chemical reaction. Even though there is no precise standard of complexity, there is no disagreement about such comparisons as these.

3. Probabilistic generalizations do not assert that the relations of dependence hold in all cases of the sort referred to in the law, while there is no such qualification in ideal laws.

4. Probabilistic generalizations, especially in the present stage of the social sciences, are severely limited in application, compared to ideal laws.

5. The source of the certitude, or the reasons for the acceptability of ideal laws lie mainly in their consistency with other laws, and in their explanatory power—that is, the number and variety of phenomena which they explain. The acceptability of a probabilistic generalization, however, is ordinarily based on techniques of getting a representative sample.

SUMMARY

Hume maintained that scientific laws assert only that there is a constant conjunction of two (or more) events, properties or things. This view is criticized in various ways:

First, some claim that all scientific laws are logical truths—which are, thus, true by virtue of the meanings of the terms of the law. We note that undoubtedly, in some contexts, laws are in fact regarded in this way. But there are various roles that laws have in science, and not all of them are compatible with the view that laws are (merely) logical truths.

Second, the Humean view neglects certain differences between the universal generalizations which are laws of science and those universal generalizations which, for example, express only coincidentally constant conjunctions of events, properties and things, such as:

Laws are not limited in scope by references to particular places and times.
Laws support counterfactual conditionals.
Laws gain support in ways other than by simple enumeration of confirming instances.
Laws are seldom falsifiable by a single direct observation of the absence of a conjunction of things, properties or events. It is often not possible to specify exactly the conditions under which they would be regarded as falsified.

---

since there are entities which are both theoretical and ideal, (1) is not universally true. Also, in the purely mathematical treatment of probability, a statement such as "If two coins are tossed the probability is $\frac{1}{4}$ that they will both come up heads" must be taken to refer to "ideal" coins.

Ideal laws, which are characteristic of the highly formalized physical sciences, are those which involve "ideal" entities or limiting conditions or both. An "ideal" entity is one which lacks some properties (or possesses others) which every physical object possesses (or which none possesses). By neglecting, maximizing, or minimizing certain properties of objects, laws and the deductive relations between laws are considerably simplified.

It is not always possible, however, to formulate ideal laws and so achieve the logical elegance that some sciences possess. Often, especially in the social sciences, it is necessary to express relations between events, properties and things in terms of the probability that these relations obtain, or in terms of some statistical measure.

EXERCISES I

A. Review the earlier exercises and examples found in the preceding chapters of Part III and indicate the law statements. Classify the laws as empirical or theoretical. Classify the laws as ideal laws, non-ideal universal generalizations, or probabilistic generalizations.

B. Find the counterfactual conditionals in the first exercises (pages 210–211) of Chapter Eight.

C. Here are some statements about laws. Criticize each on the basis of the discussion in this chapter.

1. In its empirical aspect, natural science is a collection of generalizations which summarize the past and point to the future.
2. Laws describe the way in which things have happened in the past, and predict the way things will happen in the future.
3. All highly confirmed hypotheses are scientific laws, and all scientific laws are highly confirmed general hypotheses.
4. A law asserts that whenever there are specified kinds of conditions, a specified kind of event will occur.
5. Laws express the presence of causal connections.
6. Laws govern different classes of phenomena.
7. Laws are universal conjunctions of terms.
8. Laws describe regularities in phenomena.
9. Laws of nature are the laws of our way of representing it.

A law is:
10. A rule or formula according to which anything exists or comes into being.
11. A decree of the divine powers governing all things.
12. The binding practices of nature.

SCIENCE AND COMMON SENSE

It is sometimes said that science conflicts or can conflict with common sense. There are a number of different ways to understand this charge. Understood in the one way the charge is true; understood in the other ways it is false. Let us critically examine, then, the ways in which the charge can be understood.

Genuine Conflicts with Common Sense

From time to time people have held views which were later found to be false. For example, for a time most people believed that the sun revolves around the earth. If we call a belief which is held by most people at some time or other a "common sense" belief, then there have been times when the discoveries of science have proven certain common sense beliefs to be false, as in this example.

A more intriguing example of a conflict between science and common sense is that of the nonadditive properties of the velocity of light. The simple addition and subtraction of velocity seems to rest on common sense. If a man walking at the rate of two miles per hour moves toward the rear of a train moving at the rate of sixty miles per hour, his velocity relative to the track is 58 miles per hour. Or suppose the train is approaching a viaduct at twenty yards per second, and a man is blowing a whistle on the viaduct. The sound waves from the whistle travel outward from the whistle at 400 yards per second. The velocity of the sound relative to the moving train, however, is 420 yards per second as the train approaches the viaduct and 380 yards per second after it has passed the viaduct. This principle of the addition of velocities was a standard and fundamental law in pre-Einsteinian science.

But suppose a man on the viaduct shines a flashlight toward the oncoming train. The light has velocity v and the train has velocity c. "Common sense"—which seems to be addicted to reasoning by analogy— supposed that the velocity of light relative to the train should be $v + c$, as in the case when we are talking about sound. But it is not—it is v. And when the train has passed the viaduct the velocity of the light rays from the viaduct is still v relative to the train.

The mistake of "common sense" here is the assumption that the "movement" of light is *like* that of sound and of gross material bodies. The conflict is actually between knowledge and ignorance. There is a host of such conflicts between science and common sense; other examples are the conflicts between what the scientist knows about the behavior of solids at very low temperatures, the properties of the elementary particles, the consequences of relativity theory, and what a man ignorant of these matters is inclined to believe.

If the charge that science conflicts with common sense, then, is understood to mean that such common sense beliefs have been found to conflict with the discoveries of science, then the charge is true.

Common Knowledge and Science

Consider the following statements:

Most substances expand when heated.
Water solidifies on sufficient cooling.
Sunlight refracts when it enters a body of water.
Wood is ordinarily solid and relatively durable.

Most of us know these things and know a great many other things like this, so we are justified in calling such knowledge "common sense knowledge." Notice how this "common sense" knowledge differs from the "common sense" belief that the sun revolves around the Earth or that the velocity of light is additive.

Statements such as the four mentioned above can be, and are, seen to be true. But those who believed that the Sun revolves around the Earth did not "see" that the Sun revolves about the Earth. It only appeared to do so. And those who believed that the velocity of light should be added to the velocity of the oncoming train did not *see* that it should, but only supposed so. It is obvious that many casual observers who are relatively uncritical can be wrong if conclusions are drawn in ignorance of the fact that they are not in a position to make correct observations and if their beliefs are based simply on an analogy.

The scientist's results can, of course, conflict with beliefs based on analogy or uncritical observations, but his results cannot conflict with or confirm common knowledge. For, as we have seen, one of his primary aims is to *explain* why substances expand when heated and why water solidifies, and so on—in a word, explain known phenomena.

Common Words and Science

People are sometimes guilty of misrepresenting the discoveries of science. This must also be noted if we wish to understand some alleged contradictions between science and common knowledge. It has been said, for example, that science has shown that an ordinary wooden table is not solid—as we ordinarily think—but is largely empty space. This view is supported by citing the fact that the distances between the elementary particles are very great relative to the dimensions of the particles. This is paradoxical. Is the table solid or is it not? The question, however, is suspicious. It is the question someone would ask in order to befuddle us. Suppose it were asked: Is the table solid? and Is the molecular theory true? This is less puzzling and less paradoxical. The answer to both questions is clearly affirmative. And when we remember that it is *by means* of the molecular theory, molecular adhesion, and other properties of the elementary particles, that we *explain* such properties of wood as solidity, toughness, and so on, it is clear that the one who would claim that tables are not solid, and that we are mistaken when we ordinarily say that tables are solid because the molecular theory is true, has represented the discovery of elementary particles as being another *kind* of discovery than it is. For the discovery of elementary particles is *not* a discovery that we were mistaken in thinking the table is solid, but a discovery of *why* the table is solid. The discovery that the Earth revolves about the Sun, on the other hand, was *not* a discovery of *why* the Sun revolves about the Earth, but a discovery that the Sun did *not* revolve around the Earth.

Let us consider another approach to this difficulty. Notice that "solidity" is a very common and pervasive criterion of our use of "wood," that "becoming ice upon sufficient cooling" is a common and pervasive criterion of our use of "water," and so on. That is, if someone spoke of water cooled to −10°F. without freezing, we would ask, "Is this ordinary water?"—that is, "Is this the substance that we ordinarily refer to as 'water'?" And we ask this because a common criterion is missing. So if it were said that wood is not solid or that water does not solidify when cooled to −10°F., our first response might well be to ask whether what we have here should be called "wood" or "water." (Of course, we might say of a particular piece of wood that it is not solid, meaning by this that it is highly porous or rotten. Furthermore, someone in stressing that wood can be compressed in the way metal cannot might say "Wood is not solid." If this is how the sentence were used, we would of course not raise the question whether what we have should or should not be called wood.)

Now when in a context of science it is sometimes said that wood is not solid, the difference between wood and metal is not what is being pointed out, for metal—in this context—would also be said to be not solid. In addition, it is not being announced that someone has found a substance which has all the usual characteristics of that which we call wood but which lacks solidity, and is not rotten, and so on. Furthermore no one—in this context—is saying that we utter false statements when we say, for example, "The table is solid, so it will hold the box up" or "Water will not leak through the table top." However, the word "wood" in the statement that wood is not solid is to be understood in its ordinary sense. How, then, is this statement to be understood? It would seem that it should be understood as a (misleading) way of saying that wood is composed of elementary particles.

Does the fact that wood is composed of atoms show us that solidity is not really a criterion for a substance being called wood? Has the atomic theory shown us the real meaning of the word "wood"? There is no real meaning of a word independent of use. What a word means depends on how it is used. In the context of science the word "wood" might be so used that solidity is not one of its criteria. For example, chemical composition might be the criteria for something being wood. But this does not imply that the ordinary use of the word is mistaken in any way any more than the fact that we ordinarly use solidity as one of the criteria for the use of the word "wood" in ordinary discourse shows that the use to which the scientists put the word is mistaken. Sometimes the scientist uses the same word with different criteria. The scientist frequently alters, extends and stipulates new meaning for words which are used in ordinary discourse. The meanings of words in ordinary discourse are also altered, extended, refined, and changed by stipulation. But to use a word with different criteria, to alter, extend, or stipulate a use for a word does not entail the incorrectness of its other uses or former uses.

SUMMARY

Sometimes there are genuine conflicts between the findings of science and common beliefs. These conflicts are factual disputes and present no problems to the logician. But sometimes what appears to be a factual dispute can be seen to be a dispute about language. This usually takes the form of a suggestion or claim that the findings of science make necessary the alteration of the meaning of a word or a change in the criteria governing its use. It is not necessary to do this, nor is it always desirable or of any importance.

EXERCISES II

Do the following involve conflicts between science and common knowledge?

1. We often hear that the sun sets in the west and rises in the east. But astronomers tell us this is not true.

2. A noted psychologist—a behaviorist—recounts that a number of years ago it suddenly occurred to him that he was not conscious and, further, that he had never been conscious.

3. What would you do if a weatherman announced, "A cyclone is coming"?

Some people would run for cover. However, they would probably be running unnecessarily. In its most general sense the term *cyclone* refers to an area of low pressure around which the air is circulating. . . . They are the largest storm centers nature produces, but, fortunately, they are also the tamest. The winds usually are not strong enough to cause damage to property, injuries or fatalities.

(LOUIS J. BATTAN, *The Nature of Violent Storms*) [16]

4. "Structure" may seem an odd word to apply to liquids, implying as it does an enduring form. Is not the lack of structure-fluidity the very essence of a liquid? I shall argue here that it is not: that liquids do have, if only instantaneously, an internal molecular architecture in which the key to understanding their properties lies.

(J. D. BERNAL, "The Structure of Liquids") [17]

5. What happens when a projectile strikes a target at extremely high velocity? Experiments indicate that impacts at speeds greater than about 8,000 feet per second cause metals to flow like liquids.

(A. C. CHARTERS, "High-Speed Impact") [18]

6. As long ago as 1870 the British physicist John Tyndall demonstrated that light, which, as everyone knows, travels in straight lines, can be conducted along a curved path. His "light pipe" was simply a thin stream of water issuing from a hole in the side of a tank. Light shined into the tank emerged at the hole and followed the downward-curving stream.

(NARINDER S. KAPANY, "Fiber Optics") [19]

7. An electron is no more (and no less) hypothetical than a star. Nowadays we count electrons one by one in a Geiger counter, as we count stars one by one on a photographic plate. In what sense can an electron be called more unobservable than a star? I am not sure whether I ought to say that I have seen an electron; but I have just the same doubt whether I have seen a star. If I have seen one, I have seen the other. I have seen a small disc of light surrounded by diffraction rings which has not the least resemblance to what a star is supposed to be; but the name "star" is given to the object in the physical world which some hundreds of years ago started a chain of causation which has resulted in this particular light-pattern. Similarly, in a Wilson expansion chamber I have seen a trail not in the least resembling what an electron is supposed to be; but

16 Louis J. Battan, *The Nature of Violent Storms* (New York: Anchor Books, 1961), pp. 129–130.

17 J. D. Bernal, "The Structure of Liquids" in *Scientific American*, Vol. 203, No. 2, August 1960, p. 124.

18 A. C. Charters, "High-Speed Impact" in *Scientific American*, Vol. 203, No. 4, October 1960, p. 128.

19 Narinder S. Kapany, "Fiber Optics" in *Scientific American*, Vol. 203, No. 5, November 1960, p. 72.

the name electron is given to the object in the physical world which has caused this trail to appear. How can it possibly be maintained that a hypothesis is introduced in one case and not in the other.

(SIR ARTHUR EDDINGTON, *New Pathways in Science*) [20]

EXERCISES III

Read each item and answer the questions.

1. This writer obviously believes he has located a number of common sense beliefs which conflict with science. What are they? And is he correct?

Consider how the universe appears to any man, however wise . . . who has never heard one word of what science has discovered. To him the earth is flat; the sun is a shining object of small size that pops up daily above an eastern rim, moves through the upper air, and sinks below the western edge; obviously it spends the night somewhere underground. The sky is an inverted bowl made of some blue material . . . the "solar system" has no meaning . . . bodies do not fall because of any "law of gravitation," but rather because there is nothing to hold them up. . . . For him the blood does not circulate, nor the heart pump blood; he thinks it is a place where love, kindness, and thoughts are kept. Cooling is not a removal of heat but an addition of "cold"; leaves are green . . . from a "greenness" in them. . . .

(BENJAMIN LEE WHORF, "Language, Mind, and Reality") [21]

2. Gilbert Ryle in his book *Dilemmas* writes:

When we are in a certain intellectual mood, we seem to find clashes between the things that scientists tell us about our furniture, clothes and limbs and the things that we tell about them. We are apt to express these felt rivalries by saying that the world whose parts and members are described by scientists is different from the world whose parts and members we describe ourselves, and yet, since there can be only one world, one of these seeming worlds must be a dummy-world. Moreover, as no one nowadays is hardy enough to say "Boo" to science, it must be the world that we ourselves describe which is the dummy-world.

. . . .

In the way in which a landscape-painter paints a good or bad picture of a range of hills, the geologist does not paint a rival picture, good or bad, of those hills, though what he tells us the geology of are the same hills that the painter depicts or misdepicts. The painter is not doing bad geology and the geologist is not doing good or bad landscape painting. In the way in which the joiner tells us what a piece of furniture is like and gets his description right

20 Sir Arthur Eddington, *New Pathways in Science* (New York: Macmillan; Cambridge, England: The University Press, 1935).

21 Benjamin Lee Whorf, "Language, Mind, and Reality," in *Etc.*, Spring, 1952. Copyright 1952, *Etc.* Used by permission of *Etc.*

or wrong (no matter whether he is talking about its colour, the wood it is made of, its style, carpentry or period), the nuclear physicist does not proffer a competing description, right or wrong, though what he tells us the nuclear physics of covers what the joiner describes. They are not giving conflicting answers to the same questions or to the same sort of question, though the physicist's questions are, in a rather artificial sense of 'about', about what the joiner gives his information about. The physicist does not mention the furniture; what he does mention are, so to speak, bills for such goods as, *inter alia*, bits of furniture.

Part of this point is sometimes expressed in this way. As the painter in oils on one side of the mountain and the painter in water-colours on the other side of the mountain produce very different pictures, which may still be excellent pictures of the same mountain, so the nuclear physicist, the theologian, the historian, the lyric poet and the man in the street produce very different, yet compatible and even complementary pictures of one and the same 'world'. But this analogy is perilous. It is risky enough to say that the accountant and the reviewer both give descriptions of the same book, since in the natural sense of 'describe' in which the reviewer does describe or misdescribe the book, the accountant does neither. But it is far riskier to characterize the physicist, the theologian, the historian, the poet and the man in the street as all alike producing 'pictures', whether of the same object or of different objects. The highly concrete word 'picture' smothers the enormous differences between the businesses of the scientist, historian, poet and theologian even worse than the relatively abstract word 'description' smothers the big differences between the businesses of the accountant and the reviewer. It is just these smothered differences which need to be brought out into the open. If the seeming feuds between science and theology or between fundamental physics and common knowledge are to be dissolved at all, their dissolution can come not from making the polite compromise that both parties are really artists of a sort working from different points of view and with different sketching materials, but only from drawing uncompromising contrasts between their businesses. To satisfy the tobacconist and the tennis-coach that there need be no professional antagonisms between them, it is not necessary or expedient to pretend that they are really fellow-workers in some joint but unobvious missionary enterprise. It is better policy to remind them how different and independent their trades actually are. Indeed, this smothering effect of using notions like *depicting, describing, explaining,* and others to cover highly disparate things reinforces other tendencies to assimilate the dissimilar and unsuspiciously to impute just those parities of reasoning, the unreality of which engenders dilemmas.

(GILBERT RYLE, *Dilemmas*) [22]

What is the world we ourselves describe? Why are some led to believe it is a dummy-world? Why, according to Ryle, isn't the world we describe ourselves a rival of the world described by scientists? Do you see any weakness in this analogical argument?

[22] Gilbert Ryle, *Dilemmas* (Cambridge: The University Press, 1954), p. 68 and pp. 80–81. Used by permission of the Cambridge University Press.

3. This passage is also taken from Ryle's book:

Our alarming and initially paralysing question was this. 'How is the World of Physics related to the Everyday World?' I have tried to reduce its terrors and dispel its paralysing effect, by asking you to reconstrue the question thus, 'How are the concepts of physical theory logically related to the concepts of everyday discourse?' I have asked you to see this question as having much in common with the questions 'How are the special terms of Bridge or Poker logically related to the terms in which the observant child describes the cards that are shown to him?' and 'How are the special terms of traders logically related to the terms in which we describe their commodities after we have brought them home?'

(GILBERT RYLE, *Dilemmas*) [23]

What is the point Ryle is making? If the questions are analogous, what are the consequences?

4. The distance from the sun to the nearest star is about 4.2 light years, or 25×10^{12} miles. This is in spite of the fact that we live in an exceptionally crowded part of the universe, namely the Milky Way, which is an assemblage of about 300,000 million stars. This assemblage is one of an immense number of similar assemblages; about 30 million are known, but presumably better telescopes would show more. The average distance from one assemblage to the next is about 2 million light years. But apparently they still feel they haven't elbow-room, for they are all hurrying away from each other; some are moving away from us at the rate of 14,000 miles per second or more. The most distant of them so far observed are believed to be at a distance from us of about 500 million light years, and what we see is what they were 500 million years ago. And as to mass: the sun weighs about 2×10^{27} tons, the Milky Way about 16,000 million times as much as the sun, ... It is not easy to maintain a belief in one's own cosmic importance in view of such overwhelming statistics.

(BERTRAND RUSSELL, *The Impact of Science on Society*) [24]

Sir Arthur Eddington in his *The Nature of the Physical World* writes that such astronomical facts impress us with our "insignificance." Sir James Jeans is not only reduced to a humble frame of mind before the vastness of the heavens, but writes that he finds it "terrifying" because of our extreme loneliness and because of the material insignificance of our home in space—"a millionth part of a grain of sand out of all the sea sand in the world."

Does the vastness of the universe produce such feelings of humility and terror? Does it follow from the fact that the universe is vast that man is unimportant or insignificant?

5. I have settled down to the task of writing these lectures and have drawn

23 *Ibid.*, p. 91. Used by permission of the Cambridge University Press.
24 Bertrand Russell, *The Impact of Science on Society* (New York: Columbia University Press, 1951), pp. 13–14. Copyright, 1951 Columbia University Press. Used by permission of the Columbia University Press.

up my chairs to my two tables. Two tables! Yes; there are duplicates of every object about me—two tables, two chairs, two pens.

. . . One of them has been familiar to me from earliest years. It is a commonplace object of that environment which I call the world. How shall I describe it? It has extension; it is comparatively permanent; it is coloured; above all, it is *substantial*. . . . Table No. 2 is my scientific table. It is a more recent acquaintance and I do not feel so familiar with it. . . . My scientific table is mostly emptiness. Sparsely scattered in that emptiness are numerous electric charges rushing about with great speed; but their combined bulk amounts to less than a billionth of the bulk of the table itself. Notwithstanding its strange construction it turns out to be an entirely efficient table. It supports my writing paper as satisfactorily as table No. 1; for when I lay the paper on it the little electric particles with their headlong speed keep on hitting the underside, so that the paper is maintained in shuttlecock fashion at a nearly steady level. If I lean upon this table I shall not go through; or, to be strictly accurate, the change of my scientific elbow going through my scientific table is so excessively small that it can be neglected in practical life. . . . There is nothing *substantial* about my second table. It is nearly all empty space—space pervaded it is true by fields of force, but these are assigned to the categories of "influences," not of "things."

(SIR ARTHUR EDDINGTON, *The Nature of the Physical World*) [25]

In the above passage, what exactly does Eddington mean when he speaks of two tables?

Are there really two such tables?

Why is it misleading to speak of "two tables"?

Can this passage be understood in a way which avoids these criticisms?

6. In view of the width of the cosmos and the slim hold on existence that Nature has provided for *Homo sapiens,* it would seem properly modest if we talked less about man being superior, less about his being the anointed of the gods. Who was anointed, and by whom, we ask, throughout the half billion manless Paleozoic and Mesozoic years when thousands of kinds of wonderful animals sought and fought for survival on the earth? Who then was the Anointed?

(HARLOW SHAPELY, "The Human Response to an Expanding Universe") [26]

Prof. Shapley explains the phrase "slim hold on existence" by comparing the newborn housefly with infants: The housefly was born with her training completed. She uses not only her own nervous ganglia for the planning and executing of life's operations, making emergency decisions and doting thereon, but she uses also and mainly her generic mind—something that we largely

[25] Eddington, *The Nature of the Physical World* (Cambridge, The University Press, 1928).

[26] Harlow Shapley, "The Human Response to an Expanding Universe," in *The Hibbert Journal,* Vol. LVIII, July 1960, p. 323. Copyright 1960, *The Hibbert Journal.* Used by permission of George Allen and Unwin, Ltd., publishers of *The Hibbert Journal.*

lack. The ratio of the number of our personal decisions to the number that the experience of the race has built into us is high, because so little is built in. The housefly makes some decisions of her own, but mostly uses the gradually acquired, the slowly trained mind of thousands of generations of flies.

Does the width of the cosmos imply that man is not the anointed of the gods?

What in the comparison between man and the housefly can be criticized? For example, can "mind," "decisions," etc. be meaningfully used in the same sense with men and houseflies?

In what way can this passage be understood so as to avoid these criticisms?

ARISTOTELIAN AND BOOLEAN SQUARES OF OPPOSITION

THE ARISTOTELIAN SQUARE OF OPPOSITION

The relationships between these four categorical statements:

All *S* is *P*	*A*	Universal affirmative
No *S* is *P*	*E*	Universal negative
Some *S* is *P*	*I*	Particular affirmative
Some *S* is not *P*	*O*	Particular negative

according to traditional logic, are indicated below in what is called the *square of opposition:*

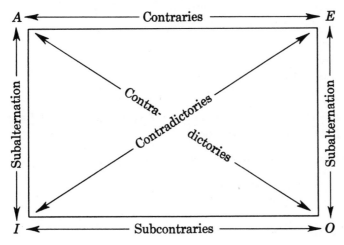

To say that **A** and **O** are contradictories is to say that they cannot both be true and they cannot both be false. If one is true the other is false and vice versa. **E** and **I**, as we can see, are also contradictories. For example, if

    1. All cowboys are TV stars. **(A)**

is supposed to be true, then

    2. Some cowboys are not TV stars. **(O)**

is false, and if (2) were true, then (1) would be false. **A** and **E** are indicated as being *contraries*—this means that they cannot both be true, although both might be false. Thus, for example, if (1) is true, then

    3. No cowboys are TV stars. **(E)**

is false and vice versa. The falsity of **A** does not determine the truth or falsity of **E** and the falsity of **E** does not determine the truth or falsity of **A**. **I** and **O** are given as *subcontraries*. Both can be true but they both can not be false. To say that **A** is related by *subalternation* to **I** means that **A** implies **I**. In turn, **E** implies **O**. Thus, for example, (1) implies that

Some cowboys are TV stars. **(I)**

THE BOOLEAN SQUARE
OF OPPOSITION

Following the symbolism introduced in Chapter Eleven, the four categorical statements would be translated:

    5. $(x) (Sx \supset Px)$ **(A)**
    6. $(x) (Sx \supset \sim Px)$ **(E)**
    7. $(\exists x) (Sx \cdot Px)$ **(I)**
    8. $(\exists x) (Sx \cdot \sim Px)$ **(O)**

In this symbolism **A** and **O** are contradictories and **E** and **I** are contradictories. This can easily be shown.

    9. '$(x) Fx$' is equivalent to '$\sim (\exists x) \sim Fx$'.

Thus if we deny (5) we have

    $\sim (x) (Sx \supset Px)$

which following (9) is equivalent to

10. $(\exists x) \sim (Sx \supset Px)$.

'$\sim (Sx \supset Px)$' can be treated in the same manner that statements are treated in Chapter Fourteen, so we can transform (10) in the following ways:

11. $(\exists x) \sim (\sim Sx \lor Px)$ from (10) by Imp.
12. $(\exists x) (Sx \cdot \sim Px)$ from (11) by DM

and, as we can see, (12) is the **O** statement (8). Thus **A** is the negation of **O**.

But in our symbolism **I** does not follow from **A** by subalternation and **O** does not follow from **E** by subalternation. As we have seen from Chapter Eleven:

13. $(x) (\cdots x \cdots) \equiv (\cdots a \cdots) \cdot (\cdots b \cdots) \cdots \cdot (\cdots n \cdots)$
14. $(\exists x) (\cdots x \cdots) \equiv (\cdots a \cdots) \lor (\cdots b \cdots) \lor \ldots \lor (\cdots n \cdots)$,

supposing n is the number of objects in the world.
Thus,

15. $(x) (Sx \supset Px)$ (**A**)

is equivalent to

16. $(Sa \supset Pa) \cdot (Sb \supset Pb) \cdot (Sc \supset Pc) \cdots (Sn \supset Pn)$

and

17. $(\exists x) (Sx \cdot Px)$ (**I**)

is equivalent to

18. $(Sa \cdot Pa) \lor (Sb \cdot Pb) \lor (Sc \cdot Pc) \lor \cdots \lor (Sn \cdot Pn)$.

Now if for 'S' we substitute "purple cows," then (15) is true. For nothing in the world is a purple cow. Thus 'Sa', 'Sb', 'Sc', and so on, are all false, and consequently each conjunct is true, since a conditional is true if the antecedent is false. Thus the truth value of the conjunctive chain is true, and thus (15) is true. On the other hand, if 'Sa', 'Sb', and so on, are all false, then each disjunct in (18) is false and thus the truth value of the disjunctive chain is false, and, so (17) is false. Hence an **A** may be true while its corresponding **I** is false. Similarly, if 'S' in **E** is replaced by a term which does not denote any existing entities (that is, a term which stands for a *null class*), **E** would be true while its corresponding **O** would be false. Thus **A** does not imply **I** and **E** does not imply **O**. The relation of subalternation does not hold.

Since when 'S' is replaced by a term standing for a null class, **A** and **E** are both true and **I** and **O** are both false, **A** and **E** are not contraries and *I* and *O* are not subcontraries. Consequently, in our symbolism the only relations between the four categorical statements are

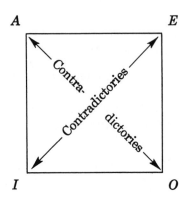

This is commonly called the *Boolean square of opposition* after the famous logician George Boole, who was one of the early contributors to symbolic logic.

CRITICISMS AND DEFENSE
OF ARISTOTELIAN SQUARE

Criticisms of the traditional system have centered around the question of "existential import." That is, when we use one of the four categorical statements, do we commit ourselves to the existence of something corresponding to the subject term? It is commonly held that in the case of *I* and *O* statements they do carry existential import. For example, to say some policemen are corrupt, is to say *that there are* some (one or more) policemen (and they are corrupt).

If *I* and *O* have existential import, and if the class designated by the subject term in either is empty or null, as in the case of "purple cows," then

(*I*) Some purple cows are friendly.
(*O*) Some purple cows are not friendly.

it is argued, are both false. Hence it is a mistake to say that *I* and *O* are subcontraries. Furthermore, since in the Aristotelian square *I* and *O* follow validly from *A* and *E*, *A* and *E* must also have existential import. But, it is argued, if they do, then, for example

(*A*) All purple cows are friendly.
(*E*) No purple cows are friendly.

would both be false. If, then, corresponding *I, O, A,* and *E* statements could all be false, then *A* and *O* are not contradictories and *E* and *I* are not contradictories.

If, on the other hand, we interpret *A* and *E* as not having existential import, then the square would break down because *I* and *O* would not follow from *A* and *E* by subalternation. *A* and *E* would not be contraries, and, whether or not *A* and *E* have existential import, *I* and *O* are not subcontraries.

A defense of the traditional square against these criticisms is provided by P. F. Strawson in his *Introduction to Logical Theory*.[1] Suppose someone says:

(*I*) Some of John's children are asleep.

The speaker obviously believes that John has children. But suppose he is mistaken. That is, suppose John has no children—the class designated by the subject term, "John's children," is a null class. Is the speaker's statement false? This question is like "Are purple cows friendly?" Our response to the latter question is that purple cows are neither friendly nor unfriendly, for there *are no* purple cows. Similarly to the first question we would not say either that it is true or that it is false, but rather that John *has no* children. Thus in order for this *I* statement to be either true or false, a necessary precondition is the existence of John's children.

Strawson suggests a possible interpretation of the Aristotelian square. Aristotle, he suggests, was treating *A, E, I, O* statements which are such that the question whether they are true or false is one which cannot arise unless the subject terms designate nonnull classes. Or, to put it another way, he was treating *A, E, I, O* statements which we ordinarily speak of as either true or false—that is, statements which presuppose the existence of that designated by the subject term. Thus, on this interpretation,

Some purple cows are friendly.

would not be treated in Aristotle's system, since we would not ordinarily say it is either true or false.

If all the *A, E, I, O* statements treated in the Aristotelian system do presuppose the existence of that designated by the subject term, then the objections to the Square of Opposition are undercut. The supposed breakdown of the square occurs when *A, E, I, O* statements with subject terms designating null classes are introduced. Furthermore, if *A, E, I, O* statements are given our symbolic interpretation *and* it is presupposed

[1] *Introduction to Logical Theory* (London: Methuen, 1952).

that the subject terms designate classes with members, then all the relations set forth in the traditional square hold.

CRITICISMS AND DEFENSE
OF THE BOOLEAN SQUARE

Two criticisms of the Boolean square which are sometimes made are: (1) statements such as

Some purple cows are friendly.

are false on the Boolean square or in symbolic logic. And statements such as

All purple cows are friendly.
No purple cows are friendly.
All purple cows are archbishops.

are true. This does not accord with the ordinary English use of "true" and "false." (2) In ordinary English, *A* statements and *E* statements imply *I* and *O* statements. And *A* and *E* are ordinarily contraries, and *I* and *O* are subcontraries. None of these relations hold in symbolic logic.

The answer to (1) is that this use of "true" and "false" is not in accordance with the ordinary English use, but why should it be, if the symbolic system achieves its *purposes*? In the system *all* statements are either *T* or *F*. And this system achieves its purposes. For example, we can translate all formal arguments into it and employ its techniques to determine whether the arguments are valid or invalid.

With respect to the second objection, it is true that in ordinary everyday discourse, *A* statements commonly imply corresponding *I* statements, and so forth. For example, if, in the customary context, someone told us "All Luppy's cows are brucellosis-free," it would follow that some of Luppy's cows are brucellosis-free. Now this relation can be captured in translating these statements into symbolic logic. We can translate "All Luppy's cows are brucellosis-free" (B) as

1. $(x) (Lx \supset Bx) \cdot (\exists x) (Lx)$.

And from (1), the corresponding *I* statement—$(\exists x) (Lx \cdot Bx)$—can be validly derived. Thus the structure and sense of statements in everyday discourse can be preserved in the symbolic notation.

Assuming that ordinary *A, E, I, O* statements do presuppose the existence of that designated by the subject term, the second objection thus can be answered by merely recognizing that in the Boolean square *A, E, I, O* statements do not preserve the sense of *A, E, I, O* statements as they are ordinarily used. But, as we have seen, the symbolic apparatus allows us to preserve the sense of ordinary discourse of *A, E, I, O* statements. And, in addition, this apparatus allows us to represent in symbolic terms statements found in areas other than ordinary discourse, such as mathematics and the theoretical sciences. For example, this apparatus allows us to represent in symbolic terms statements which treat of subject terms which denote classes with no members and which we regard as true, for example, ideal laws, such as the law of inertia: "All moving bodies not acted upon by external forces continue in a state of uniform motion in a straight line."

SUBJECT INDEX

Ad hoc explanations, 418, 420
Ambiguity, 181–183
Ambiguous names, 274–281
Analogies, 141–155
  argumentative, 141–142, 146–155
  criticism by, 153–155
  evaluating analogical arguments, 148–151
  explanatory, 141–155
  and similes, 141
  which suggest hypotheses, 141–142, 145–146
Antinomies, *see* Paradoxes
Arguments, 3
  ad hoc, see Ad hoc explanations
  conclusion of, 3
  correctness or incorrectness of, 9–11, 14, 189
  deductive, 11 n., 187 f.
  general circumstances of, 12–14
  inductive, 11 n., 187 f.
  logical appraisal of, 3
  premisses of, 3
  reductio ad absurdum (RAA), 177 n., 237–238
  valid, 11 n., 188–189
Aristotelian logic, 266 f., 457–463
Axiom sets
  completeness of, 301–302, 308–311, 437

Axiom sets (*Cont.*):
  consistency of, 300, 304–307, 437
  independence of, 300, 307–308, 437
  proof of consistency of, 305–307
  proof of independence of, 307–308
Axiom systems, 293–311, 329
  axioms of, 295–296, 300–301
  and Boolean algebra, 328–329
  derived rules of, 303–304
  formation rules of, 294–295, 298–299
  interpreted and uninterpreted, 296, 304
  proof in an axiom system, 299–300
  rules of inference of, 296–297, 299–300
  and scientific theory, 436–439
  theorems of, 301–302
  vocabulary of, 293–294, 298–299
  well-formed formulae in, 298–299

Boolean algebra, 328–329, 330

Categorical statements, 266–268
  and classes, 320–321
  distribution of terms of, 268
  major and minor terms of, 267–268
  particular affirmative (I), 267
  particular negative (O), 267
  relations between, 457–462

Categorical statements (*Cont.*):
  and square of opposition, *see* Square
    of opposition
  subject-predicate terms of, 267
  universal affirmative (A), 267
  universal negative (E), 267
  and Venn diagrams, 321–325
C-characteristics, 74–78
Circumstances, 12–14, 19–20, 28, 70
Classes, 314 f.
  class complement, 317–318
  class-identify, 316, 326–328
  class-inclusion, 314–317
  class-inclusion (C) and class-inclusion
    proper (C), 316–317
  class-membership (∈), 314–317
  intersection (∩) of, 318–320
  the null class, 317–318, 460–462
  operation on, 318–320
  proper subclass, 317
  subclass, 317
  union (∪) of, 319–320
  universe of discourse, 317–318
  Venn diagrams of, 321–325
Conclusion, 3
Conditional validation (RCP), 235–237
Conjunctive normal form (CNF), 309
Connotation, 79–80
Consistency
  of axioms, *see* Axiom systems
  consistency (S), 239–240
  of premisses, 232, 238–240
  proving consistency (S) of premisses,
    238–240
Constant conjunction, 429–434
Constants, 274–275
  in axiom systems, 297
Contingent truth, 192–193, 219–222
  contingent (S), 220–221
Contradiction, 187–188, 193–195, 219–222
Contrary-to-fact conditionals, 206, 432–433
Correctness
  and truth and falsity, 10–11, 14
  see also Arguments
Corroboration, 349, 418–420, 433
Criteria, 72–78
  and C-characteristics, 74–78
  for genuine scientific explanations,
    410–417

Criteria (*Cont.*):
  and mental acts, 73 n.
  and ordinary words, 72–78
  for satisfactory scientific explana-
    tions, 410–417
  and statements, 73 n.
Crucial experiments, 363–369
  and death blows, 367–368
  and empirical hypotheses, 363–364,
    433–435
  and fact of the cross, 368–369
  and theoretical hypotheses, 364–369,
    433–435

Death blow to a theory, 367–368
Deductive arguments, 187 f.
  and nondeductive arguments, 187–189
  in science, 353–355, 389–394, 436–439
  valid and invalid, 187 f.
  see also Arguments
Deductive systems, *see* Axiom systems
Definitional disputes, 91–92
Definitions, 66 f.
  by analysis, 99–100
  analytic, 99–100
  in axiom systems, 297
  dictionary, 72
  exact, 66–69, 100
  by example, 98–99
  by *genus* and *differentia*, 99–100
  implicit, 97 n.
  lexical, 100
  methods and types of, 97 f.
  ostensive, 98
  persuasive, 102–104
  real and nominal, 104–105
  recursive, 298
  reportive, 67
  and scientific laws, 430–431
  stipulative, 100–101
  by synonym, 97–98
  theoretical, 101–102
Demarcation, problem of, 416–417
"Denote," 67
Dilemmas, 164–175
  complex and simple, 165
  counterdilemma, 170–172
  destructive and constructive, 165
  realistic and unrealistic, 166, 172

Dilemmas (*Cont.*):
  slipping between the horns of, 167–170, 172
  taking the —— by the horns, 168–170, 172

Entelechy, 419–420
Enthymemes, 269–271
Equivalence, logical, 207, 218–219
Existential quantifier ($\exists x$), 250–252
Explanations, *see* Hypotheses *and* Scientific explanations
Explicandum, 389
Explicans, 389
Extending the use of a word, 88–91

Fact of the cross, 368–369
Fallacies, 11–12, 19 f.
  of accent, 52–53
  of accident, 31–32
  ad baculum, 25
  ad hominem, 11, 19, 20–22, 32
  ad ignorantiam, 27–28
  ad misericordiam, 24
  ad populum, 23–25
  ad verecundiam, 25–27
  of ambiguity, 19, 46 f.
  amphiboly, 49–50
  category-mixing, 131–136
  circular argument, 29, 415
  complex question, 30–31
  composition, 50–51
  context-mixing, 131–136
  division, 50–51
  equivocation, 47–49, 51
  false cause, 39
  genetic, 32–33
  hasty generalization, 41–42, 374–375
  ignoratio elenchi, 33–34, 48–49
  and incorrect arguments, 11
  of insufficient evidence, 19, 39 f.
  material —— of relevance, 19, 20 f.
  opposition, 42–45
  petitio principii, 29–34
  post hoc, 39–40
  quoting out of context, 52–53
  special pleading, 40–41
  tu quoque, 22–23
  use mixing, 120–123, 132–133
Falsifiability, 412–417
Form(s) of an argument, 191–192
Formulae, 214

Galileo's law of motion, 76, 394, 428, 435–437, 439–440, 441

Hypotheses
  corroboration of, *see* Corroboration
  direct testing of, 343, 416–417
  discovery and justification of, 352–353
  empirical (or experimental), 348–350, 363–364, 414–415
  and "free creation of mind," 353
  William Harvey's hypothesis, 340–343
  indirect testing of, 343, 416–417
  and inductivism, 352
  Lorenz-Fitzgerald contraction hypothesis, 417–418
  Newton's corpuscular hypothesis, 343–345, 411
  Rumford's hypothesis, 345–348
  in science, 339
  theoretical, 348–350, 364–369, 414–415
  theoretical entities in, 348
  Torricelli's hypothesis, 338–340, 416
  Velikovsky's hypothesis, 420
  see also Theories *and* Scientific explanations
Hypothetico-deductive method, 355

Ideal entities, 440–441
Implies and "$\supset$", 231–232
Individual constants, 257–259
  and quantified statements, 258–259, 286–289
Individual variables, 250
Induction
  and deduction compared, 351–355
  by enumeration, 351, 374–375
  and laws, 433–435
  and Mill's methods, 351 n., 376–383; *see also* Mill's methods
  and sampling, 375
  and scientific explanations, 410–411
  type A, 351–352, 374, 377 n., 410, 433
  type B, 351–352
Inductive arguments, 340, 348–349
  and nondeductive arguments compared, 187
Inductive logic, 355
Inductivism, 352–353

Inference rules (elementary), 230–234, 329
  absorption, 234
  addition, 233
  association, 234
  in axiom systems, 296–297
  commutation, 234
  conjunction, 233
  constructive dilemma, 233
  De Morgan's theorems, 233
  disjunctive syllogism (DS), 233
  distribution, 234
  double negation, 233
  equivalence, 234
  existential generalization (EG), 279, 281, 284–285
  existential instantiation (EI), 278–281, 284–285
  exportation, 234
  hypothetical syllogism, 233
  implication, 234
  modus ponens (MP), 230–231, 299
  modus tollens (MT), 232
  simplification, 233
  tautology, 234
  transposition, 234
  universal generalization (UG), 273–274, 281, 284–285
  universal instantiation (UI), 276–278, 280, 281, 284–285
Invalidity, *see* Validity

Kepler's laws, 432

Language
  directive use of, 112–118
  expressive use of, 112–118
  informative use of, 112–118
  logic of, 330
  see also Words
Laws of nature, 204, 295–296, 390
  and constant conjunction, 429–435
  empirical, 350, 433–435, 436–439, 440
  falsifying empirical, 433–435
  ideal, 350 n., 439–440, 444–446, 463
  logical character of, 428–435
  logical necessity of, 430–431
  nomological universality of, 432–433
  theoretical, 350, 433–435, 436–439, 444 n.
Logical form, 189–192

Logical structure of a statement, 249–263
Logical truth, 192–193

Mathematic induction, 330
Metaphor, 134–135
Michelson-Morley experiment, 417–418
Mill's methods, 376–383
  and induction type A, 355 n., 377 n.
  method of agreement, 376–377
  method of agreement and difference, 378
  method of concomitant variations, 378–379
  method of differences, 377
  method of residues, 378
  using Mill's methods, 379–383

Names and descriptions, 257, 274–276
  ambiguous, 274–281
Necessary and sufficient conditions, 207
Newton's laws of motion, 393–394, 437, 440–441, 463
Nonscientific explanations, 409–410
Nonsense, 128–138
  kinds of, 129–132
  and metaphor, 134–135

Observable and unobservable entities, 343 n., 348 n.
Observation and scientific explanations, 411–412
Ordinary words, 66–85
  and ambiguity, 81–84
  and criteria, 72–78
  and exact definitions, 67–69, 81–84
  and extension, 88–91
  and lack of boundaries, 80–81
  and paradigm examples, 69–72
  and science, 448–450
  and vagueness, 81–84

P's, 338 n.
Paradigm examples, 69–72
Paradoxes, 175–183
  and antinomies, 179–181
  falsidical and veridical, 177–178
  logical, 175
Predicates, 250
  complex, 260
  many-placed, 259–263

Predicates (*Cont.*):
  relational, 260
  single-placed, 262
  variables, 330
Premisses, 3
  irrelevant, 11–12, 14
Probabilistic explanations, 394–396
Probabilistic (or statistical) generality,
  395, 441–446
Problem of demarcation, 410–417
Pseudo-disputes, 92–93

Quantification, 249–263
  existential, 250–252
  multiple, 259–263
  universal, 252–254
  unquantified, 250

Relational predicates, 260
Relational theory, 263
Rules
  of derivation, 296–300
  derived, 303–304
  elementary rules of inference, *see* In-
    ference
  formation, 294–295, 298–299
  of inference of axiom systems, 296–
    297, 299–300
  substitution, 299
  of transformation, 296–300

Sampling, 375
Science
  and common sense, 447–450
  and deduction, 354, 436–439
  and formal axiom systems, 436–439
  horizontal and vertical organization
    of, 435–439
  ideal form of, 436–439
  ideal of, 337–338
  and induction, 340, 352–355
  observations in, 347
  practical aim of, 337–338
  theoretical aim of, 337–338
  and types of explanations, 389–421
Scientific explanations
  corroboration of, *see* Corroboration
  deductive, 389–394
  direct and indirect testing of, 416–
    417

Scientific explanations (*Cont.*):
  empathetic, 398–400
  and falsifiability, 412–415
  functional, 398
  genuine and pseudoscientific, 409–
    417
  historical, 396–397
  laws in, *see* Laws of nature
  and observation, 411–412
  patterns of, 389–401
  probabilistic, 394–396, 442–446
  reason and, 397
  satisfactory and unsatisfactory, 418–
    420
  see also Hypotheses
Scientific knowledge, 337
Scope
  of logical connectives, 208–209
  of quantifiers, 261–262, 275
Sentence
  and statement, 112–113, 193–195,
    430–431
Simile, 141
Sorites, 269–270
Square of opposition
  Aristotelian, 457–458
  Boolean, 458–460
  criticism of Aristotelian, 460–462
  criticism of Boolean, 462–463
Statement, *see* Sentence
Statement connectives, 192, 199–210,
  329
  '·' and "and", 199–200
  '≡' and "if and only if", 207
  '⊃' and "if—then", 204–206
  '~' and "not", 199–200
  '∨' and "or", 202–204
  relations between, 216–219
  and truth tables, 214–215
Statement variables, 214, 257
Syllogisms, 266–271
  traditional rules for validity of, 268

Tautologies, 219–222
Terms and *t*, 275
Theoretical entities, 343 n., 348, 441
Theories
  abandonment of, *see* Crucial experi-
    ments
  caloric theory, 345–347, 365
  Copernicus' theory, 391–392

Theories (*Cont.*):
  Einstein's gravitational theory, 414–415
  Einstein's relativity theory, 418
  empirical and theoretical, *see* Hypotheses
  ether theory, 416–417
  Galenic theory, 341–342, 409, 411, 416
  Huygens' wave theory, 368–369, 416
  kinetic theory, 348 n.
  Newton's corpuscular theory, 343–345, 367–369
  Ptolemaic theory, 390–392, 409
  and truth, 340 n.
  see also Hypotheses
Truth tables, 214–228
  and proof of consistency, independence, and completeness of axiom systems, 305–311
  short-cut, 227–228, 239
  and statement connectives, 214–215
  and validity(S), 223–225
Truth value, 210

Uses of language, 112–123
  countless uses, 118–120
  expressive use, 112–116, 119–123
  directive use, 112–116, 119–123
  form, purpose, and effect of, 116–118
  informative use, 112–116, 121–123, 128–129, 134
  three common, 112–116, 123

Vagueness, 81–84
Validity and invalidity, 187–195
  of arguments, 11 n., 188–189

Validity and invalidity (*Cont.*):
  and logical form, 189–192
  showing invalidity(S) of arguments, 223–225
  showing invalidity of arguments involving single-placed predicates, 286–289
  and structure of statements, 249 f., 273
  of syllogisms, 268
  testing for, 223–225
  truth tables for, 223–225
  valid and invalid(S), 191–192, 224, 250, 329
  validation involving quantifiers, 278–286
  validation of (S) arguments, 234–238
Variables
  and ambiguous names, 274–276
  in axiom systems, 297
  bound and free, 262, 276
  individual, 250
  predicate, *see* Predicates
Venn diagrams, 321–325
Verbal disputes, 88–93
  definitional disputes, 91–92
  pseudo-verbal disputes, 92–93
  word-extension disputes, 89–91
Verstehen, 400–401

Well-formed formulae, *see* . Axiom systems
Word-extension disputes, 89–91
Words
  honorific, 102
  indefinable, 98
  pejorative, 103
  see also Ordinary words

INDEX OF NAMES

Achilles, 176–177
Adam, 169
Adler, 413–414, 416
Anthony, Susan B., 60–61
Arago, Jean, 368
Aristotle, 19, 64, 107, 266 f., 340, 424, 461
Ascoli, Max, 105
Austin, J. L., 88 n., 130–131
Avogadro, 359

Babson, Roger, 39
Bacon, Francis, 29
Bagdikian, Ben, 395
Bargmann, V., 420 n.
Battan, Louis J., 402, 451
Baxter, Richard, 399
Becher, 371
Bendiner, Robert, 16
Bentham, J., 136
Berkeley, G., 65
Berlin, 162
Bernal, J. D., 451
Bernays, Paul, 300
Bernbach, William, 63
Berry, G. G., 182
Birkhoff, Garrett, 330 n.
Black, Max, 183
Blackett, P. M. S., 396, 416
Blaine, James G., 23

Boole, George, 273, 460
Booth, Edwin, 421
Boring, Edwin G., 373
Boswell, James, 6, 65
Brewster, Sir David, 357
Brutus, 173
Bryan, William J., 23

Caesar, Julius, 173
Carnap, 107
Carroll, Lewis, 5, 6, 85, 88, 129, 131–132, 137–138, 151, 155, 271
Castro, Fidel, 53
Cavendish, 372
Charters, A. C., 451
Chase, Stuart, 22, 56, 64
Christ, see Jesus Christ
Clebourne, Gen., 174
Commager, Henry S., 164
Conant, J. B., 357–359
Cope, Edward D., 406
Copernicus, 392
Curran, Joseph, 15

Darwin, C., 146, 347 n.
Davis, Kingsley, 408
De Morgan, Augustus, 154, 233
Descartes, René, 159, 161–162
Doolittle, James, 425
Dostoyevsky, F., 125

Douglas, Paul, 175
Driesch, Hans, 419
Dubos, René, 371, 386–387, 407
Duhem, P., 364 n.

Eddington, Sir Arthur, 452, 454–455
Eijkman, Christian, 384
Einstein, A., 413–414, 418, 439
Eiseley, Loren C., 406
Eisenhower, Dwight, 57
Eliot, T. S., 135
Elliot, Hugh, 62, 160
Empedocles, 156
Engels, F., 54
Epimenides, 178, 181
Erasistratus, 340
Eulathus, 171–172
Euler, 321
Euthyphro, 85–86
Evans, Bergen, 169 n.

Fabricius, 342
Festinger, Leon, 427
Feyerabend, P. K., 348 n.
Fibiger, Johannes, 356
Flanders, Ralph E., 57
Ford, Gerald, 107
Fort, Charles, 138
Foucault, 367–369
Frege, Gottlob, 88 n., 181 n., 273
Freud, S., 10–11, 38, 152, 197, 405, 413–
414, 416, 421, 444 n.
Fulbright, J. W., 8–10

Galbraith, J. K., 137, 143, 402–403
Galen, 340
Galileo, 76, 338, 356–357, 390–392, 394,
416, 429–430, 432–434, 439–441
Gardner, Martin, 28 n., 39 n., 40 n.,
139, 423, 425
Gavin, Clark, 36–37
Gemar, Joanne, 380 n.
Glaser, Hugo, 384
Goldwater, Barry, 94–95, 105
Gove, Philip, 110
Grunbaum, Adolph, 364

Hall, A. R., 342
Hall, Alexander, 28
Hall, J., 370
Halle, Louis J., 144

Hamilton, Alexander, 59
Hammond, E. Cuyler, 385
Hanson, N. R., 431 n.
Harvey, William, 340 f.
Hegel, G., 421
Herberg, Will, 60
Herophilus, 340
Hilgard, Ernest L., 408
Hitler, A., 435
Hoffa, James, 15
Hohn, Fronz E., 330 n.
Homer, 119
Hoover, J. Edgar, 44–45
Horowitz, Al, 197
Hull, Clark L., 407
Hume, David, 6, 140, 161, 174–175, 429,
445
Hutton, James, 370
Huygens, C., 368–369
Hyman, Sidney, 9

Ingen-Housz, Jan, 387

Jacobs, W. P., 361
Jaffe, Bernard, 356
James, W. T., 58
James, William, 89–90, 108, 158–159
Jeans, James, 454
Jefferson, Thomas, 55
Jesus Christ, 36, 38, 96, 108, 113, 120,
156–157, 174
Jevons, William S., 52
Johnson, Samuel, 6, 65, 109
Joshua, 420
Jourdain, P. E. B., 183
Joyce, James, 124

Kamke, E., 180 n.
Kapany, Narinder S., 451
Kaufman, Lloyd, 373
Kemeny, John, 437 n.
Kempton, Murray, 107
Kennedy, John F., 8, 38, 71
Kepler, J., 432
Khrushchev, N., 71
Korzybski, Count Alfred, 424

Lander, Bernard, 405
Laurenti, Luigi, 380–383
Lavoisier, Antoine, 358–359, 372
Lear, Edward, 129

Le May, Curtis, 7
Lenin, N., 16, 55
Lewis, C. I., 86
Lincoln, Abraham, 56, 165, 167
Lindsay, John, 107
Lippmann, Walter, 106
Lodge, 417
Long, Oren E., 59
Lorenz, 417, 417 n.

McCarthy, Joseph, 36, 58
McComb, Marshall, 61–62
McKie, Douglas, 372 n.
Maclane, Saunders, 330 n.
McNamara, Robert, 7, 396
Malthus, Robert, 146
Marskak, Robert E., 409
Marx, Karl, 15, 54, 56, 166
Mason, James, 165, 167
Mason, S. F., 161, 370
Means, Gardiner, 403
Michelson, 417–418
Mill, J. S., 32, 351 n., 355 n., 376–379, 383–384
Mills, Wilbur, 55
Molière, 29, 54
Moore, G. E., 65, 104, 109, 130
Moore, Wilbert E., 408
Morley, 417–418
Moses, 10–12, 152, 420
Motz, L., 420 n.
Murchison, 371

Nagel, Ernest, 145 n., 156, 162–163, 442 n.
Neuman, Alfred E., 476
Newton, Issac, 343 f., 367–369, 374–376, 390, 392–393, 431, 433–434, 440
Nielsen, Harry, 17, 58, 152, 423, 426
Nietzsche, F., 7, 124
Nossiter, Bernard, 404

Oesterle, John A., 423
Orwell, George, 86, 153

Packard, Vance, 424
Page, Melvin, 40
Paine, Thomas, 37
Pascal, Blaise, 339, 351, 379–380
Pasteur, Louis, 357–358, 371, 386–387
Paul, Saint, 178

Peano, 295
Plato, 85–86, 104, 126, 157, 168, 173
Pope, Alexander, 154
Popper, Karl R., 347 n., 349, 352, 412–416
Post, C. W., 36
Priestly, Dr., 387
Protagoras, 171–172
Proust, Marcel, 141–142

Quine, W. V., 176

Rapoport, Anatole, 405
Rayleigh, 363–364
Redi, Francesco, 357
Reid, Thomas, 146
Robespierre, 272
Rock, Irvin, 373
Romanoff, Noodles, 17, 35, 315
Roosevelt, F. D., 155, 158
Ross, Edmund, 38
Rovere, Richard, 36, 59, 106
Rumford, Count, 345 f., 365, 367
Ruskin, John, 37
Russell, Bertrand, 64, 87, 101, 106, 107–108, 140, 142, 147, 156–160, 179–182, 273, 297 n., 429 n., 454
Rutherford, 144 n.
Ryle, Gilbert, 452–454

Sandburg, Carl, 135
Schlauch, Margaret, 80
Schlick, Moritz, 419 n.
Schumann, Clara, 49
Sedgwick, 371
Servetus, 342
Seton-Watson, Hugh, 16
Seward, 165, 167
Shakespeare, William, 15, 56, 123, 134, 135, 173
Shapley, Harlow, 15, 455
Shorenstein, Hymie, 157–158
Shylock, 56
Silone, Ignazio, 158
Sledd, James, 110–111
Slidell, John, 165, 167
Socrates, 24, 85–86, 125–126, 157, 167–168, 173
Sophocles, 30
Spinoza, B., 107
Spitz, René, 388

Stahl, 371
Stalin, Josef, 55
Stebbing, L. Susan, 377 n., 378 n.
Stevenson, C. L., 102
Strawson, P. F., 461
Suppes, P., 325 n., 437 n.
Swift, Jonathan, 57, 125, 138
Symington, Stuart, 396

Tolstoy, Leo, 103–104
Torricelli, 338 f., 353–354, 416
Toynbee, Arnold, 62–63
Tucker, R. W., 46
Twain, Mark, 45, 138
Tyndall, John, 451

Velikovsky, Immanuel, 420
Venn, 321
Vesalius, 341
Vicary, James, 423–424
Von Frisch, Karl, 362
Von Mayer, Julius Robert, 402

Walton, Harold F., 407
Washington, George, 27
Weber, Max, 398–399
Welch, Robert, 26, 43
Wells, William, 385–386
Werner, Abraham, 370
Whately, Richard, 129
Whistler, James, 37
White, Theodore H., 158
Whitehead, A. N., 179 n., 182, 273, 297 n.
Whorf, Benjamin L., 452
Wilkes, Captain, 165, 167
Williams, Edward B., 58
Woolsey, John M., 91
Wittgenstein, Ludwig, 87, 108, 118–119, 127, 136, 138

Yeats, W. B., 30
Yukawa, Hideki, 408–409

Zeno, 176–177